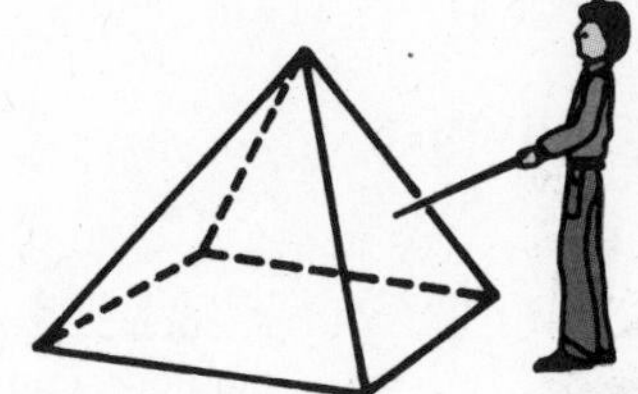

heath mathematics

CLYDE A. DILLEY
WALTER E. RUCKER

D. C. HEATH AND COMPANY
Lexington, Massachusetts Toronto London

About the authors

CLYDE A. DILLEY Associate Professor, University of Toledo, Toledo, Ohio, is teaching methods courses in elementary and secondary mathematics. He has taught mathematics in public schools and is a coauthor of several successful mathematics programs.

WALTER E. RUCKER Former Specialist in Education with the Curriculum Laboratory of the University of Illinois, has taught mathematics in public schools and is a coauthor of several successful mathematics programs.

Illustrations: Bill Davis
Technical Art: CS&S Design Associates, Inc.

Published simultaneously in Canada.

Printed in the United States of America.

International Standard Book Number: 0-669-96297-X

Contents

1 Numbers and Equations

Simplifying numerical expressions

These are **numerical expressions**:

$30 + 1 \qquad 31 \qquad 3 + (4 \times 7) \qquad (3 \times 7) + (2 \times 5)$

Numerical expressions may contain numerals, operation signs, and grouping symbols. Each of the expressions above stands for the same number. The simplest expression for the number is: 31

When we **simplify** a numerical expression, we write the simplest name for the number.

Examples.	Numerical Expression	Simplified Form
	3×7	21
	$14 + 2$	16
	$\frac{20}{2}$	10
	$(4 \times 7) + (5 \times 2)$	38

The expression below has more than one operation sign and no grouping symbols. There could be some confusion about how to simplify it:

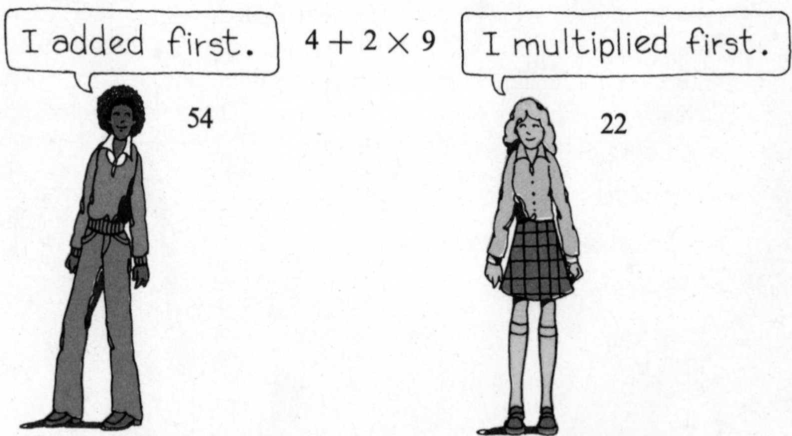

In order to clear up this possible confusion, mathematicians have agreed on some rules about the order of operations.

(1) First do multiplications and divisions in order from left to right.
(2) Next do additions and subtractions in order from left to right.
(3) Use grouping symbols when you wish to have the operations done in a different order.

Examples.

$12 \div 2 \times 3 = 18$ (operations done in order: ÷ 1, × 2) — Left to right.

$14 - 7 - 2 = 5$ (operations done in order: first − 1, second − 2) — Left to right.

$8 - 2 \times 3 = 2$ (operations done in order: − 2, × 1) — Multiply or divide first.

$20 - 12 \div 2 \div 3 = 18$ (operations done in order: − 3, first ÷ 1, second ÷ 2) — Multiply or divide first from left to right.

$(3 + 4) \times 2 = 14$ (operations done in order: + 1, × 2) — Grouping symbols tell us to add first.

EXERCISES

Simplify.

1. $7 \times 5 - 2$

2. $7 \times (5 - 2)$

3. $12 \div 3 \times 4$

4. $12 \div (3 \times 4)$

5. $30 - 2 \times 10$

6. $4 \times 2 \times 3$

7. $6 + 5 + 3$

8. $12 - 3 - 1$

9. $12 - (3 - 1)$

10. $12 \div 6 \div 2$

11. $12 \div (6 \div 2)$

12. $\frac{8 \times 4}{2}$

Remember that the bar means division.

13. $5 + 4 + 3 \times 5$

14. $12 - (3 - 2) - 5$

15. $2 \times 3 + 4 \times 5$

16. $7 + 3 \times 4 - 5 \times 2$

17. $(15 - 2 \times 3) \times 3 + 4$

18. $6 + 7 \times 4 \div 2 + 10$

19. $(4 + 3) \times 7 + 10 \div 5$

20. $(3 \times 4 - 5 \times 2) \times 7$

21. $(4 \div 2 \times 7 - 4) \times 5$

22. $12 \div 3 \times (8 - 3) \div 2$

23. $6 + 15 \div 3 \div 5 \times (12 - 4 - 3)$

24. Make up numerical expressions of your own and simplify them.

EXCURSION

Imagine 27 cubical blocks put together as a cube, then the entire outside painted red:

How many of the blocks are painted red on 3 sides?
On 2 sides? On 1 side?
On 0 sides?

Answer the same questions about this cube.

Supplementary Exercises, Set 1, page 374

Placeholders

The letter ***n*** in this expression is a **placeholder.**

$$6 \times n$$

It can be replaced by a numeral. Replacing a placeholder with a numeral is called **substitution**. For example, if we **substitute** 9 for ***n***, we get:

$$6 \times 9$$

If we substitute $7\frac{1}{2}$ for ***n***, we get:

$$6 \times 7\frac{1}{2}$$

Here is another expression:

$$3 \times a + (9 - b)$$

$3 \times 5 + (9 - 2)$ $\qquad$ $3 \times 7 + (9 - 7)$

EXERCISES

The table shows the replacements for the placeholders. Substitute. Do not simplify.

a	A	b	m
3	5	9	5

1. $3 \times A$ **2.** $7 + b$ **3.** $12 - m$ **4.** $12 - A$

5. $a + 16$ **6.** $a + b$ **7.** $A + b$ **8.** $m + b$

9. $a + a$ **10.** $A \times A$ **11.** $2 \times a + b$ **12.** $a \times A \times m$

13. $2 \times (m + b)$ **14.** $2 \times m + b$ **15.** $\frac{a}{A}$ **16.** $\frac{a}{b}$

17. $(a + A) \times (b + 7)$ **18.** $\frac{4}{a} + m$ **19.** $A \div m + a$ **20.** $2 \times (3 \times A + b)$

Substitute and simplify.

S	y	Z	d	N	R
1	3	7	5	0	0

21. $4 \times y$
22. $12 + Z$
23. $d - 5$
24. $6 \times N$
25. $2 \times (S + R)$
26. $d + Z$
27. $S \times 7$
28. $6 \times (d + y)$
29. $Z + R$
30. $R + y + d$
31. $R \times (y + d)$
32. $(S + y) + Z$
33. $S + (y + Z)$
34. $(2 \times y) \times d$
35. $2 \times (y + d)$
36. $N + 7$

Substitute and simplify.

a	B	b	d	g
2	4	8	3	5

37. $10 \times b$
38. $10 \times B$
39. $2 \times g \times B$
40. $a + b$
41. $b \div a$
42. $b \div B$
43. $32 \div b$
44. $32 \div b \div a$
45. $32 \div (b \div a)$
46. $a \times b \times d$
47. $a \times (B \times d)$
48. $B + b + g$
49. $B + (b + g)$
50. $16 - b - B$
51. $16 - (b - B)$
52. $b \times 0$

53. Substitute your age for n.
- **a.** I am n years old.
- **b.** In 5 years I will be $n + 5$ years old.
- **c.** Three years ago I was $n - 3$ years old.

54. Substitute your height for m.
- **a.** I am m inches tall.
- **b.** If I grow 3 inches taller, I will be $m + 3$ inches tall.

55. Substitute your weight for y.
- **a.** I weigh y pounds.
- **b.** If I lose 12 pounds, I will weigh $y - 12$ pounds.
- **c.** If I weighed two times as much, I would weigh $2 \times y$ pounds.

EXCURSION

Imagine this $4 \times 4 \times 4$ cube of blocks. The cube is painted red on the outside.

How many blocks are painted on 3 sides? On 2 sides? On 1 side? On 0 sides?
Repeat with a $5 \times 5 \times 5$ cube.

Skill Maintenance, Set 1, page 397

Exponents

Mathematicians always try to simplify mathematical notations. Here are two examples of how they use shortcuts in expressions.

(1) Multiplication signs between two placeholders or between a numeral and a placeholder are omitted.

times

$a \cdot b = ab$

$m \times n \times g = mng$

$2 \times a = 2a$

$3 \cdot c \cdot d = 3cd$

$6 \cdot (4 + 1) = 6(4 + 1)$

This multiplication sign is not omitted: 2×7. Why not?

(2) Instead of writing the same factor several times, exponents are used.

5 factors

exponent

$m \cdot m \cdot m \cdot m \cdot m = m^5$ Read this as "m to the 5th power."

$7 \times 7 \times 7 = 7^3$ Read as "7 cubed" or "7 to the 3rd power."

$aa = a^2$ Read as "a squared" or "a to the 2nd power."

$aa \cdot bbb = a^2b^3$

Here are two special exponents:

$b^1 = b$ b to the 1st power equals b.

$x^0 = 1$ x to the 0th power equals 1.

EXERCISES

Rewrite each expression. Omit multiplication signs wherever possible.

1. $7 \times a$
2. $6 \cdot 3$
3. $9 \times b$
4. $m \times n$
5. $6 \cdot r$
6. $a \times b \times c$
7. $2 \cdot d \cdot h$
8. $7 \times 3 \times 5$
9. $6 \times 4 \times a$
10. 2×47
11. $3 \times (a + b)$
12. $7 \cdot (12 - 4)$
13. $8 \times (3 \times 4)$
14. $(a + b) \times (2 + c)$
15. $4 \times (3 \times a + b)$

Complete this table.

	16.	17.	18.	19.	20.	21.	22.
Without exponents	$8 \times 8 \times 8$		*ggggg*			*ggghh*	$(3 + 4)(3 + 4)(3 + 4)$
With exponents		4^2		m^7	10^8		

Substitute and simplify.

a	g	H	N	Y	Z
2	4	3	5	7	1

23. ag **24.** HY **25.** $6N$ **26.** $10a$ **27.** $10Y$

28. $4(a + g)$ **29.** $2(7 + N)$ **30.** agH **31.** $a(gH)$ **32.** g^2

33. a^3 **34.** a^4 **35.** a^5 **36.** a^6 **37.** H^3

38. 6^a **39.** g^0 **40.** Y^1 **41.** N^0 **42.** Y^0

43. Z^0 **44.** Z^1 **45.** Z^2 **46.** Z^3 **47.** Z^4

48. Z^5 **49.** Z^{10} **50.** Z^{234} **51.** 0^N **52.** $(a + g)^2$

In exercises 53–58 use the expression $3n + 2$. Substitute the given values for n and simplify.

53. 7 **54.** 5 **55.** 8 **56.** 10 **57.** 0 **58.** 1

$3 \times 7 + 2$

Substitute and simplify to complete this table.

	n	$n^2 + 1$
59.	3	$3^2 + 1 = ?$
60.	4	
61.	5	
62.	6	
63.	7	
64.	8	
65.	9	
66.	0	

EXCURSION

Collect the data about the numbers of blocks that are painted on 0 sides, 1 side, 2 sides, and 3 sides in the Excursions on pages 3 and 5.

	Sides			
Cube	0	1	2	3
$2 \times 2 \times 2$				
$3 \times 3 \times 3$				
$4 \times 4 \times 4$				
$5 \times 5 \times 5$				
$6 \times 6 \times 6$				
$7 \times 7 \times 7$				

Can you find any patterns? Can you predict the data in the last two rows? Check.

Supplementary Exercises, Set 2, page 374

Properties

The grouping symbols tell us the order in which to perform the operations when we simplify this expression.

$$\underset{1}{\uparrow}\quad\underset{2}{\uparrow}$$

$$(6 + 3) + 7 = 16$$

(↑ 1 under the first +, ↑ 2 under the second +)

If we change the grouping symbols, we change the order of the operations.

$$6 + (3 + 7) = 16$$

(↑ 2 under the first +, ↑ 1 under the second +)

Notice that changing the order of the operations did not change the sum. This is *always* true for expressions involving only additions.

No matter what substitutions are made,

$$(a + b) + c = a + (b + c).$$

This is called the **associative property of addition.**

There is also an **associative property of multiplication**:

For all substitutions,

$$(a \times b) \times c = a \times (b \times c)$$

There is no associative property of subtraction or of division. Can you write examples to show this?

Here are the basic properties that you should know.

Commutative Property of Addition
For all substitutions, $a + b = b + a$

Commutative Property of Multiplication
For all substitutions, $a \cdot b = b \cdot a$

Associative Property of Addition
For all substitutions, $(a + b) + c = a + (b + c)$

Associative Property of Multiplication
For all substitutions, $(a \cdot b) \cdot c = a \cdot (b \cdot c)$

Adding 0 Property (Identity property of addition)
For all substitutions, $a + 0 = a$

Multiplying by 1 Property (Identity property of multiplication)
For all substitutions, $a \cdot 1 = a$

This property involves both addition and multiplication.

Multiplying by 0 Property
For all substitutions, $a \cdot 0 = 0$

Distributive Property of Multiplication over Addition
For all substitutions, $a \cdot (b + c) = a \cdot b + a \cdot c$

EXERCISES

Match a property with each example.

1. $(7 + 3) + 9 = 7 + (3 + 9)$
2. $8 \times 7 = 7 \times 8$
3. $583 + 279 = 279 + 583$
4. $261 \times 0 = 0$
5. $9 \times (40 + 5) = 9 \times 40 + 9 \times 5$
6. $48 \times 1 = 48$
7. $863 + 0 = 863$
8. $(7 \times 0) \times 1 = 7 \times (0 \times 1)$
9. Show that subtraction and division are not commutative.

a. commutative property of addition
b. commutative property of multiplication
c. associative property of addition
d. associative property of multiplication
e. adding 0 property
f. multiplying by 1 property
g. multiplying by 0 property
h. distributive property

Complete.

10. $18 \times 7 = 7 \times$ ___?___
11. $49(9 + 5) = 49 \cdot 9 +$ ___?___ $\cdot 5$
12. $36 + (14 +$ ___?___$) = (36 + 14) + 71$
13. $15 + 91 =$ ___?___ $+ 15$
14. $3 \cdot 7 + 9 \cdot 7 = (3 + 9)$___?___
15. $68 \cdot 0 =$ ___?___

CHECKUP
for pages 2–5

Simplify.

1. $3 + 7 \times 2$
2. $(3 + 7) \times 2$
3. $14 - 6 - 2$
4. $12 \div 6 \div 2$
5. $\dfrac{6 \times 3 + 2}{2}$
6. $7 \times (4 + 5) + 3$

Substitute and simplify.

a	A	b	x
2	4	3	7

7. $a \times b$
8. $b \times b$
9. $a \times a \times a$
10. $5 \times X$
11. $A + b$
12. $(A + a)$

Answers on page 425.

Skill Maintenance, Set 2, page 397

Sets and subsets

We write about **sets** in two ways:

By listing the elements in a loop.

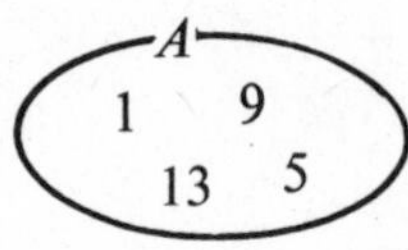

By listing the **elements** between braces.

$$A = \{1, 5, 9, 13\}$$

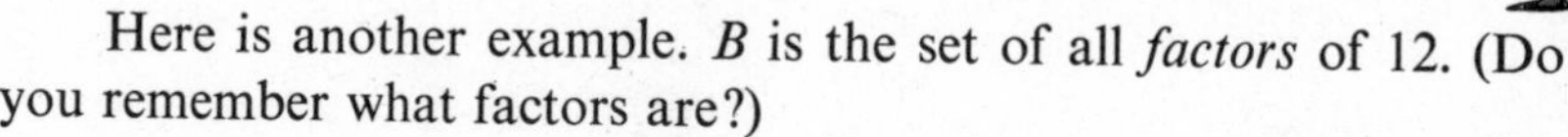

Here is another example. B is the set of all *factors* of 12. (Do you remember what factors are?)

$$B = \{1, 2, 3, 4, 6, 12\}$$

Some sets are **infinite**. This means that the list of elements would go on forever. For example, suppose that G is the set of all *multiples* of 3. (Do you remember what multiples are?) We could write G like this:

$$G = \{0, 3, 6, 9, 12, \ldots\}$$

One set has no elements. It is **the empty set**. We usually name the empty set with the symbol $\varnothing$, and we often show it like this:

Study this diagram of sets X and Y.

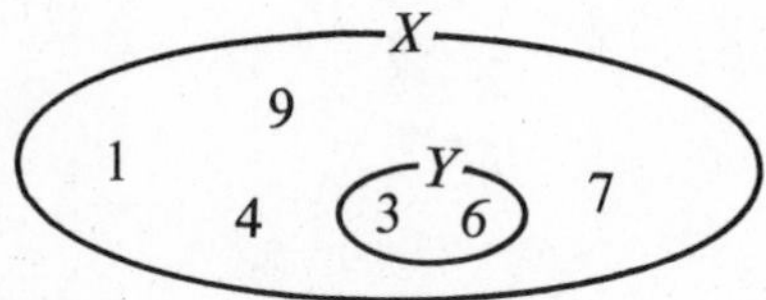

Each element of Y is also an element of X. We say that Y is a **subset** of X and we write:

$$Y \subseteq X$$

The empty set is a subset of every set.

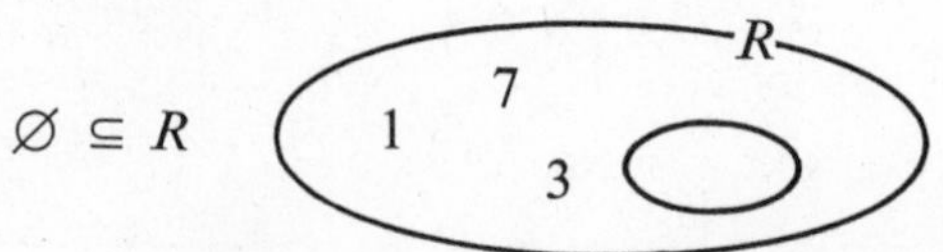

EXERCISES

True or false?

1. 6 is an element of {2, 4, 6, 8}.
2. 10 is an element of {2, 4, 6, 8}.
3. 1 is an element of {9, 10, 11, 12}.
4. 11 is an element of {1, 3, 5, 7, . . .}.
5. 12 is an element of {1, 3, 5, 7, . . .}.
6. 30 is an element of {5, 10, 15, 20, . . .}.
7. 5 is an element of the set of factors of 20.
8. 5 is an element of the set of multiples of 20.

Name these sets, using braces.

9. The set of all factors of 18.
10. The set of all factors of 32.
11. The set of all multiples of 2.
12. The set of all multiples of 7.
13. The set of all odd numbers.
14. The set of factors of 1.

True or false?

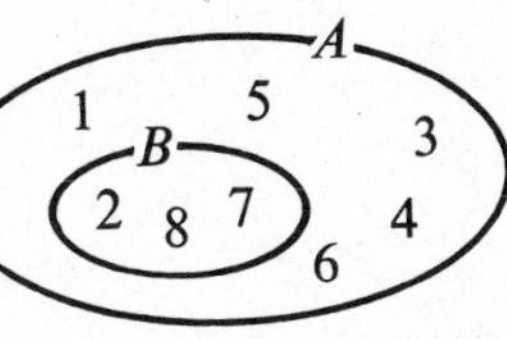

15. 7 is an element of B.
16. 7 is an element of A.
17. $B \subseteq A$
18. 6 is an element of B.
19. 6 is an element of A.
20. $A \subseteq B$
21. $\varnothing \subseteq A$
22. $\{1, 2\} \subseteq \{1, 2, 3, 4\}$
23. $\{1, 2, 3, 4\} \subseteq \{2, 3, 4, 5, 6, 7, 8\}$
24. $\varnothing \subseteq \{7, 9, 15\}$
25. $\{1, 6, 8\} \subseteq \{1, 6, 8\}$
26. There are 3 elements in {2, 9, 27}.
27. 3 is an element of {2, 9, 27}.

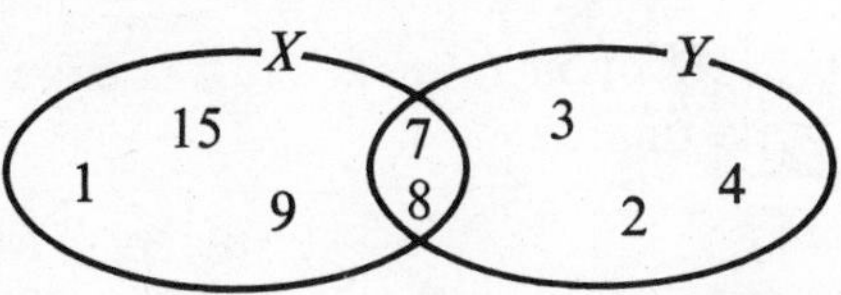

28. 8 is in X.
29. 8 is in Y.
30. 7 is in X.
31. 7 is in Y.
32. 9 is in X.
33. 9 is in Y.
34. 2 is in X.
35. 2 is in Y.
36. $X \subseteq Y$
37. $Y \subseteq X$

38. The set of multiples of 6 is a subset of the set of multiples of 2.
39. The set of factors of 6 is a subset of the set of factors of 2.

EXCURSION

These pictures show oblong numbers.

First oblong number	Second oblong number	Third oblong number
2	6	12

Fourth oblong number	Fifth oblong number	Sixth oblong number
20	?	?

Can you give a rule?

Skill Maintenance, Set 3, page 397

Unions and intersections of sets

Study the two sets A and B.

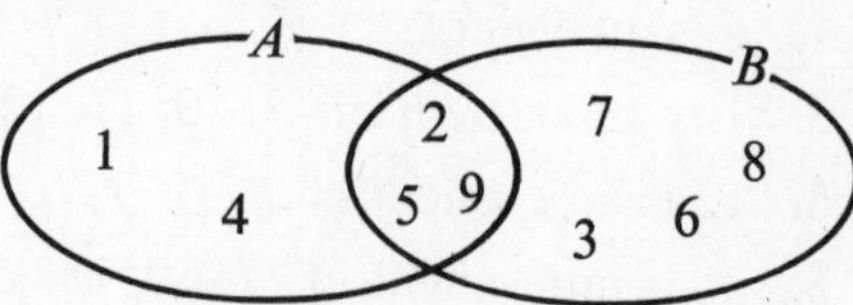

$A = \{1, 2, 4, 5, 9\}$

$B = \{2, 3, 5, 6, 7, 8, 9\}$

Notice that the elements 2, 5, and 9 are in both A and B. The set of elements that are common to A and B is called the **intersection** of A and B. We write this:

$A \cap B = \{2, 5, 9\}$

Here are two other examples.

(1) (2)

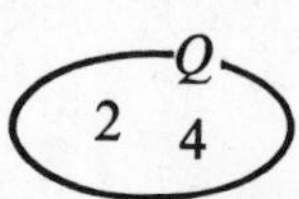

$X = \{1, 2, 3, 4, 5\}$

$Y = \{3, 5\}$

$X \cap Y = \{3, 5\}$

$P = \{1, 3, 5\}$

$Q = \{2, 4\}$

$P \cap Q = \varnothing$

Now study the sets M and N.

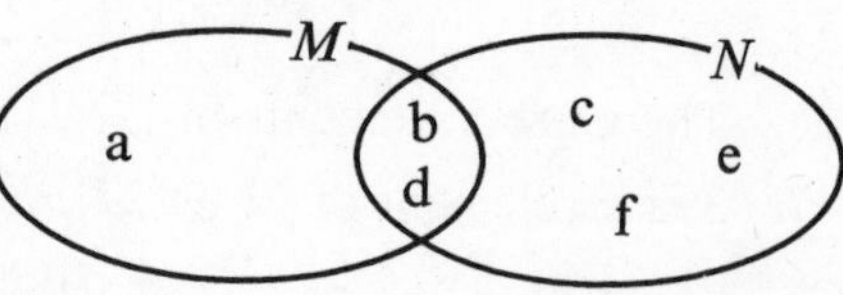

$M = \{a, b, d\}$

$N = \{b, c, d, e, f\}$

The set of elements that are in M or in N or in both is called the **union** of sets M and N. We write this:

$M \cup N = \{a, b, c, d, e, f\}$

Here are two more examples.

(1) (2)

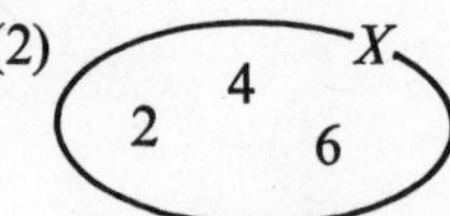

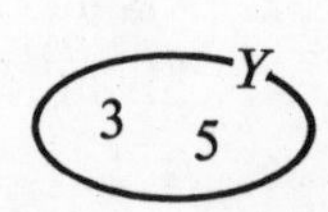

$A = \{1, 2, 3,. 4, 5\}$

$B = \{3, 5\}$

$A \cup B = \{1, 2, 3, 4, 5\}$

$X = \{2, 4, 6\}$

$Y = \{3, 5\}$

$X \cup Y = \{2, 3, 4, 5, 6\}$

EXERCISES

List the elements of each set.

1. A
2. B
3. $A \cap B$
4. $A \cup B$

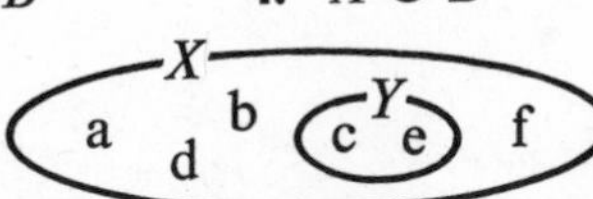

5. X
6. Y
7. $X \cap Y$
8. $X \cup Y$

9. M
10. N
11. $M \cap N$
12. $M \cup N$

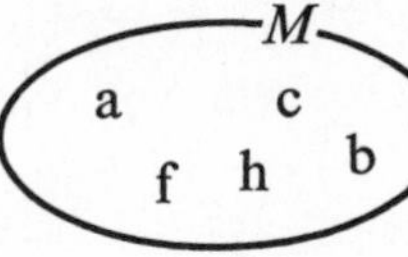

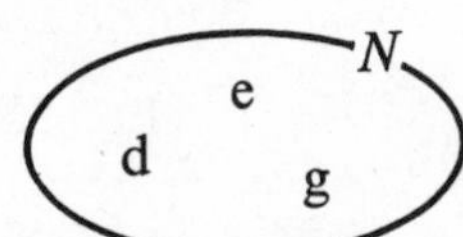

Complete.

13. $G = \{1, 2, 3, 4, 5\}$
    $H = \{2, 4, 6, 8\}$
    a. $G \cup H = ?$
    b. $G \cap H = ?$

14. $P = \{a, b, c, d\}$
    $Q = \{w, x, y, z\}$
    a. $P \cup Q = ?$
    b. $P \cap Q = ?$

15. $R = \{3, 5, 7, 9\}$
    $S = \varnothing$
    a. $R \cup S = ?$
    b. $R \cap S = ?$

16. $X = \{1, 2, 3\}$
    $Y = \{1, 2, 3\}$
    a. $X \cup Y = ?$
    b. $X \cap Y = ?$

17. The set of factors of 12 = {1, 2, 3, 4, 6, 12}.
    The set of factors of 18 = {1, 2, 3, 6, 9, 18}.
    The set of **common factors** of 12 and 18 is the intersection of those two sets.
    List the common factors. What is the **greatest common factor (GCF)?**

18. The set of multiples of 6 = {0, 6, 12, 18, 24, . . .}.
    The set of multiples of 8 = {0, 8, 16, 24, 32, . . .}.
    List the set of **common multiples** of 6 and 8. What is the **least common multiple (LCM)?**

List all common factors of the numbers. Which is the GCF?

19. 8, 12
20. 9, 24
21. 27, 36
22. 50, 56
23. 9, 12, 18
24. 27, 33, 48

List 3 common multiples, including the LCM.

25. 2, 7
26. 2, 4
27. 6, 9
28. 3, 5
29. 3, 5, 8
30. 2, 4, 6
31. Remember that **prime numbers** have exactly two factors. List 10 prime numbers.

CHECKUP
for pages 10–13

True or false?

1. 1 is an element of A.
2. 1 is an element of B.
3. 3 is an element of A.
4. 3 is an element of B.
5. $A \subseteq B$.
6. $B \subseteq A$.

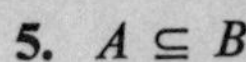

Answers on page 425.

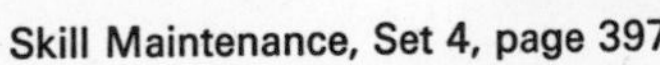

Skill Maintenance, Set 4, page 397

Greatest common factor, least common multiple

You have found common factors and the greatest common factor (GCF) of two numbers by using sets.

Example.

The set of factors of 18 = {1, 2, 3, 6, 9, 18}

The set of factors of 42 = {1, 2, 3, 6, 7, 14, 21, 42}

$\{1, 2, 3, 6, 9, 18\} \cap \{1, 2, 3, 6, 7, 14, 21, 42\} = \{1, 2, 3, 6\}$

Here is another method for finding a greatest common factor. Remember that a prime number is a number having exactly two factors. Below, 18 and 42 have been factored as a product of prime numbers.

The prime factorizations of 18 and 42.

$18 = 2 \times 3 \times 3$

$42 = 2 \times 3 \times 7$

2 and 3 are the common prime factors. The GCF is 2×3 or 6.

You have also found common multiples of two numbers by using sets. Here is the intersection of the set of multiples of 12 and the set of multiples of 20:

$\{0, 12, 24, 36, 48, 60, 72, \ldots\} \cap \{0, 20, 40, 60, 80, \ldots\}$
$= \{0, 60, 120, \ldots\}$

You probably remember that the least nonzero common multiple is called the least common multiple (LCM). What is the LCM of 12 and 20?

Here is another way to find the LCM of two numbers by using the prime factorization of each number.

$12 = 2 \times 2 \times 3$ — Each multiple of 12 will have these factors.

$20 = 2 \times 2 \times 5$ — Each multiple of 20 will have these factors.

$12 = 2 \times 2 \times 3$

$20 = 2 \times 2 \times 5$

Each common multiple of 12 and 20 will have these factors.

The LCM of 12 and 20 is $2 \times 2 \times 3 \times 5 = 60$.

EXERCISES

Copy and complete each prime factorization.

1. $24 = 6 \cdot 4 = 2 \cdot 3 \cdot 2 \cdot \underline{?}$
2. $32 = 8 \cdot 4 = 2 \cdot 4 \cdot 4 = 2 \cdot 2 \cdot 2 \cdot 4 = 2 \cdot 2 \cdot 2 \cdot 2 \cdot \underline{?}$
3. $30 = 5 \cdot 6 = 5 \cdot 2 \cdot \underline{?}$
4. $35 = 5 \cdot \underline{?}$
5. $66 = 2 \cdot 33 = 2 \cdot 3 \cdot \underline{?}$

Use the prime factorization method to find the GCF.

6. 8, 12 **7.** 16, 24 **8.** 18, 28 **9.** 35, 15 **10.** 16, 42 **11.** 32, 24
12. 16, 36 **13.** 14, 21 **14.** 20, 8 **15.** 48, 36 **16.** 50, 15 **17.** 48, 32

Use the prime factorization method to find the LCM.

18. 20, 35 **19.** 18, 42 **20.** 10, 12 **21.** 40, 24 **22.** 16, 20 **23.** 18, 24
24. 20, 36 **25.** 21, 14 **26.** 12, 20 **27.** 60, 15 **28.** 20, 28 **29.** 36, 48

Copy and complete this table.

	x	y	xy	GCF of x and y	LCM of x and y	GCF $\times$ LCM
30.	6	8				
31.	12	15				
32.	12	18				
33.	18	32				
34.	16	36				
35.	17	18				

Who are we?

36. Our sum is 15.
Our LCM is 18.
Our GCF is 3.

37. Our sum is 28.
Our LCM is 48.
Our GCF is 4.

EXCURSION

With 12 toothpicks and some clay, form:
a. 4 congruent squares.
b. 6 congruent squares.

Supplementary Exercises, Set 3, page 374

Equations

A sentence with an equals sign (=) is called an **equation.** Here are three equations.

$4 + 7 = 11$ $\quad$ $2 \times 6 = 25$ $\quad$ $4a = 12$

The first equation is true and the second is false. The third is called an **open equation** because it has a placeholder in it. We can make it a true equation by substituting 3 for a, and we can make it a false equation by substituting 7 (or any number other than 3).

$4a = 12$ $\quad$ $4a = 12$

$4 \times 3 = 12$ (true) $\quad$ $4 \times 7 = 12$ (false)

When we **solve** an open equation we find all numbers that make the equation true. The numbers that make an equation true are called **solutions** of the equation.

Examples.

Equation: $3 + a = 17$ $\quad$ Equation: $\frac{g}{6} = 7$ $\quad$ Equation: $\frac{12}{b} = 2$

Solution: 14 $\quad$ Solution: 42 $\quad$ Solution: 6

EXERCISES

Is the number given in red a solution of the equation?

1. 7 $5a + 1 = 36$ **2.** 9 $36 - 3g = 0$ **3.** 7 $\frac{3m + 1}{2} = 11$

4. 5 $x^2 = 25$ **5.** 2 $y^3 = 6$ **6.** 10 $h^3 = 1000$

7. 3 $2(5m - 4) = 33$ **8.** 4 $(a + 1)^2 = 25$ **9.** 5 $a^2 + 1 = 25$

10. 2 $(a - 2)(a + 3) = 0$ **11.** 2 $\frac{12 - 5n}{2} = 1$ **12.** 2 $\frac{24}{3a} = 4$

Solve.

13. $a + 7 = 15$
14. $d + 9 = 24$
15. $x + 12 = 48$
16. $y + 75 = 187$
17. $6 + c = 13$
18. $8 + g = 17$
19. $10 + m = 45$
20. $34 + Z = 266$
21. $12 - a = 7$
22. $30 - b = 22$
23. $58 - n = 21$
24. $156 - m = 131$
25. $x - 3 = 5$
26. $y - 7 = 10$
27. $r - 15 = 24$
28. $q - 73 = 100$
29. $3a = 12$
30. $5r = 35$
31. $7g = 70$
32. $8A = 72$
33. $2b = 9$
34. $3x = 25$
35. $3g = 29$
36. $5h = 48$
37. $\frac{6}{a} = 3$
38. $\frac{15}{b} = 5$
39. $\frac{32}{g} = 4$
40. $\frac{63}{a} = 7$
41. $\frac{r}{2} = 6$
42. $\frac{m}{3} = 8$
43. $\frac{x}{5} = 9$
44. $\frac{y}{9} = 10$

45. Jean thought that 7 was a solution of this equation:

$$3(5x + 10) = 150$$

Prove that she was wrong.

46. Jean thought that 5 was a solution of this equation:

$$\frac{7y + 5}{4} = 10$$

Prove that she was correct.

Copy and number the arrows to show the order of operation.

47. $3a + 7$
↑ ↑
? ?

48. $7 + 3a$
↑ ↑
? ?

49.
? ?
↓ ↶
$\frac{5 + a}{2}$

50.
? ?
↓ ↓
$2(a + 6)$

51. $5(3 + 6g)$
↑ ↑ ↑
? ? ?

52.
? ? ?
↓ ↓ ↶
$\frac{9x + 4}{2}$

53. $\frac{12}{2m + 4}$
↑ ↑ ↶
? ? ?

54. $\frac{6(4x + 3)}{5 + 2}$
? ? ?
↓ ↓ ↓ ↶
↑
? ?

CHECKUP
for pages 6–9

Rewrite these expressions and omit as many multiplication signs as possible.

1. $4 \times a$
2. 6×7
3. $a \times b$
4. $2 \times (3 + 7)$
5. $2 \times 3 \times a$
6. $a \times b \times c$

Simplify.

7. 2^3
8. 3^2
9. 10^5
10. 9^2

Here are examples of some properties. Name the properties.

11. $7 + 4 = 4 + 7$
12. $3 \times (4 \times 2) = (3 \times 4) \times 2$
13. $6 \times 1 = 6$
14. $3 \times (6 + 1) = 3 \times 6 + 3 \times 1$

Answers on pages 425.

Supplementary Exercises, Set 4, page 374

Solving 2- and 3-step equations

Study these examples.

<table>
<tr>
<td>
Find the last operation.

$2(x + 7) = 24$

$\uparrow \; \uparrow$

2 1

</td>
<td>
What do you multiply by 2 to get 24?

$2 \, \boxed{} = 24$

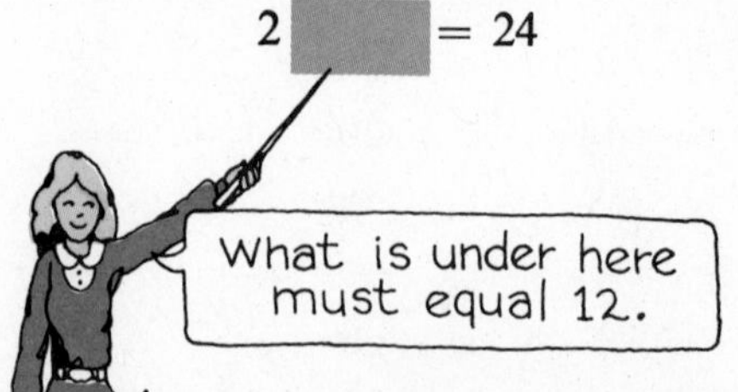

</td>
</tr>
<tr>
<td>
Write the new equation.

$2(x + 7) = 24$

$x + 7 = 12$
</td>
<td>
What do you add 7 to to get 12?

$2(x + 7) = 24$

$x + 7 = 12$

5
</td>
</tr>
</table>

<table>
<tr>
<td>
Find the last operation.

1 2

$\downarrow \; \downarrow$

3 → $\frac{3x - 1}{2} = 10$
</td>
<td>
What do you divide by 2 to get 10?

$\frac{\boxed{}}{2} = 10$

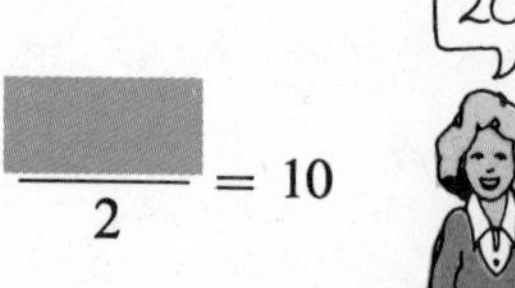

</td>
</tr>
<tr>
<td>
Make a record of that fact.

$\frac{3x - 1}{2} = 10$

$3x - 1 = 20$
</td>
<td>
Find the last operation.

$\frac{3x - 1}{2} = 10$

$3x - 1 = 20$

$\uparrow \; \uparrow$

1 2
</td>
</tr>
<tr>
<td>
What do you subtract 1 from to get 20?

$\frac{3x - 1}{2} = 10$

$3x - 1 = 20$

</td>
<td>
Make a record.

$\frac{3x - 1}{2} = 10$

$3x - 1 = 20$

$3x = 21$
</td>
</tr>
</table>

What multiplied by 3 is 21?

$$\frac{3x - 1}{2} = 10$$

$$3x - 1 = 20$$

$$3x = 21$$

$$7$$

Here is another example.
Can you explain each step?

$$2(12 - 3a) = 6$$

$$12 - 3a = 3$$

$$3a = 9$$

$$3$$

EXERCISES

What is the last operation?

1. $6a + 4 = 54$
2. $6(a + 4) = 54$
3. $28 - 3a = 1$
4. $\frac{4 + g}{7} = 3$
5. $\frac{2x + 7}{5} = 5$
6. $5(12 - 3r) = 45$

Pretend that you are helping a friend solve equations as on page 18. What part of the equation would you cover first?

7. $3g + 7 = 34$
8. $3(g + 7) = 33$
9. $5 + 7r = 33$
10. $\frac{12 + 2y}{2} = 4$
11. $6(3x - 5) = 35$
12. $\frac{2(3a + 1)}{5} = 10$

Solve.

13. $\frac{5x}{3} = 10$
14. $7r + 2 = 30$
15. $8(x + 2) = 48$
16. $\frac{2c}{8} = 2$
17. $7 + 3a = 22$
18. $20 - 3d = 2$
19. $4y - 7 = 29$
20. $10 + 9m = 73$
21. $100 - 10n = 10$
22. $2(3x + 5) = 34$
23. $\frac{5y - 2}{2} = 19$
24. $\frac{7c + 1}{9} = 4$
25. $4(2r - 7) = 36$
26. $\frac{3g - 4}{2} = 10$
27. $\frac{5x + 1}{4} = 9$
28. $\frac{2(3a - 1)}{5} = 8$
29. $\frac{2(5 + 8y)}{7} = 6$
30. $\frac{4(20 - 2m)}{2} = 16$

EXCURSION

The letters M, E, and Y stand for digits. ME stands for a 2-digit number. Do not multiply M by E.

$$\begin{array}{r} \text{ME} \\ +\text{MY} \\ \hline \text{EYE} \end{array}$$

Can you find the numbers?

Supplementary Exercises, Set 5, page 375

Solution sets, replacement sets

You know that the only solution of the equation $2x + 3 = 15$ is 6. This means that the set of all solutions of the equation is $\{6\}$. This set of all solutions is called the **solution set** of the equation.

The set of numbers from which we can choose a solution is called the replacement set. For example, if the replacement set is the set of whole numbers, $\{0, 1, 2, 3, \dots\}$, the equation $5x = 8$ has no solution. That is, the solution set is the empty set, $\varnothing$. If the replacement set is the set of fractional numbers, the solution set is

$$\left\{\frac{5}{8}\right\}$$

We can write other kinds of open sentences and find their solution sets. Here are some of the other symbols that we can use in sentences:

$\neq$	$<$	$>$	$\leq$	$\geq$
is not equal to	is less than	is greater than	is less than or equal to	is greater than or equal to

Sentences that contain these symbols are called **inequalities.**

Examples.

Inequality	Replacement Set	Solution Set
$2x \neq 8$	{whole numbers}	$\{0, 1, 2, 3, 5, \dots\}$
$a + 7 < 10$	{odd numbers}	$\{1\}$
$a + 7 \leq 10$	{odd numbers}	$\{1, 3\}$
$g - 3 > 5$	{whole numbers}	$\{9, 10, 11, 12, 13, \dots\}$
$g - 3 \geq 5$	{whole numbers}	$\{8, 9, 10, 11, 12, \dots\}$
$\frac{16}{y} \geq 8$	{even numbers}	$\{2\}$ Notice that 0 is not a solution because we don't divide by 0.

EXERCISES

True or false?

1. $6 \neq 7$ **2.** $6 \neq 6$ **3.** $5 < 8$ **4.** $5 \leq 8$

5. $9 < 9$ **6.** $9 \leq 9$ **7.** $3 > 1$ **8.** $3 \geq 1$

9. $3 > 3$ **10.** $3 \geq 3$ **11.** $7 < 4$ **12.** $7 \leq 4$

13. $4 > 7$ **14.** $4 \geq 7$ **15.** $\frac{1}{2} \neq 0$ **16.** $\frac{1}{2} > 0$

Does the number given in red make the sentence true or false?

17. 7 $8a \neq 32$ **18.** 4 $8a \neq 32$ **19.** 1 $g + 7 < 9$

20. 12 $\frac{a}{2} > 5$ 21. 6 $12 - b \leq 4$ 22. 8 $12 - b \leq 4$

23. 9 $12 - b \leq 4$ 24. 13 $c - 9 \geq 6$ 25. 3 $5x + 3 \leq 18$

Give each solution set. The replacement set is {0, 1, 2, 3, . . .}.

26. $5a \neq 20$
27. $a - 3 \neq 6$
28. $a - 3 = 6$
29. $2b > 12$
30. $2b = 12$
31. $2b \geq 12$
32. $a + 5 = 9$
33. $a + 5 < 9$
34. $a + 5 \leq 9$
35. $\frac{a}{3} \geq 5$
36. $\frac{g}{3} > 7$
37. $\frac{k}{2} \leq 5$
38. $8 - y \leq 2$
39. $m - 3 \leq 8$
40. $\frac{8}{y} \leq 2$
41. $\frac{8}{z} \geq 2$
42. $17 - n \geq 15$
43. $q - 7 \leq 5$
44. $2a + 1 = 9$
45. $2a + 1 < 9$
46. $2a + 1 \leq 9$
47. $3(x - 2) = 6$
48. $3(x - 2) > 6$
49. $3(x - 2) \geq 6$
50. $5m + 4 < 34$
51. $\frac{r + 3}{2} > 4$
52. $\frac{3m - 2}{2} \neq 7$

53. Karl thought that 6 was a solution of $\frac{3x + 2}{2} < 10$.

Prove that he was wrong.

54. Can you guess what the $\nless$ symbol means?

55. What other symbol means the same as $\ngeq$?

EXCURSION

Study these special numbers that we call *triangular numbers*.

First triangular number	Second triangular number	Third triangular number	Fourth triangular number	Fifth triangular number

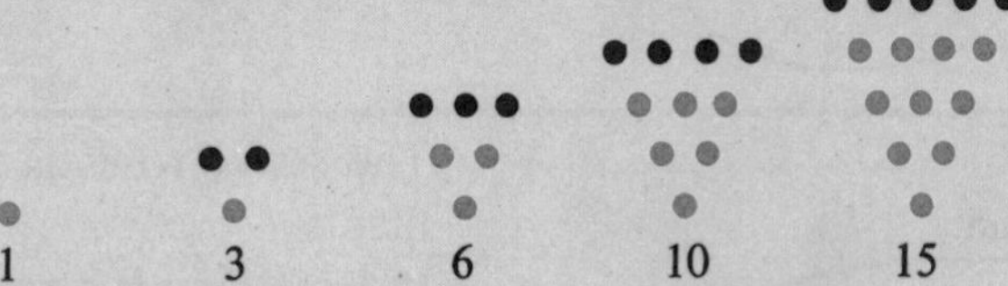

1	3	6	10	15

Can you find the next five triangular numbers?

Can you give a rule for finding any triangular number?

Skill Maintenance, Set 5, page 398

Logic

We don't often use the words *intersection*, *union*, and *subset* in everyday conversation. We use more ordinary words instead. Study the examples to see how the two kinds of language are related.

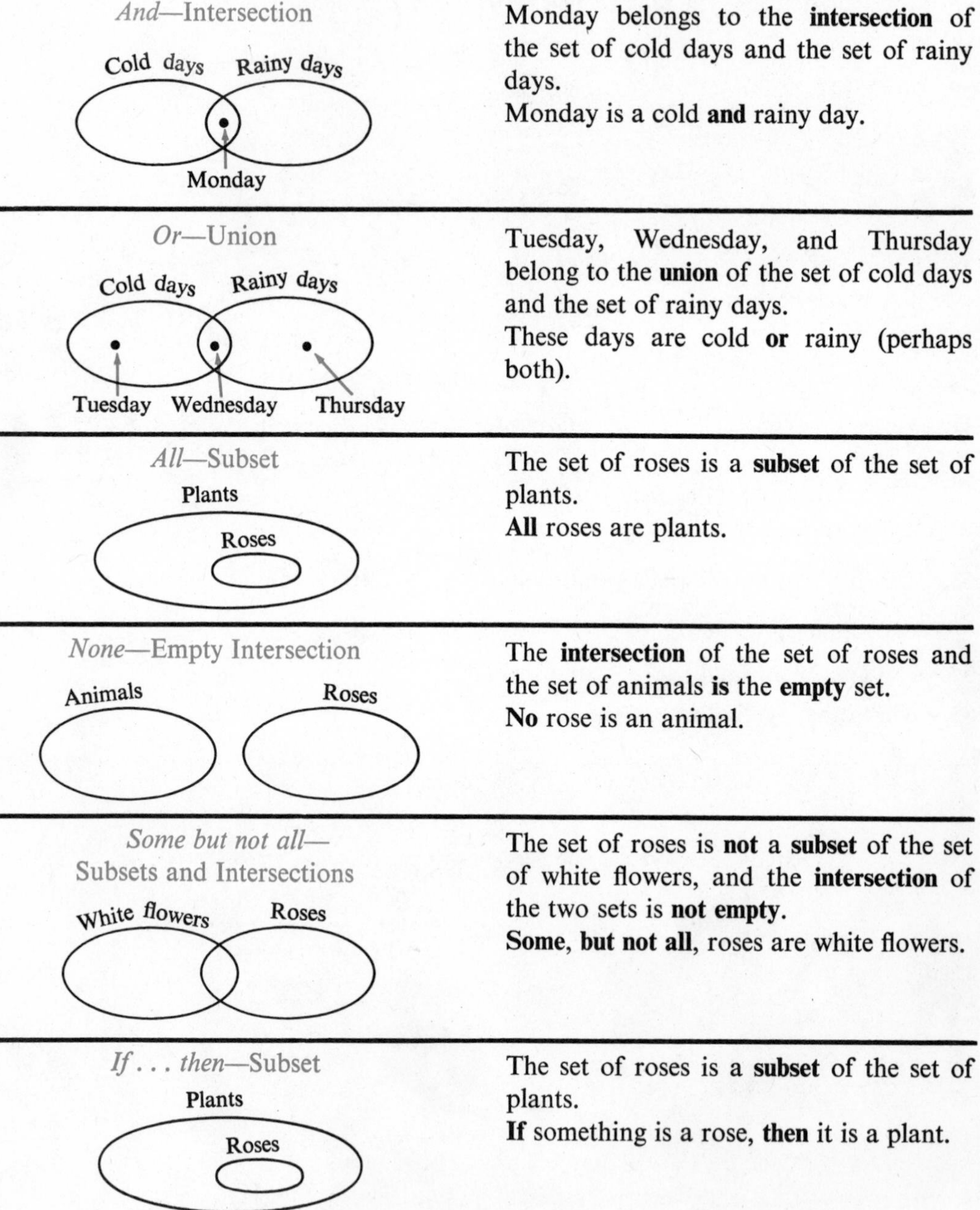

And—Intersection

Monday belongs to the **intersection** of the set of cold days and the set of rainy days.
Monday is a cold **and** rainy day.

Or—Union

Tuesday, Wednesday, and Thursday belong to the **union** of the set of cold days and the set of rainy days.
These days are cold **or** rainy (perhaps both).

All—Subset

The set of roses is a **subset** of the set of plants.
All roses are plants.

None—Empty Intersection

The **intersection** of the set of roses and the set of animals **is** the **empty** set.
No rose is an animal.

Some but not all—
Subsets and Intersections

The set of roses is **not** a **subset** of the set of white flowers, and the **intersection** of the two sets is **not empty**.
Some, **but not all**, roses are white flowers.

If . . . then—Subset

The set of roses is a **subset** of the set of plants.
If something is a rose, **then** it is a plant.

EXERCISES

The statements go with the pictures. Is the statement true or false?

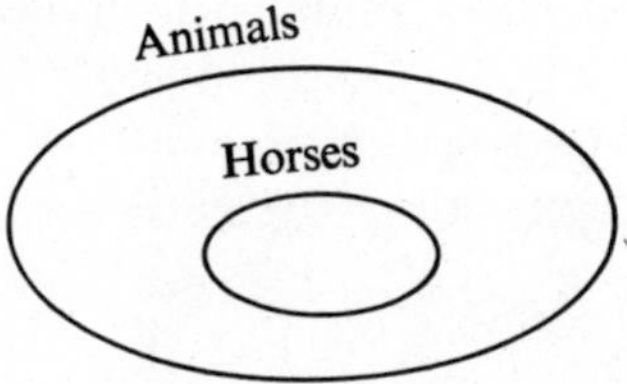

1. All horses are animals.
2. No horses are animals.
3. If something is a horse, then it is an animal.
4. Some, but not all, animals are horses.
5. Some, but not all, horses are animals.

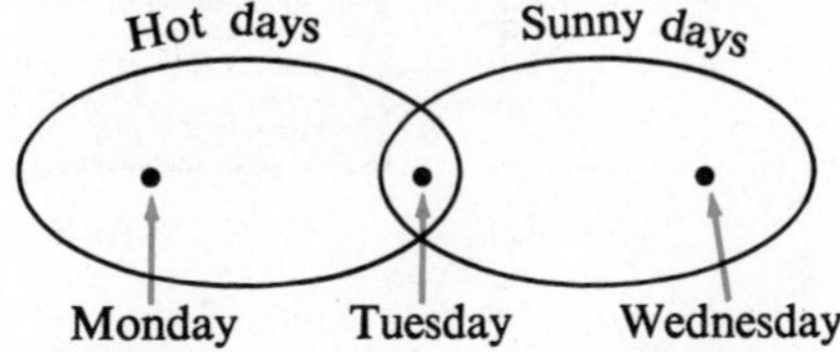

6. Monday was hot and sunny.
7. Tuesday was hot and not sunny.
8. Wednesday was hot or sunny.

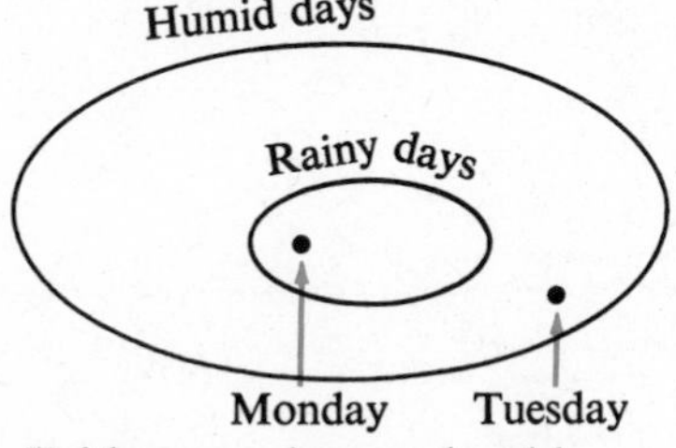

9. Monday was rainy and humid.
10. Tuesday was rainy.
11. Monday was rainy or humid.
12. Tuesday was rainy and humid.

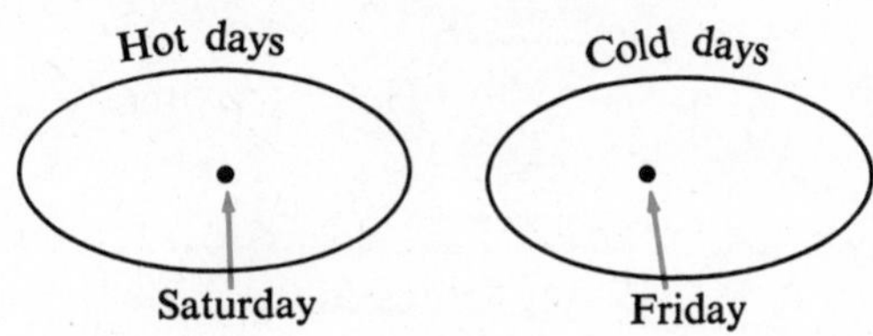

13. Friday was hot and cold.
14. Friday was hot or cold.
15. If Saturday was hot, then it was cold.
16. No days are hot and cold.

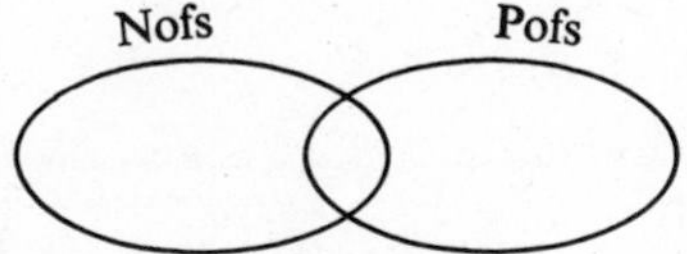

17. All nofs are pofs.
18. Some pofs are nofs.
19. No nofs are pofs.
20. If something is a nof, then it is a pof.

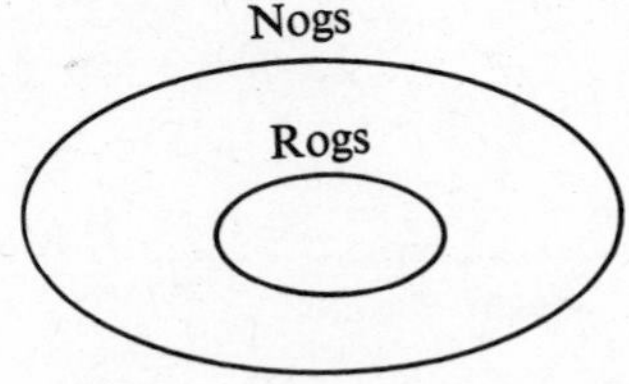

21. All nogs are rogs.
22. All rogs are nogs.
23. If something is a rog, then it is a nog.
24. If something is a nog, then it is a rog.
25. No nogs are rogs.
26. No rogs are nogs.

Skill Maintenance, Set 6, page 398

Functions

In mathematics a **function** is like a machine that puts together pairs of numbers according to a rule. Here is an example:

7 goes into the machine.

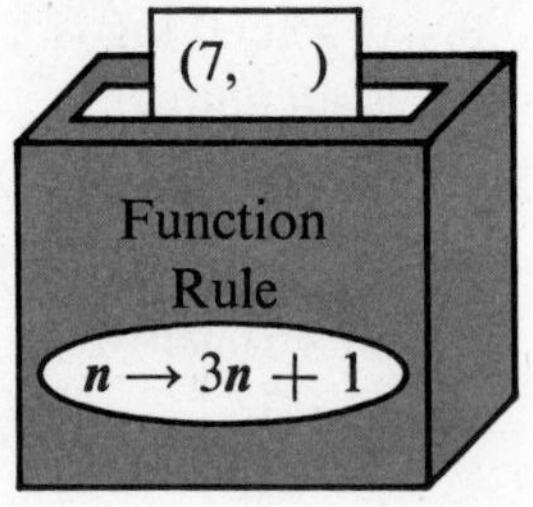

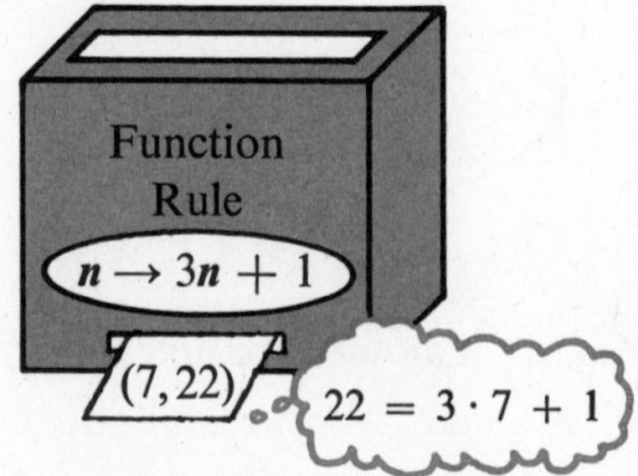

The machine pairs 7 and 22.

Here are other pairs of numbers for the rule:

$$n \rightarrow 3n + 1$$

(6, 19) $6 \rightarrow 3 \cdot 6 + 1$

(10, 31) $10 \rightarrow 3 \cdot 10 + 1$

(0, 1) $0 \rightarrow 3 \cdot 0 + 1$

Here is another function rule and some of its pairs:

$$m \rightarrow m^2 + 3$$

(4, 19) $4 \rightarrow 4^2 + 3$

(9, 84) $9 \rightarrow 9^2 + 3$

(0, 3) $0 \rightarrow 0^2 + 3$

EXERCISES

Complete each pair.

1. Function Rule

$a \rightarrow a + 9$

a. (3, ?)
b. (5, ?)
c. (9, ?)
d. (?, 10)
e. (?, 15)

2. Function Rule

$n \rightarrow 7n$

a. (6, ?)
b. (8, ?)
c. (9, ?)
d. (?, 49)
e. (?, 70)

3. Function Rule

$x \rightarrow x^2$

a. (1, ?)
b. (0, ?)
c. (5, ?)
d. (?, 81)
e. (?, 64)

4. Function Rule

$y \rightarrow 4y - 3$

a. (8, ?)
b. (9, ?)
c. (10, ?)
d. (?, 29)
e. (?, 25)

5. Function Rule

$b \rightarrow \frac{b+3}{2}$

a. (7, ?)
b. (15, ?)
c. (4, ?)
d. (?, 8)
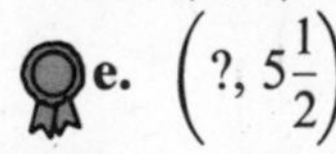
e. $\left(?, 5\frac{1}{2}\right)$

6. Function Rule

$g \rightarrow 7g + 1$

a. (10, ?)
b. (8, ?)
c. (6, ?)
d. (?, 36)
e. (?, 64)

7. Function Rule

$z \rightarrow 3z^2$

a. (0, ?)
b. (1, ?)
c. (3, ?)
d. (?, 12)
e. (?, 300)

8. Function Rule

$m \rightarrow \frac{2m - 4}{2}$

a. (5, ?)
b. (2, ?)
c. (8, ?)
d. (?, 8)
e. (?, 5)

Complete each function rule.

9. Function Rule

$n \rightarrow ?$

(1, 2)
(3, 6)
(9, 18)

10. Function Rule

$m \rightarrow ?$

(1, 2)
(3, 4)
(9, 10)

11. Function Rule

$a \rightarrow ?$

(9, 1)
(7, 3)
(5, 5)

12. Function Rule

$c \rightarrow ?$

(2, 1)
(6, 3)
(18, 9)

13. Function Rule

$h \rightarrow ?$

(2, 6)
(4, 12)
(8, 24)

14. Function Rule

$a \rightarrow ?$

(4, 14)
(7, 17)
(13, 23)

15. Function Rule

$m \rightarrow ?$

(15, 5)
(27, 17)
(41, 31)

16. Function Rule

$x \rightarrow ?$

(8, 4)
(7, 5)
(11, 1)

17. Function Rule

$b \rightarrow ?$

(5, 13)
(7, 17)
(10, 23)

18. Function Rule

$n \rightarrow ?$

(5, 29)
(9, 53)
(2, 11)

19. Function Rule

$f \rightarrow ?$

(2, 5)
(4, 17)
(8, 65)

20. Function Rule

$h \rightarrow ?$

(3, 10)
(5, 16)
(6, 19)

CHECKUP
for pages 16–19

Solve.

1. $7x = 35$
2. $a + 9 = 16$
3. $2a + 5 = 23$
4. $18 - 3x = 9$
5. $\frac{b+8}{3} = 6$
6. $4(a + 7) = 40$
7. $\frac{2c+8}{2} = 11$
8. $\frac{5(r+4)}{10} = 4$

Answers on page 425.

Supplementary Exercises, Set 6, page 375

Writing about functions

Mathematicians often name functions with such letters of the alphabet as f, g, and h. For example, here is a rule for a function we will call f:

$$f: n \rightarrow n + 3.$$

This function pairs each number with the number that is 3 more. For example, the function pairs 4 with 7.

We think: The number that f pairs 4 with is 7.

We write: $f(4) = 7$

We say:

Here are other examples.

$f(1) = 4$ $\quad f(10) = 13$ $\quad f(97) = 100$

In general we can write: $f(n) = n + 3$ (f of n equals $n + 3$)

Here is another function, which we'll call g. g pairs each number with its double:

$$g: x \rightarrow 2x$$

$g(3) = 6$ $\quad g(10) = 20$ $\quad g(5) = 10$ $\quad g(6) = 12$

EXERCISES

Here is a function rule for a function f: $n \rightarrow 2n + 1$.

Complete.

1. $f(1) = ?$ **2.** $f(2) = ?$ **3.** $f(3) = ?$ **4.** $f(7) = ?$

5. $f(?) = 19$ **6.** $f(10) = ?$ **7.** $f(?) = 13$ **8.** $f(?) = 25$

Here is a function rule for a function g: $m \rightarrow 12 - m$.

Complete.

9. $g(7) = ?$ **10.** $g(5) = ?$ **11.** $g(10) = ?$ **12.** $g(?) = 0$

13. $g(?) = 4$ **14.** $g(?) = 12$ **15.** $g(6) = ?$ **16.** $g(1) = ?$

Here are three functions:

$f: n \to 3n - 2 \qquad g: x \to x^2 + 1 \qquad h: c \to \dfrac{c + 5}{2}$

Complete.

17. $f(1) = ?$ **18.** $g(1) = ?$ **19.** $h(1) = ?$ **20.** $f(5) = ?$
21. $g(5) = ?$ **22.** $h(5) = ?$ **23.** $f(?) = 22$ **24.** $g(?) = 37$
25. $h(?) = 6$ **26.** $f(10) = ?$ **27.** $g(10) = ?$ **28.** $h(10) = ?$
29. $g(0) = ?$ **30.** $f(x) = ?$ **31.** $g(n) = ?$ **32.** $h(b) = ?$

Here are three functions:

$f(y) = 7y \qquad g(y) = y - 1 \qquad h(y) = y + 9$

Complete.

33. $f: m \to ?$ **34.** $g: n \to ?$ **35.** $h: a \to ?$
36. $f(6) = ?$ **37.** $g(6) = ?$ **38.** $h(6) = ?$ **39.** $f(?) = 0$
40. $g(?) = 0$ **41.** $h(?) = 9$ **42.** $h(9) = ?$ **43.** $h(7) = ?$
44. $f(9) = ?$ **45.** $f(8) = ?$ **46.** $g(38) = ?$ **47.** $g(?) = 38$

In each exercise you are given three true sentences. Complete the fourth sentence.

48. $f(1) = 8$
$f(2) = 16$
$f(5) = 40$
$f(n) = ?$

49. $g(24) = 12$
$g(8) = 4$
$g(0) = 0$
$g(x) = ?$

50. $h(8) = 17$
$h(7) = 16$
$h(3) = 12$
$h(y) = ?$

51. $g(9) = 81$
$g(5) = 25$
$g(7) = 49$
$g(a) = ?$

52. $f(3) = 18$
$f(7) = 38$
$f(8) = 43$
$f(c) = ?$

53. $f(4) = 20$
$f(9) = 55$
$f(10) = 62$
$f(m) = ?$

CHECKUP
for pages 10–11, 22–23

List the elements.

1. $A \cup B$
2. $A \cap B$
3. $X \cup Y$
4. $X \cap Y$
5. $X \cap Z$
6. $Y \cup Z$

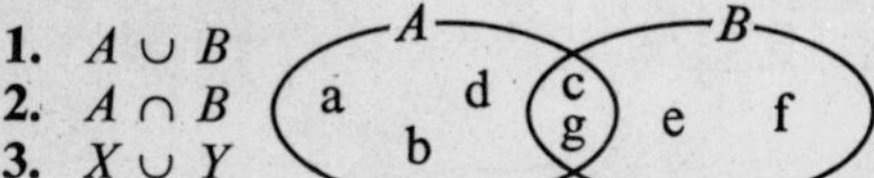

Is the statement true or false?

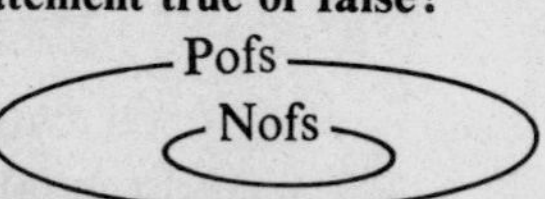

7. All nofs are pofs.
8. All pofs are nofs.
9. If something is a nof, then it is a pof.
10. Some, but not all, pofs are nofs.

Answers on page 425.

Supplementary Exercises, Set 7, page 375

Base six notation

Our numeration system is based on the number ten, probably because we have ten fingers. If we had only six fingers, three on each hand, we would probably have a base six system. When we count in a base six system, we group by sixes, not by tens. Study these examples.

	Sixes	Ones
One single block		1
Two		2
Three		3
Four		4
Five		5
One group of six	1	0
	1	1
	1	2
	1	3
	1	4
	1	5
	2	0

Here are other examples.

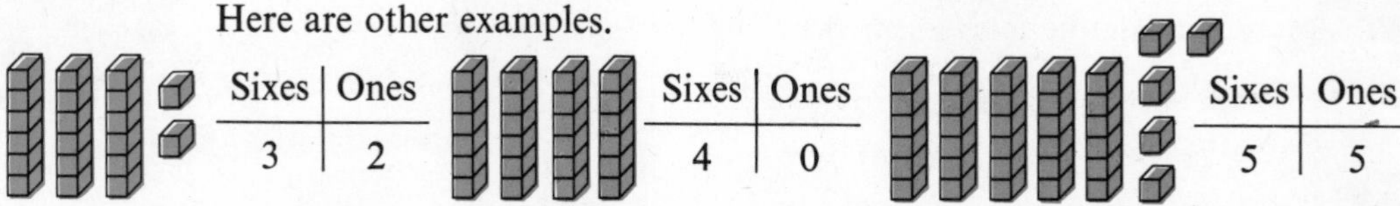

Sixes	Ones
3	2

Sixes	Ones
4	0

Sixes	Ones
5	5

When we get six groups of 6, we make a group of thirty-six. Then we need another column in the table.

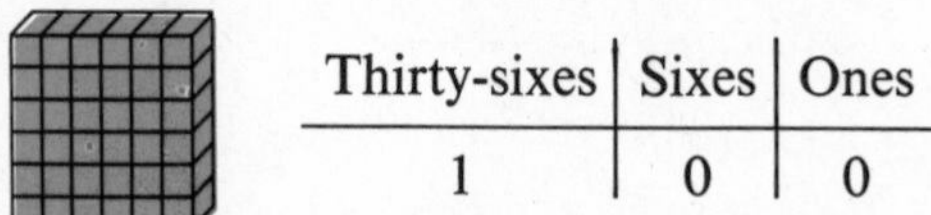

Thirty-sixes	Sixes	Ones
1	0	0

Of course, if we remember the values of the places we don't need the table.

Sixes	Ones	
2	3	$\rightarrow 23_{six}$

Read as "two three base six."

Sixes	Ones	
5	2	$\rightarrow 52_{six}$

Thirty-sixes	Sixes	Ones	
2	3	5	$\rightarrow 235_{six}$

EXERCISES

Write base six numerals for the number of blocks.

1.

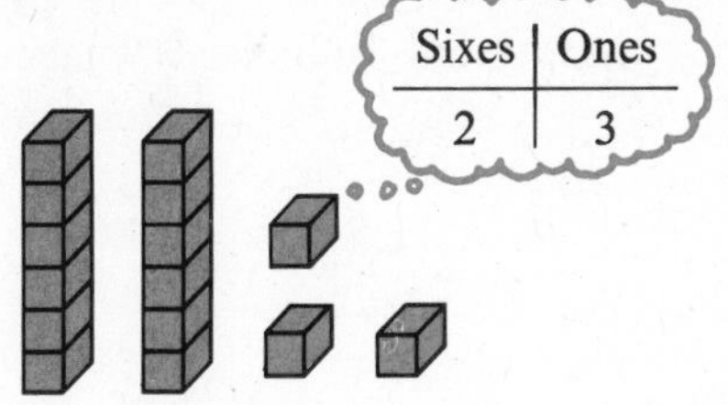

2.

3.

Copy and complete this table.

	4.	5.	6.	7.	8.	9.	10.	11.	12.	13.	14.	15.
Base ten		2	3	4	5	6	7	8	9	10	11	12
Base six	1_{six}											

	16.	17.	18.	19.	20.	21.	22.	23.	24.	25.	26.	27.
Base ten			35	36		40	50	60				
Base six	31_{six}	45_{six}			103_{six}				200_{six}	324_{six}	412_{six}	525_{six}

Answer each question, using base six numerals.

28. How old are you?

29. How many days in a week?

30. How many days in June?

31. How many days in January?

32. How many centimeters tall are you?

33. How many students in your class?

34. How many boys in your class?

35. How many girls in your class?

36. Copy and complete this addition table.

+	0_{six}	1_{six}	2_{six}	3_{six}	4_{six}	5_{six}
0_{six}						
1_{six}						
2_{six}						
3_{six}				10_{six}		
4_{six}						
5_{six}						

37. Copy and complete this multiplication table.

×	0_{six}	1_{six}	2_{six}	3_{six}	4_{six}	5_{six}
0_{six}						
1_{six}						
2_{six}						
3_{six}				13_{six}		
4_{six}						
5_{six}						

Skill Maintenance, Set 7, page 398

Base twelve notation

In a base twelve numeration system we would use a place-value table like this one.

One hundred forty-fours	Twelves	Ones

This means that we must name the numbers ten and eleven by using single digits in the ones place. (Why can't we use "10" and "11"?) We will have to invent these symbols. Let's use ⊖ to name ten and ⊕ to name eleven. The examples below show how we can use base twelve numerals to name some numbers.

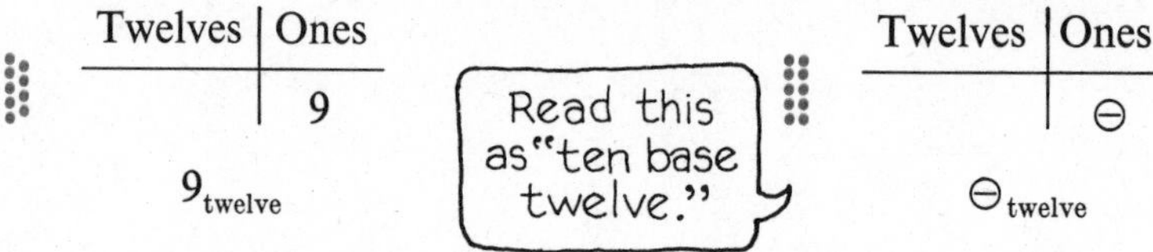

Twelves	Ones
	9

9_{twelve}

Twelves	Ones
	⊖

⊖$_{twelve}$

Twelves	Ones
	⊕

⊕$_{twelve}$

Twelves	Ones
1	0

10_{twelve}

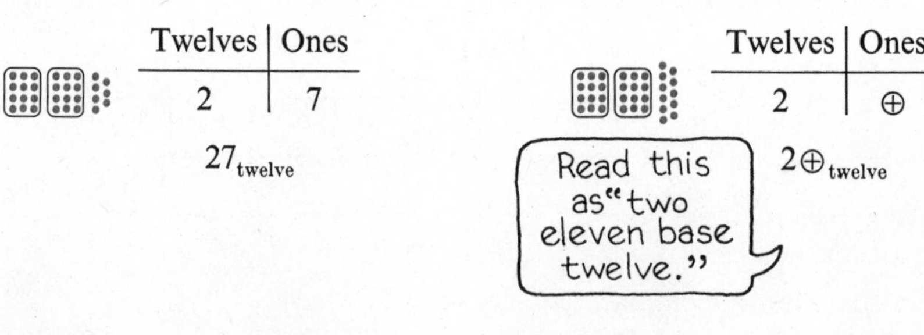

Twelves	Ones
2	7

27_{twelve}

Twelves	Ones
2	⊕

2⊕$_{twelve}$

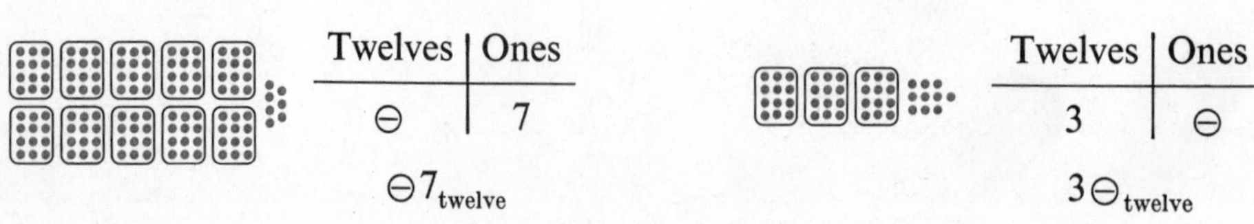

Twelves	Ones
⊖	7

⊖7_{twelve}

Twelves	Ones
3	⊖

3⊖$_{twelve}$

EXERCISES

Write the base twelve numeral.

1. 

2. 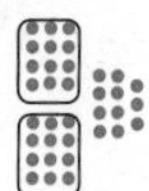

3.

4. 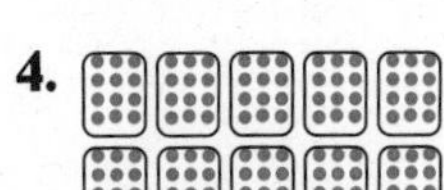

5.  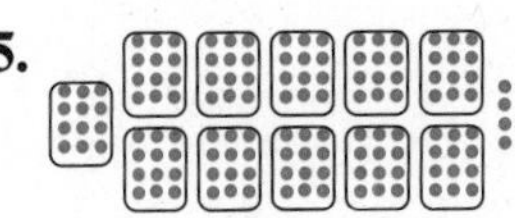

6. 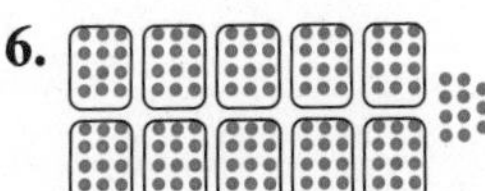

Complete this table.

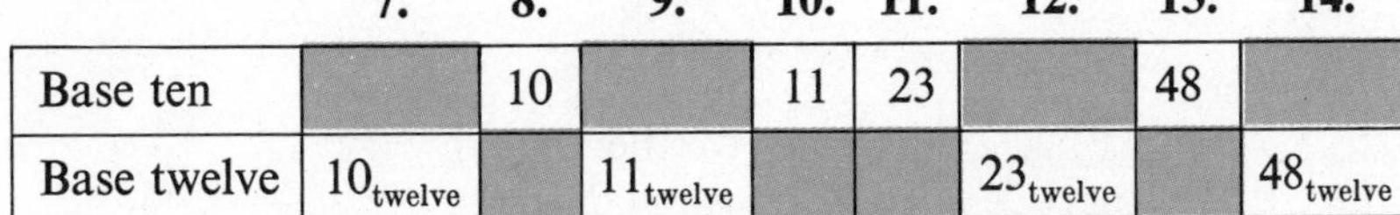

	7.	8.	9.	10.	11.	12.	13.	14.
Base ten		10		11	23		48	
Base twelve	10_{twelve}		11_{twelve}			23_{twelve}		48_{twelve}

	15.	16.	17.	18.	19.	20.	21.	22.
Base ten	50		83		120			143
Base twelve		50_{twelve}		92_{twelve}		$\ominus 7_{twelve}$	$\ominus \ominus_{twelve}$	

23. How would you name 144 in base twelve?

Answer each question in base twelve notation.

24. How old are you?

25. How many boys in your class?

26. How many girls in your class?

27. How many students in your class?

28. How many days in January?

29. How many days in a year?

Complete. Use base twelve notation.

30. $7_{twelve} + 3_{twelve} = ?$

31. $8_{twelve} + 3_{twelve} = ?$

32. $8_{twelve} + 4_{twelve} = ?$

33. $9_{twelve} + 9_{twelve} = ?$

34. $\ominus_{twelve} + 3_{twelve} = ?$

35. $\oplus_{twelve} + 7_{twelve} = ?$

36. $\ominus_{twelve} + \ominus_{twelve} = ?$

37. $\oplus_{twelve} + \oplus_{twelve} = ?$

38. Make a basic addition-fact table in base twelve.

39. Make a basic multiplication-fact table in base twelve.

Try these problems.

40. $\begin{array}{r} 27_{twelve} \\ +58_{twelve} \\ \hline \end{array}$

41. $\begin{array}{r} 3\oplus_{twelve} \\ +16_{twelve} \\ \hline \end{array}$

42. $\begin{array}{r} 1\ominus_{twelve} \\ -\oplus_{twelve} \\ \hline \end{array}$

43. $\begin{array}{r} 43_{twelve} \\ \times 4_{twelve} \\ \hline \end{array}$

44. $\begin{array}{r} 10_{twelve} \\ \times 7_{twelve} \\ \hline \end{array}$

Skill Maintenance, Set 8, page 399

Clock arithmetic

We can use this 6-hour "clock" to do a different kind of arithmetic, which has only 6 numbers. It is called a **modular arithmetic**. In this case the **modulus** is 6 (mod 6). Study these examples to see how to add, subtract, multiply, and divide.

Addition Mod 6

To add 3 + 5:
Start at 0 and move 3 spaces clockwise.

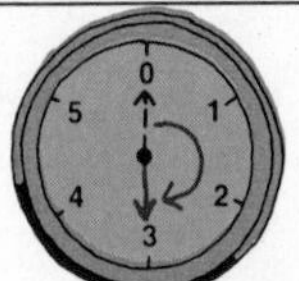

Then move the hand 5 more spaces clockwise.

$3 + 5 = 2 \pmod 6$

Subtraction Mod 6

To subtract 5 from 3:
Start at 0 and move the hand 3 spaces clockwise.

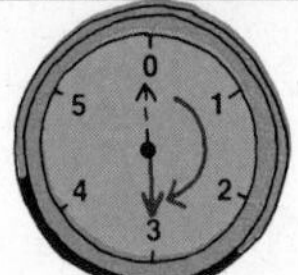

Then move the hand 5 spaces *counterclockwise.*

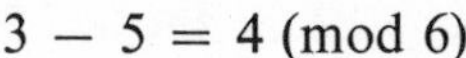

$3 - 5 = 4 \pmod 6$

Multiplication Mod 6

To multiply 2 × 4:
Start at 0.

Then make two 4-hour jumps clockwise.

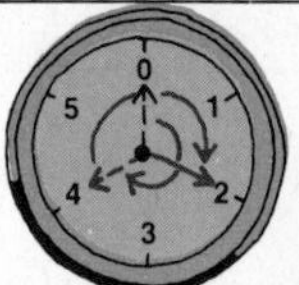

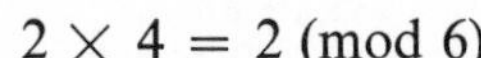

$2 \times 4 = 2 \pmod 6$

Division Mod 6

To divide 2 by 4:
Start at 2.

Then make 4-hour jumps *counterclockwise* until you land on 0. Your answer is the number of jumps.

$2 \div 4 = 2 \pmod 6$

EXERCISES

Do these mod 6 problems. Think about the clock.

1. 1 + 1 **2.** 1 + 2 **3.** 1 + 3 **4.** 1 + 4 **5.** 1 + 5
6. 2 + 1 **7.** 2 + 2 **8.** 2 + 3 **9.** 2 + 4 **10.** 2 + 5
11. 3 + 1 **12.** 3 + 2 **13.** 3 + 3 **14.** 3 + 4 **15.** 3 + 5
16. 4 + 1 **17.** 4 + 2 **18.** 4 + 3 **19.** 4 + 4 **20.** 4 + 5
21. 5 + 1 **22.** 5 + 2 **23.** 5 + 3 **24.** 5 + 4 **25.** 5 + 5

26. Is there a commutative property of addition mod 6?

27. $5 + 0$ **28.** $0 + 3$ **29.** $2 + 0$ **30.** $4 + 0$

31. Is there an adding 0 property of addition mod 6?

32. $(4 + 3) + 2$ **33.** $4 + (3 + 2)$ **34.** $(2 + 5) + 3$ **35.** $2 + (5 + 3)$

36. Is there an associative property of addition mod 6?

37. $5 - 2$ **38.** $2 - 5$ **39.** $4 - 1$ **40.** $1 - 4$ **41.** $2 - 3$

42. $3 - 2$ **43.** 3×5 **44.** 4×3 **45.** 4×4 **46.** 2×2

47. 2×3 **48.** 5×5 **49.** 0×1 **50.** 1×5 **51.** 3×1

52. $2 \div 2$ **53.** $2 \div 4$ **54.** $3 \div 3$ **55.** $2 \div 5$ **56.** $3 \div 2$

57. Complete this multiplication table.

×	0	1	2	3	4	5
0						
1						
2						
3			0			
4						
5						

58. Does multiplication mod 6 have these properties?
- **a.** a commutative property
- **b.** an associative property
- **c.** a multiplying by 0 property
- **d.** a multiplying by 1 property

59. Solve the equation $3m = 2$ (mod 6).

60. What does your answer to exercise 59 tell you about $2 \div 3$?

61. What other numbers, besides 2, cannot be divided by 3?

62. Are there any numbers that cannot be divided by 2?

63. Are there any numbers that cannot be divided by 5?

64. Why, do you think, are the answers to exercises 62 and 63 different?

65. Use this 5-hour clock to complete the addition table and the multiplication table for a mod 5 system.

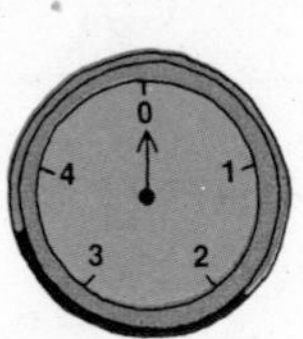

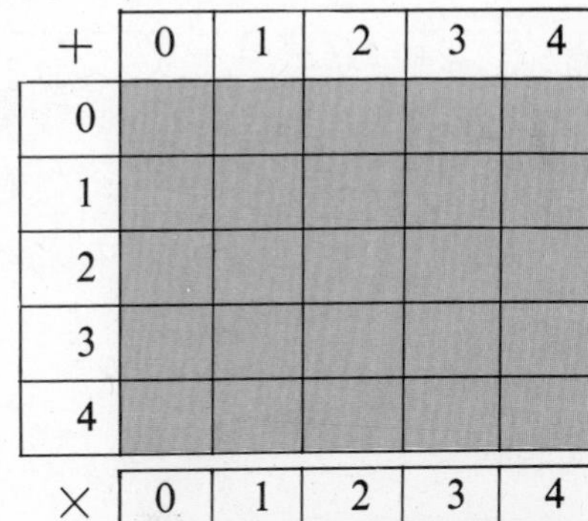

+	0	1	2	3	4
0					
1					
2					
3					
4					

×	0	1	2	3	4
0					
1					
2					
3					
4					

66. Do addition and multiplication mod 5 have commutative properties, associative properties, etc.?

67. Are there any division problems that do not have answers?

Skill Maintenance, Set 9, page 399

CHAPTER CHECKUP

Simplify. [*page 2*]

1. $9 - 3 - 2$ **2.** $6 + 4 \times 5$ **3.** $12 \div 6 \div 2$ **4.** $3 \times (5 + 4)$

Substitute and simplify. [*pages 4, 6*]

a	b	D	d	x
3	2	5	4	7

5. $5a$ **6.** db **7.** $b(D + d)$ **8.** $9 - ab$ **9.** $\frac{a + D}{d}$

10. a^2 **11.** b^3 **12.** x^2 **13.** $3b^2$ **14.** $(d + D)^2$

Answer each question. [*page 10*]

15. Is 2 an element of B?

16. Is 2 an element of A?

17. Is 3 an element of B?

18. Is B a subset of A?

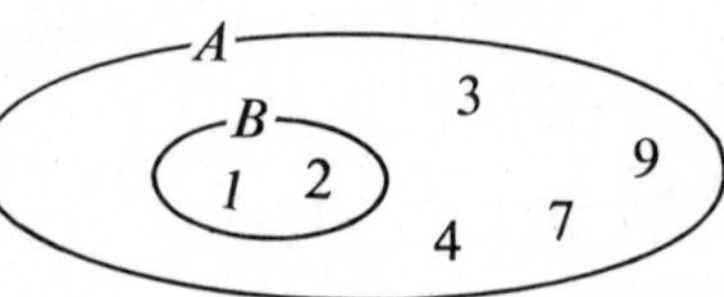

19. Is A a subset of B?

List the elements of each union or intersection. [*page 12*]

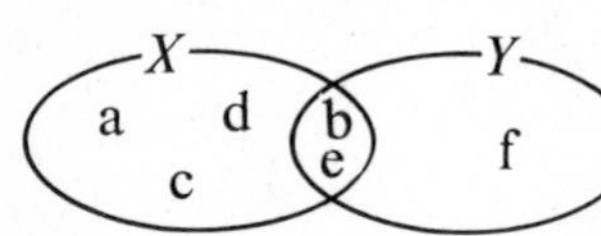

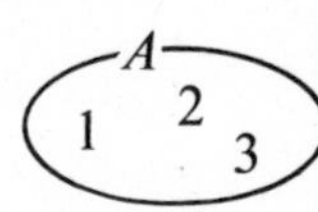

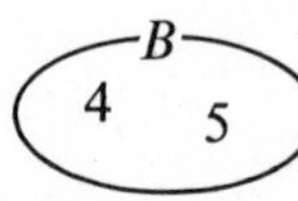

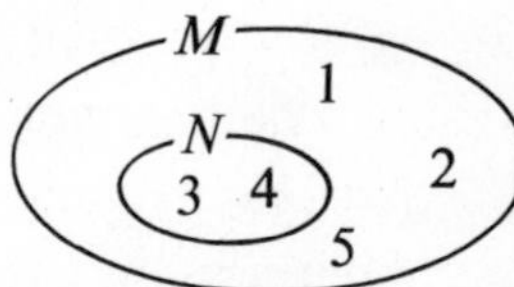

20. $X \cap Y$ **21.** $X \cup Y$ **22.** $A \cap B$ **23.** $A \cup B$ **24.** $M \cap N$ **25.** $M \cup N$

Give the LCM and GCF. Use prime factors. [*page 14*]

26. 30, 16 **27.** 52, 64 **28.** 48, 72 **29.** 256, 144

Solve. [*pages 16, 18*]

30. $4a = 24$ **31.** $g + 7 = 12$ **32.** $15 - c = 9$ **33.** $\frac{a}{3} = 6$

34. $4a - 7 = 29$ **35.** $8(y + 2) = 48$ **36.** $20 - 3m = 2$ **37.** $\frac{2(4n - 3)}{3} = 6$

Complete. [*page 24*]

38. Function Rule
$b \rightarrow 2b + 3$

a. (3, ?)
b. (7, ?)
c. (?, 13)

39. Function Rule
$n \rightarrow n^2$

a. (9, ?)
b. (4, ?)
c. (?, 9)

40. $f: m \rightarrow 3(2 + m)$

a. $f(4) = ?$
b. $f(7) = ?$
c. $f(?) = 21$

41. $g: x \rightarrow \frac{x + 5}{2}$

a. $g(5) = ?$
b. $g(4) = ?$
c. $g(?) = 7$

Some seventh- and eighth-graders were taking orders for school sweatshirts. The following numbers of orders were taken.

Seventh-grade orders

	Small	Medium	Large
White	2	3	5
Blue	1	8	4

Eighth-grade orders

	Small	Medium	Large
White	1	6	2
Blue	1	3	9

The seventh- and eighth-graders then combined the orders and sent them to a supply company.

	Small	Medium	Large
White	3	9	7
Blue	2	11	13

How did the seventh- and eighth-graders "combine" their orders?

Notice that the orders are in the form of rectangular arrays of numbers. Mathematicians often work with rectangular arrays of numbers and place them in parentheses. Such an array is called a **matrix.** Each of these is a matrix:

$$\begin{pmatrix} 2 & 3 & 5 \\ 1 & 8 & 4 \end{pmatrix} \qquad \begin{pmatrix} 3 & 9 \\ 2 & 6 \\ 9 & 4 \end{pmatrix} \qquad \begin{pmatrix} 10 & 6 \\ 5 & 3 \end{pmatrix}$$

Matrices (the plural of matrix) may have any number of rows or columns. Two matrices with the same number of rows and columns can be added. Study the following example of matrix addition. How is it like the sweatshirt orders above?

$$\begin{pmatrix} 2 & 3 & 5 \\ 1 & 8 & 4 \end{pmatrix} + \begin{pmatrix} 1 & 6 & 2 \\ 1 & 3 & 9 \end{pmatrix} = \begin{pmatrix} 3 & 9 & 7 \\ 2 & 11 & 13 \end{pmatrix}$$

Practice adding these matrices.

1. $\begin{pmatrix} 3 & 7 & 10 \\ 6 & 5 & 8 \end{pmatrix} + \begin{pmatrix} 2 & 4 & 7 \\ 3 & 9 & 10 \end{pmatrix}$ **2.** $\begin{pmatrix} 2 & 4 & 7 \\ 3 & 9 & 10 \end{pmatrix} + \begin{pmatrix} 3 & 7 & 10 \\ 6 & 5 & 8 \end{pmatrix}$ **3.** $\begin{pmatrix} 3 & 9 \\ 2 & 6 \\ 9 & 4 \end{pmatrix} + \begin{pmatrix} 6 & 4 \\ 3 & 2 \\ 0 & 5 \end{pmatrix}$

Do you think matrix addition is commutative? Associative?

2 Decimals and Problem Solving

Expanded and standard forms

Here is part of a base ten place-value table.

		Thousands	Hundreds	Tens	Ones		Tenths	Hundredths	Thousandths	
	...	___	___	___	___	.	___	___	___	...
powers of ten		10^3	10^2	10^1	10^0		$\frac{1}{10^1}$	$\frac{1}{10^2}$	$\frac{1}{10^3}$	

We can write about numbers using expanded form or we can use standard place-value form.

Expanded form: $3 \times 10^2 + 0 \times 10^1 + 2 \times 10^0 + 7 \times \frac{1}{10^1} + 5 \times \frac{1}{10^2}$

Standard form: 3 0 2 . 7 5

Examples.

Expanded Form	Standard Form
6×10^1	60
8×10^0	8
$3 \times \frac{1}{10^1}$	.3
$1 \times \frac{1}{10^2}$	.01
$7 \times 10^3 + 5 \times 10^0 + 9 \times \frac{1}{10^3}$	7005.009

EXERCISES

Write in standard form.

1. 5×10^2 **2.** 4×10^1 **3.** 6×10^0 **4.** $7 \times \frac{1}{10}$

5. $9 \times \frac{1}{10^2}$ **6.** $5 \times 10^2 + 4 \times 10^1 + 6 \times 10^0 + 7 \times \frac{1}{10^1} + 9 \times \frac{1}{10^2}$

7. $2 \times 10^3 + 5 \times 10^2$ **8.** $4 \times 10^2 + 7 \times \frac{1}{10^2}$

9. $7 \times 10^5 + 4 \times 10^4 + 6 \times 10^3$ **10.** $9 \times \frac{1}{10^2} + 8 \times \frac{1}{10^4}$

11. $9 \times 10^7 + 6 \times 10^4 + 2 \times 10^0$

12. $8 \times 10^4 + 7 \times \frac{1}{10^4}$

13. $4 \times \frac{1}{10^2} + 6 \times \frac{1}{10^3} + 9 \times \frac{1}{10^4}$

14. $1 \times 10^3 + 1 \times 10^0 + 1 \times \frac{1}{10^4}$

Write in expanded form.

15. 9 16. 90 17. 900 18. .9 19. .09

20. 74 21. 243.1 22. 5.43 23. 200.002

How many hundred-dollar bills would it take to make each value?

24. $700 25. $800 26. $900 27. $1000 28. $2000

29. $4100 30. $5700 31. $80,000 32. $82,000 33. $84,000

How many hundreds in all in each number?

34. 800 35. 1000 36. 1900 37. 6700 38. 50,000

39. 57,200 40. 600,000 41. 751,200 42. 8200 43. 75,000

44. 50 *Answer.* .5 because 50 is 5 tenths of 100

45. 60 46. 70 47. 80 48. 90 49. 100

50. 3 51. 9 52. 36 53. 242 54. 1567

55. 3852 56. 47,386

How many tens in all?

57. 80 58. 100 59. 300

60. 520 61. 7 62. 8

63. 28 64. 728 65. 5283

How many tenths?

66. .2 67. .9 68. 1.0

69. 3.0 70. 4.1 71. 20.0

72. 23.4 73. .02 74. .08

75. .35 76. 4.27 77. 21.35

How many hundredths?

78. .03 79. .09 80. .10

81. .19 82. .45 83. 2.00

84. 2.35 85. 42.77 86. .008

87. .024 88. .357 89. 2.684

EXCURSION

The Roman numeral system is not a place-value system. These symbols are used:

I	V	X	L	C	D	M
1	5	10	50	100	500	1000

and the symbols are written in strings:

CXXVI

The values of the single symbols are then added. The numeral above names 126. Notice that the symbol for the greatest value is on the left. The symbols are in order of their values.

What is the value of each numeral?

1. LXXVII 2. CCLXI
3. MDCLXVI 4. MMXXVIII
5. XXXVI 6. MDCCXVII

You will learn another rule on page 39.

Skill Maintenance, Set 10, page 399

Decimal exercises

One centimeter (cm) is .1 decimeter (dm).

Decimeter: •—•—•—•—•—•—•—•—•—•—•

Centimeter: •—•

Complete, using decimals.

1. 1 cm = ___?___ dm
2. 2 cm = ___?___ dm
3. 5 cm = ___?___ dm
4. 9 cm = ___?___ dm
5. 10 cm = ___?___ dm
6. 11 cm = ___?___ dm
7. 13 cm = ___?___ dm
8. 24 cm = ___?___ dm
9. ___?___ cm = 1 dm
10. ___?___ cm = 2 dm
11. ___?___ cm = 1.5 dm
12. ___?___ cm = .8 dm
13. ___?___ cm = 2.9 dm
14. ___?___ cm = 3.8 dm
15. ___?___ cm = 7.2 dm
16. ___?___ cm = 10 dm

A cent has a value of .1 dime.

Complete, using decimals.

17. 1 cent = ___?___ dimes
18. 7 cents = ___?___ dimes
19. 17 cents = ___?___ dimes
20. 35 cents = ___?___ dimes
21. 127 cents = ___?___ dimes
22. ___?___ cents = 3 dimes
23. ___?___ cents = 4 dimes
24. ___?___ cents = 3.3 dimes
25. ___?___ cents = 7.5 dimes

One centimeter is .01 meter (m).

Complete, using decimals.

26. 1 cm = ___?___ m
27. 2 cm = ___?___ m
28. 9 cm = ___?___ m
29. 10 cm = ___?___ m
30. 11 cm = ___?___ m
31. 24 cm = ___?___ m
32. 57 cm = ___?___ m
33. 99 cm = ___?___ m
34. 100 cm = ___?___ m
35. 200 cm = ___?___ m
36. 523 cm = ___?___ m
37. 4286 cm = ___?___ m
38. ___?___ cm = .04 m
39. ___?___ cm = .07 m
40. ___?___ cm = .32 m
41. ___?___ cm = .50 m
42. ___?___ cm = 1 m
43. ___?___ cm = 1.07 m
44. ___?___ cm = 3.22 m
45. ___?___ cm = 4.30 m

One meter is .001 kilometer (km).

Complete, using decimals.

46. 2m = ___?___ km
47. 12 m = ___?___ km
48. 37 m = ___?___ km
49. 500 m = ___?___ km
50. 725 m = ___?___ km
51. 1000 m = ___?___ km
52. 2834 m = ___?___ km
53. 5286 m = ___?___ km
54. ___?___ m = 5 km
55. ___?___ m = 5.2 km
56. ___?___ m = 5.23 km
57. ___?___ m = 5.235 km

Copy the digits and put in a decimal point so that the number makes sense.

58. This car averaged 13742 miles per hour in a race.

59. This plane averaged 5756 miles per hour on a flight.

60. Bill said that he was 5467 inches tall.

61. Mary weighed 1273 pounds.

62. The Glenbrook High School Building is 5322 feet high.

63. A slice of bread is 934 centimeters thick.

64. One automobile gasoline tank holds 185 gallons of gas.

65. In 6 hours Mrs. Hart drove 3247 miles.

Answer the questions.

66. What is half of 100?

67. What is half of 10?

68. What is half of 1?

69. What is half of .1?

70. What is half of .01?

71. What is half of .001?

What is the midpoint of each segment?

72.	6 — 7	**73.**	50 — 60
74.	10 — 11	**75.**	.3 — .4
76.	.9 — 1.0	**77.**	1.0 — 1.1
78.	.04 — .05	**79.**	.99 — 1.00

EXCURSION

On page 37 you learned an addition rule for writing Roman numerals. There is also a subtraction rule: If a symbol is followed by a symbol for a greater value, subtract the smaller value from the greater value.

IV: $5 - 1 = 4$ XXIX: $10 + 10 + (10 - 1) = 29$

Find each value.

1. IX **2.** XI
3. XL **4.** LX
5. CM **6.** MC
7. XXIV **8.** XLVI
9. XLIV **10.** MCM
11. CCXCIV **12.** MCMLXXVI

Make up other Roman numerals and find their values.

Supplementary Exercises, Set 8, page 375

Rounding

Study these examples of rounding.

Round to the nearest hundred: 5273
Find the "neighboring" multiples of 100. Choose the nearer one.

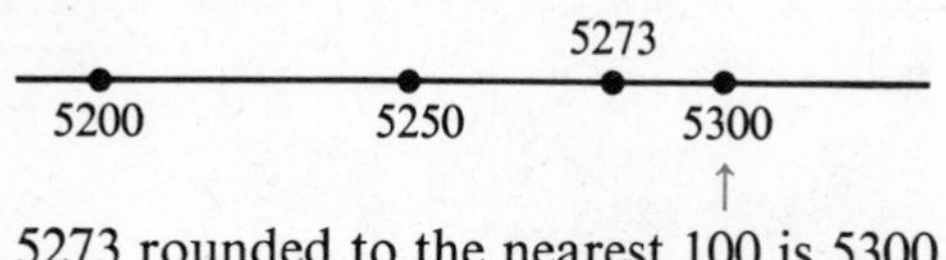

5273 rounded to the nearest 100 is 5300

Round to the nearest hundredth: 7.532
Find the "neighboring" multiples of .01. Choose the nearer one.

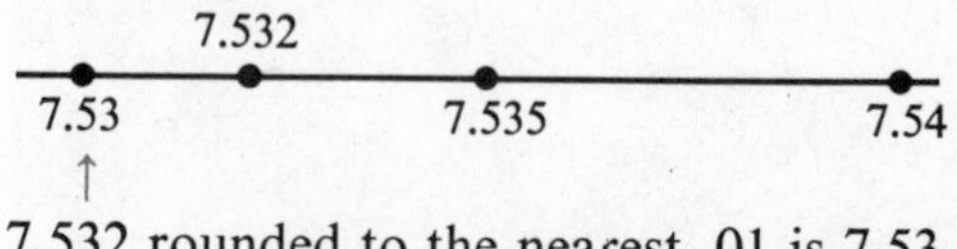

7.532 rounded to the nearest .01 is 7.53

Notice that when we round we introduce some error. Once we have decided on the place to which we will round, we make that error as small as possible. That is what the word "nearest" tells us. Here is an example of a trouble spot.

Round to the nearest ten: 435

Notice that 430 and 440 are equally good choices. Some people always choose the greater of the two choices, but there is another rule that is often used.

> When the number that is to be rounded is halfway between the two choices, choose the one with the *even* digit rather than the one with the odd digit.

Study these examples.

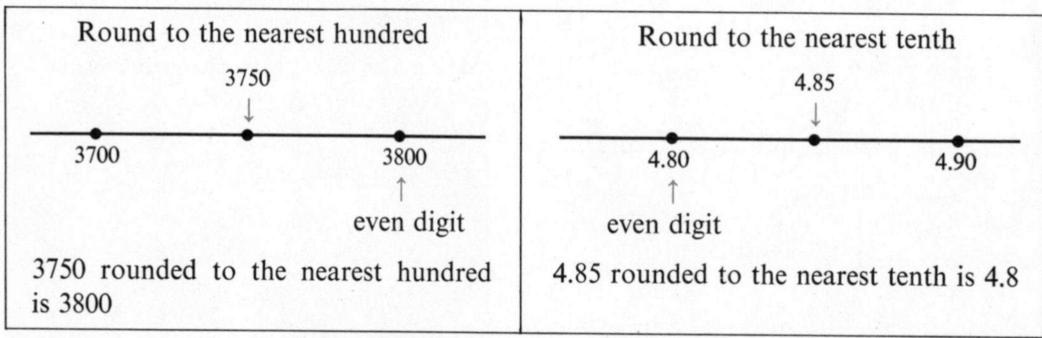

When you use this rule you sometimes round "upward" and sometimes "downward." If you are rounding several numbers in the same problem, the rounding errors tend to cancel out.

EXERCISES

Round to the nearest hundred.

1. 768 **2.** 823 **3.** 27562 **4.** 3850 **5.** 950

Round to the nearest tenth.

6. 8.57 **7.** 9.52 **8.** 127.635 **9.** 4.49 **10.** 4.449

11. 25.35 **12.** 35.45 **13.** .062 **14.** .7499 **15.** 567.451

Round to the nearest whole number.

16. 6.8 **17.** 7.3 **18.** 287.632 **19.** 18.5 **20.** 8.49

21. When Dr. Cooke went grocery shopping he always estimated his grocery bill. He rounded the prices to the nearest ten cents and then added "in his head." How would he round each of these prices?

a. 84¢ **b.** 39¢ **c.** 29¢ **d.** 55¢ **e.** 45¢

f. \$2.43 **g.** \$1.98 **h.** 99¢ **i.** 70¢ **j.** \$3.10

22. A number rounded to the nearest whole number is 27. What can you tell about the number?

23. A number rounded to the nearest million is 623,000,000. What can you tell about the number?

24. A newspaper article stated that \$25,000 had been collected for the United Fund. Do you think that *exactly* \$25,000 was collected? What can you tell about the amount that was collected?

Estimate each product or quotient by rounding each number to the nearest whole number.

25. 3.75×2.1 **26.** 5.277×4.932

27. $6.7\overline{)41.88}$ **28.** $3.21\overline{)27.42}$

CHECKUP
for pages 36–37

How many hundreds in each number?

1. 600 **2.** 1600 **3.** 620

4. 623 **5.** 3623 **6.** 2654.1

How many thousands?

7. 8000 **8.** 28000 **9.** 8600

10. 38200 **11.** 5342 **12.** 5342.6

Write in standard form.

13. 6.2 million

14. 5.77 billion

Answers on page 425.

Supplementary Exercises, Set 9, page 376

Adding and subtracting—decimals

You can add and subtract with decimals in exactly the same ways that you do with whole numbers. These examples using blocks and tenth-blocks show why.

Example 1. Addition

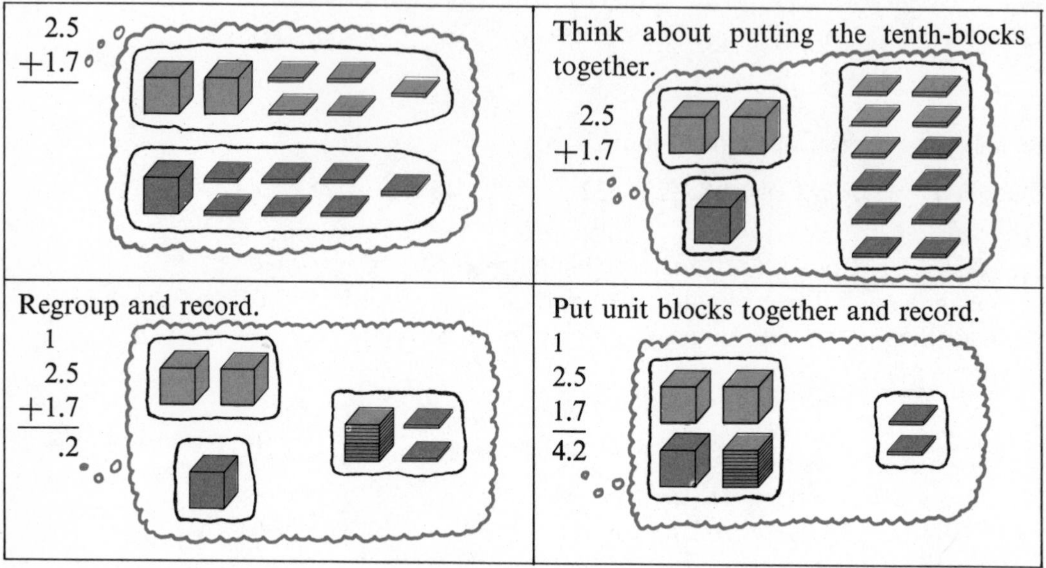

Example 2. Subtraction

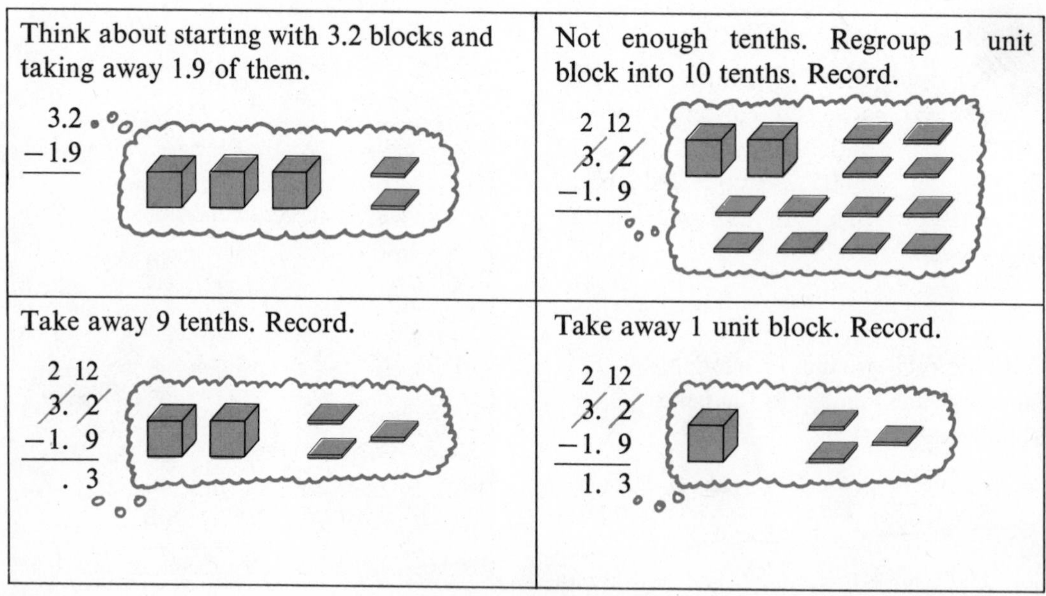

Example 3. 3.27 + .754

```
  1 1
  3.27    (Line up decimal points. 0 thousandths)
+ .754
 4.024
```

Example 4. 78.5 − .606

```
   14 9
  7 15 10 10
  7 8 . 5  0  0    (It may help to write the zeros.)
    − . 6  0  6
  7 7 . 8  9  4
```

EXERCISES

Add.

1. 3.7 + 2.8

2. .461 + .329

3. 28.6 + 54.3

4. 6.88 + 9.75

5. 4.07 + 7.03

6. 7.3 + 4.56

7. 23.8 + 3.96

8. 7.47 + .993 + 1.048

9. 88.6 + 5.79 + 30.7

10. .2735 + .9115 + .2673

11. 2.7 + 3.5 + 4.3

12. 8.88 + .276 + 95 + .014

Subtract.

13. 5.3 − 2.7

14. 9.0 − 3.5

15. 1.83 − .91

16. 26.1 − 15.9

17. .544 − .27

18. 20.7 − .48

19. 5.02 − .196

20. 6.000 − .437

21. 4 − .898

22. 2.3 − .781

23. 4.387 − 1.59

24. 40.1 − 7.666

25. .0843 − .0099

Add.

26. 9.853 + 6.788 + 5.571 + 1.609

27. 8.74 + .7935 + .0177 + 3.0099

28. 316.5 + 63.27 + 78.04 + 258.16

29. .04596 + .81443 + .00997 + .57348

30. 260.016 + 35.4 + 18.8 + 6.756

31. 27.36 + .09 + .038 + 6.5 + .45 + .0634

> **EXCURSION**
>
> All the digits in the numeral 1976 can be used to name 9:
>
> 9 + 7 − (6 + 1)
>
> Name as many numbers from 0 through 15 as you can. You may add, subtract, multiply, or divide. You may also place digits next to each other in place-value form and use exponents.
>
> 9 + 7 − 16 (0) 9 − 7 + 6^1 (8)

Supplementary Exercises, Set 10, page 376

Estimating

People often need to know approximate answers to problems. When they do, they estimate.

One method of estimating is to round the numbers before adding or subtracting. Study these examples.

Problem	Estimate	Problem	Estimate	Problem	Estimate
57 + 29	60 + 30 = 90	81 − 38	80 − 40 = 40	703 − 289	700 − 300 = 400
6.73 + 9.80	7 + 10	5.05 − 2.88	5 − 3	37 + 21 + 58	40 + 20 + 60

There is no rule about how we should round when we estimate. You should notice, however, that the more you round, the more accuracy you lose. However, the computation becomes easier.

	Nearest 1	Nearest 10	Nearest 100
573.5	574	570	600
+482.7	+483	+480	+500
	1057	1050	1100
	Most accurate estimate		Easiest computation

EXERCISES

Multiple choice. First estimate, and then choose the answer.

1. $53.77 + 82.31$ — **a.** 126.28 **b.** 136.08 **c.** 147.08 **d.** 251.28

2. $703.11 - 498.26$ — **a.** 304.85 **b.** 204.85 **c.** 145.85 **d.** 263.85

3. $25.8 + 36.5 + 41.1$ — **a.** 103.4 **b.** 92.4 **c.** 123.4 **d.** 96.4

4. $2.7(3.1 + 5.3)$ — **a.** 35.28 **b.** 22.68 **c.** 16.98 **d.** 43.58

5. $\dfrac{50.21 - 36.44}{5.1}$ — **a.** 5.8 **b.** 1.7 **c.** 4.6 **d.** 2.7

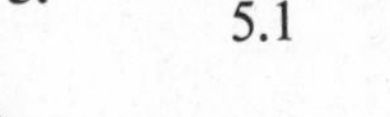

6. 3.14×5.1^2 — **a.** 81.6714 **b.** 93.2124 **c.** 15.2673 **d.** 60.5134

In each case an estimate is given. Tell whether the estimate is too small or too large. Do not compute.

7. $42.3 + 51.9$ ($40 + 50 = 90$)
8. $406 - 297$ ($400 - 300 = 100$)
9. $52.83 + 22.11$ ($50 + 20 = 70$)
10. 6.75×8.93 ($7 \times 9 = 63$)
11. 10.14×6.23 ($10 \times 6 = 60$)
12. $4.8(2.71 + 3.87)$ ($5(3 + 4) = 35$)
13. $\pi(2.3)^2$ ($3 \times 2^2 = 12$)

1. Estimate the number of times your heart beats in a day.
2. Estimate the number of breaths you take in a day.

EXCURSION

Suppose that there are three empty seats in a classroom.

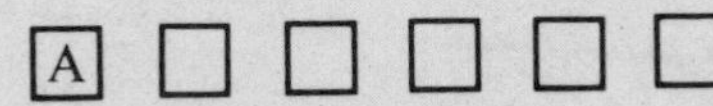

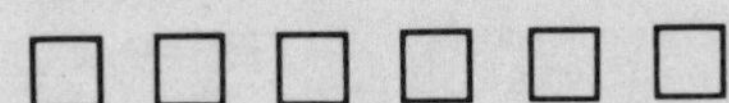
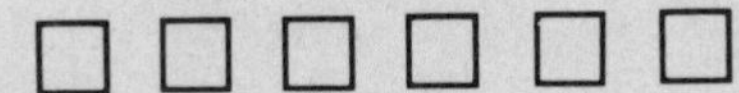
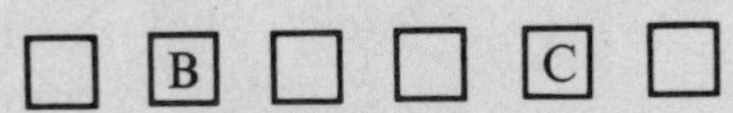

Suppose that two new students join the class. How many different ways can they be assigned the empty seats? How many ways if there were four empty seats? Five empty seats? Is there a rule?

Skill Maintenance, Set 11, page 399

Flow charts

Computers work with great speed and they do very complex things, but they are not intelligent. They must be told what to do, right down to the smallest detail. The set of instructions that tells a computer what to do is called a **program**. It is written by a **programmer.** Later in this book you will have an opportunity to learn to write some simple programs. First you must learn to write **flow charts**, which are more general plans, or sets of instructions.

Here is a simple flow chart that tells how to start a car.

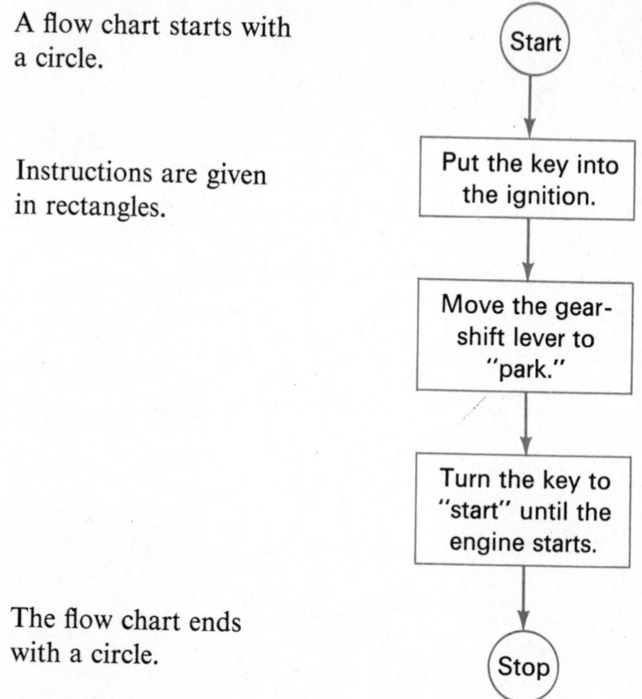

Here is an example with numbers. Notice that the first box tells what the letters stand for, the second tells how to use the numbers to compute D, and the third tells you to write the *value* of D. You would write 10.

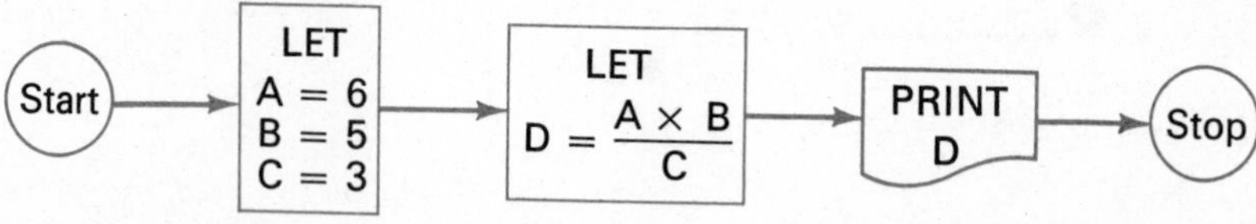

Notice the shape of a PRINT box.

EXERCISES

1. Follow this flow chart. What word do you get?

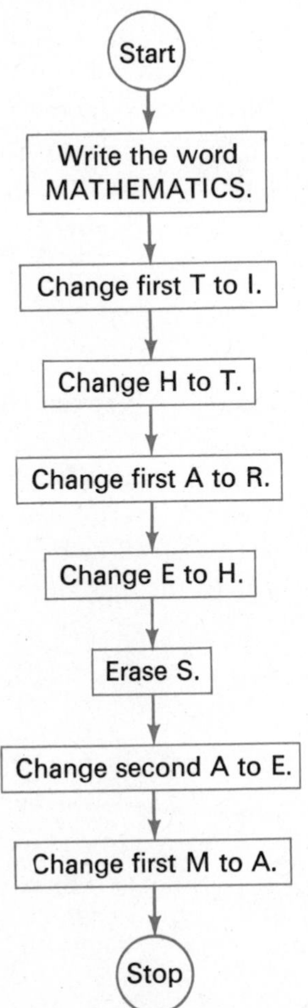

2. Follow this flow chart.

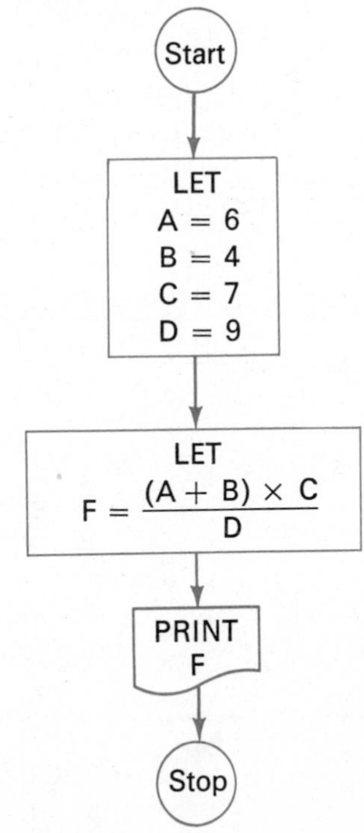

3. Write a flow chart to tell how to change the word "THIRTY" to the word "EIGHTY."
4. Write a flow chart to tell how to change 30 to 80.
5. Write a flow chart to tell how to open a combination lock with this combination:

   21 5 6

6. Write a flow chart that tells how to get ready for school in the morning.

CHECKUP
for pages 42–43

Add or subtract.

1. 4.7 + 3.9	**2.** 4.7 − 3.9	**3.** 2.06 − 1.73
4. .482 + .775	**5.** 3.55 − 1.97	**6.** 16.00 − 7.84

Estimate.

7. 503.7 − 299.8	**8.** 6.8 + 7.5 + 9.6 + 8.7	**9.** 6.12 − 3.99

Answers on page 425.

Skill Maintenance, Set 12, page 400

Decision boxes and loops

Here is a flow chart that tells how to open a combination lock that has a three-number combination. Questions are in diamonds.

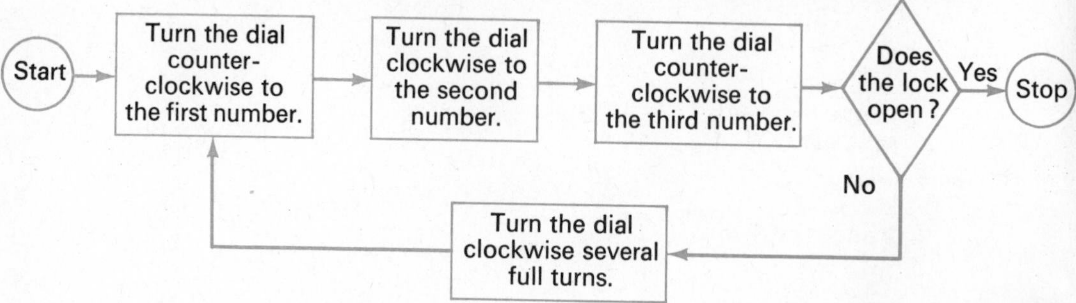

Notice that this flow chart has a question that can be answered *yes* or *no*. Your path through the flow chart depends on your answer to the question. Notice, too, that there is a **loop** in the flow chart. If your answer to the question is *no*, you go back and start the combination over again. According to this flow chart you keep trying the combination over and over until the lock opens.

EXERCISES

1. Copy and complete this flow chart that tells how to sharpen a pencil.

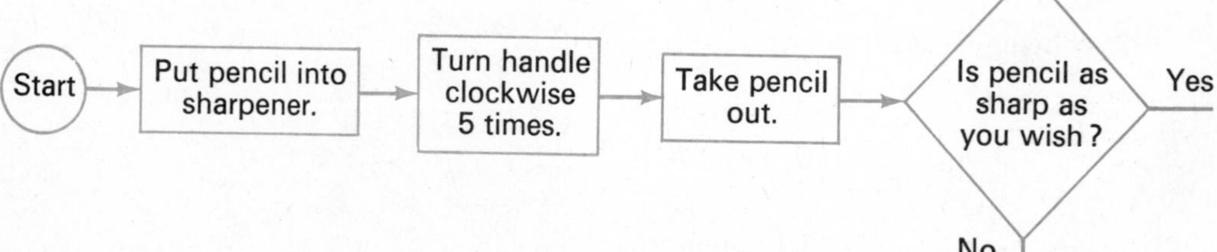

2. Complete this flow chart that tells how to take a test.

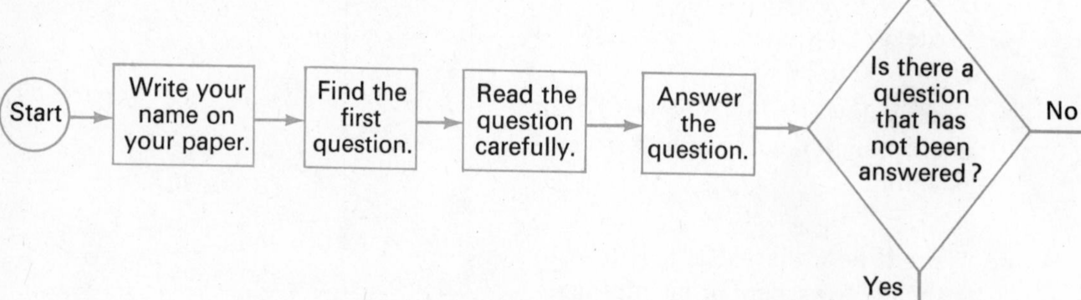

Follow these flow charts.

3.

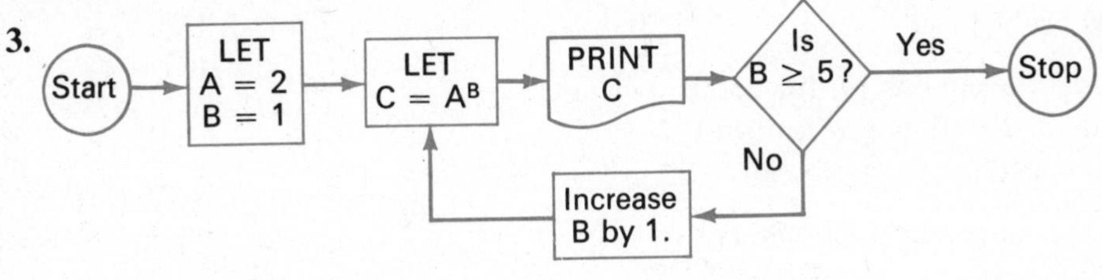

4.

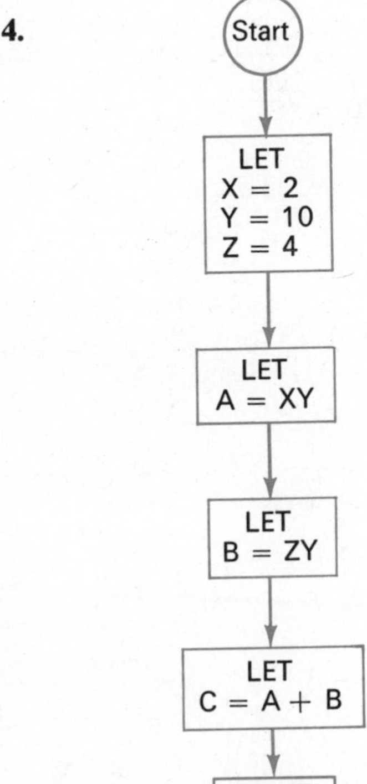

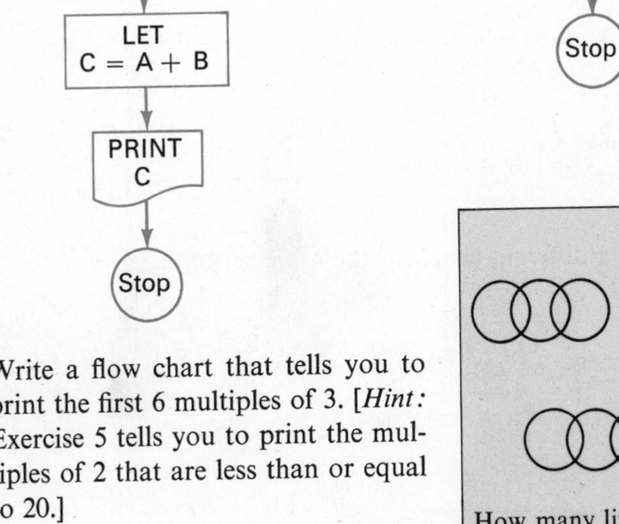

5.

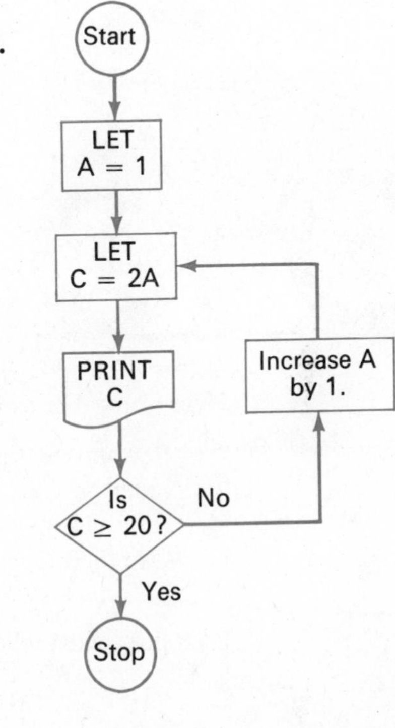

6. Write a flow chart that tells you to print the first 6 multiples of 3. [*Hint:* Exercise 5 tells you to print the multiples of 2 that are less than or equal to 20.]

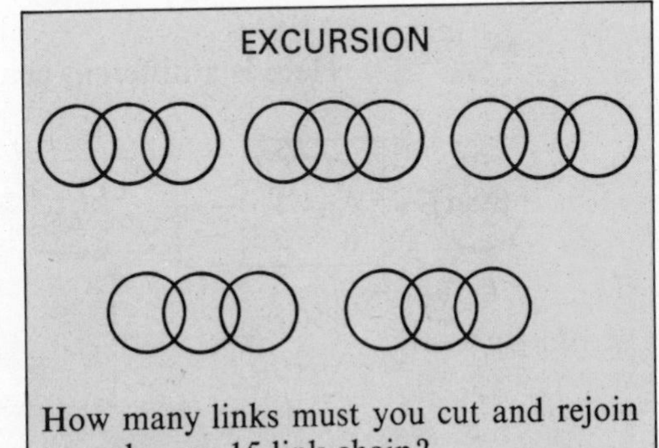

How many links must you cut and rejoin to make one 15-link chain?

Skill Maintenance, Set 13, page 400

Flow charts for word problems

Here is a word problem.

> Karen bought a motorcycle for \$300 down and 12 monthly payments of \$80. How much did she pay in all?

This flow chart gives instructions for solving the problem.

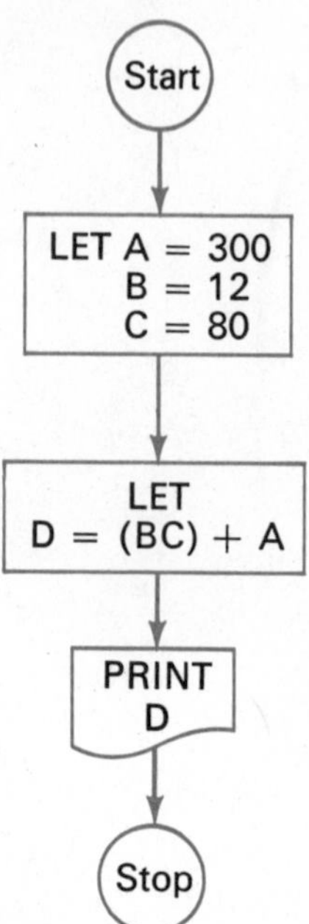

Here is another example.

> Jim started saving \$25 per week in order to buy a stereo set for \$475. How many weeks will it take him to save the money?

This flow chart tells how to get the answer.

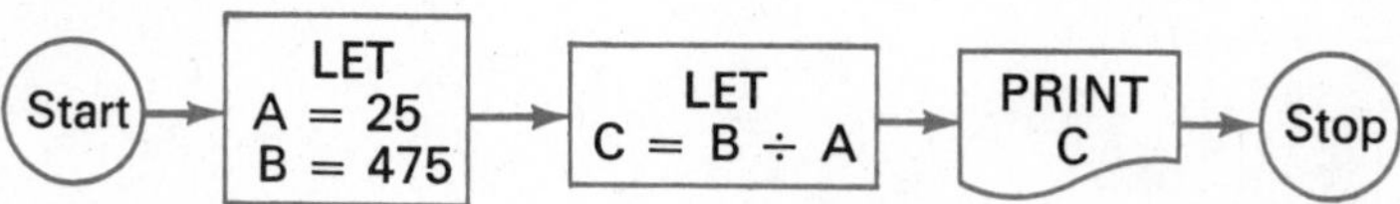

Here is a different chart for the same problem.

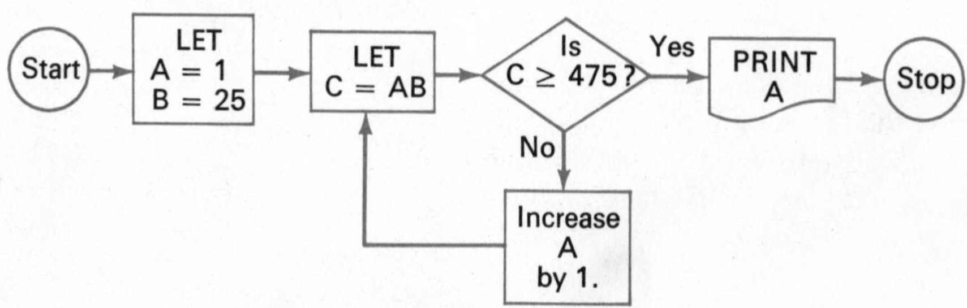

EXERCISES

Write flow charts for these problems. Do not solve.

1. Jill bought two baseballs for \$4.95 each. How much change would she get from a \$10 bill?
2. In one season Robert scored 7 touchdowns (6 points each), kicked 3 field goals (3 points each), and kicked 13 extra points (1 point each). How many points did he score in all?
3. Cora had some money in her checking account. During one two-month period she made deposits of \$45.20, \$36.50, and \$12.90. She also made withdrawals of \$30.75 and \$20.75. At the end of that two-month period she had \$258.63 in her account. How much did she have in her account at the beginning of the two-month period?
4. Jack worked as a waiter. One night he earned \$2.00 per hour for 6 hours. He also earned \$20.35 in tips. How much did he earn in all?
5. Mrs. Clark was planting her lawn, which had an area of 600 square meters. If a kilogram of grass seed will cover 275 square meters, how many kilograms of seed does she need?
6. Here is a flow chart for finding some pairs for the function rule $n \rightarrow n^2 + 1$. Follow the directions.

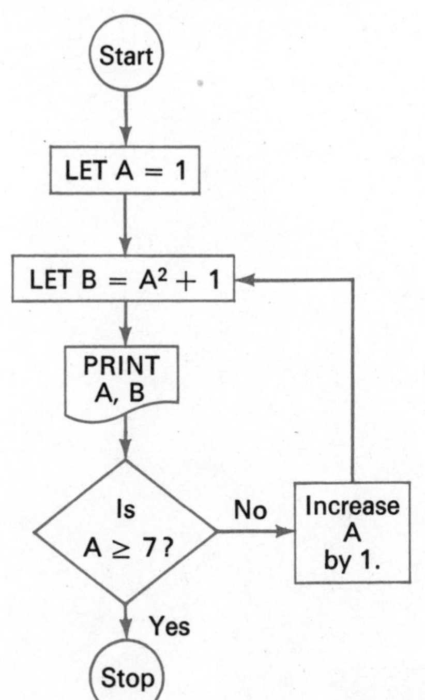

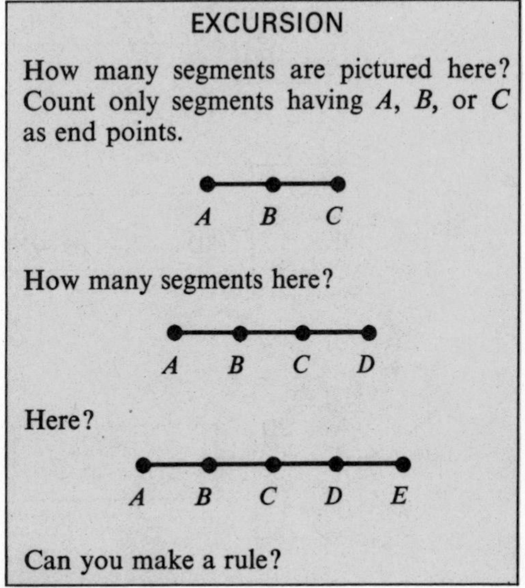

Skill Maintenance, Set 14, page 400

Flow charts for word problems

Read this problem carefully.

> Karl scored 20 points, 17 points, and 35 points on his first 3 tests in English class. He needs a total of 100 points on the first 4 tests to get an A. How many points does he need on his fourth test in order to get an A?

Many flow charts can be written for this problem.
Which of the following flow charts fit the problem?

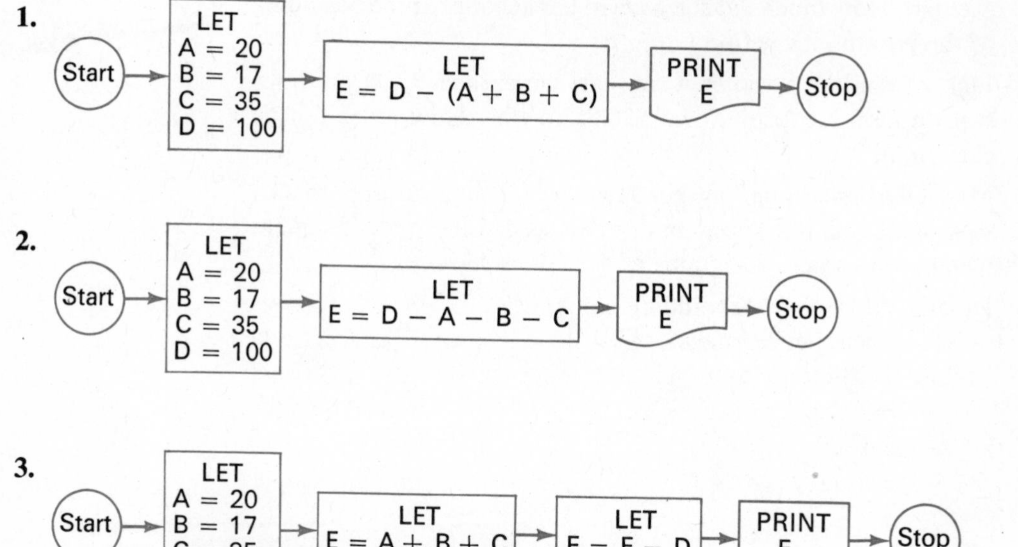

3.

Start → LET A = 20, B = 17, C = 35, D = 100 → LET E = A + B + C → LET F = E − D → PRINT F → Stop

4.

Start → LET A = 20, B = 17, C = 35 → LET D = A + B + C → LET E = 100 − D → PRINT E → Stop

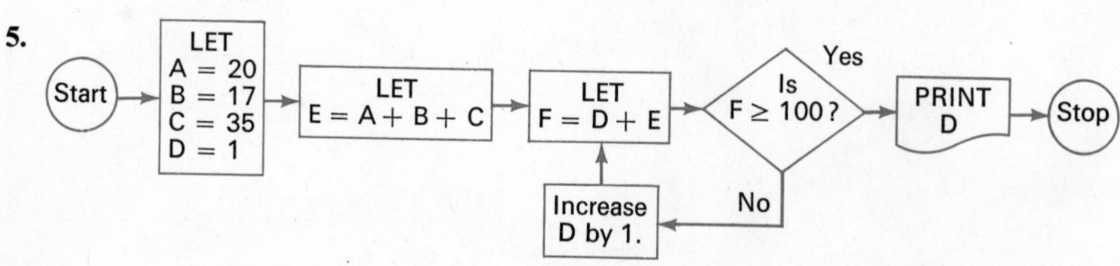

EXERCISES

Solve these problems. Write several flow charts first.

1. Bill worked 8 hours a day on Monday through Friday and 5 more hours on Saturday. How many hours did he work in the week?
2. Mr. Holt earned $835 one month. Of that amount, $124 was taken out for withholding tax, $35 was taken out for health insurance, and $50 was taken out for a savings plan. How much did he receive that month?
3. Mrs. Hyde worked at two jobs. One paid her $375 per month after deductions and the other paid $280 after deductions. Her rent was $175 per month, payments on her car were $118 per month, and her family grocery bill for the month was $280. How much did she have left each month for other expenses?
4. In a school there are 425 girls and 396 boys. How many more girls than boys are there?
5. Mary was a long-distance runner. For conditioning she ran 5 miles twice each day for six days, and on the seventh day she ran 7 miles. How many miles per week did she run?
6. Jill bought a used car that was priced at $1850 cash. She bought it on the installment plan and over a two-year period she paid $2325. How much extra did she pay for the car by buying on the installment plan?

7. a. How much do these items cost in all?
   b. How much more than the tomato juice does the meat cost?

EXCURSION

Each letter stands for a digit. SE does not mean S × E. It is a two-digit number. Find the digits for the letters.

```
$   S E.N D
+  M O.R E
$ M O N.E Y
```

Supplementary Exercises, Set 11, page 376

Problem solving

In this lesson we are going to look at a different kind of problem solving. But first you should try to solve the following problem about networks.

Definitions. This is a **closed network**.

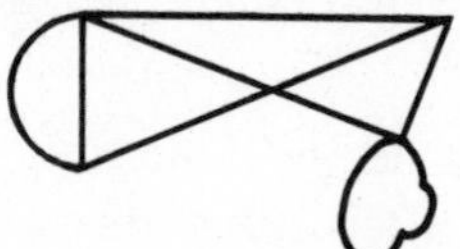

This network is not closed. It has "loose ends" sticking out.

A closed network is made up of **arcs** and usually some **vertices**.

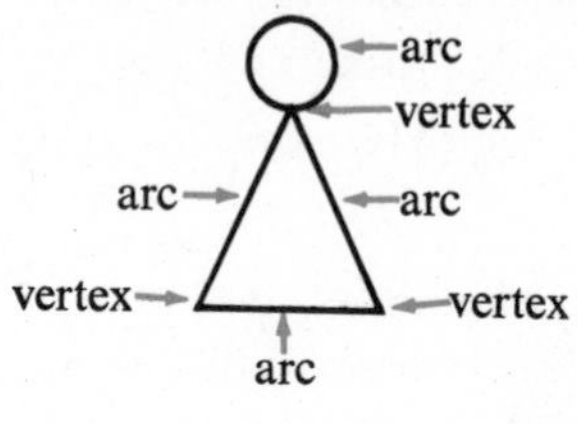

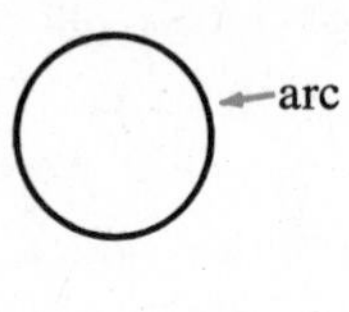

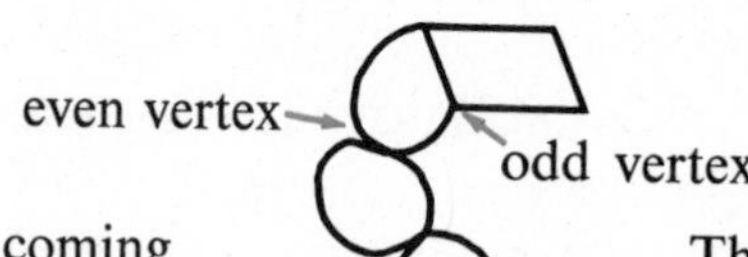

There are 4 "spokes" coming from the vertex and 4 is an even number.

There are 3 "spokes" coming from the vertex and 3 is an odd number.

If there is an even number of "spokes" from a vertex, it is called an **even vertex**. If there is an odd number of "spokes" from a vertex, it is called an **odd vertex**.

Check to see that you understand the definitions of odd and even vertices. Tell whether these vertices are odd or even.

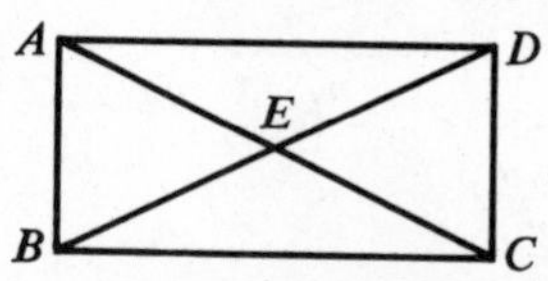

Problem. It is possible to draw a closed network that has 2 odd vertices and 1 even vertex.

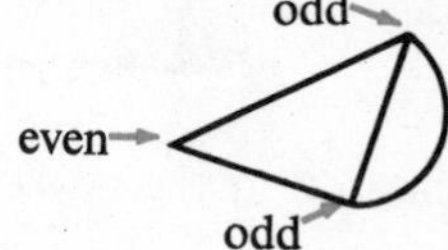

It is impossible to draw a closed network that has 2 even vertices and 1 odd vertex. (Try to draw one.) Find a rule that tells which closed networks can be drawn and which cannot be drawn.

After you have solved the problem read this page.

There are many ways of solving problems. Many people try to solve problems by using these steps.

Collect Data Some people get more information or data by drawing other networks and counting odd and even vertices. Other people try to draw special networks.

Organize Data Some people make a table like this.

Possible	Impossible
2 odd, 0 even	1 odd, 2 even
4 odd, 0 even	1 odd, 3 even
4 odd, 1 even	1 odd, 1 even

Other people make a table like this.

1 even, 0 odd—possible
1 even, 1 odd—impossible
1 even, 2 odd—possible
1 even, 3 odd—impossible

Analyze Data Look for patterns in your data.

State Hypothesis State the rule that you think you have found.

Test Hypothesis Draw more networks to check your rule, or explain *why* your rule works.

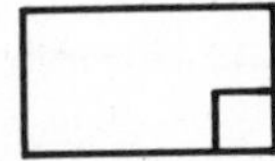

Revise Hypothesis (if necessary) If your rule doesn't work, analyze the data again and make a new rule.

EXERCISES

Solve this problem.

This closed network is *traceable*. You can trace all of it without lifting your pencil and without tracing any arc twice.

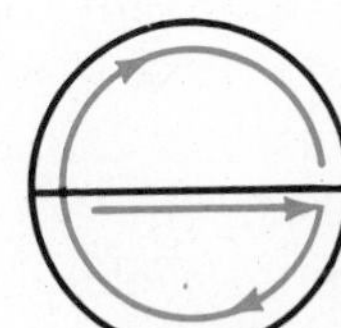

This closed network is not traceable. Try it.

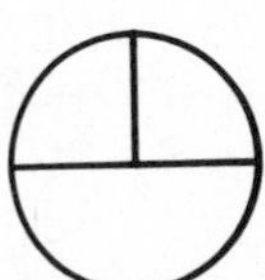

Find a rule that tells how the traceability of a closed network is related to the number of odd or even vertices.

Skill Maintenance, Set 15, page 401

Problem solving

Here, again, are the steps that some people use when they solve problems. The example used is the one given on page 55.

Collect Data

2 odd	4 odd	4 even	3 even	2 odd, 2 even
			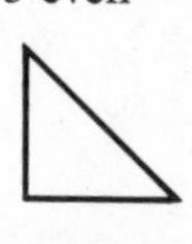	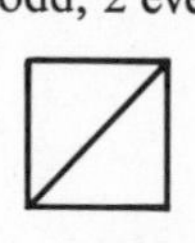
traceable	not traceable	traceable	traceable	traceable

Organize Data

Traceable	Not traceable
2 odd, 0 even	4 odd, 0 even
0 odd, 4 even	4 odd, 2 even
0 odd, 3 even	
2 odd, 2 even	

Think about other ways to organize the data.

Analyze Data

The number of even vertices doesn't seem to make any difference. The untraceable networks have 4 odd vertices.

State Hypothesis

Closed networks with 0 or 2 odd vertices are traceable and those with 4 odd vertices are not traceable.

Test Hypothesis

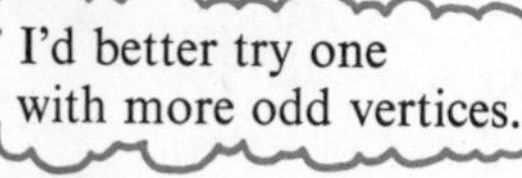

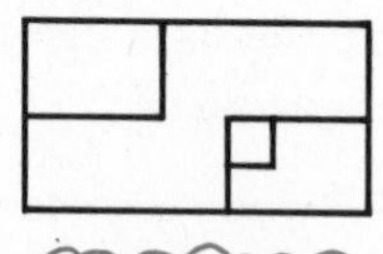

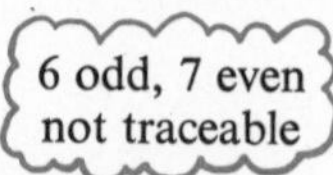

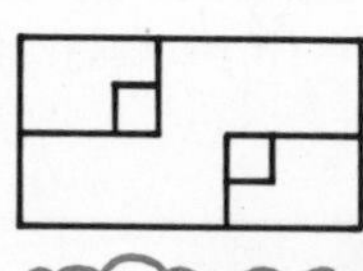

8 odd, 8 even
not traceable

Revise Hypothesis Closed networks with 0 or 2 odd vertices are traceable and those with 4 or more odd vertices are not traceable.

Test New Hypothesis

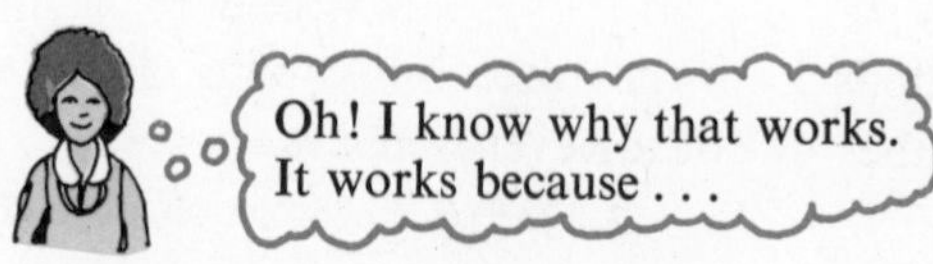

EXERCISES

Solve the problems. Try to use the steps given on page 56.

1. A triangle has 0 diagonals.

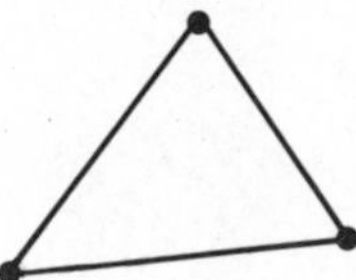

A 4-sided figure has 2 diagonals.

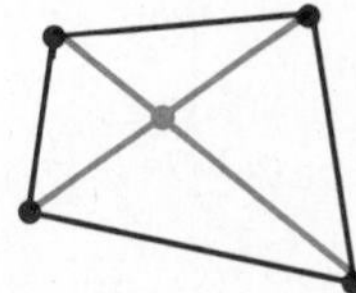

A 5-sided figure has 5 diagonals.

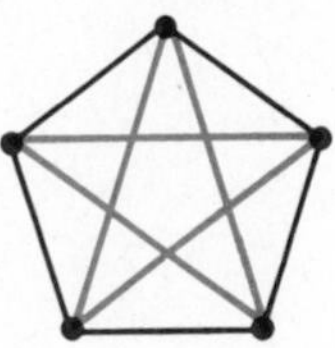

Find a rule that tells how many diagonals a figure has.

2. This closed network has 8 arcs, 5 vertices, and 4 interior regions.

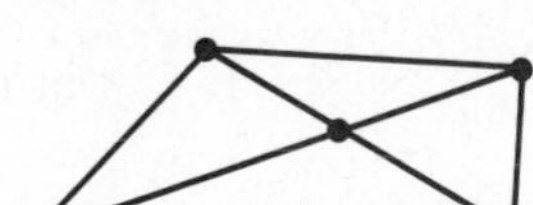

This closed network has 4 arcs, 3 vertices, and 2 interior regions.

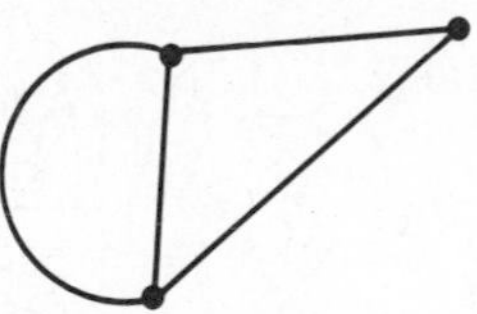

Find a rule that relates the numbers of arcs, vertices, and interior regions.

3. One segment can divide a circle into 2 regions.

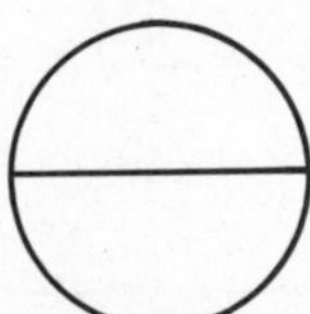

Two segments can divide a circle into 4 regions.

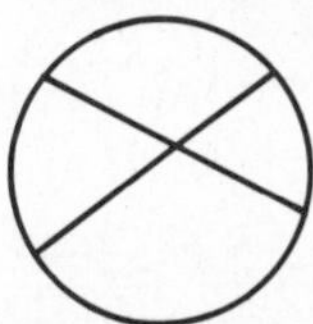

Three segments can divide a circle into 7 regions.

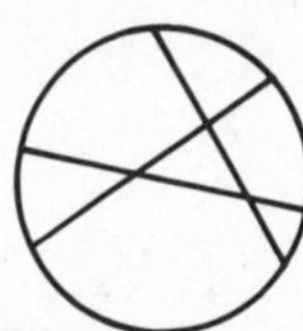

Find a rule that relates the number of regions and the number of segments.

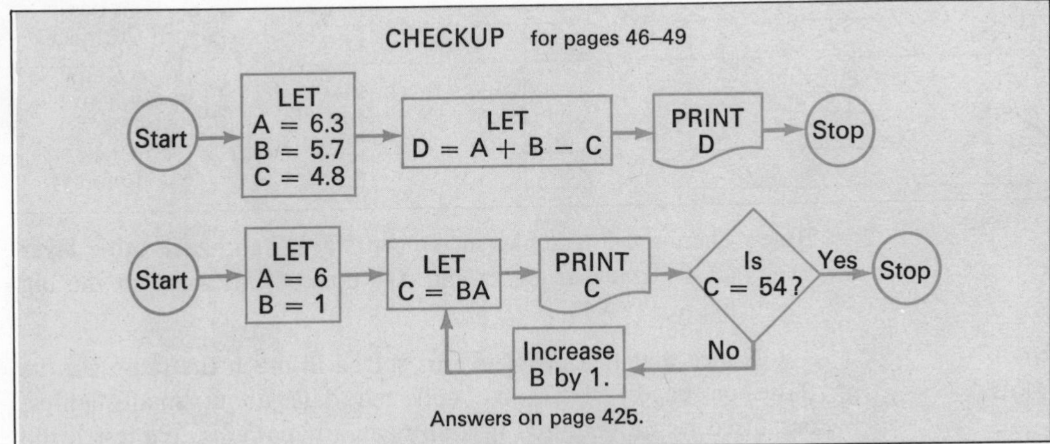

Answers on page 425.

Skill Maintenance, Set 16, page 401

Little problems from big ones

Sometimes when we have a difficult problem to solve we can find a solution by looking at simpler but similar problems. Here is an example. Try to solve the problem before you read the solution.

Example.

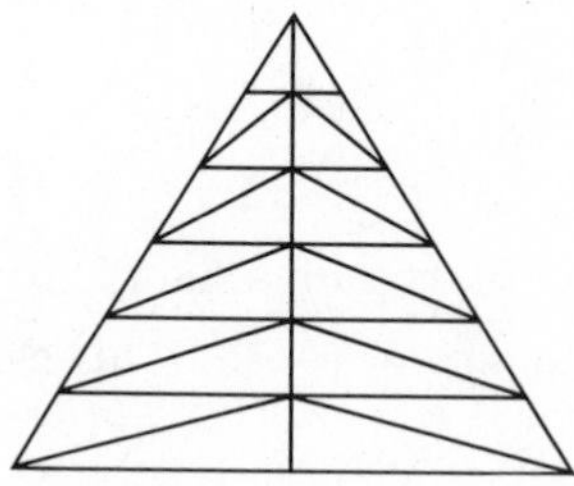

How many triangles are in this figure?

Solution. Instead of trying to count all the triangles in the large figure, let's look at smaller figures.

First. Count the triangles in the top "layer."

Three.

Second. Count the *new* triangles when the second "layer" is added.

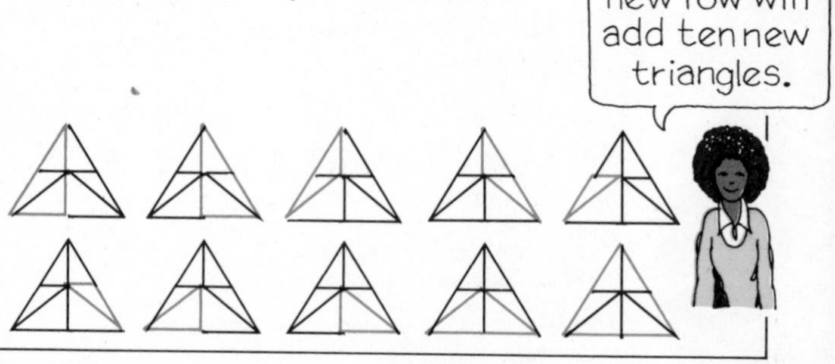

I think each new row will add ten new triangles.

Third. Count *new* triangles when a third "layer" is added.

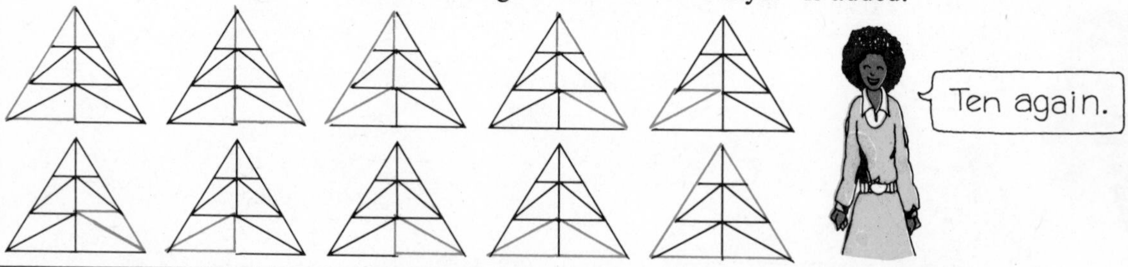

Ten again.

Rule: There are 3 triangles in the top "layer" and each other layer adds 10 new triangles. So, there are 53 triangles in the big figure.

Notice that this problem was solved in much the same way as those on pages 54–57. We collected data about small figures, organized it and analyzed it, and made a hypothesis. We tested the hypothesis, and then used it to solve our big problem.

EXERCISES

Solve each problem. Think about similar problems that are simpler.

1. How many triangles are in these figures?

a.

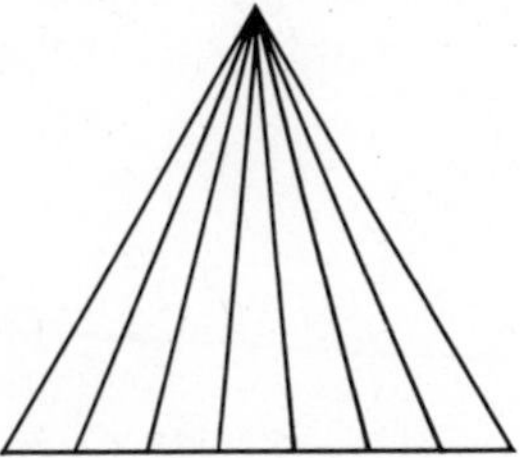

b.

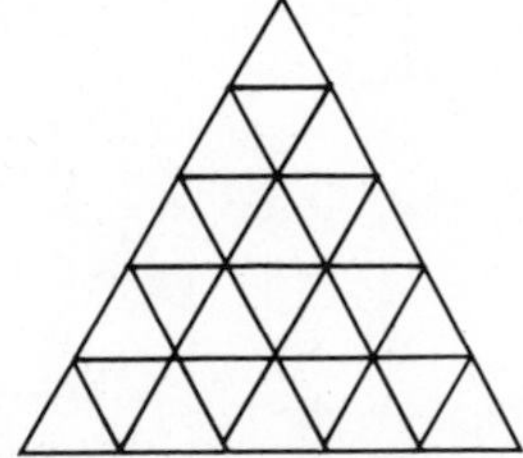

2. How many squares are on a checkerboard? The answer is *not* 64. That is merely the number of small squares. Think about small checkerboards first!

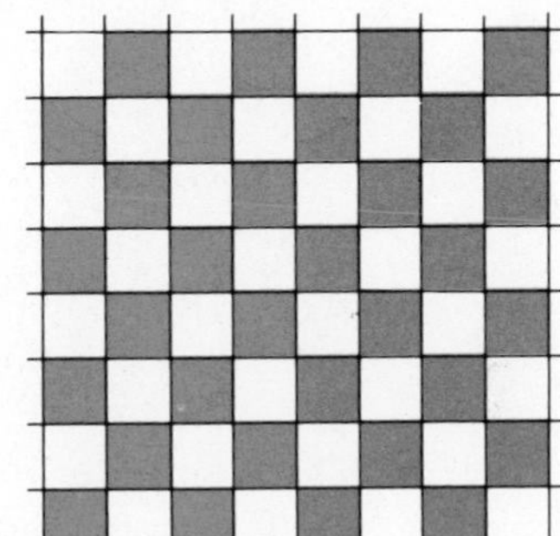

3. How many subsets does this set have?

{a, b, c, d, e, f}

Think about smaller sets first!

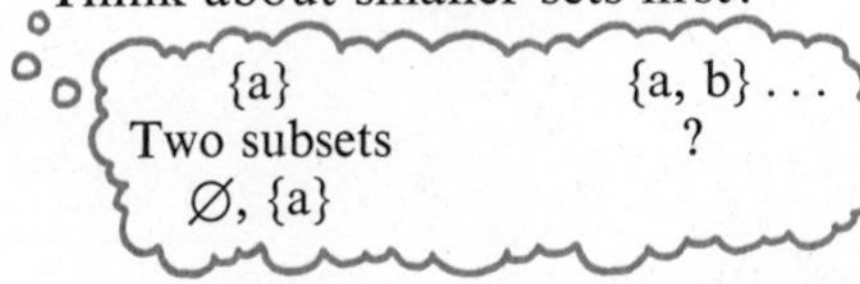

4. How many paths from Joan's house to school, if she always follows arrows?

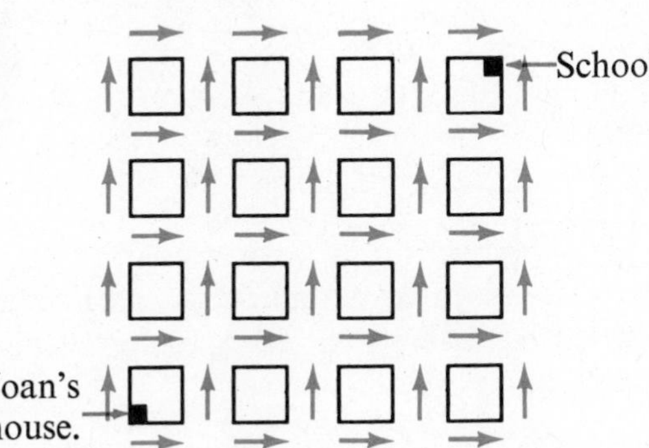

Think about "smaller" problems with school closer to Joan's house.

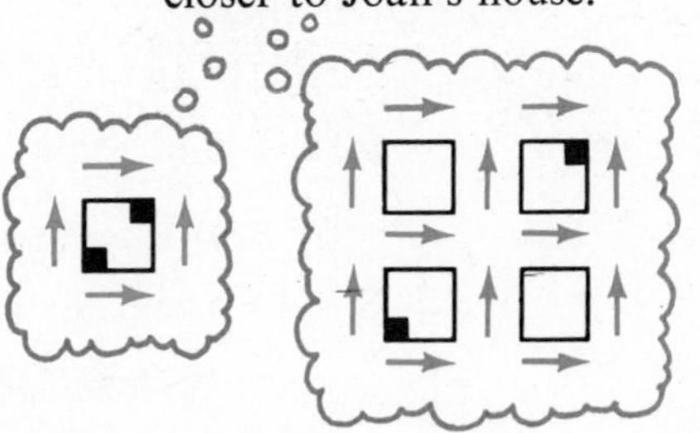

Skill Maintenance, Set 17, page 401

Writing computer programs in BASIC

Once a flow chart is written for a computer, a detailed set of instructions, a program, must be written in a language that the computer understands. One simple computer language is BASIC. Here is a sample program. Study it carefully.

```
10  LET A = 8
20  LET B = 9
70  LET C = A + B
80  PRINT C
90  END
```

In this program there are 5 statements; each is on a separate line. The last statement must be "END."

Each line is numbered. Any numbers between 0 and 9999 may be used. As you can see, numbers may be skipped but the numbers must be in order. The same number cannot be used more than once.

This program tells the computer to store the number 8 in a location in its memory referred to as A, to store 9 in a location referred to as B, and store the sum in location C. Finally, in line 80, the computer is told to print the number stored in C. The last line tells the computer to stop.

These symbols can be used in BASIC programs:

+	(add)	/	(divide)
–	(subtract)	↑	(raise to a power)
*	(multiply)	( )	(grouping symbols)

The computer also recognizes the words LET, PRINT, and END. You will learn other words later.

Here are some sample program statements. Notice that the line number can be any number you choose.

```
15  LET X = A*B - 5
```

(Multiply A and B and then subtract 5.)

```
483  LET G = (A - B)/D
```

(Subtract B from A and divide that answer by D.)

```
37  LET R = M↑3 - K
```

(Raise M to the third power and then subtract K.)

EXERCISES

Be a computer. Follow each program.

1.
```
10  LET G = 10
20  LET H = 7
30  LET I = 2
40  LET K = G*H + I
50  PRINT K
60  END
```

2.
```
200  LET A = 7
300  LET B = 1
400  LET C = A↑2 + B
500  PRINT C
600  END
```

3.
```
1000  LET X = 56
2000  LET Y = 2
3000  LET Z = (X - Y)/6
4000  PRINT Z
5000  END
```

4.
```
110  LET A = 5
120  LET B = 4
125  LET C = (A + B)*2
130  PRINT C
140  END
```

5.
```
1100  LET M = 5
1150  LET N = 3*M + 1
1200  PRINT M, N
1250  END
```

6.
```
10  LET A = 6
11  LET B = 2
12  LET C = A↑B
13  PRINT C
14  END
```

7.
```
10  LET X = 63
20  LET Y = 9
30  LET Z = 5
40  LET A = (X/Y - Z)*5
50  PRINT A
60  END
```

8.
```
100  LET A = 19
200  LET B = 23
300  LET C = 5
400  LET D = 10
500  LET E = B - A
600  LET F = (C*E/D)↑2
700  PRINT F
800  END
```

9. Write a program for this flow chart.

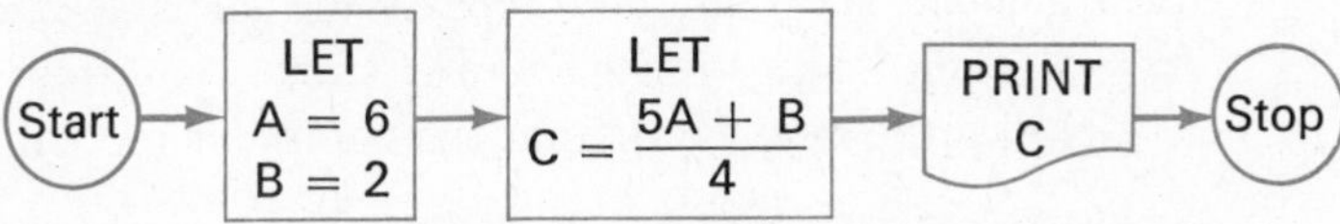

10. Write a program that tells how to solve the equation $2(3x + 1) = 8$.

Skill Maintenance, Set 18, page 402

BASIC—branches and loops

Study this flow chart.

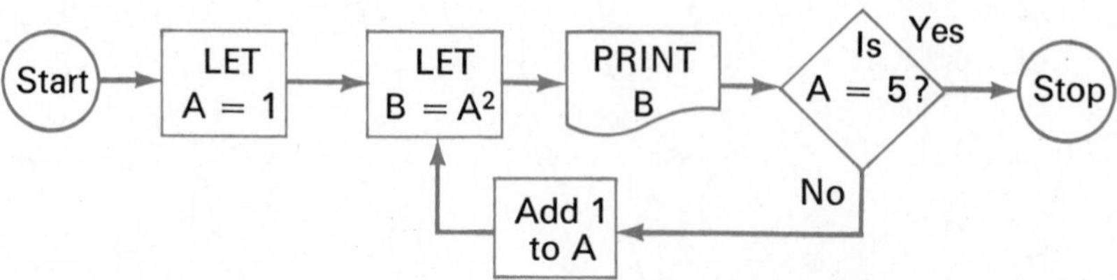

Now study this program to see how the program *branches* at a question, how *loops* are written, and how to tell the computer to skip steps.

```
10  LET A = 1
20  LET B = A↑2
25  PRINT B
30  IF A = 5 THEN 60
40  LET A = A + 1
50  GØ TØ 20
60  END
```

At line 30 there is a **branch**. The statement tells the computer to skip to line 60 (END) if A = 5. If A is not 5, then the computer goes on to the next line, line 40.

Line 40 is a little strange since it is impossible for a number to *equal* a number 1 greater. This statement tells the computer to add 1 to the number stored in A and then to store that new number back in A. This means that the old value of A is lost, but that's OK since it has already served its purpose.

Line 50 tells the computer to go back to line 20 and do the computation with the new value of A. Lines 20, 25, 30, 40, and 50 form a **loop**. The computer repeats the steps over and over until A = 5. Then it skips to line 60 and stops.

Notice the new words that the computer recognizes.

```
IF . . . THEN
GØ TØ
```

EXERCISES

Be the computer. Follow the program.

1.
```
10  LET A = 1
20  LET C = 2*A
30  PRINT C
40  IF A = 10 THEN 70
50  LET A = A + 1
60  GØ TØ 20
70  END
```

2.
```
100  LET G = 1
200  LET H = 1
300  LET I = G + H
400  PRINT I
500  IF H = 6 THEN 900
600  LET G = G + 1
700  LET H = H + 1
800  GØ TØ 300
900  END
```

3.
```
100  LET M = 1
110  LET N = 2↑M
120  PRINT N
130  IF N = 32 THEN 160
140  LET M = M + 2
150  GØ TØ 110
160  END
```

4.
```
1000  LET A = 1
2000  LET B = A↑2
3000  PRINT B
4000  IF A = 10 THEN 7000
5000  LET A = A + 1
6000  GØ TØ 2000
7000  END
```

5.
```
10  LET A = 1
20  LET C = 3*A
30  PRINT C
40  IF A = 20 THEN 70
50  LET A = A + 1
60  GØ TØ 20
70  END
```

6.
```
10  LET A = 1
20  LET B = 3.14*(A↑2)
30  PRINT B
40  IF A = 5 THEN 80
60  LET A = A + 1
70  GØ TØ 20
80  END
```

7. Write flow charts for the programs in exercises 1–4.

8. Write a program for this flow chart.

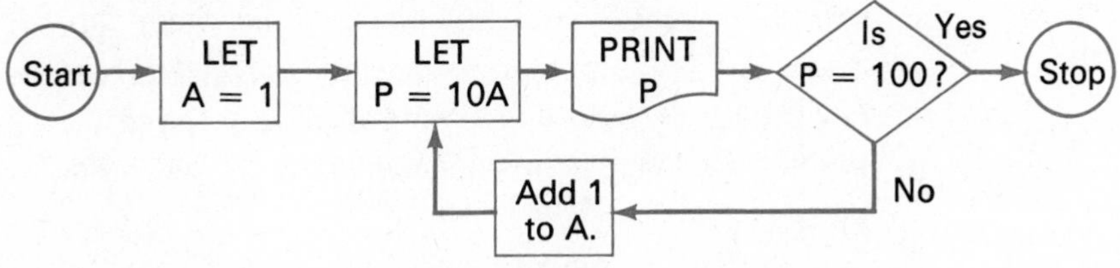

Skill Maintenance, Set 19, page 402

Problem solving

Solve.

1. A jet airliner flew from Chicago to Toledo with 145 passengers. At Toledo 37 passengers got off and 48 new passengers got on. Then the plane flew to Cleveland where 129 passengers got off and 153 new passengers got on. Then the plane flew to Boston. How many different passengers flew on the plane?
2. Jill went shopping. She bought a book for \$4, a bookmark for 29¢, some gum for 3¢, and a box of candy for \$2.98. How much change did she get from a ten-dollar bill?
3. In an eighth-grade class, 16 students had no pets, 13 students had 1 pet each, 8 students had 2 pets each, and 2 students had 3 pets each. How many pets were owned by the eighth-grade class?
4. Jeff bought a tennis racket for \$12.75 and a football that cost \$4 more than the tennis racket. How much did he spend?
5. Lucille bought some pencils at 15¢ each, the same number of erasers at 10¢ each, and the same number of large clips at 9¢ each. She spent \$2.38. How many of each item did she buy?
6. Tom worked for 7 hours on Saturday. Half the time he mowed lawns, a tenth of the time he pulled weeds, and the rest of the time he delivered newspapers. How long did he deliver newspapers?
7. Mr. Graham planted a flower bulb every 6 centimeters along a fence that was 2.04 meters long. How many bulbs did he plant?

CHAPTER CHECKUP

Write in standard form. [*page 36*]

1. $3 \times 10^2 + 7 \times 10^1 + 6 \times 10^0 + 4 \times \frac{1}{10^1} + 9 \times \frac{1}{10^2}$

2. $8 \times 10^3 + 2 \times 10^0 + 7 \times \frac{1}{10^2}$

Complete. [*page 38*]

3. 25 cents = ___?___ dimes
4. 246 cents = ___?___ dimes
5. ___?___ cents = 6.4 dimes
6. 3 cm = ___?___ m
7. 538 cm = ___?___ m
8. ___?___ cm = .018 m

Round to the nearest whole number. [*pages 40–41*]

9. 3.44
10. 38.995
11. .08
12. 56.5

Add or subtract. [*pages 42–43*]

13. $\begin{array}{r} 4.34 \\ +2.87 \\ \hline \end{array}$
14. $\begin{array}{r} .065 \\ +.937 \\ \hline \end{array}$
15. $\begin{array}{r} 47.8 \\ -8.2 \\ \hline \end{array}$
16. $\begin{array}{r} .672 \\ -.445 \\ \hline \end{array}$
17. $\begin{array}{r} 2.002 \\ -.013 \\ \hline \end{array}$

Follow this flow chart. [*pages 46–49*]

18.

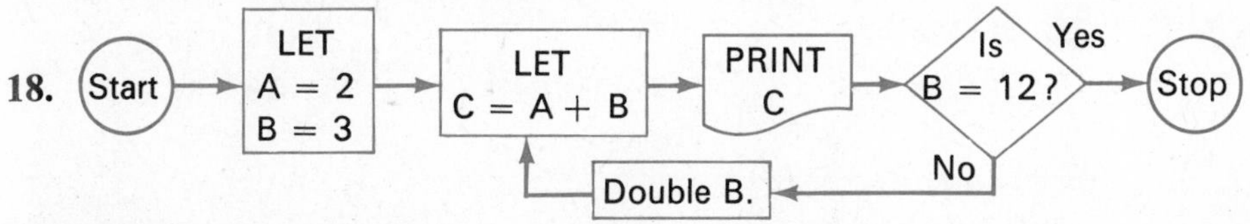

Write a flow chart that tells a computer how to solve this problem. [*pages 50–53*]

19. Ken bought 8 doughnuts for 12¢ each and a quart of milk for 38¢. How much did he spend in all?

Solve. [*pages 50–53, 59*]

20. Nine adults and a group of students went on a field trip. There were fifty-seven students in a bus and 8 students in each of 7 station wagons. How many students went on the field trip?

21. Mr. Jenner gives four 30-point tests during a grading period. To get an A a student must have a total of 105 points; to get a B, 96 points; a C, 84 points; and a D, 72 points. Kelly had scores of 20, 25, and 18 on her first three tests. What is the highest possible grade she can get?

MAJOR CHECKUP

Substitute and simplify. [*pages 2–5*]

x	y	z	Y	a
4	3	7	5	2

1. $12 - Y - a$ **2.** $12 - (Y - a)$ **3.** $16 \div x \div x$

4. $16 \div (x \div x)$ **5.** xy **6.** $3az$ **7.** $2(y + Y)$ **8.** y^2

True or false? [*page 10*]

9. 1 is an element of A.

10. 6 is an element of A.

11. 3 is an element of A.

12. $B \subseteq A$ **13.** $C \subseteq A$ **14.** $A \subseteq B$

List the elements of the sets. [*page 12*]

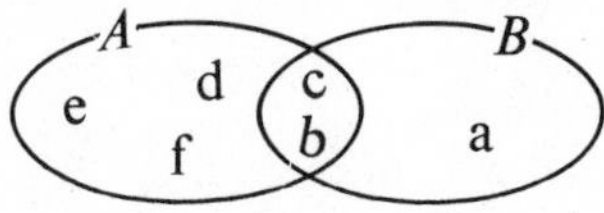

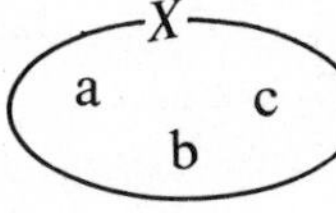

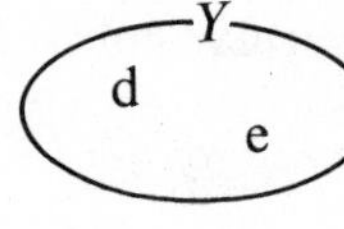

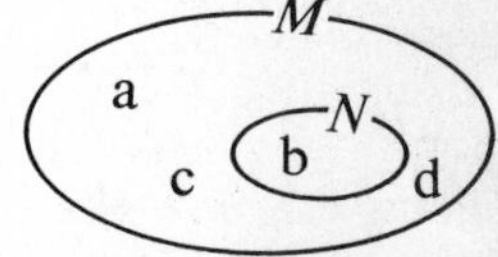

15. $A \cap B = ?$ **17.** $X \cap Y = ?$ **19.** $M \cap N = ?$

16. $A \cup B = ?$ **18.** $X \cup Y = ?$ **20.** $M \cup N = ?$

Solve. [*pages 16, 18*]

21. $4x = 20$ **22.** $a + a = 15$ **23.** $y - 8 = 4$

24. $8 - g = 4$ **25.** $3a + 4 = 19$ **26.** $35 - 2g = 19$

27. $9r + 52 = 79$ **28.** $\frac{15 + h}{6} = 8$

Give each solution set. The replacement set is $\{0, 1, 2, \ldots\}$. [*page 20*]

29. $4y \neq 12$ **30.** $x - 7 < 15$ **31.** $\frac{x}{4} \geq 5$ **32.** $y + 9 > 14$

Here are three functions. Complete each sentence. [*pages 24, 26*]

$f: m \rightarrow 5m$ $g: x \rightarrow \frac{x}{2} + 6$ $h: n \rightarrow 3 + n^2$

33. $f(0) = ?$ **34.** $g(0) = ?$ **35.** $h(0) = ?$ **36.** $f(?) = 35$

37. $g(12) = ?$ **38.** $g(14) = ?$ **39.** $g(?) = 15$ **40.** $h(9) = ?$

Project

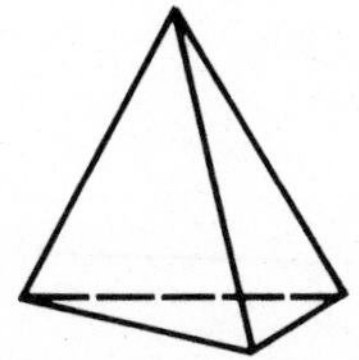

TETRAHEDRON
4 faces
6 edges
9 vertices

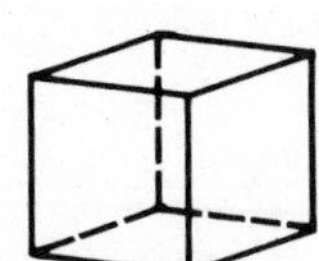

HEXAHEDRON (CUBE)
6 faces
12 edges
8 vertices

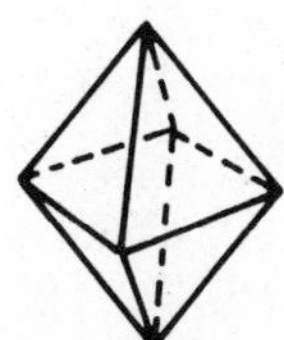

OCTAHEDRON
8 faces
12 edges
6 vertices

A **polyhedron** is a solid formed by four or more plane faces. All the faces of a **regular polyhedron** are congruent regular polygons. There are five regular polyhedrons, often called the platonic solids because they were studied by the disciples of Plato. The platonic solids are pictured.

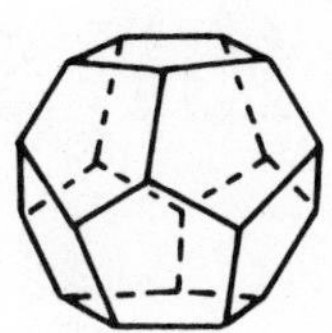

DODECAHEDRON
12 faces
30 edges
20 vertices

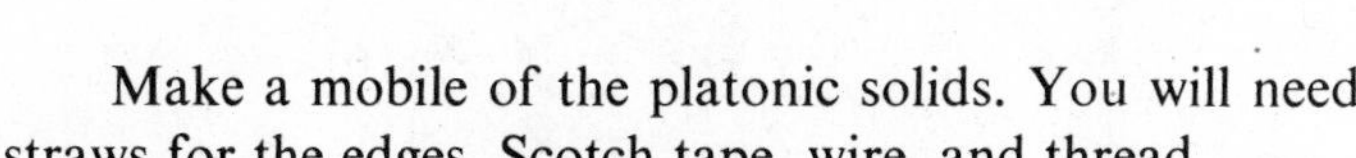

Make a mobile of the platonic solids. You will need straws for the edges, Scotch tape, wire, and thread.

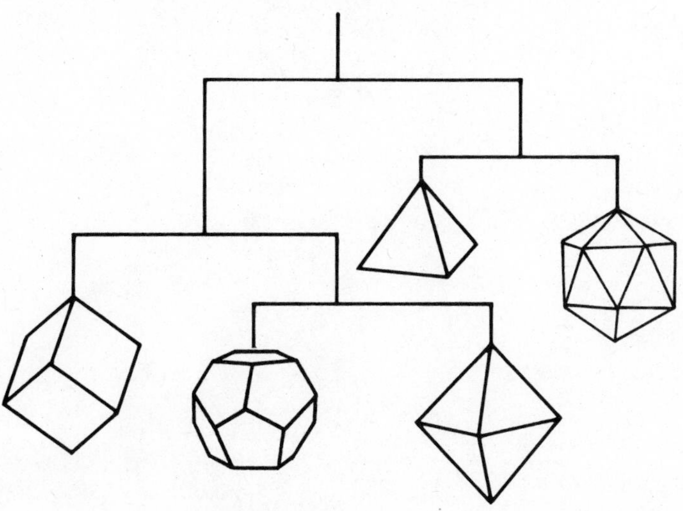

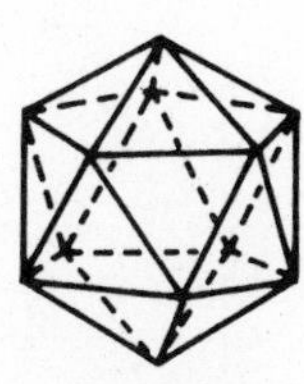

ICOSAHEDRON
20 faces
30 edges
12 vertices

3 Multiplication and Division

Multiplying by a one-digit number

You probably remember how to multiply by a one-digit number. If you have forgotten, study these examples.

Think about 3 sets with 2 unit blocks, 3 tenth-blocks, and 1 hundredth-block in each set.

2.31
×3

Step 1. Multiply 1 by 3 to find the number of hundredths.

2.31
×3
.3

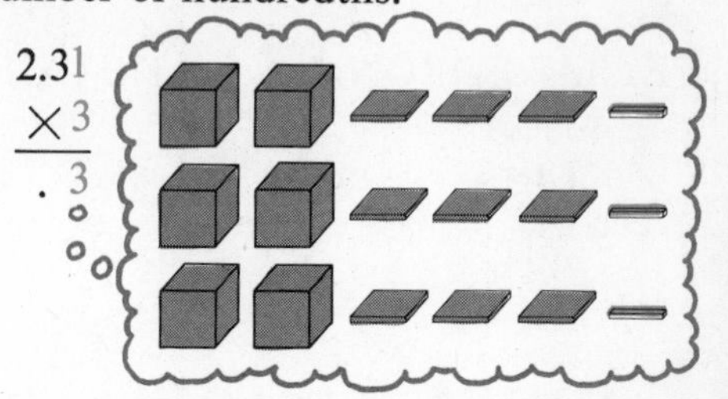

Step 2. Multiply 3 by 3 to find the number of tenths.

2.31
×3
.93

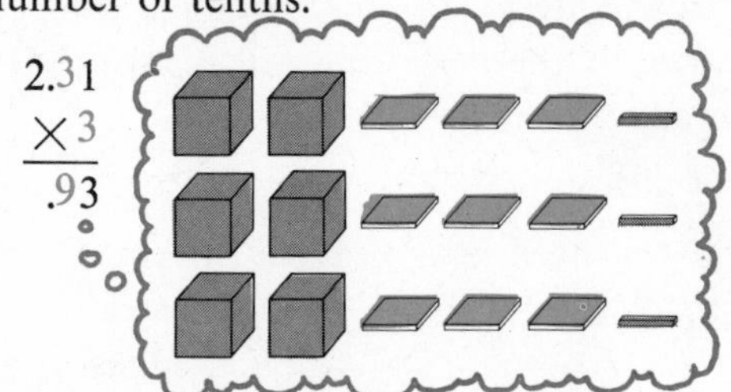

Step 3. Multiply 2 by 3 to find the number of unit blocks.

2.31
×3
6.93

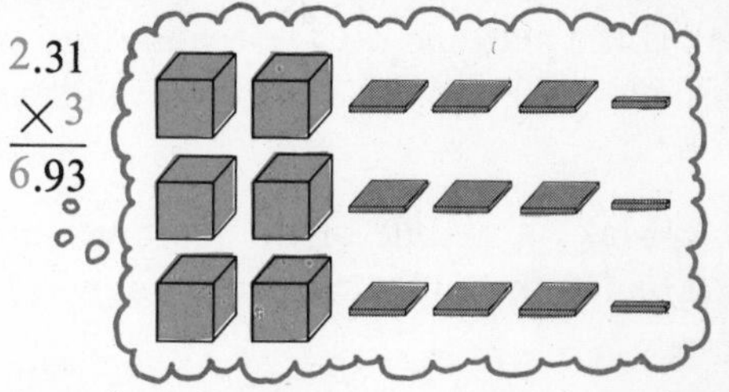

Multiply and regroup.	Multiply, add, and regroup.	Multiply, add, and regroup.
4 63.7 ×6 .2	24 63.7 ×6 2.2	24 63.7 ×6 382.2

EXERCISES

Multiply.

1. 4.23 ×2	**2.** 5.73 ×4	**3.** .827 ×5	**4.** 243 ×7	**5.** 5.2 ×8
6. 5.6 ×5	**7.** 3.77 ×8	**8.** .053 ×9	**9.** 6.005 ×9	**10.** .734 ×6

Solve.

11. 2 shirts
$4.95 each
How much in all?

12. 3 pounds of apples
49¢ per pound
How much in all?

13. 6 buses
54 students on each bus
How many students in all?

14. 6 buses with the same number of students on each
54 students in all
How many students on each bus?

15. 9 boxes
202.6 grams each
How much do the boxes weigh in all?

16. 7 jars
5.9 liters in each
What is the total volume?

17. Carol's mother bought her a 10-speed bicycle. She paid $15 down and $10.25 per week for 9 weeks. What was the total cost?

18. Carl cut a strip of wood into 8 pieces. Each piece was 57.2 centimeters long. Each cut was .2 centimeter wide. How long was the strip?

Follow the flow charts.

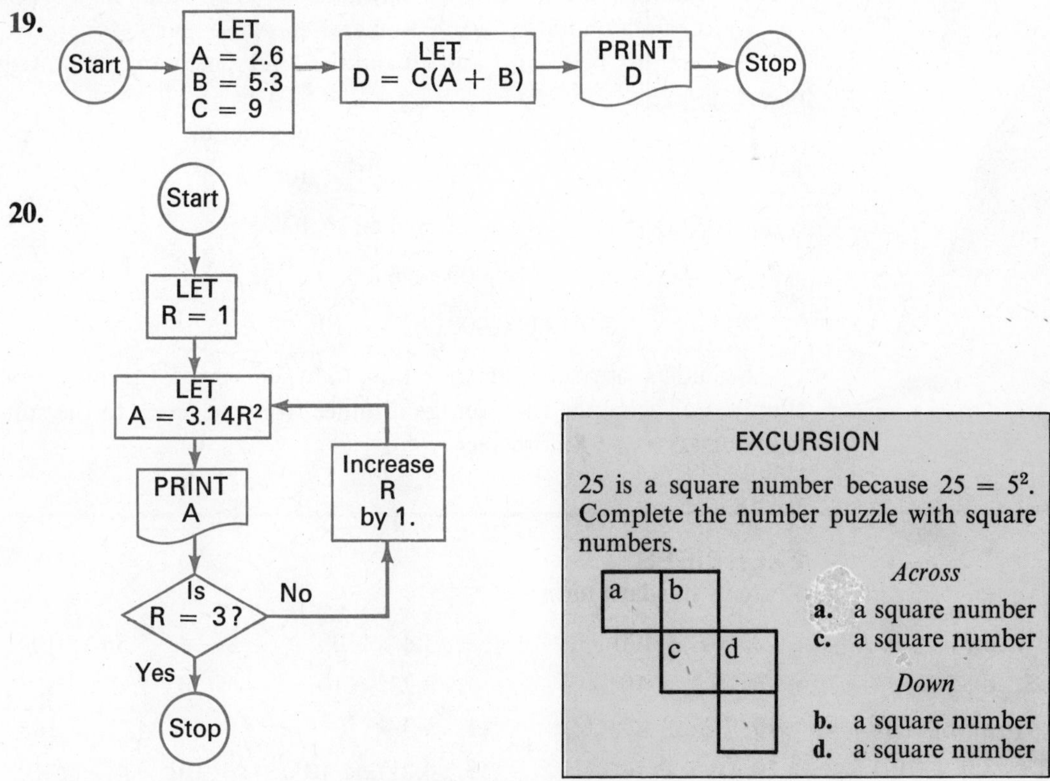

EXCURSION

25 is a square number because $25 = 5^2$. Complete the number puzzle with square numbers.

Across

a. a square number
c. a square number

Down

b. a square number
d. a square number

Supplementary Exercises, Set 12, page 377

Mathematics and science

Multiplying by powers of 10 leaves the digits unchanged but moves the decimal point.

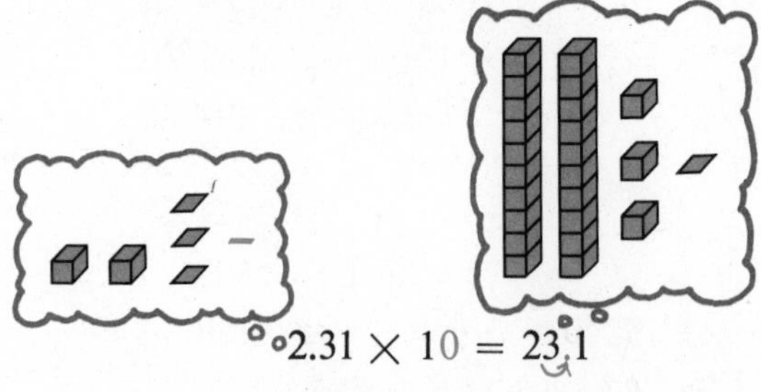

$2.31 \times 10 = 23.1$

$2.31 \times 100 = 231.$

$2.31 \times 1000 = 2310.$

Scientists often use this fact to write numerals in **scientific notation.**

In scientific notation each numeral has two parts—one part names a number between 1 and 10 and the other part names a power of 10.

Standard Form	Scientific Notation
231 =	2.31×10^2
46.2 =	4.62×10^1
68,000 =	6.8×10^4
2,000,000 =	2×10^6

Scientists use scientific notation to write very large numbers simply. For example, the average distance from the earth to the sun is about 1.5×10^8 kilometers.

EXERCISES

Write in standard form.

1. 4.31×10 **2.** 67×100 **3.** 3.4×100 **4.** 5.76×10

5. 8×10^2 **6.** 9.3×10^3 **7.** 8.23×10^3 **8.** 283×10^4

9. 8.31×10^4 **10.** 3.721×10^6 **11.** 5.3×10^6 **12.** 4.21×10^8

13. 3.9×10^7 **14.** 6.5×10^9 **15.** 4.217×10^2 **16.** 3.472×10^0

Complete.

17. $378.2 = 3.782 \times 10^?$
18. $42.9 = 4.29 \times 10^?$
19. $6280 = 6.28 \times 10^?$
20. $53{,}600 = 5.36 \times 10^?$
21. $200{,}000 = 2 \times 10^?$
22. $5216 = 5.216 \times 10^?$
23. $8430 = 8.43 \times 10^?$
24. $843 = 8.43 \times 10^?$
25. $84.3 = 8.43 \times 10^?$
26. $48.2 = \underline{\ ?\ } \times 10^1$
27. $3754 = \underline{\ ?\ } \times 10^3$
28. $54{,}320 = \underline{\ ?\ } \times 10^4$
29. $67{,}300 = \underline{\ ?\ } \times 10^4$
30. $843.2 = \underline{\ ?\ } \times 10^2$
31. $260{,}000 = \underline{\ ?\ } \times 10^5$

Write in scientific notation.

32. 53.4
33. 680
34. 7240
35. 56,300
36. 28,000
37. 5,200,000
38. 37,000,000
39. 8,000,000,000
40. 27 trillion

Write the number in scientific notation.

41. The moon is about 250,000 miles from the earth.
42. The speed of light is about 300,000 kilometers per second.
43. The average distance of Mars from the sun is 141 million miles.
44. The most distant visible bodies in the universe are 12 billion light-years from the earth.
45. The diameter of the body of the sun is about 14,000,000 kilometers.
46. The temperature at the center of the sun is about 20,000,000° Celsius (about 36,000,000° Fahrenheit).
47. The average distance from the earth to the sun is 92,957,000 miles.
48. The sun weighs about 331,950 times as much as the earth.

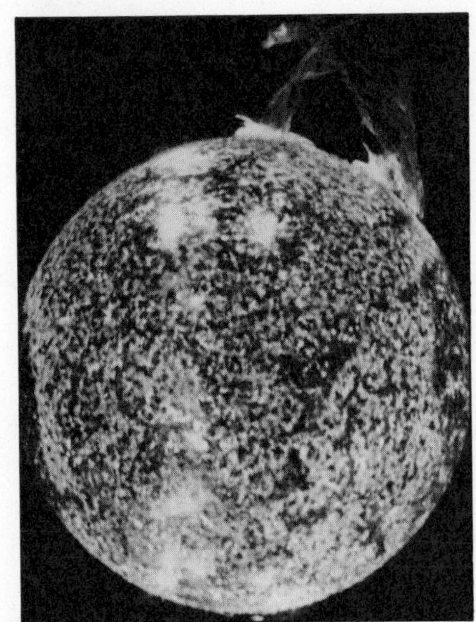

EXCURSION

$a \times b = a + b$

Can you find pairs of numbers that make the equation true?
How many pairs are whole numbers?
How many pairs are fractions?

Skill Maintenance, Set 20, page 402

Multiplying by multiples of 10 or 100

When you first learned to multiply by 30, you probably used two steps.

$$\begin{array}{r} 4.7 \\ \times 30 \\ \hline \end{array}$$

First multiply by 10,

$$\begin{array}{r} 4.7 \\ \times 10 \\ \hline 47.0 \end{array}$$

then multiply by 3.

$$\begin{array}{r} 4.7 \\ \times 10 \\ \hline 47.0 \\ \times 3 \\ \hline 141.0 \end{array}$$

This method works because of the associative property of multiplication:

$$4.7 \times 30 = 4.7 \times (10 \times 3) = (4.7 \times 10) \times 3$$

Now you probably use this shortcut.

Write 1 zero.	Multiply by 3.
$\begin{array}{r} 4.7 \\ \times 30 \\ \hline .0 \end{array}$	$\begin{array}{r} 4.7 \\ \times 30 \\ \hline 141.0 \end{array}$

Write 2 zeros.	Multiply by 5.
$\begin{array}{r} 5.2 \\ \times 500 \\ \hline 0.0 \end{array}$	$\begin{array}{r} 5.2 \\ \times 500 \\ \hline 2600.0 \end{array}$

EXERCISES

Multiply.

1. $\begin{array}{r} 3.8 \\ \times 20 \\ \hline \end{array}$ **2.** $\begin{array}{r} .95 \\ \times 30 \\ \hline \end{array}$ **3.** $\begin{array}{r} 8.2 \\ \times 60 \\ \hline \end{array}$ **4.** $\begin{array}{r} 53 \\ \times 70 \\ \hline \end{array}$ **5.** $\begin{array}{r} .041 \\ \times 60 \\ \hline \end{array}$ **6.** $\begin{array}{r} 3.6 \\ \times 50 \\ \hline \end{array}$

7. $\begin{array}{r} 5.1 \\ \times 200 \\ \hline \end{array}$ **8.** $\begin{array}{r} .84 \\ \times 300 \\ \hline \end{array}$ **9.** $\begin{array}{r} 1.23 \\ \times 600 \\ \hline \end{array}$ **10.** $\begin{array}{r} 340 \\ \times 700 \\ \hline \end{array}$ **11.** $\begin{array}{r} 1.56 \\ \times 500 \\ \hline \end{array}$ **12.** $\begin{array}{r} 32.4 \\ \times 800 \\ \hline \end{array}$

13. a. 84×20
b. 84×200
c. 84×2000

14. a. 1.27×30
b. 1.27×300
c. 1.27×3000

15. a. $.035 \times 70$
b. $.035 \times 700$
c. $.035 \times 7000$

16. a. 9.3×80
b. 9.3×800
c. 9.3×8000

17. a. 43.6×40
b. 43.6×400
c. 43.6×4000

18. a. $.16 \times 90$
b. $.16 \times 900$
c. $.16 \times 9000$

19. Follow this flow chart.

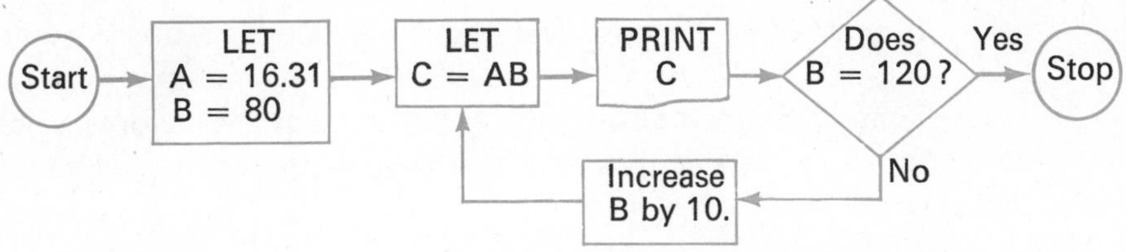

Solve.

20. Mrs. Sholty bought a $3400 car on the installment plan. She paid $1000 down and $96.25 each month for 30 months. How much did she pay for the car?

CAPACITY 58

21. How much will 20 of these boxes weigh?

22. How many people can 40 buses carry?

23. Twenty apples all the same size weigh 2000 grams. What does each apple weigh?

Estimate each product.

24. 21×78

25. 29×72

26. 54×83

27. 56×87

28. 393×41

29. 68×532

30. 987×406

31. 750×850

32. 4.8×7.1

33. 3.2×9.1

34. 5.74×8.91

35. 6.03×9.11

36. 67.41×3.99

37. 58.62×81.14

EXCURSION

Put a checker in one corner of a checkerboard.

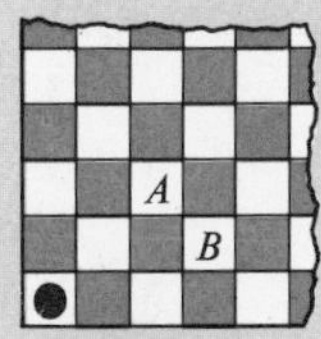

To decide how to move the checker, flip a coin.

1. Move 1 square up for a head.
2. Move 1 square right for a tail.

There are 4 paths that you could take to get to square B. Show them.
How many paths take you to A?
Which square, A or B, are you more likely to land on?

Supplementary Exercises, Set 13, page 377

Multiplying by two- and three-digit numbers

If you know how to multiply by a one-digit number and by a multiple of 10, then you should be able to multiply by a two-digit number. Study the example. Do you see that one factor was "broken" into two parts and then the distributive property was used?

$$\begin{array}{r} 6.4 \\ \times 37 \\ \hline \end{array} \rightarrow \begin{array}{r} 6.4 \\ \times 30 \\ \hline 192.0 \end{array} + \begin{array}{r} 6.4 \\ \times 7 \\ \hline 44.8 \end{array} = 236.8$$

You probably use this shortcut.

$$\begin{array}{r} 6.4 \\ \times 37 \\ \hline 44.8 \\ 192.0 \\ \hline 236.8 \end{array}$$

6.4 × 7

6.4 × 30

6.4 × 37

Here the shortcut is used to multiply by a three-digit number.

$$\begin{array}{r} 3.17 \\ \times 516 \\ \hline 19.02 \\ 31.70 \\ 1585.00 \\ \hline 1635.72 \end{array}$$

EXERCISES

Complete.

1. a. 56 × 3 = ___?___
b. 56 × 30 = ___?___
c. 56 × 33 = ___?___

2. a. 4.5 × 7 = ___?___
b. 4.5 × 30 = ___?___
c. 4.5 × 37 = ___?___

3. a. 526 × 9 = ___?___
b. 526 × 40 = ___?___
c. 526 × 49 = ___?___

4. a. 207 × 3 = ___?___
b. 207 × 60 = ___?___
c. 207 × 63 = ___?___

Multiply.

5. 48 ×23 **6.** 4.8 ×23 **7.** .48 ×23 **8.** 4.8 ×230 **9.** 480 ×23 **10.** 480 ×230

11. 523 ×41 **12.** 52.3 ×41 **13.** 5.23 ×41 **14.** .523 ×41 **15.** 523 ×410 **16.** 52.3 ×410

17. 4.7 ×36 **18.** .58 ×53 **19.** 75 ×22 **20.** 437 ×82 **21.** 503 ×261 **22.** 721 ×604

Solve.

23. Mark saved \$8.75 each week for a year (52 weeks). How much money did he save in the year?

24. Marcia bought a sewing machine on the installment plan. She paid \$35 down and \$9.50 per month for a year. How much did she pay in all?

25. How much does the whole case cost?

26. How many students can be carried on 25 buses?

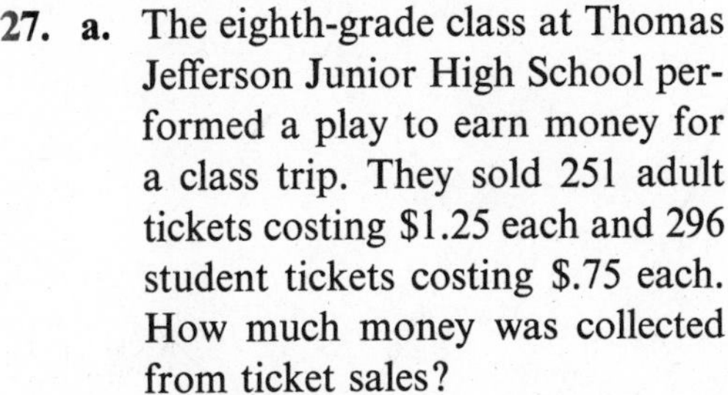

27. a. The eighth-grade class at Thomas Jefferson Junior High School performed a play to earn money for a class trip. They sold 251 adult tickets costing \$1.25 each and 296 student tickets costing \$.75 each. How much money was collected from ticket sales?
    b. The expenses for putting on the play totaled \$257.45. How much profit was made?

28. Mr. Davison bought 125 pounds of beef for his freezer. The beef cost \$.87 per pound. How much did it cost in all?

29. A basketball player scored 15 points per game for 19 games. How many points did he score in all?

30. Juanita wanted to buy Christmas presents for 6 of her friends, her brother, and her sister. If she spent \$1.75 on each present, how much would she spend in all?

EXCURSION

Write the numbers 1, 2, 3, 4, 5, 7, 12 in the empty circles so that the sum of the numbers in the three circles on any red segment or on any blue segment is 22.

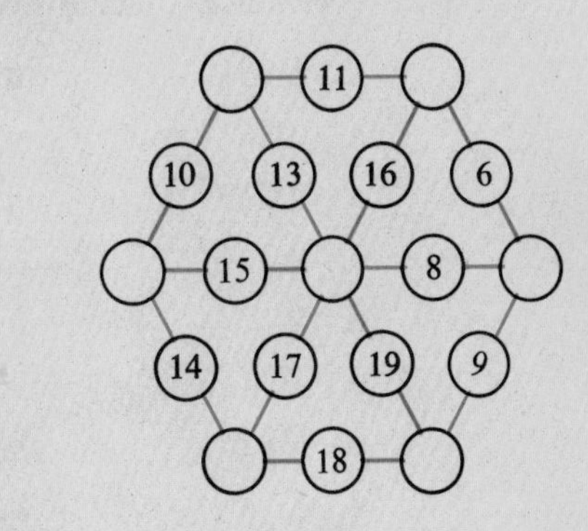

Supplementary Exercises, Set 14, page 377

Estimating products

You can estimate products by rounding the factors and then multiplying. Study these examples.

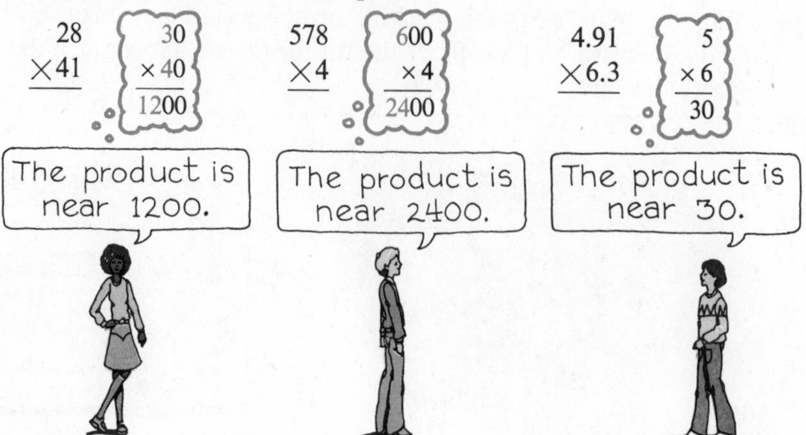

EXERCISES

Estimate each product.

1. 39×68	**2.** 73×2	**3.** 88×9	**4.** 572×3	**5.** 813×7	**6.** 493×11
7. 5734×2	**8.** 89×73	**9.** 750×39	**10.** 985×47	**11.** 3.7×2.8	**12.** 5.9×3.1
13. 9.42×7.31	**14.** 9.87×7.31	**15.** $.86 \times .93$	**16.** 31.57×8.4	**17.** 58.3×9.7	**18.** 6.57×8.2

In each exercise you are given an estimate (in red) and four numbers. Which number is nearest the estimate?

19. 63	**a.** 5.831	**b.** 58.31	**c.** 583.1	**d.** 5 831
20. 8	**a.** .086	**b.** .86	**c.** 8.6	**d.** 86
21. 16	**a.** .0213	**b.** .213	**c.** 2.13	**d.** 21.3
22. 90	**a.** .83	**b.** 8.3	**c.** 83	**d.** 830
23. 90	**a.** 11.7	**b.** 117	**c.** 1170	**d.** 11,700
24. .6	**a.** .734	**b.** 7.34	**c.** 73.4	**d.** 734
25. 1	**a.** .082	**b.** .82	**c.** 8.2	**d.** 82
26. 500	**a.** 37.8	**b.** 378	**c.** 3780	**d.** 37,800
27. .9	**a.** .163	**b.** 1.63	**c.** 16.3	**d.** 163

Estimate. Then choose the correct product.

28. $\begin{array}{r} 48 \\ \times 21 \\ \hline \end{array}$ **a.** 1.008 **b.** 10.08 **c.** 100.8 **d.** 1008

29. $\begin{array}{r} 52 \\ \times 33 \\ \hline \end{array}$ **a.** 17.16 **b.** 171.6 **c.** 1716 **d.** 17160

30. $\begin{array}{r} 78 \\ \times 3 \\ \hline \end{array}$ **a.** 2.34 **b.** 23.4 **c.** 234 **d.** 2340

31. $\begin{array}{r} 102 \\ \times 8 \\ \hline \end{array}$ **a.** 8.16 **b.** 81.6 **c.** 816 **d.** 8160

32. $\begin{array}{r} 587 \\ \times 4 \\ \hline \end{array}$ **a.** 2.348 **b.** 23.48 **c.** 234.8 **d.** 2348

33. $\begin{array}{r} 6.7 \\ \times 8 \\ \hline \end{array}$ **a.** 5.36 **b.** 53.6 **c.** 536 **d.** 5360

34. $\begin{array}{r} 7.13 \\ \times 5 \\ \hline \end{array}$ **a.** .3565 **b.** 3.565 **c.** 35.65 **d.** 356.5

35. $\begin{array}{r} 8.2 \\ \times 2.1 \\ \hline \end{array}$ **a.** 1.722 **b.** 17.22 **c.** 172.2 **d.** 1722

36. $\begin{array}{r} 12.8 \\ \times 2.9 \\ \hline \end{array}$ **a.** .3712 **b.** 3.712 **c.** 37.12 **d.** 371.2

Estimate. Then copy and put a decimal point in the "product."

37. $\begin{array}{r} 5.2 \\ \times 8 \\ \hline 416 \end{array}$

38. $\begin{array}{r} 2.3 \\ \times 1.5 \\ \hline 115 \\ 230 \\ \hline 345 \end{array}$

39. $\begin{array}{r} 4.77 \\ \times 2.9 \\ \hline 4293 \\ 9540 \\ \hline 13833 \end{array}$

40. $\begin{array}{r} 17.6 \\ \times 3.4 \\ \hline 704 \\ 5280 \\ \hline 5984 \end{array}$

CHECKUP

for pages 69–70, 74–75

Multiply.

1. $\begin{array}{r} 3.2 \\ \times 3 \\ \hline \end{array}$ **2.** $\begin{array}{r} 5.7 \\ \times 6 \\ \hline \end{array}$

3. $\begin{array}{r} .48 \\ \times 7 \\ \hline \end{array}$ **4.** $\begin{array}{r} 54.2 \\ \times 9 \\ \hline \end{array}$

5. $\begin{array}{r} 9.3 \\ \times 21 \\ \hline \end{array}$ **6.** $\begin{array}{r} .86 \\ \times 32 \\ \hline \end{array}$

7. $\begin{array}{r} .075 \\ \times 47 \\ \hline \end{array}$ **8.** $\begin{array}{r} 62.3 \\ \times 281 \\ \hline \end{array}$

Answers on page 425.

Skill Maintenance, Set 21, page 402

Multiplying by a decimal

You *could* use this method to do most multiplication exercises in which both factors are in decimal form:

Step 1. Multiply as you would with whole numbers.

$$\begin{array}{r} 4.7 \\ \times 3.2 \\ \hline 94 \\ 1410 \\ \hline 1504 \end{array}$$

Step 2. Estimate the product to place the decimal point.

$$\begin{array}{r} 4.7 \\ \times 3.2 \\ \hline 94 \\ 1410 \\ \hline 15.04 \end{array}$$

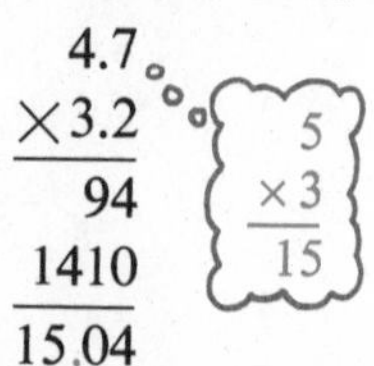

Here are two more examples.

$$\begin{array}{r} 2.78 \\ \times 5.9 \\ \hline 2502 \\ 13900 \\ \hline 16.402 \end{array} \qquad \begin{array}{r} 3 \\ \times 6 \\ \hline 18 \end{array}$$

$$\begin{array}{r} 4.1 \\ \times .98 \\ \hline 328 \\ 369 \\ \hline 4.018 \end{array} \qquad \begin{array}{r} 4 \\ \times 1 \\ \hline 4 \end{array}$$

Most people use a shortcut that does not involve estimating. Study these examples of the shortcut.

$$\begin{array}{r} 4.7 \\ \times 3.2 \\ \hline 94 \\ 1410 \\ \hline 15.04 \end{array}$$

2 digits to the right of the decimal points.

2 digits to the right of the decimal point.

$$\begin{array}{r} .131 \\ \times .08 \\ \hline .01048 \end{array}$$

5 digits to the right of the decimal points.

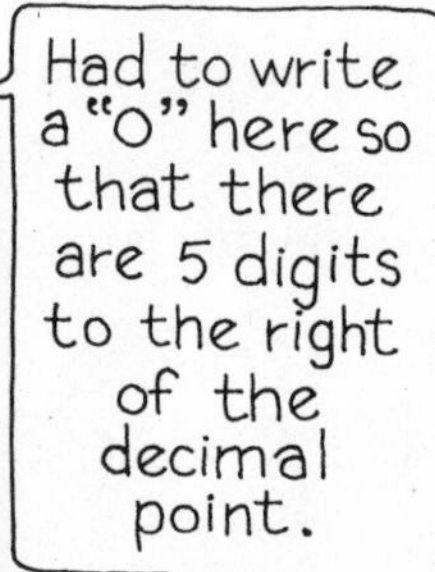

This flow chart tells you how to multiply with decimals.

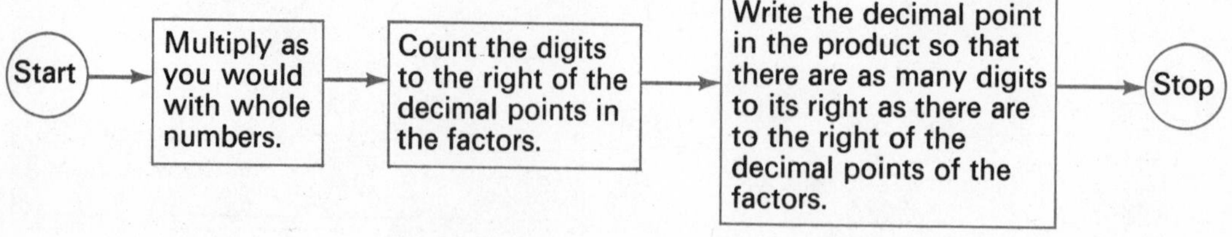

EXERCISES

Copy each "product" and put a decimal point in the proper place. You may need to write extra zeros.

1. 7.3 × 5.8 = 4234 **2.** 9.01 × 5.2 = 46,852 **3.** .34 × .16 = 544

4. 200 × 7.1 = 14,200 **5.** 6.9 × .15 = 1035 **6.** .06 × .07 = 42

Multiply.

7. 3.2 ×7.5 **8.** 5.9 ×6.5 **9.** 3.21 ×.6 **10.** 4.03 ×2.1 **11.** .06 ×.7 **12.** 3.41 ×.23

13. 52.1 ×8 **14.** 43.2 ×.5 **15.** 6.2 ×.35 **16.** .75 ×.43 **17.** .08 ×.06 **18.** .03 ×.02

Solve.

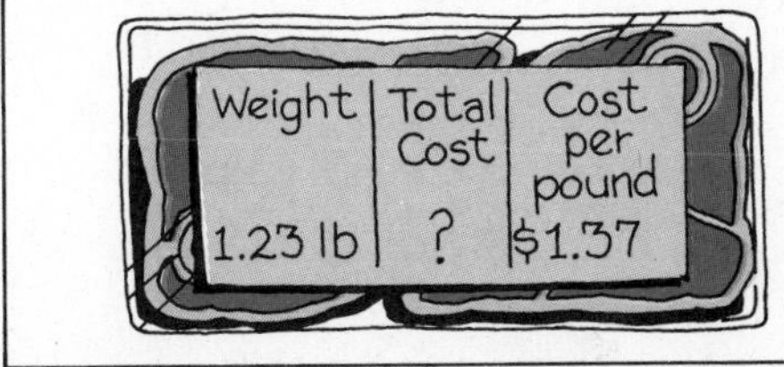

19. What is the total cost?

20. What is the total cost?

21. A race-car driver drove at an average rate of 123.62 miles per hour for 2.5 hours. How far did she drive?

Copy and complete.

22. 230 = 2.3 × __?__

23. 23 = 2.3 × __?__

24. 2.3 = 2.3 × __?__

25. .23 = 2.3 × __?__

26. .023 = 2.3 × __?__

27. .00531 = 5.31 × __?__

28. .000042 = 4.2 × __?__

29. .01732 = 1.732 × __?__

30. .017 = 1.7 × __?__

31. .0035 = 3.5 × __?__

32. .00500 = 5.00 × __?__

33. .0006 = 6 × __?__

EXCURSION

Here is a 2-player game that is similar to tic-tac-toe.

One player uses 1, 3, 5, 7, and 9. The other player uses 2, 4, 6, 8, and 10.

Each number can be used only once. Players take turns writing their numbers in the squares. The first player who *completes* a row, column, or diagonal with a sum of 15 wins.

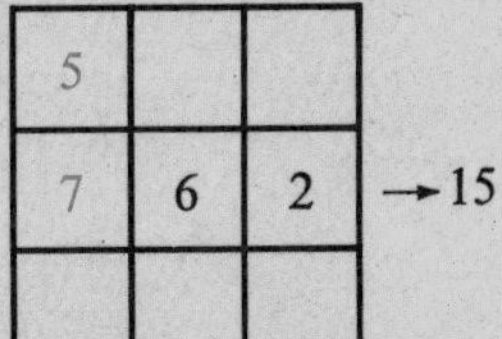

Study this game. The first player's numbers are in red. The second player won.

Supplementary Exercises, Set 15, page 378

Problem solving

Solve the problems. You may wish to write a flow chart for each problem.

1. Mrs. Stark bought 16.5 gallons of gas for 53.8¢ per gallon and a quart of oil for 95¢. How much did she spend in all?

2. Mr. Carter bought 3 shirts for $8.95 each and 3 ties for $5.75 each. How much did he spend in all?

3. Mr. Hooper bought 3 shirt and tie sets. The price of each shirt was $8.95 and the price of each tie was $5.75. What was the cost of each set? What was the total cost? (Your flow chart will have *two* PRINT instructions.)

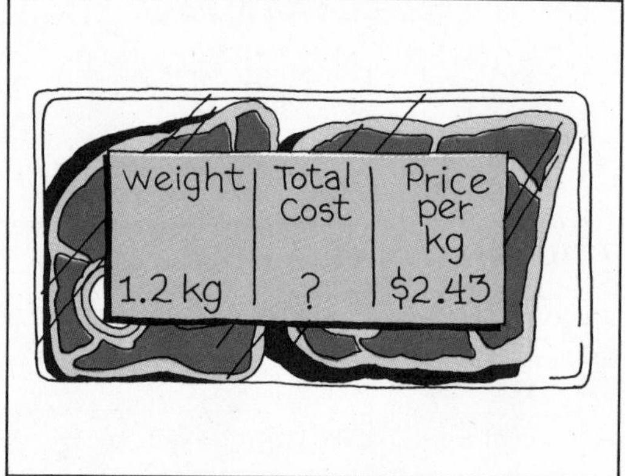

4. What is the total cost?

5. What is the cost of the whole bolt of cloth?

6. There were 295 adult tickets sold, at $1.75 each, for a basketball game. There were also 538 student tickets sold at $1.25 each and 73 free passes given away. How many people attended the game and how much money was collected?

7. A used car was listed for $1375 cash. It was bought on the installment plan for $400 down and $51.71 per month for 2 years. How much more did the car cost on the installment plan?

8. Jim bought 12 old coins for $7.75 each. Ten years later he sold them for $23.50 each. How much profit did he make?

9. Carol scored 27, 35, and 15 points on her first three math tests. How many points does she need on the next test to have a total of 100 points?

KEEPING SKILLS SHARP

Here are rules for three functions, f, g, and h:

$$f: n \rightarrow 2(n + 1) \qquad g: n \rightarrow n^2 \qquad h: n \rightarrow 3.1n + 6.7$$

Complete.

1. $f(6) =$ _?_ **2.** $f(10.1) =$ _?_ **3.** $f(13.9) =$ _?_ **4.** $f($_?_$) = 30$

5. $g(27) =$ _?_ **6.** $g(12.6) =$ _?_ **7.** $g(35.2) =$ _?_ **8.** $g($_?_$) = 196$

9. $h(7) =$ _?_ **10.** $h(3.2) =$ _?_ **11.** $h(.7) =$ _?_ **12.** $h(.07) =$ _?_

Add or subtract.

13. $.03 + .356 + .403 + 2.3$ **14.** $.9 - .084$ **15.** $2.9 + .007 + .84 + 1$

16. $3.5 - .35$ **17.** $88.37 + 1.64 + .305 + .9 + .0084$

18. $34.52 - 1.883$ **19.** $.85 - .063$ **20.** $49.7 - 5.2006$

Substitute and simplify.

A	b	d	D
0	4.1	7	3.2

21. A^5 **22.** d^4 **23.** db **24.** bD **25.** D^2 **26.** d^A

27. $3(b + d)$ **28.** $\frac{5D}{4}$ **29.** $2.7(b + D)$ **30.** $AbdD$ **31.** $(b - D)d$

Follow each flow chart.

32. Start → LET A = 27, B = 54, C = 18, D = 43 → LET E = A + C, F = AB + CD → PRINT E and F → Stop

33. Start → LET A = 5 → LET B = A² → PRINT B → Is A ≤ 55? — No → Stop; Yes → Increase A by 10. → LET B = A²

Write a flow chart for this problem.

34. Out of 34 students in a class, 4 were absent. Each of the students who was present paid 75¢ for school lunch. How much was paid by the class?

Skill Maintenance, Set 22, page 403

Dividing by a one-digit number

You may have learned how to divide by using place-value blocks.

$2\overline{)15.2}$

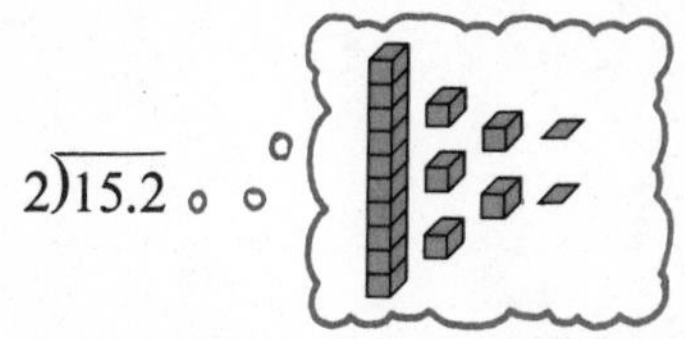

Think about 15.2 blocks that are to be divided into 2 equally large groups.

$2\overline{)15.2}$

There are not enough tens to go around. Regroup to get 15 unit blocks.

$$\begin{array}{r} 7 \\ 2\overline{)15.2} \\ -14 \\ \hline 1 \end{array}$$

Put 7 unit blocks into each group. This uses 14 and leaves 1.

$$\begin{array}{r} 7 \\ 2\overline{)15.2} \\ -14 \\ \hline 12 \end{array}$$

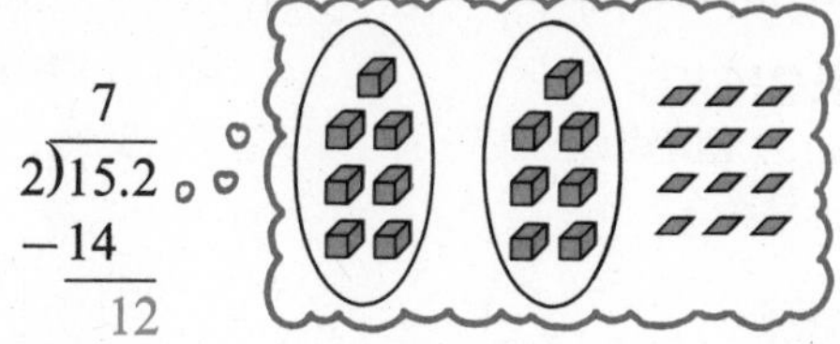

Regroup to get 12 tenth-blocks.

$$\begin{array}{r} 7.6 \\ 2\overline{)15.2} \\ -14 \\ \hline 12 \\ -12 \\ \hline 0 \end{array}$$

Put 6 tenth-blocks into each group. This uses all 12 of the tenth-blocks.

Here is another example. Can you explain it, using blocks?

$$\begin{array}{r} 1.34 \\ 5\overline{)6.70} \\ -5 \\ \hline 17 \\ -15 \\ \hline 20 \\ -20 \\ \hline 0 \end{array}$$

Sometimes the division will not "come out even." When this happens, you have to stop dividing and round the quotient to some place. The place to which you round will depend on the problem. For example, if you were solving a problem about money, you would probably round to the nearest cent. For the exercises that follow we tell you where to round.

Example. Divide 5.6 by 3 and round to the nearest hundredth.

Step 1. Divide to the thousandths place.

$$\begin{array}{r} 1.866 \\ 3\overline{)5.600} \\ -3 \\ \hline 26 \\ -24 \\ \hline 20 \\ -18 \\ \hline 20 \\ -18 \\ \hline 2 \end{array}$$

Step 2. Round to the nearest hundredth.

$$\begin{array}{r} 1.866 \rightarrow 1.87 \\ 3\overline{)5.600} \end{array}$$

EXERCISES

Divide. If the division does not come out even, round to the nearest hundredth.

1. $2\overline{)580}$	**2.** $2\overline{)5.8}$	**3.** $4\overline{)2.5}$	**4.** $8\overline{)1}$	**5.** $8\overline{)2}$
6. $5\overline{).32}$	**7.** $4\overline{)84}$	**8.** $2\overline{)7.32}$	**9.** $3\overline{).039}$	**10.** $4\overline{)3.4}$
11. $3\overline{)2.2}$	**12.** $7\overline{)1.1}$	**13.** $9\overline{)31.2}$	**14.** $7\overline{)370}$	**15.** $8\overline{)47}$
16. $9\overline{)100}$	**17.** $7\overline{)100}$	**18.** $5\overline{)4.1}$	**19.** $6\overline{)10}$	**20.** $3\overline{)931}$

Solve.

21. Four boys shared the cost of a used car that sold for $830. How much did each boy pay?

22. Suppose only 3 boys had bought the car in exercise 21. How much would each boy have paid?

23. If 10 apples are divided equally among 3 people, what will be each person's share?

24. If 10 cents is divided equally among 3 people, what will be each person's share?

What are the basic multiplication facts for the numbers?

25. 50 (50 × 1 = ? ⋮ 50 × 9 = ?) **26.** 20 **27.** 70

28. 80 **29.** 90

30. 200 **31.** 400

CHECKUP
for pages 78–79

Multiply.

1. $\begin{array}{r} 3.2 \\ \times .2 \\ \hline \end{array}$	**2.** $\begin{array}{r} 4.8 \\ \times .7 \\ \hline \end{array}$
3. $\begin{array}{r} .52 \\ \times .4 \\ \hline \end{array}$	**4.** $\begin{array}{r} 6.7 \\ \times .05 \\ \hline \end{array}$
5. $\begin{array}{r} 3.8 \\ \times 2.6 \\ \hline \end{array}$	**6.** $\begin{array}{r} .58 \\ \times .41 \\ \hline \end{array}$
7. $\begin{array}{r} 3.08 \\ \times 1.9 \\ \hline \end{array}$	**8.** $\begin{array}{r} 48.6 \\ \times 3.21 \\ \hline \end{array}$

Answers on page 425.

Supplementary Exercises, Set 16, page 378

Estimating in division

There are many ways of estimating the quotient of two numbers. When the divisor is a one-digit number, perhaps the easiest way of getting an estimate is to divide to find the first nonzero digit and then write zeros in the other places. Study this example.

Example. Estimate the quotient 8)6273.4.

8)6273.4 Not enough thousands.	7 8)6273.4 The first digit is 7, in the hundreds place	700 8)6273.4

You can get a better estimate by finding the first *two* nonzero digits and then rounding.

```
  780. → 800
8)6273.4
  56          A closer estimate.
  --
   67
```

You can use similar methods for two-digit divisors. First, however, you should round the divisor.

Example. Estimate the quotient 58)132.67.

(60) ~~58~~)132.67 Not enough hundreds.	(60) ~~58~~)132.67 Not enough tens.	(60) 2. ~~58~~)132.67 A good estimate is 2.

Here is an example with a decimal divisor.

Example. Estimate the quotient 4.3)2159.3.

(4) ~~4.3~~)2159.3 Not enough thousands.	(4) 5 ~~4.3~~)2159.3 5 in the hundreds place.	(4) 500. ~~4.3~~)2159.3 A good estimate is 500.

EXERCISES

Estimate.

1. $7\overline{)2387}$	**2.** $4\overline{)335.6}$	**3.** $8\overline{)1.756}$	**4.** $5\overline{)8351.4}$	**5.** $6\overline{).2754}$
6. $9\overline{)538.62}$	**7.** $8\overline{).0275}$	**8.** $3\overline{)6.8342}$	**9.** $2\overline{)102.77}$	**10.** $9\overline{)1.7663}$
11. $5\overline{)723.4}$	**12.** $50\overline{)723.4}$	**13.** $500\overline{)723.4}$	**14.** $4\overline{)2.987}$	**15.** $40\overline{)2.987}$
16. $7\overline{)8674.1}$	**17.** $70\overline{)8674.1}$	**18.** $700\overline{)8674.1}$	**19.** $3\overline{)1479}$	**20.** $30\overline{)1479}$
21. $60\overline{)8163}$	**22.** $20\overline{)5.411}$	**23.** $90\overline{)43.668}$	**24.** $80\overline{)2.513}$	**25.** $60\overline{)159300}$
26. $41\overline{)2835.1}$	**27.** $39\overline{)2835.1}$	**28.** $58\overline{)413.2}$	**29.** $62\overline{)413.2}$	**30.** $77\overline{)3.866}$

Estimate the answers.

31. 5 pounds of apples for \$1.68.
How much for 1 pound?

32. 4 kilograms of meat for \$8.79.
How much for 1 kilogram?

33. A dozen eggs for 79¢.
How much for each egg?

34. 2173 students on 41 buses.
How many students on each bus?

Estimate.

35. $78\overline{)39.416}$	**36.** $82\overline{)59341}$	**37.** $29\overline{)135.41}$	**38.** $38\overline{)2674.1}$	**39.** $97\overline{)543.67}$
40. $31\overline{)67.62}$	**41.** $3.1\overline{)67.62}$	**42.** $58\overline{)135.66}$	**43.** $5.8\overline{)135.66}$	**44.** $4.2\overline{)3884}$
45. $91\overline{)377.4}$	**46.** $.91\overline{)377.4}$			

Estimate.

47. What is the price per kilogram?

48. What is the weight?

EXCURSION

The smallest whole number having exactly 3 factors is 4.

What is the smallest whole number that has exactly

6 factors? 7 factors?

8 factors? 9 factors?

Skill Maintenance, Set 23, page 403

Dividing by two- or three-digit numbers

Dividing by a two-digit number is usually more difficult than dividing by a one-digit number. This is because we have not memorized the basic multiplication facts for most two-digit numbers. One way of doing a division exercise with a two-digit divisor is to first compute all 9 "basic" multiplication facts. Study this example.
First compute basic multiplication facts for 42:

$42\overline{)155.4}$

42	42	42	42	42	42	42	42	42
×1	×2	×3	×4	×5	×6	×7	×8	×9
42	84	126	168	210	252	294	336	378

Use the facts to divide:

$$\begin{array}{r} 3.7 \\ 42\overline{)155.4} \\ -126 \\ \hline 29\,4 \\ -29\,4 \\ \hline 0 \end{array}$$

It is usually a waste of time to compute nine basic facts, so we estimate to save some work. Study this example.

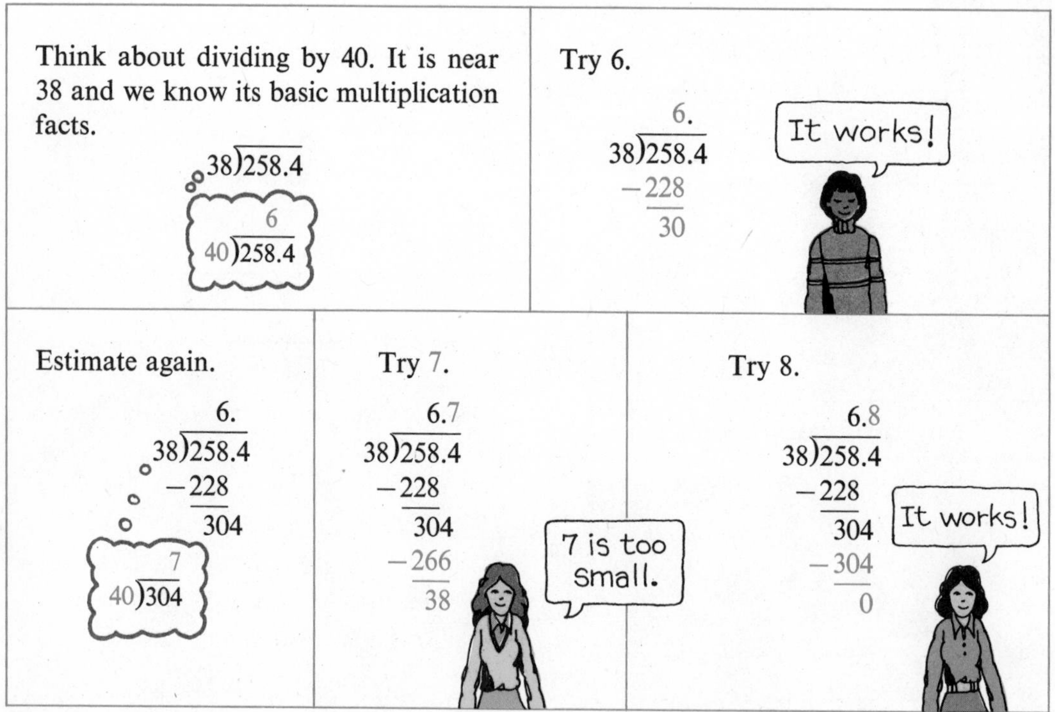

EXERCISES

Use these multiplication facts to help you divide.

58	58	58	58	58	58	58	58	58
×1	×2	×3	×4	×5	×6	×7	×8	×9
58	116	174	232	290	348	406	464	522

1. $58\overline{)232}$ **2.** $58\overline{)2088}$ **3.** $58\overline{)20.88}$ **4.** $58\overline{)5.162}$ **5.** $58\overline{)446.6}$

6. $58\overline{)58116}$ **7.** $58\overline{)5916}$ **8.** $58\overline{)696}$ **9.** $58\overline{)36.54}$ **10.** $58\overline{)504.60}$

Divide.

11. $24\overline{)168}$ **12.** $39\overline{)195}$ **13.** $72\overline{)432}$ **14.** $85\overline{)59.5}$ **15.** $73\overline{)5.84}$

16. $23\overline{)943}$ **17.** $28\overline{)159.6}$ **18.** $53\overline{)22.26}$ **19.** $952\overline{)276.08}$ **20.** $771\overline{)370.08}$

Divide. Round quotients to the nearest hundredth.

21. $19\overline{)58.3}$ **22.** $32\overline{)5.11}$ **23.** $42\overline{)17.2}$ **24.** $83\overline{)268}$ **25.** $47\overline{)57.6}$

26. $11\overline{)56.3}$ **27.** $17\overline{)86.41}$ **28.** $283\overline{)977.4}$ **29.** $562\overline{)426.7}$

Estimate each quotient.

30. $2\overline{)4}$ **31.** $20\overline{)40}$ **32.** $200\overline{)400}$

33. $5\overline{)35}$ **34.** $50\overline{)350}$ **35.** $500\overline{)3500}$

36. $3\overline{)6}$ **37.** $30\overline{)60}$ **38.** $300\overline{)600}$

1. Ask about 20 schoolmates for the number of people in their family.
2. Compute the average family size. Round your quotient to the nearest tenth.
3. Compare your findings with those of other classmates.

EXCURSION

Think of a number.
Add 10.
Multiply by 2.
Divide by 4.
Subtract 5.
Multiply by 2.
What is your answer?
Repeat, starting with a different number.
What is your answer?
Can you explain why?

Supplementary Exercises, Set 17, page 378

Negative exponents and scientific notation

Mathematicians and scientists often use negative numbers as exponents. Study these examples.

$$\begin{aligned} 1000 &= 10^{3} \qquad & .1 &= 10^{-1} \\ 100 &= 10^{2} \qquad & .01 &= 10^{-2} \\ 10 &= 10^{1} \qquad & .001 &= 10^{-3} \\ 1 &= 10^{0} \qquad & .0001 &= 10^{-4} \end{aligned}$$

Using negative exponents, we can write scientific notation for numbers that are less than 1. Remember that numerals in scientific notation have two parts—one part for a number between 1 and 10 and one part for a power of 10.

$$\begin{aligned} .25 &= 2.5 \times 10^{-1} \\ .025 &= 2.5 \times 10^{-2} \\ .0025 &= 2.5 \times 10^{-3} \\ .000000025 &= 2.5 \times 10^{-8} \end{aligned}$$

Scientists use scientific notation when they write about very small quantities. For example:

9×10^{-5} meters (diameter of a human hair)

1.675×10^{-24} grams (approximate weight of a hydrogen atom)

EXERCISES

Write, using negative exponents.

1. .1 **2.** .01 **3.** .001 **4.** .0001 **5.** .00001

6. .00000001 **7.** .0000000001 **8.** $\frac{1}{10^1}$ **9.** $\frac{1}{10^2}$ **10.** $\frac{1}{10^3}$

11. $\frac{1}{10^4}$ **12.** $\frac{1}{10^5}$ **13.** $\frac{1}{10^6}$ **14.** $\frac{1}{10^{15}}$ **15.** $\frac{1}{10^{30}}$

Write in standard notation.

16. 10^{-1} **17.** 10^{-3} **18.** 10^{-4} **19.** 10^{-7}

20. 10^{-12} **21.** 3×10^{-1} **22.** 4.2×10^{-2} **23.** 6.31×10^{-2}

24. 9.34×10^{-3} **25.** 9.34×10^{-5} **26.** 6.5×10^{-8} **27.** 1.22×10^{-5}

28. 6.4×10^{-6} **29.** 7.7×10^{-12} **30.** 8.31×10^{-14} **31.** 2.49×10^{-20}

Write in scientific notation.

32. .037 **33.** .0037 **34.** .00037 **35.** .000037 **36.** .00000037

37. .453 **38.** .00291 **39.** .0000067 **40.** .000000000000000912

Write each number in scientific notation.

41. The angstrom is a unit of length used to measure very small distances, such as the diameter of a molecule. One angstrom equals .0000000001 meter.

42. One antenna received a signal one ten-billionth of a second before a second antenna.

Complete. 100 × 1000 = 10000 .01 × .001 = .00001

43. $10^2 \times 10^3 = 10^?$
44. $10^5 \times 10^2 = 10^?$
45. $10^3 \times 10^4 = 10^?$
46. $10^1 \times 10^3 = 10^?$
47. $10^6 \times 10^7 = 10^?$
48. $10^8 \times 10^{10} = 10^?$
49. $10^{19} \times 10^{25} = 10^?$
50. $10^{-2} \times 10^{-3} = 10^?$
51. $10^{-2} \times 10^2 = 10^?$
52. $10^{-3} \times 10^4 = 10^?$
53. $10^{-2} \times 10^{-2} = 10^?$
54. $10^{-4} \times 10^{10} = 10^?$
55. $10^{-6} \times 10^{-9} = 10^?$
56. $10^{-10} \times 10^{-13} = 10^?$
57. $10^{-3} \times 10^6 = 10^?$
58. $10^{-4} \times 10^{10} = 10^?$
59. $10^8 \times 10^{-3} = 10^?$
60. $10^9 \times 10^{-13} = 10^?$

Exercises 43–60 show you a rule for multiplying powers of 10:

Add the exponents of the factors to get the exponent of the product.

$10^2 \times 10^5 = 10^7$ $10^2 \times 10^{-4} = 10^{-2}$

100 × 100,000 = 10,000,000 100 × .0001 = .01

Do you remember how to add with negative numbers?

This rule can be used when multiplying with numerals in scientific notation.

Example 1. $19{,}000{,}000 \times 370{,}000$
$= 1.9 \times 10^7 \times 3.7 \times 10^5$
$= (1.9 \times 3.7) \times (10^7 \times 10^5)$
$= 7.03 \times 10^{12}$

Example 2. $43{,}000 \times .000065$
$= 4.3 \times 10^4 \times 6.5 \times 10^{-5}$
$= (4.3 \times 6.5) \times (10^4 \times 10^{-5})$
$= 27.95 \times 10^{-1}$
$= 2.795$

Simplify.

61. $(3.1 \times 10^4)(2.6 \times 10^5)$
62. $(4.7 \times 10^7)(2.1 \times 10^3)$
63. $(3.2 \times 10^4)(3.2 \times 10^4)$
64. $(2.3 \times 10^{-1})(4.1 \times 10^{-5})$
65. $(1.6 \times 10^7)(3.2 \times 10^{-4})$
66. $(2.8 \times 10^{-5})(3.1 \times 10^2)$
67. $(4.9 \times 10^{-13})(6.8 \times 10^6)$
68. $48{,}000{,}000 \times 320{,}000$
69. $670{,}000{,}000 \times 220{,}000$
70. $.000034 \times .00051$
71. $.000047 \times .00000031$
72. $.000034 \times 67{,}000{,}000$

Skill Maintenance, Set 24, page 403

Dividing by a decimal

Here is one way to do problems that involve dividing by a decimal: First, divide as you would with whole numbers. Second, estimate to find where the decimal point goes in the quotient.

Examples.

	Forget about the decimal points and divide.	Estimate to place the decimal point.
$5.4\overline{)9.18}$	$54\overline{)918}$ = 17; 54; 378; 378	$5.4\overline{)9.18}$ = 1.7; 54; 378; 378 (Thought: $5\overline{)9}$ Quotient is near 2.)
$1.87\overline{)6.358}$	Divide with whole numbers. $187\overline{)6358}$ = 34; 561; 748; 748	Estimate to place the decimal point. $1.87\overline{)6.358}$ = 3.4; 561; 748; 748 (Thought: $2\overline{)6}$ Quotient is near 3.)

Most people use a more mechanical method. They remember that you can multiply both the divisor and the dividend by the same number without changing the quotient. They use this fact to change all divisors to whole numbers. Study these examples.

Examples.

$5.4\overline{)9.18}$	Multiply both divisor and dividend by 10. $5.4\overline{)9.18}$	Divide. $5.4\overline{)9.18}$ = 1.7; 54; 378; 378
$1.87\overline{)6.358}$	Multiply both divisor and dividend by 100. $1.87\overline{)6.358}$	Divide. $1.87\overline{)6.358}$ = 3.4; 561; 748; 748

When you use the second method, it's still a good idea to estimate as a check on your work.

EXERCISES

Copy each exercise and place the decimal point in the "quotient."

1. $\begin{array}{r}57\\62\overline{)35.34}\end{array}$ 2. $\begin{array}{r}57\\6.2\overline{)35.34}\end{array}$ 3. $\begin{array}{r}57\\.62\overline{)35.34}\end{array}$ 4. $\begin{array}{r}57\\6.2\overline{)3.534}\end{array}$ 5. $\begin{array}{r}57\\.62\overline{)3.534}\end{array}$

6. $\begin{array}{r}403\\73\overline{)29.419}\end{array}$ 7. $\begin{array}{r}403\\.73\overline{)29.419}\end{array}$ 8. $\begin{array}{r}403\\7.3\overline{)294.19}\end{array}$ 9. $\begin{array}{r}403\\.73\overline{)2941.9}\end{array}$ 10. $\begin{array}{r}403\\7.3\overline{)29.419}\end{array}$

Divide. Round your quotients so that they have at most 3 digits.

11. $.4\overline{)2.7}$ 12. $.5\overline{)37}$ 13. $.6\overline{).57}$ 14. $.2\overline{).6}$ 15. $.9\overline{)32.5}$

16. $.05\overline{)81}$ 17. $.08\overline{).3}$ 18. $.07\overline{)32}$ 19. $.06\overline{)5.132}$ 20. $.003\overline{)1.3}$

21. $2.1\overline{)57.3}$ 22. $3.8\overline{).42}$ 23. $.47\overline{)5.661}$ 24. $.035\overline{)63}$ 25. $9.2\overline{)61.4}$

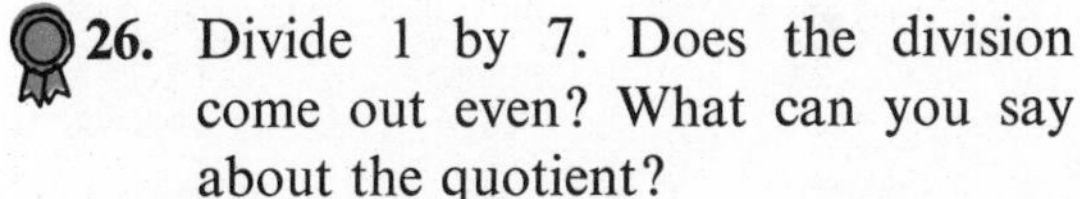

26. Divide 1 by 7. Does the division come out even? What can you say about the quotient?

27. Divide 1 by 9. Does the division come out even? What can you say about the quotient?

EXCURSION

In the computer programs that you wrote in Chapter 2, you told the computer what numbers to use and how to use them like this:

```
10  LET A = 6
20  LET B = 4
30  LET C = A + B
```

Here is another way that is very useful when there are many data or if the same computations are to be done several times with different numbers.

Suppose that you wish to tell the computer to find the areas of circles that have radii 7, 3.4, 6.2, 5.4, and 13.

You could use this program.

```
10  READ R
20  LET A = 3.14*(R↑2)
30  PRINT A
40  GØ TØ 10
50  DATA 7, 3.4, 6.2, 5.4, 13
60  END
```

The READ instruction of line 10 tells the computer to use the first number of the DATA line for R. When the computer loops back to line 10, it uses the second number of the DATA line for R. When there are no data left to read, the program ends.

Write a program to tell a computer to compute the circumferences of the same circles.

Supplementary Exercises, Set 18, page 378

Problem solving

Solve each problem.

1. Mr. Hardy bought a washing machine on the installment plan. The total cost to him was $242. He paid $50 down and the rest in 12 equal installments. How much was each installment?

2. Mrs. Underwood had a small orchard with 54 apple trees. From each tree she harvested about 250 apples. About how many apples did she harvest in all? The apples were packed in boxes, with about 100 apples per box. She sold the boxes for $6.95 per box. How much money did she collect when she sold all the boxes?

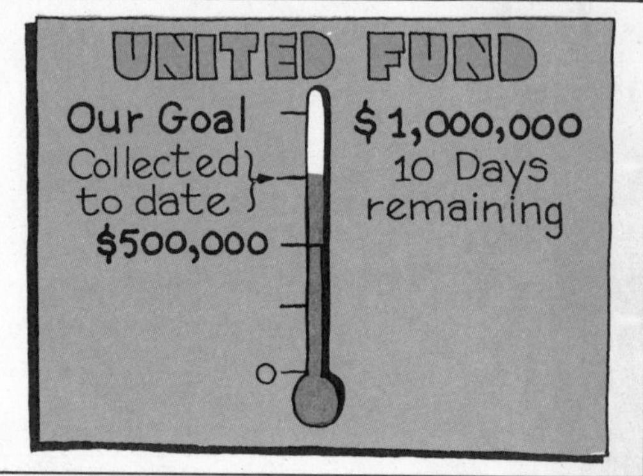

3. About how many kilometers in a mile?

4. On the average how much must be collected on each of the next 10 days to reach the goal?

5. There are 475 students going on a field trip. Mrs. Hunt, the principal, must order enough buses. If each bus holds 54 students, how many buses should she order?

6. Jerry played Little League baseball. One season he got 21 hits in 70 official times at bat. Find his batting average by dividing the number of hits by the number of times at bat. Round to the nearest thousandth.

7. A magazine offered new subscribers a special subscription rate of 6 issues for $1.98. The same 6 issues would cost $4.50 at a newsstand. How much is saved on *each* issue at the subscription rate?

8. A delivery service delivers packages in a small city. The delivery charge is 50¢ per package plus a charge by weight of 50¢ for the first pound and 10¢ for each pound after the first pound. How much would it cost to have a 6-pound package delivered?

Divide. Round so that there are 3 digits in your quotients.

1. $45\overline{)297.4}$ **2.** $4.5\overline{)297.4}$ **3.** $.45\overline{)297.4}$ **4.** $4.5\overline{)29.74}$ **5.** $.45\overline{)2974}$

6. $59\overline{)4.36}$ **7.** $1.9\overline{)175.33}$ **8.** $.6\overline{)1}$ **9.** $.03\overline{)1}$ **10.** $9\overline{).1}$

Follow each flow chart.

11.

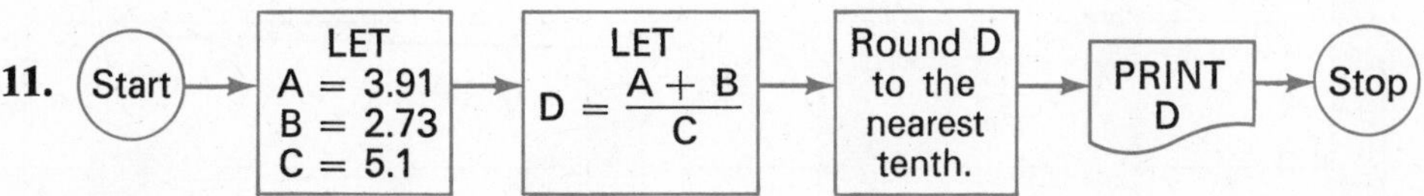

12.

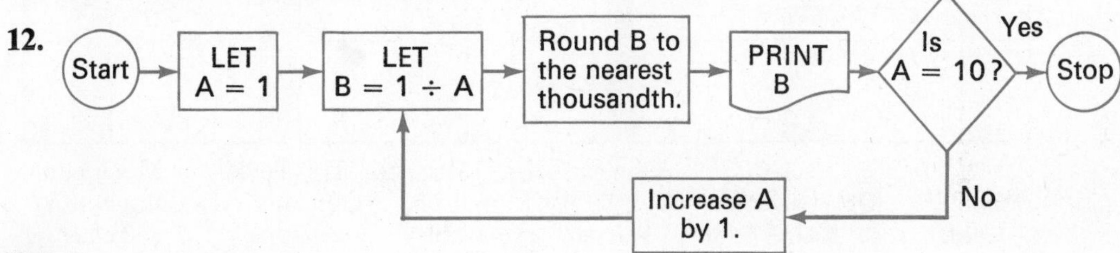

Solve.

13. $4.7a = 1.645$

14. $\frac{b}{.53} = 1.8$

15. $g^2 = 4$

16. $m^2 = .04$

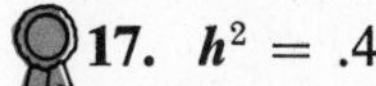

17. $h^2 = .4$

18. $\frac{(.3a + 6.5)}{5} = 1.45$

Complete.

$f: n \rightarrow .4n$

19. $f(6) =$ ___?___

20. $f(.6) =$ ___?___

21. $f(60) =$ ___?___

22. $f($_?_$) = .032$

$g: n \rightarrow n \div .6$

23. $g(3) =$ ___?___

24. $g(.1) =$ ___?___

25. $g(10) =$ ___?___

26. $g($_?_$) = 7.2$

CHECKUP

for pages 82–87, 90–91

Divide.

1. $6\overline{)15.6}$ **2.** $3\overline{).213}$

3. $4\overline{)10}$ **4.** $5\overline{)3.2}$

5. $12\overline{)1.56}$ **6.** $28\overline{)4.76}$

7. $.9\overline{)34.2}$ **8.** $.3\overline{).261}$

9. $.5\overline{)32}$ **10.** $1.2\overline{)2.88}$

11. $.37\overline{)2.183}$ **12.** $5.6\overline{)8512}$

Divide. Round your quotient to the nearest hundredth.

13. $4.3\overline{)279.8}$ **14.** $2.9\overline{)378.2}$

Answers on page 425.

Skill Maintenance, Set 25, page 404

Graphs

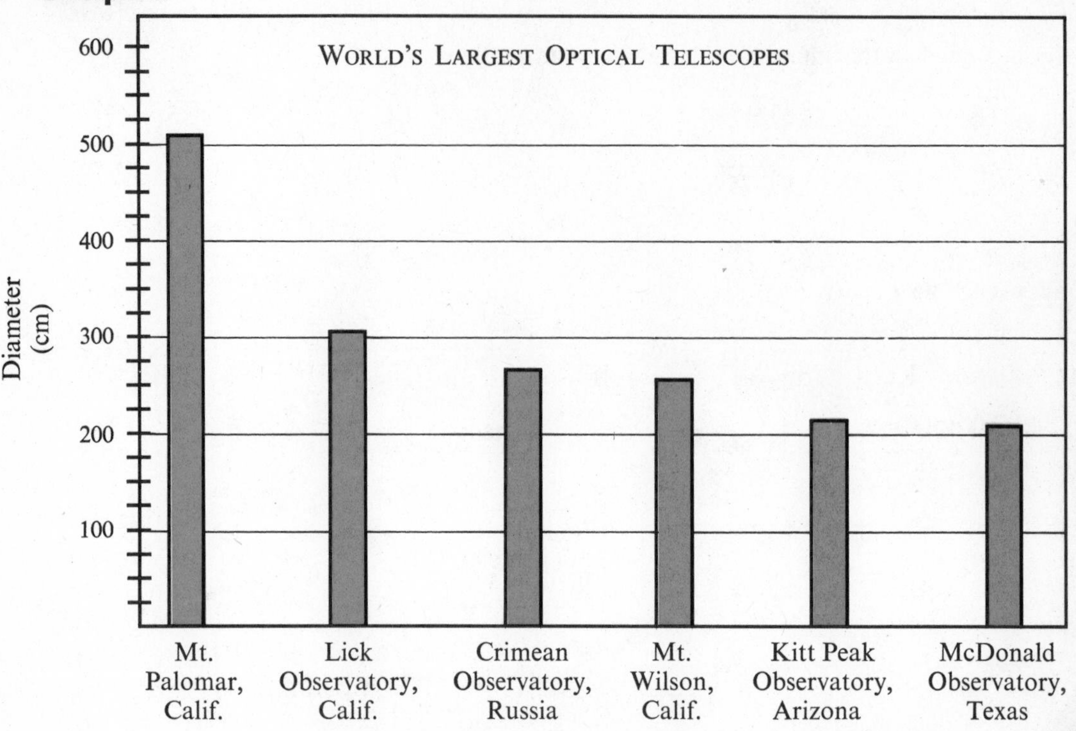

1. Which telescope shown is the largest? Smallest?
2. What is the approximate diameter of the telescope at the Lick Observatory? At the Crimean Astrophysical Observatory?
3. Which telescope is half as large as the one at Mt. Palomar?
4. One of the world's largest radio telescopes has a diameter of 30,480 cm. How many times greater is that than the diameter of the largest optical telescope?

5. What is the approximate difference in the diameter of the largest and smallest telescopes shown on the graph?
6. The Mt. Palomar telescope has a diameter of 508 cm, or 200 in. How many centimeters in an inch?

Project

Find some interesting data and show them on a bar graph.

CHAPTER CHECKUP

Multiply. [*page 68*]

1. 2.4×2 **2.** $.38 \times 4$ **3.** 26.7×5 **4.** 60.77×8

Complete this table. [*page 70*]

	5.	6.	7.	8.	9.
Standard notation		72,300		62,000,000	
Scientific notation	4.3×10^4		5.33×10^6		7.02×10^9

Multiply. [*page 72*]

10. 25×41 **11.** 3.6×52 **12.** 4.21×78 **13.** 51.3×256 **14.** $.716 \times 305$

Multiply. [*page 76*]

15. 37×1.6 **16.** $.48 \times 3.9$ **17.** $6.25 \times .06$ **18.** $.773 \times 9.5$ **19.** 7.04×61.1

Divide. [*page 84*]

20. 2)2.84 **21.** 3)1.35 **22.** 5).41 **23.** 8)10 **24.** 9)34.11

Divide. Round so that your quotients have at most three digits. [*page 86*]

25. 21)44.1 **26.** 38)523 **27.** 25)1 **28.** 45)17.53 **29.** 312)684.7

Divide. Round so that your quotients have at most three digits. [*page 90*]

30. .5)2.75 **31.** .03)91.41 **32.** 4.2)684.1 **33.** .37)12.4 **34.** 4.11)3754.2

Solve. [*pages 80, 92*]

35. Karen bought a typewriter for $57. She paid for it in 12 equal installments. How much was each installment?

36. Joe bought 4.5 kilograms of frankfurts for a picnic. They cost $2.18 per kilogram. How much did he pay?

MAJOR CHECKUP

Match. [*page 8*]

1. commutative property of addition
2. associative property of addition
3. adding 0 property
4. distributive property

a. $0(7 + 0) = 0 \times 7 + 0 \times 0$
b. $7 + 0 = 7$
c. $7 + 0 = 0 + 7$
d. $(7 + 0) + 0 = 7 + (0 + 0)$

Solve. [*pages 16–19*]

5. $7x + 4 = 60$ **6.** $7(x + 4) = 35$ **7.** $12.4 - 3a = 2.2$

8. $\frac{m + 25}{5} = 11$ **9.** $\frac{50}{a + 3} = 2$ **10.** $\frac{7m + 10}{10} = 15$

Complete. [*page 38*]

11. 2000 m = __?__ km **12.** 4387 m = __?__ km **13.** 70 m = __?__ km

14. __?__ m = 3.4 km **15.** __?__ m = .56 km **16.** __?__ m = .0089 km

Add or subtract. [*pages 42–43*]

17. 1.08 + .79

18. .768 + .272

19. 73.9 + 8.1

20. .4948 + .2107

21. 65.43 + 2.58

22. 9.64 − .19

23. 2.38 − .75

24. .8380 − .3039

25. .49 − .0476

26. 60 − 55.98

Follow this flow chart. [*pages 46–49*]

27.

28. Write a flow chart that will tell someone to compute and print the multiples of 9 that are less than 1000. [*pages 46–49*]

City geometry

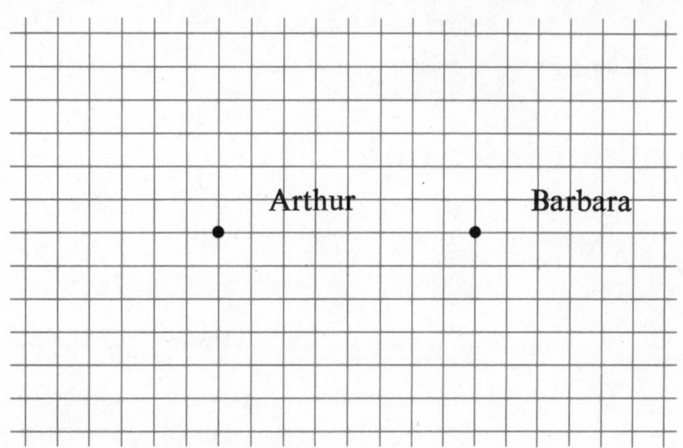

The grid above represents streets in a city. The points show where Arthur and Barbara live.

1. If Arthur starts at home and walks away from home for 5 blocks (along the streets), where might his walk end? Get a sheet of graph paper, mark a point (where two lines cross) to represent Arthur's home, and mark in red all the points that are 5 blocks from home.
2. Are there the same number of routes to each end point?
3. Mark in blue the points that are the same number of blocks from Arthur's home as they are from Barbara's home.

4. On graph paper mark the points given below and see if you can find where the school and the ice-cream parlor are located. The school is 6 blocks from houses *C*, *D*, and *E*. The ice-cream parlor is the same number of blocks (not 6) from houses *F*, *G*, and *H*.

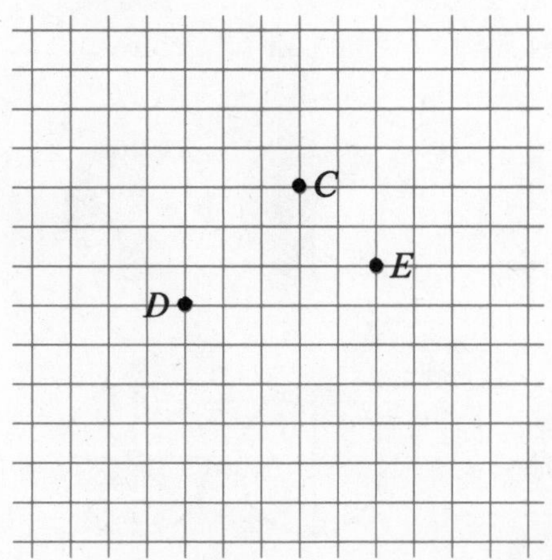

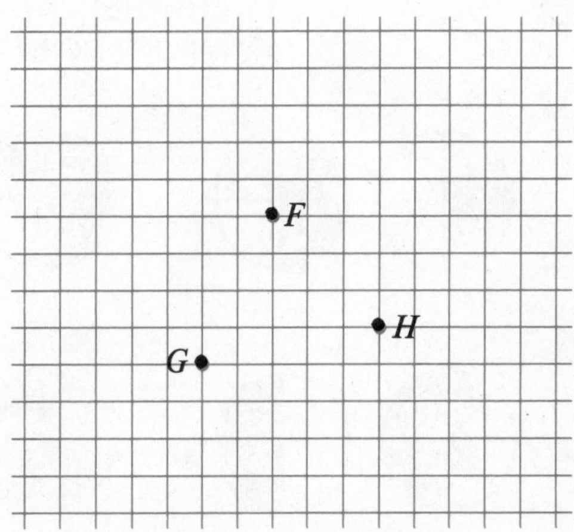

4 Computing with Fractional Numbers

Equivalent fractions

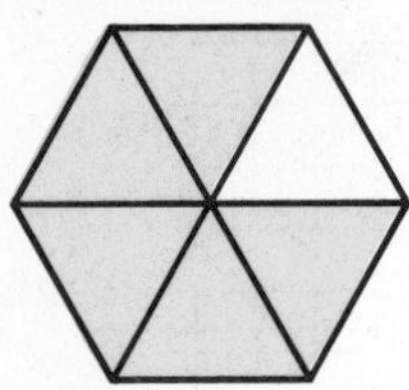

You know that such numerals as $\frac{1}{3}$, $\frac{4}{9}$, and $\frac{0}{6}$ are **fractions.** You have used fractions to tell what part of a set or region has a given quality. For example, the fraction $\frac{5}{6}$ tells the part of the figure that is yellow. The numerator, 5, tells the number of yellow regions; the denominator, 6, tells the number of regions the same size. You have also used fractions to name points on the number line. The fractions $\frac{1}{3}$ and $\frac{2}{6}$ both name the red point on the number line below. They are called **equivalent fractions.**

$$\begin{array}{ccccccc} & & \frac{1}{3} & \frac{1}{2} & \frac{2}{3} & & \\ \bullet & \bullet & \bullet & \bullet & \bullet & \bullet & \bullet \\ 0 & \frac{1}{6} & \frac{2}{6} & \frac{3}{6} & \frac{4}{6} & \frac{5}{6} & 1 \end{array}$$

All the fractions in this set of equivalent fractions are names for the same fractional number:

$$\left\{\frac{1}{3}, \frac{2}{6}, \frac{3}{9}, \frac{4}{12}, \frac{5}{15}, \ldots\right\}$$

Every fractional number can be named by an infinite set of equivalent fractions.

EXERCISES

Give the two equivalent fractions shown by the pair of pictures.

1.

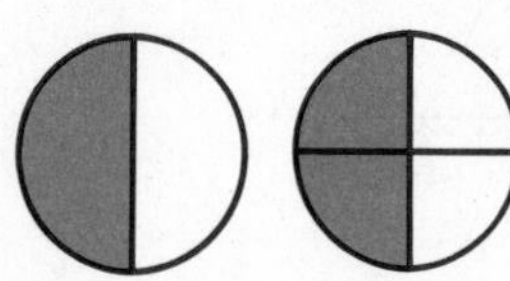

2.

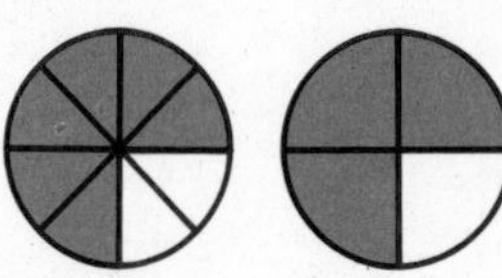

3.

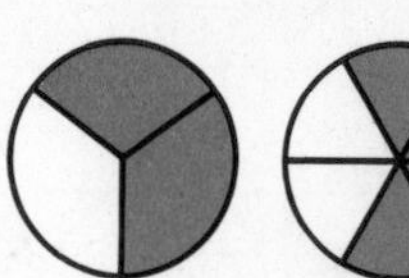

4.

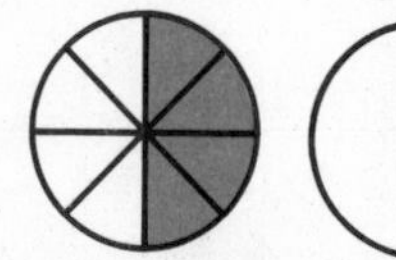

5.

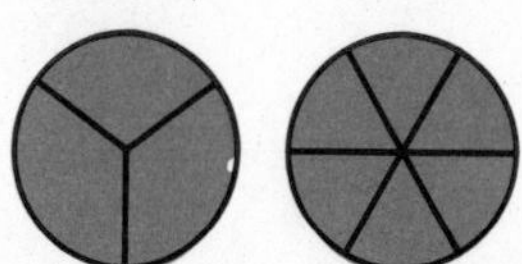

6.

Use the divisions on the ruler to find equivalent fractions for the red mark.

7. INCHES 1 2

8. INCHES 1 2

9. INCHES 1 2

10. INCHES 1 2

Match each set of equivalent fractions with its point on the number line.

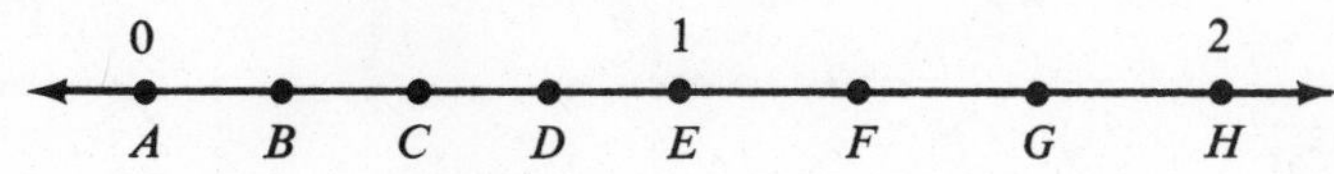

11. $\left\{\frac{1}{2}, \frac{2}{4}, \frac{3}{6}, \frac{4}{8}, \ldots\right\}$

Answer. C

12. $\left\{\frac{1}{1}, \frac{2}{2}, \frac{3}{3}, \frac{4}{4}, \ldots\right\}$

13. $\left\{\frac{3}{4}, \frac{6}{8}, \frac{9}{12}, \frac{12}{16}, \ldots\right\}$

14. $\left\{\frac{0}{1}, \frac{0}{2}, \frac{0}{3}, \frac{0}{4}, \ldots\right\}$

15. $\left\{\frac{5}{3}, \frac{10}{6}, \frac{15}{9}, \frac{20}{12}, \ldots\right\}$

16. $\left\{\frac{2}{1}, \frac{4}{2}, \frac{6}{3}, \frac{8}{4}, \ldots\right\}$

17. $\left\{\frac{4}{3}, \frac{8}{6}, \frac{12}{9}, \frac{16}{12}, \ldots\right\}$

18. $\left\{\frac{1}{4}, \frac{2}{8}, \frac{3}{12}, \frac{4}{16}, \ldots\right\}$

Who am I?

19. I am a fraction equivalent to $\frac{1}{4}$. My denominator is 8.

20. I am a fraction equivalent to $\frac{2}{3}$. My numerator is 6.

21. I am a fraction equivalent to $\frac{3}{8}$. My denominator is 15 greater than my numerator.

Give another equivalent fraction.
Draw a number line if you need to.

22. $\frac{1}{2}, \frac{2}{4}$ 23. $\frac{1}{4}, \frac{2}{8}$ 24. $\frac{1}{8}, \frac{2}{16}$

25. $\frac{2}{3}, \frac{4}{6}$ 26. $\frac{4}{3}, \frac{8}{6}$ 27. $\frac{0}{1}, \frac{0}{2}$

28. $\frac{1}{1}, \frac{2}{2}$ 29. $\frac{3}{4}, \frac{6}{8}$ 30. $\frac{3}{2}, \frac{6}{4}$

31. $\frac{5}{8}, \frac{10}{16}$ 32. $\frac{7}{5}, \frac{14}{10}$ 33. $\frac{1}{10}, \frac{2}{20}$

34. $\frac{5}{2}, \frac{10}{4}$ 35. $\frac{8}{3}, \frac{16}{6}$ 36. $\frac{7}{8}, \frac{14}{16}$

EXCURSION

Write the following numbers as the sum and/or difference of not more than three square numbers:

59, 62, 78, 84, 91, 99

Here are some examples:

$$58 = 7^2 + 3^2$$
$$53 = 6^2 + 4^2 + 1^2$$
$$51 = 8^2 - (3^2 + 2^2)$$

Supplementary Exercises, Set 19, page 378

Fractions in higher or lower terms

The numerator and denominator of a fraction are called **terms** of the fraction. Here are two equivalent fractions:

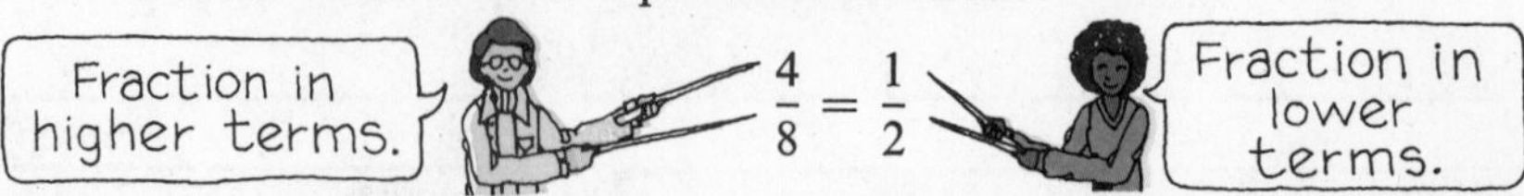

To get an equivalent fraction in higher terms, multiply both terms of the fraction by a whole number greater than 1.	To get an equivalent fraction in lower terms, divide both terms of the fraction by a whole number greater than 1.
Example.	*Example.*

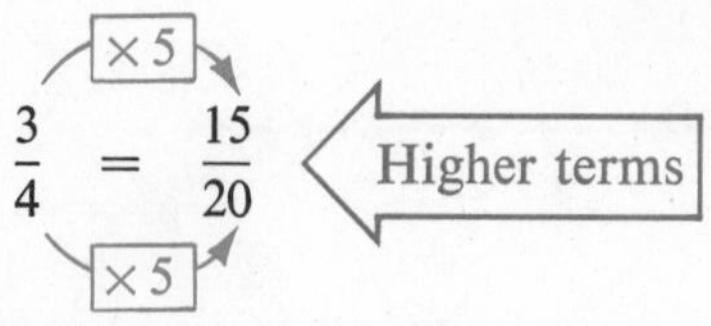

$$\frac{9}{12} = \frac{3}{4}$$ (÷3, ÷3) Lower terms

To reduce a fraction to lowest terms, divide both terms by their greatest common factor.

Example.

To reduce to lowest terms a fraction that is equivalent to a whole number, write it as a whole number.

Example.

$$\frac{12}{3} = \frac{4}{1} = 4$$

A fraction is in lowest terms if the greatest common factor of both terms is 1.

EXERCISES

Give an equivalent fraction in higher terms.

1. $\frac{1}{2}$ **2.** $\frac{2}{3}$ **3.** $\frac{4}{3}$ **4.** $\frac{3}{4}$ **5.** $\frac{3}{5}$ **6.** $\frac{8}{7}$ **7.** $\frac{3}{2}$ **8.** $\frac{7}{4}$

9. $\frac{1}{8}$ **10.** $\frac{2}{5}$ **11.** $\frac{1}{3}$ **12.** $\frac{9}{4}$ **13.** $\frac{6}{5}$ **14.** $\frac{5}{3}$ **15.** $\frac{1}{6}$ **16.** $\frac{5}{4}$

17. $\frac{3}{8}$ **18.** $\frac{12}{5}$ **19.** $\frac{8}{5}$ **20.** $\frac{7}{3}$ **21.** $\frac{11}{4}$ **22.** $\frac{8}{3}$ **23.** $\frac{11}{3}$ **24.** $\frac{7}{10}$

First give the greatest common factor of the terms. Then give the equivalent fraction in lowest terms.

25. $\frac{2}{6}$ **26.** $\frac{2}{4}$ **27.** $\frac{6}{8}$ **28.** $\frac{4}{16}$ **29.** $\frac{12}{9}$ **30.** $\frac{14}{16}$ **31.** $\frac{24}{30}$ **32.** $\frac{14}{18}$

33. $\frac{18}{32}$ **34.** $\frac{9}{12}$ **35.** $\frac{27}{36}$ **36.** $\frac{15}{25}$ **37.** $\frac{16}{24}$ **38.** $\frac{21}{14}$ **39.** $\frac{14}{12}$ **40.** $\frac{6}{9}$

Who am I?

41. I am a fraction equivalent to $\frac{8}{12}$. I am in lowest terms

42. I am a fraction equivalent to $\frac{3}{2}$. The greatest common factor of my terms is 5.

43. I am a fractional number greater than 1. The product of my terms is 24. The sum of my terms is 11.

Solve.

44. $\frac{1}{2} = \frac{b}{6}$ (×3)

45. $\frac{1}{3} = \frac{n}{6}$

46. $\frac{1}{4} = \frac{g}{16}$

47. $\frac{2}{3} = \frac{6}{a}$

48. $\frac{2}{7} = \frac{b}{21}$

49. $\frac{5}{8} = \frac{r}{40}$

50. $\frac{3}{8} = \frac{12}{m}$

51. $\frac{5}{2} = \frac{10}{p}$

52. $\frac{6}{5} = \frac{c}{15}$

53. $\frac{3}{4} = \frac{15}{k}$

54. $\frac{3}{1} = \frac{15}{f}$

55. $\frac{4}{3} = \frac{28}{e}$

56. $\frac{2}{9} = \frac{d}{36}$

57. $\frac{3}{2} = \frac{12}{j}$

58. $\frac{5}{3} = \frac{a}{15}$

59. Copy and complete this flow chart for reducing a fraction to lowest terms.

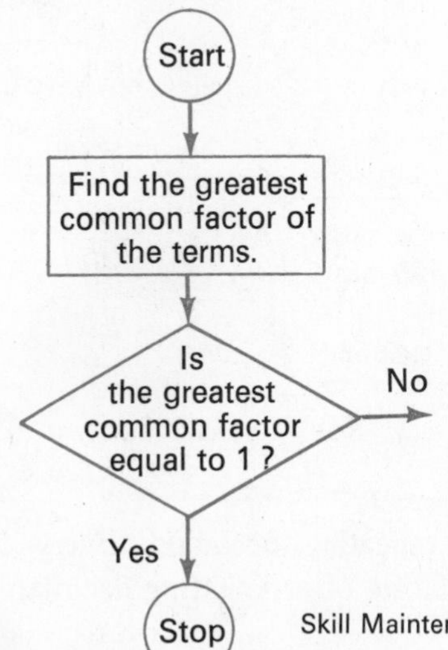

EXCURSION

Try to give the remaining products without multiplying.

37,037 × 3 = 111,111

1. 37,037 × 6 = ?
2. 37,037 × 9 = ?
3. 37,037 × 12 = ?
4. 37,037 × 15 = ?
5. 37,037 × 18 = ?
6. 37,037 × 21 = ?
7. 37,037 × 24 = ?
8. 37,037 × 27 = ?

Skill Maintenance, Set 26, page 404

Changing a fraction to a decimal

A fraction can be thought of as indicating a division.

Examples.

$\frac{4}{5}$ (4 ÷ 5) $\qquad \frac{3}{2}$ (3 ÷ 2) $\qquad \frac{7}{8}$ (7 ÷ 8)

So, a fraction can be changed to its equivalent decimal fraction by dividing its numerator by its denominator.

$\frac{4}{5} = ?$	$\frac{3}{2} = ?$	$\frac{7}{8} = ?$
$\begin{array}{r} .8 \\ 5\overline{)4.0} \\ \underline{4\,0} \\ 0 \end{array}$	$\begin{array}{r} 1.5 \\ 2\overline{)3.0} \\ \underline{2} \\ 1\,0 \\ \underline{1\,0} \\ 0 \end{array}$	$\begin{array}{r} .875 \\ 8\overline{)7.000} \\ \underline{6\,4} \\ 60 \\ \underline{56} \\ 40 \\ \underline{40} \\ 0 \end{array}$
So, $\frac{4}{5} = .8$	So, $\frac{3}{2} = 1.5$	So, $\frac{7}{8} = .875$

Since the decimals above terminate (come to an end), they are called **terminating decimals**. Some fractions are equivalent to decimals that do not terminate.

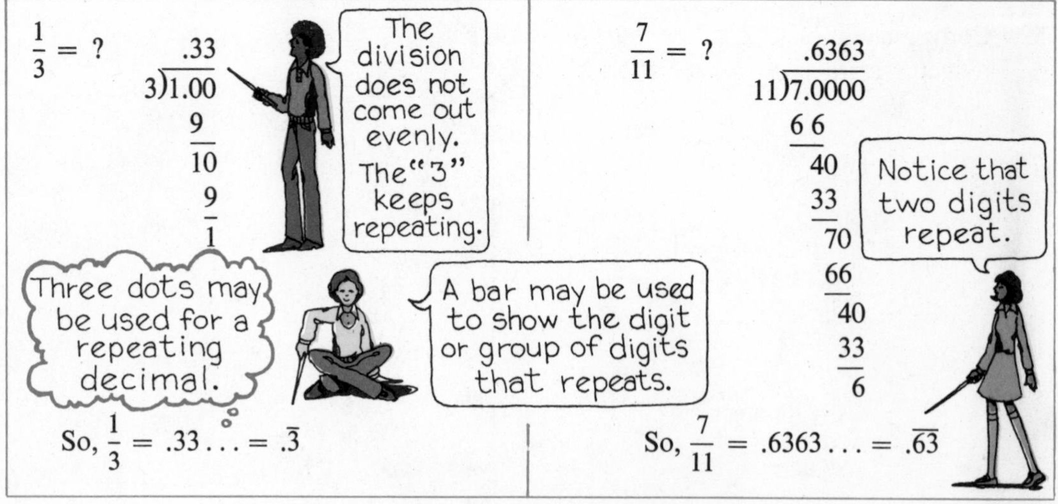

$\frac{1}{3} = ?$

$$\begin{array}{r} .33 \\ 3\overline{)1.00} \\ \underline{9} \\ 10 \\ \underline{9} \\ 1 \end{array}$$

So, $\frac{1}{3} = .33\ldots = .\overline{3}$

$\frac{7}{11} = ?$

$$\begin{array}{r} .6363 \\ 11\overline{)7.0000} \\ \underline{6\,6} \\ 40 \\ \underline{33} \\ 70 \\ \underline{66} \\ 40 \\ \underline{33} \\ 6 \end{array}$$

So, $\frac{7}{11} = .6363\ldots = .\overline{63}$

Such decimals are called **repeating decimals**. Every fraction is equivalent to either a terminating or a repeating decimal.

EXERCISES

Change each fraction to a decimal. Tell whether the decimal is terminating or repeating.

1. $\frac{1}{2}$ **2.** $\frac{1}{6}$ **3.** $\frac{1}{8}$ **4.** $\frac{5}{3}$ **5.** $\frac{3}{5}$ **6.** $\frac{2}{3}$

7. $\frac{5}{8}$ **8.** $\frac{5}{4}$ **9.** $\frac{1}{3}$ **10.** $\frac{4}{9}$ **11.** $\frac{3}{8}$ **12.** $\frac{3}{2}$

Complete.

13. If $\frac{1}{5} = .2$ then $\frac{2}{5} = ?$ $\frac{3}{5} = ?$ $\frac{4}{5} = ?$ $\frac{5}{5} = ?$ $\frac{6}{5} = ?$

14. If $\frac{1}{4} = .25$ then $\frac{2}{4} = ?$ $\frac{3}{4} = ?$ $\frac{4}{4} = ?$ $\frac{5}{4} = ?$ $\frac{6}{4} = ?$

15. If $\frac{1}{8} = .125$ then $\frac{2}{8} = ?$ $\frac{3}{8} = ?$ $\frac{4}{8} = ?$ $\frac{5}{8} = ?$ $\frac{6}{8} = ?$

16. If $\frac{1}{16} = .0625$ then $\frac{2}{16} = ?$ $\frac{3}{16} = ?$ $\frac{4}{16} = ?$ $\frac{5}{16} = ?$ $\frac{6}{16} = ?$

17. If $\frac{1}{20} = .05$ then $\frac{2}{20} = ?$ $\frac{3}{20} = ?$ $\frac{4}{20} = ?$ $\frac{5}{20} = ?$ $\frac{6}{20} = ?$

$<$, $=$, or $>$?

18. $.3 \bullet \frac{1}{3}$ **19.** $\frac{5}{9} \bullet .56$

20. $1.6 \bullet \frac{8}{5}$ **21.** $.875 \bullet \frac{7}{8}$

22. $\frac{9}{4} \bullet 2.25$ **23.** $\frac{7}{9} \bullet .77$

24. $\frac{1}{6} \bullet .16$ **25.** $\frac{5}{3} \bullet 1.67$

Change each fraction to a decimal.

26. $\frac{2}{13}$ **27.** $\frac{4}{17}$

28. $\frac{5}{19}$ **29.** $\frac{5}{21}$

EXCURSION

Here are some equations involving Roman numerals. Make each equation true by moving just one toothpick.

XI = V + IV

X − VI = VI

III + V = VI

II × V = X + IV

Supplementary Exercises, Set 20, page 379

Changing a decimal to a fraction

Below are some examples that show how to change a terminating decimal to its equivalent fraction in lowest terms.

375 thousandths

$$.375 = \frac{375}{1000} = \frac{15}{40} = \frac{3}{8}$$

32 tenths

$$3.2 = \frac{32}{10} = \frac{16}{5}$$

Now let's consider changing a repeating decimal to an equivalent fraction. To do this, let $\boldsymbol{n}$ be the fraction.

Examples.

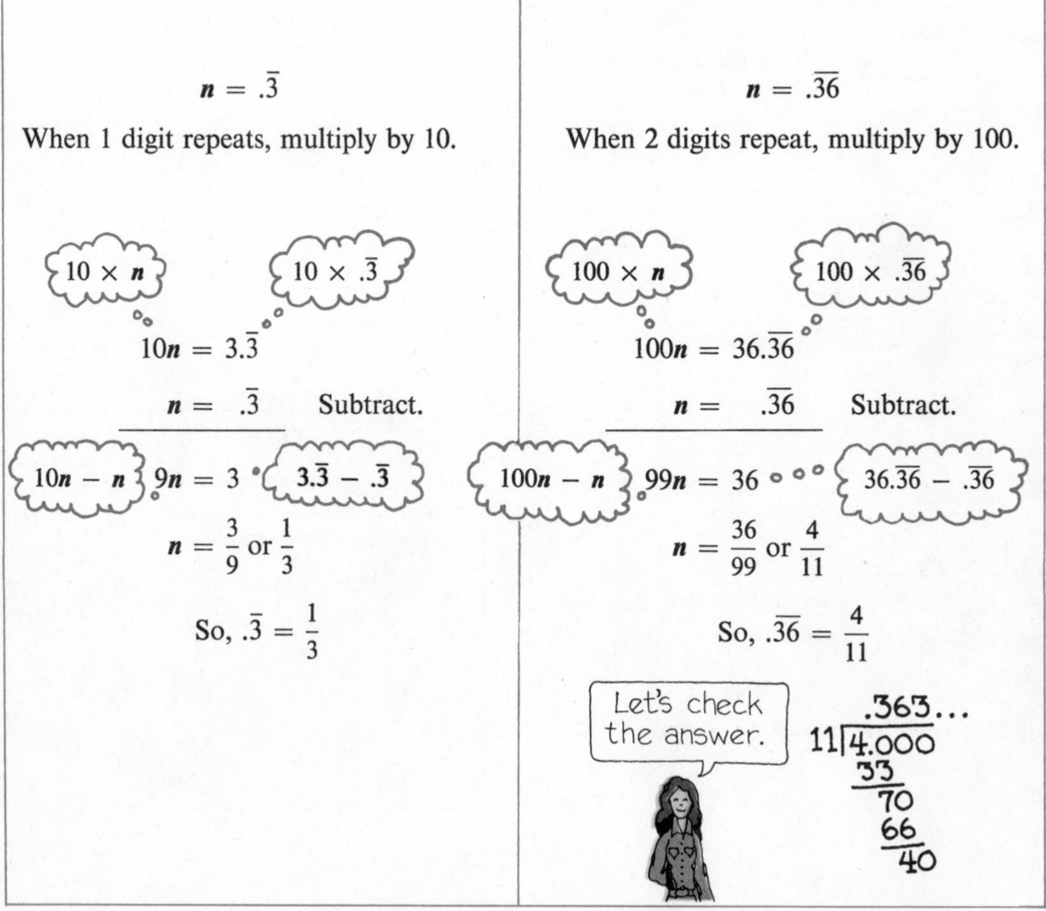

$$n = .\overline{3}$$

When 1 digit repeats, multiply by 10.

$10 \times n$ — $10 \times .\overline{3}$

$$10n = 3.\overline{3}$$
$$n = .\overline{3} \quad \text{Subtract.}$$

$10n - n$ — $3.\overline{3} - .\overline{3}$

$$9n = 3$$
$$n = \frac{3}{9} \text{ or } \frac{1}{3}$$

$$\text{So, } .\overline{3} = \frac{1}{3}$$

$$n = .\overline{36}$$

When 2 digits repeat, multiply by 100.

$100 \times n$ — $100 \times .\overline{36}$

$$100n = 36.\overline{36}$$
$$n = .\overline{36} \quad \text{Subtract.}$$

$100n - n$ — $36.\overline{36} - .\overline{36}$

$$99n = 36$$
$$n = \frac{36}{99} \text{ or } \frac{4}{11}$$

$$\text{So, } .\overline{36} = \frac{4}{11}$$

EXERCISES

Change each decimal to its equivalent fraction in lowest terms.

1. .28 **2.** .35 **3.** .6 **4.** .06 **5.** .006

6. .375 **7.** 1.3 **8.** 4.2 **9.** 1.25 **10.** .625

11. .008 **12.** 12.6 **13.** .875 **14.** .75 **15.** .075

<, =, or >?

16. $\frac{1}{3}$ ● .3 **17.** .6 ● $\frac{2}{3}$ **18.** $\frac{2}{5}$ ● .39

19. $\frac{3}{8}$ ● .35 **20.** $\frac{1}{4}$ ● .25 **21.** 1.2 ● $\frac{5}{4}$

22. 2.5 ● $\frac{5}{2}$ **23.** 1.5 ● $\frac{7}{4}$ **24.** $\frac{1}{10}$ ● .09

Write each decimal, using the bar notation.

25. **a.** .6666 . . .
b. 10 × .6666 . . .

26. **a.** .151515 . . .
b. 100 × .151515 . . .

27. **a.** .1111 . . .
b. 10 × .1111 . . .

28. **a.** .4444 . . .
b. 10 × .4444 . . .

29. **a.** .090909 . . .
b. 100 × .090909 . . .

30. **a.** .16666 . . .
b. 10 × .16666 . . .

Change each decimal to its equivalent fraction in lowest terms.

31. $.\overline{6}$ **32.** $.\overline{15}$ **33.** $.\overline{1}$ **34.** $.\overline{4}$ **35.** $.\overline{09}$ **36.** $.1\overline{6}$

Give a fractional number that is between the two numbers.

37. .3, .4 **38.** 1.8, 1.9

39. .06, .07 **40.** .34, .35

41. .09, .1 **42.** .99, 1

Give a decimal that is between the two numbers.

43. $\frac{1}{6}, \frac{1}{7}$ **44.** $\frac{1}{8}, \frac{1}{9}$

45. $\frac{2}{13}, \frac{2}{14}$ **46.** $\frac{3}{32}, \frac{1}{10}$

47. $\frac{15}{16}, 1$ **48.** $1, \frac{19}{18}$

EXCURSION

Copy and fill in the missing digits.

```
      □ □ □
    ×   □ 9
    4 □ 0 1
  □ □ □ □
  □ □ □ 4 □
```

Skill Maintenance, Set 27, page 404

Comparing fractional numbers

It is sometimes helpful to think about the number line when comparing two fractional numbers.

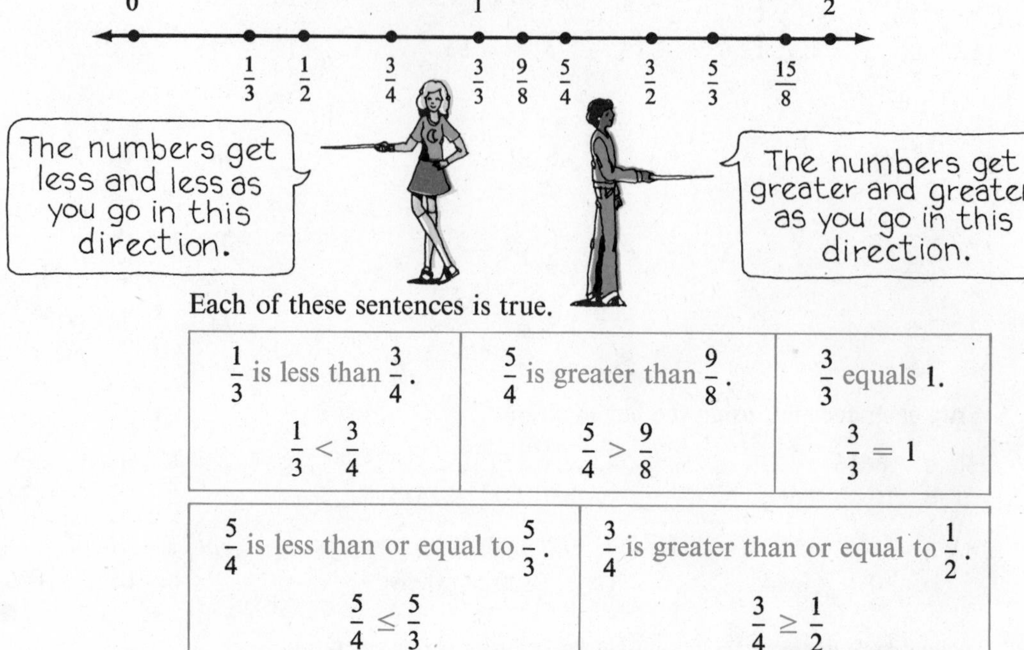

Each of these sentences is true.

$\frac{1}{3}$ is less than $\frac{3}{4}$.	$\frac{5}{4}$ is greater than $\frac{9}{8}$.	$\frac{3}{3}$ equals 1.
$\frac{1}{3} < \frac{3}{4}$	$\frac{5}{4} > \frac{9}{8}$	$\frac{3}{3} = 1$

$\frac{5}{4}$ is less than or equal to $\frac{5}{3}$.	$\frac{3}{4}$ is greater than or equal to $\frac{1}{2}$.
$\frac{5}{4} \leq \frac{5}{3}$	$\frac{3}{4} \geq \frac{1}{2}$

Two fractions, such as $\frac{5}{9}$ and $\frac{7}{9}$, that have the same denominator are called **like fractions**. To compare fractional numbers having different denominators, change to equivalent fractions that are like.

Example.

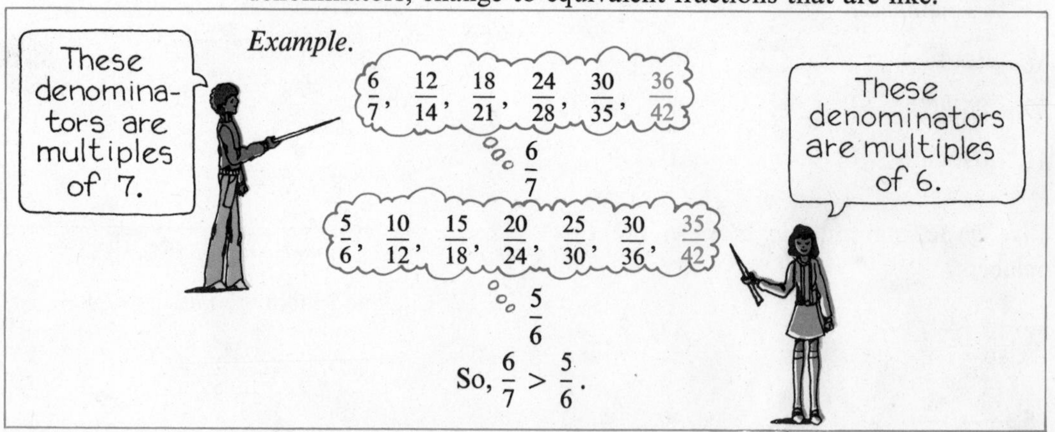

So, $\frac{6}{7} > \frac{5}{6}$.

From the example you should see that the denominator of the like fractions is the *least common multiple* of the denominators of the fractions being compared.

EXERCISES

<, =, or >?

1. $\frac{1}{2} \bullet \frac{4}{8}$
2. $\frac{3}{5} \bullet \frac{4}{5}$
3. $\frac{3}{8} \bullet \frac{1}{2}$
4. $\frac{1}{2} \bullet \frac{4}{7}$
5. $\frac{2}{3} \bullet \frac{5}{9}$
6. $\frac{3}{2} \bullet \frac{7}{4}$
7. $\frac{6}{7} \bullet \frac{5}{6}$
8. $\frac{9}{10} \bullet \frac{8}{9}$
9. $\frac{1}{4} \bullet \frac{3}{8}$
10. $\frac{3}{7} \bullet \frac{9}{21}$
11. $\frac{5}{3} \bullet \frac{5}{4}$
12. $\frac{5}{8} \bullet \frac{2}{3}$
13. $\frac{0}{4} \bullet \frac{0}{5}$
14. $\frac{9}{2} \bullet \frac{13}{3}$
15. $\frac{15}{8} \bullet \frac{17}{9}$

True or false?

16. $\frac{5}{11} \leq \frac{6}{11}$
17. $\frac{1}{2} \geq \frac{3}{6}$
18. $\frac{2}{9} \leq \frac{1}{3}$
19. $\frac{7}{8} \geq \frac{5}{6}$
20. $\frac{3}{5} \geq \frac{2}{3}$
21. $\frac{7}{2} \leq \frac{27}{8}$
22. $\frac{6}{5} \geq \frac{5}{6}$
23. $\frac{5}{25} \geq \frac{1}{5}$
24. $\frac{6}{4} \leq \frac{1}{2}$
25. $\frac{6}{7} \geq \frac{7}{8}$

Solve.

26. $\frac{1}{3}$ hour
    30 minutes
    Which is greater?

27. $\frac{3}{4}$ of a pound
    10 ounces
    Which is less?

28. 5 days
    $\frac{2}{3}$ of a week
    Which is less?

29. 16 inches
    $\frac{5}{12}$ of a yard
    Which is greater?

30. $\frac{7}{10}$ of a minute
    40 seconds
    Which is less?

31. 19 hours
    $\frac{5}{6}$ of a day
    Which is less?

32. 1300 yards
    $\frac{3}{4}$ of a mile
    Which is greater?
    (*Hint:* 1 mile = 1760 yards)

Give a fractional number that is between the given fractional numbers.

33. $\frac{1}{2}, \frac{1}{3}$
34. $\frac{4}{9}, \frac{5}{9}$
35. $\frac{5}{6}, \frac{6}{7}$
36. $\frac{18}{19}, \frac{19}{20}$

CHECKUP
for pages 102–105

Change to a decimal.

1. $\frac{3}{2}$
2. $\frac{3}{4}$
3. $\frac{2}{3}$
4. $\frac{5}{8}$
5. $\frac{1}{6}$
6. $\frac{9}{2}$
7. $\frac{7}{6}$
8. $\frac{1}{16}$
9. $\frac{3}{8}$

Change to a fraction.

10. .3
11. .03
12. .003
13. 1.25
14. .75
15. .008
16. 2.375
17. 1.875
18. 2.05

Answers on page 426.

Skill Maintenance, Set 28, page 404

Adding fractional numbers

You probably remember that to add with like fractions, you add the numerators and write the sum over the denominator. The following example shows how to add with fractions that are not like fractions.

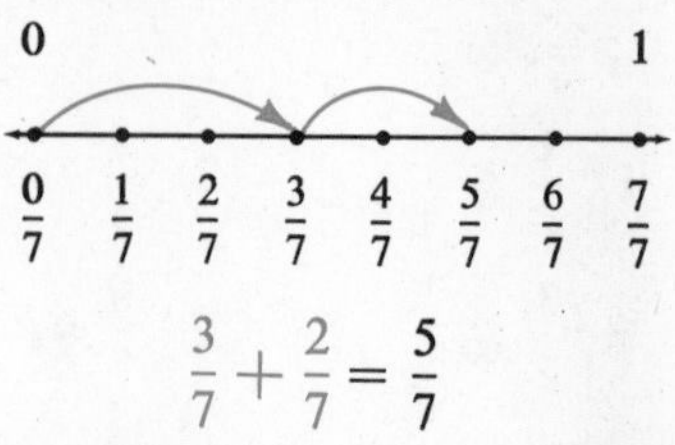

Find equivalent fractions that are like.

Notice that the least common denominator is the least common multiple (other than 0) of the denominators.

Example 1.

The least common denominator is 12.

$$\frac{3}{4} + \frac{5}{6} = \frac{9}{12} + \frac{10}{12}$$

4, 8, 12

6, 12

$$= \frac{19}{12}$$

Example 2.

3, 6, 9, 12, 15, 18, 21, 24

$$\frac{5}{3} = \frac{40}{24}$$

8, 16, 24

$$+\frac{5}{8} = \frac{15}{24}$$

$$\frac{55}{24}$$

You've learned how to use prime factors to find LCMs. Let's use the same method to find the least common denominator.

Example. $\frac{5}{28} + \frac{7}{60} = ?$

Step 1. Factor the denominators.

$28 = 4 \cdot 7 = 2 \cdot 2 \cdot 7$

$60 = 6 \cdot 10 = 3 \cdot 2 \cdot 2 \cdot 5$

Step 2. Multiply numerators and denominators of both fractions by the prime factors that make the denominators the same.

$$\frac{5}{28} = \frac{5 \cdot 3 \cdot 5}{2 \cdot 2 \cdot 7 \cdot 3 \cdot 5}$$

$$\frac{7}{60} = \frac{7 \cdot 7}{3 \cdot 2 \cdot 2 \cdot 5 \cdot 7}$$

The same.

Step 3. Multiply and add.

$$\frac{75}{420} + \frac{49}{420} = \frac{124}{420} = \frac{31}{105}$$

EXERCISES

Add. Give each sum in lowest terms.

1. $\frac{1}{5}+\frac{3}{5}$ **2.** $\frac{1}{3}+\frac{5}{6}$ **3.** $\frac{7}{8}+\frac{1}{3}$ **4.** $\frac{0}{6}+\frac{5}{6}$

5. $\frac{7}{10}+\frac{1}{2}$ **6.** $\frac{4}{3}+\frac{5}{6}$ **7.** $\frac{2}{7}+\frac{5}{7}$ **8.** $\frac{5}{4}+\frac{5}{3}$

9. $\frac{0}{2}+\frac{3}{8}$ **10.** $\frac{5}{3}+\frac{1}{8}$ **11.** $\frac{1}{6}+\frac{3}{8}$ **12.** $\frac{3}{5}+\frac{3}{2}$ **13.** $\frac{7}{4}+\frac{2}{9}$ **14.** $\frac{5}{12}+\frac{7}{4}+\frac{5}{6}$ **15.** $\frac{1}{3}+\frac{5}{9}+\frac{2}{3}$ **16.** $\frac{1}{2}+\frac{4}{5}+\frac{3}{4}$

Copy and complete these addition boxes. Give each sum in lowest terms.

17.

$\frac{1}{5}$	$\frac{2}{5}$	$\frac{3}{5}$
$\frac{1}{2}$	$\frac{1}{2}$	
$\frac{7}{10}$		

18.

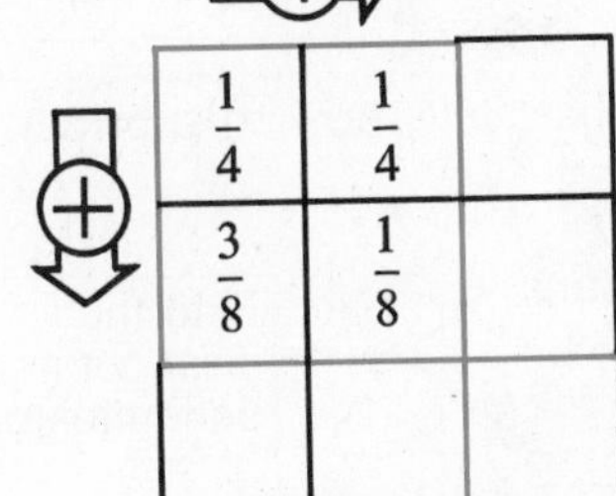

$\frac{1}{4}$	$\frac{1}{4}$	
$\frac{3}{8}$	$\frac{1}{8}$	

19.

$63 = 3 \cdot 3 \cdot 7$

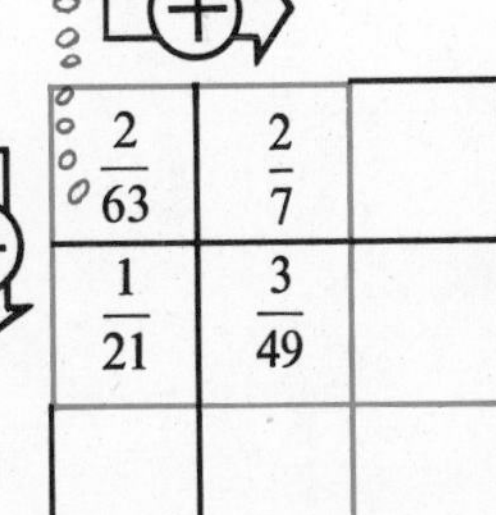

$\frac{2}{63}$	$\frac{2}{7}$	
$\frac{1}{21}$	$\frac{3}{49}$	

Solve.

20. Dolores bought $\frac{3}{4}$ of a pound of peanut clusters and half a pound of mints. How many pounds of candy did she buy?

21. Andrew read $\frac{1}{8}$ of a book on Monday, $\frac{1}{4}$ of the book on Tuesday, and $\frac{1}{2}$ of the book on Wednesday. What fraction of the book did he read during the three days?

22. To get a certain color, Mr. James mixed 1 pint of white paint with $\frac{3}{4}$ of a quart of green paint. How many quarts of the mix did he have?

CHECKUP
for pages 100–101

Reduce to lowest terms.

1. $\frac{2}{4}$ **2.** $\frac{4}{2}$ **3.** $\frac{4}{16}$

4. $\frac{0}{2}$ **5.** $\frac{2}{6}$ **6.** $\frac{6}{2}$

7. $\frac{4}{20}$ **8.** $\frac{9}{6}$ **9.** $\frac{2}{10}$

10. $\frac{3}{9}$ **11.** $\frac{3}{6}$ **12.** $\frac{14}{4}$

13. $\frac{24}{16}$ **14.** $\frac{5}{20}$ **15.** $\frac{20}{5}$

16. $\frac{4}{8}$ **17.** $\frac{3}{15}$ **18.** $\frac{4}{12}$

Answers on page 426.

Supplementary Exercises, Set 21, page 379

Subtracting fractional numbers

The following examples show how to subtract fractional numbers.

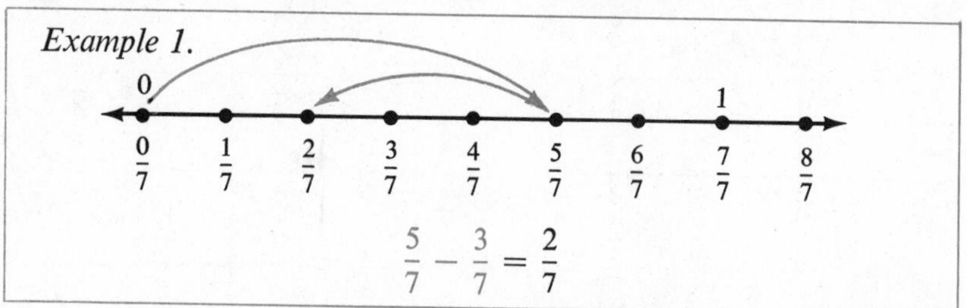

$$\frac{5}{7} - \frac{3}{7} = \frac{2}{7}$$

Example 2. $\frac{5}{8} - \frac{1}{2} = \frac{5}{8} - \frac{4}{8} = \frac{1}{8}$

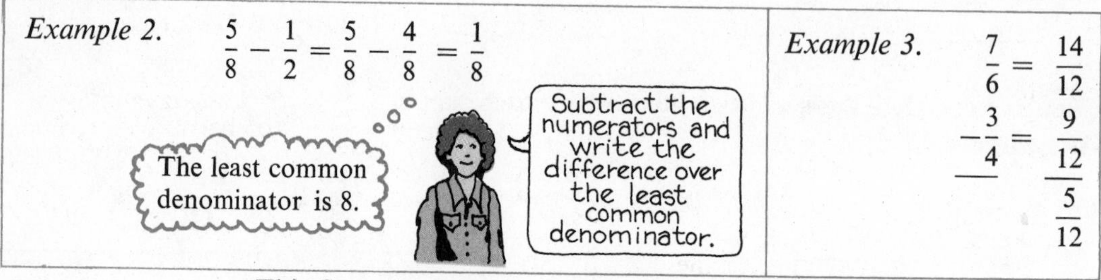

Example 3.

$$\begin{array}{rcr} \frac{7}{6} & = & \frac{14}{12} \\ -\frac{3}{4} & = & \frac{9}{12} \\ \hline & & \frac{5}{12} \end{array}$$

This flow chart tells how to subtract fractional numbers.

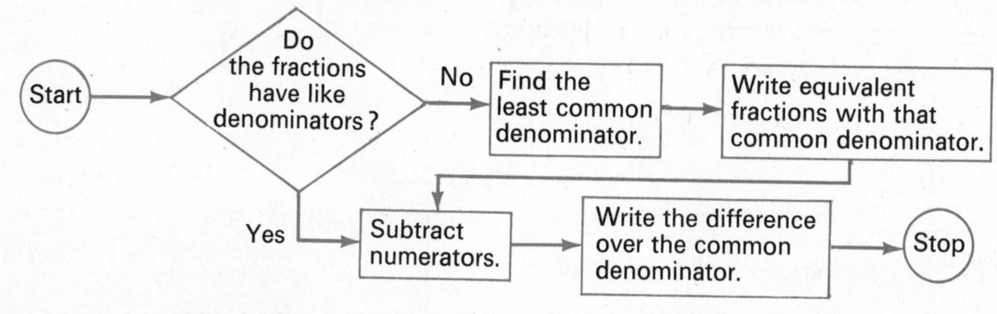

EXERCISES

Subtract. Give each difference in lowest terms.

1. $\frac{1}{3} - \frac{1}{3}$
2. $\frac{2}{5} - \frac{1}{5}$
3. $\frac{1}{2} - \frac{1}{4}$
4. $\frac{3}{4} - \frac{3}{8}$
5. $\frac{3}{4} - \frac{2}{3}$
6. $\frac{5}{6} - \frac{2}{3}$
7. $1 - \frac{2}{5}$
8. $\frac{3}{4} - \frac{0}{7}$
9. $\frac{2}{2} - \frac{5}{9}$
10. $\frac{7}{8} - \frac{3}{5}$
11. $\frac{3}{2} - \frac{2}{3}$
12. $\frac{7}{4} - \frac{7}{6}$
13. $2 - \frac{0}{3}$
14. $\frac{9}{10} - \frac{5}{8}$
15. $\frac{11}{9} - \frac{3}{4}$
16. $\begin{array}{r} \frac{3}{2} \\ -1 \\ \hline \end{array}$
17. $\begin{array}{r} 2 \\ -\frac{3}{2} \\ \hline \end{array}$
18. $\begin{array}{r} \frac{15}{9} \\ -\frac{5}{6} \\ \hline \end{array}$
19. $\begin{array}{r} 2 \\ -\frac{3}{4} \\ \hline \end{array}$
20. $\begin{array}{r} \frac{7}{8} \\ -\frac{2}{3} \\ \hline \end{array}$
21. $\begin{array}{r} 3 \\ -\frac{7}{3} \\ \hline \end{array}$
22. $\begin{array}{r} \frac{9}{5} \\ -\frac{5}{9} \\ \hline \end{array}$

Copy and complete these addition-subtraction boxes. Give each sum or difference in lowest terms.

23.

$\frac{5}{7}$	$\frac{2}{7}$	
$\frac{2}{7}$	$\frac{1}{7}$	
$\frac{3}{7}$		

24.

$\frac{7}{8}$	$\frac{1}{4}$	
$\frac{1}{4}$	$\frac{1}{8}$	

25.

$\frac{1}{12}$	$\frac{1}{24}$	
$\frac{1}{42}$	$\frac{1}{35}$	

Solve.

26. Alvin wrote $\frac{1}{3}$ of his English theme on Tuesday and $\frac{1}{2}$ of it on Wednesday. What fraction of his theme did he write during those two days?

27. Terry spent $\frac{1}{3}$ of her allowance on a movie, $\frac{1}{2}$ on magazines, and saved the rest. What fraction of her allowance did she spend? What fraction did she save?

28. A youth group held a car wash to raise money for a camp-out. They earned $\frac{3}{5}$ of the money needed. What fraction of the money did they still need to earn?

29. The Belvins spend $\frac{1}{5}$ of their income for food and $\frac{1}{3}$ of their income for housing. What fraction of their income do they spend for food and housing?

30. A recipe calls for $\frac{3}{4}$ of a cup of flour. Mrs. Petty has only $\frac{1}{3}$ of a cup. How much more flour does she need?

31. Sarah and Sally together ate $\frac{1}{2}$ of a pie. If Sally ate $\frac{1}{6}$ of a pie more than Sarah, what fraction of a pie did each girl eat?

EXCURSION

Here is a program for computing the areas of these rectangles:

length	6	9	4.3	6.8
width	4	8	9	3.1

```
100  READ A, B
200  LET D = A*B
300  PRINT D
400  GØ TØ 100
500  DATA 6, 4, 9, 8, 4.3, 9,
        6.8, 3.1
600  END
```

Line 100 tells the computer to use the first DATA number for A and the second for B. When the computer comes to line 100 again, it uses the next two DATA numbers for A and B.

Be a computer—follow the program.

Write a program for computing the perimeters of the same rectangles.

Supplementary Exercises, Set 22, page 379

Mixed numerals

The number for the red point can be written as a fraction or a mixed numeral.

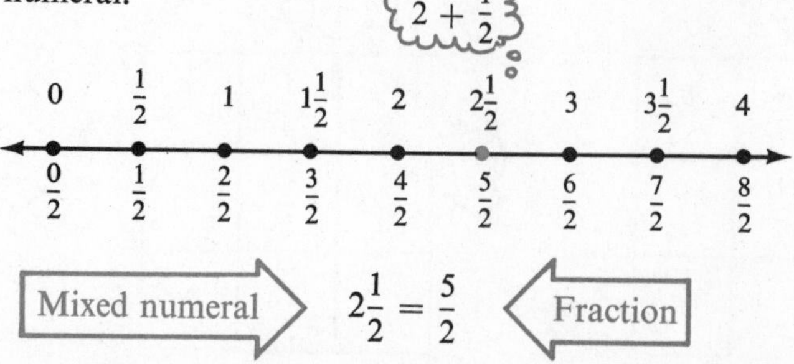

Notice that a mixed numeral combines a numeral for a whole number and a fraction (in lowest terms) for a number less than 1. Here are two methods for changing a mixed numeral to a fraction.

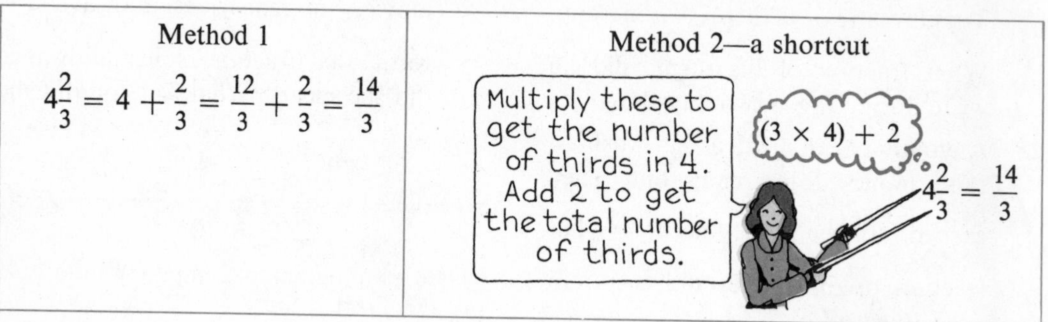

Here are two methods for changing a fraction to a mixed numeral.

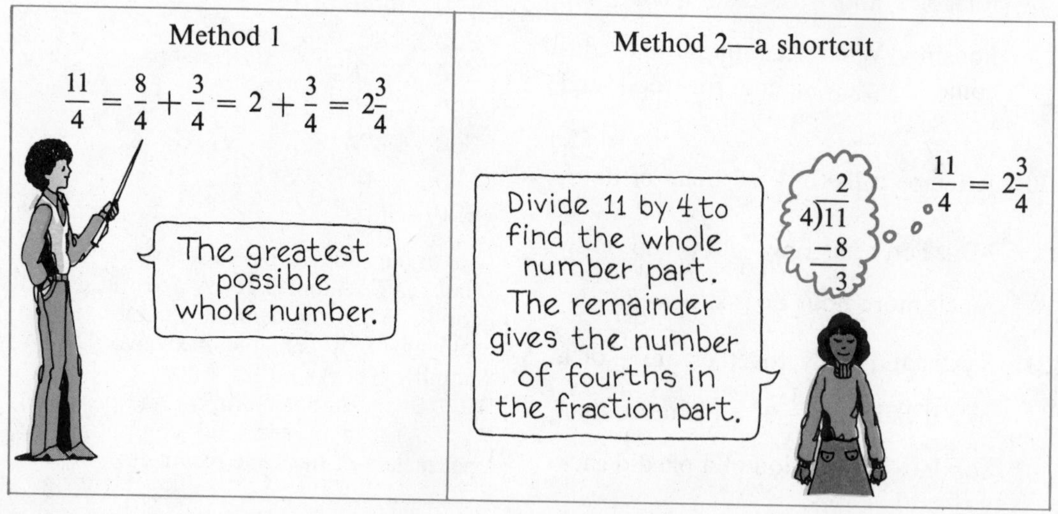

EXERCISES

Give the equivalent fraction in lowest terms.

1. $1\frac{1}{2}$ **2.** $1\frac{1}{3}$ **3.** $1\frac{2}{3}$ **4.** $2\frac{3}{4}$ **5.** $3\frac{1}{3}$ **6.** $2\frac{2}{5}$ **7.** $1\frac{3}{8}$ **8.** $4\frac{1}{2}$

9. $5\frac{1}{2}$ **10.** $4\frac{3}{8}$ **11.** $2\frac{5}{8}$ **12.** $2\frac{1}{2}$ **13.** $4\frac{5}{6}$ **14.** $2\frac{2}{3}$ **15.** $3\frac{3}{5}$ **16.** $4\frac{2}{5}$

17. $2\frac{1}{3}$ **18.** $5\frac{1}{10}$ **19.** $6\frac{3}{4}$ **20.** $3\frac{3}{4}$ **21.** $2\frac{5}{8}$ **22.** $3\frac{1}{2}$ **23.** $4\frac{3}{4}$ **24.** $4\frac{2}{3}$

Give the equivalent mixed numeral.

25. $\frac{3}{2}$ **26.** $\frac{4}{3}$ **27.** $\frac{5}{4}$ **28.** $\frac{11}{5}$ **29.** $\frac{11}{3}$ **30.** $\frac{7}{4}$ **31.** $\frac{10}{3}$ **32.** $\frac{13}{4}$

33. $\frac{18}{4}$ **34.** $\frac{19}{8}$ **35.** $\frac{9}{2}$ **36.** $\frac{5}{3}$ **37.** $\frac{19}{4}$ **38.** $\frac{18}{7}$ **39.** $\frac{19}{6}$ **40.** $\frac{7}{2}$

41. $\frac{21}{5}$ **42.** $\frac{11}{2}$ **43.** $\frac{7}{3}$ **44.** $\frac{13}{5}$ **45.** $\frac{15}{2}$ **46.** $\frac{9}{4}$ **47.** $\frac{8}{3}$ **48.** $\frac{21}{2}$

Complete.

49. 1 dozen = 12
- **a.** $1\frac{1}{2}$ doz = ?
- **b.** $2\frac{1}{3}$ doz = ?
- **c.** $3\frac{1}{4}$ doz = ?
- **d.** $2\frac{2}{3}$ doz = ?
- **e.** $2\frac{3}{4}$ doz = ?

50. 1 foot = 12 inches
- **a.** $1\frac{1}{3}$ ft = ? in.
- **b.** $1\frac{3}{4}$ ft = ? in.
- **c.** $2\frac{1}{2}$ ft = ? in.
- **d.** $3\frac{1}{3}$ ft = ? in.
- **e.** $2\frac{1}{6}$ ft = ? in.

51. 1 hour = 60 minutes
- **a.** $1\frac{1}{2}$ hr = ? min
- **b.** $1\frac{1}{4}$ hr = ? min
- **c.** $2\frac{1}{3}$ hr = ? min
- **d.** $2\frac{3}{4}$ hr = ? min
- **e.** $1\frac{3}{10}$ hr = ? min

Solve.

52. During one week Sally worked $18\frac{1}{2}$ hours. If she earned $2.40 an hour, how much did she earn during that week? (*Hint:* First find the amount she earned for 18 hours and then add the amount she earned for $\frac{1}{2}$ hour.)

53. Mrs. Alan needs $3\frac{1}{3}$ cubic yards of concrete, which costs $27 a cubic yard. What is the total cost?

CHECKUP
for pages 108–111

Add. Give answers in lowest terms.

1. $\frac{1}{8}+\frac{3}{8}$ **2.** $\frac{1}{9}+\frac{1}{3}$ **3.** $\frac{3}{4}+\frac{1}{8}$

4. $\frac{3}{4}+\frac{3}{2}$ **5.** $\frac{5}{6}+\frac{2}{3}$ **6.** $\frac{7}{8}+\frac{5}{6}$

Subtract. Give answers in lowest terms.

7. $\frac{7}{8}-\frac{3}{8}$ **8.** $\frac{5}{9}-\frac{1}{3}$ **9.** $\frac{5}{6}-\frac{2}{3}$

10. $\frac{7}{8}-\frac{3}{4}$ **11.** $\frac{7}{6}-\frac{5}{8}$ **12.** $\frac{6}{5}-\frac{5}{6}$

Answers on page 426.

Skill Maintenance Set 29, page 404

Adding and subtracting with mixed numerals

These examples show how to add with mixed numerals.

Example 1.

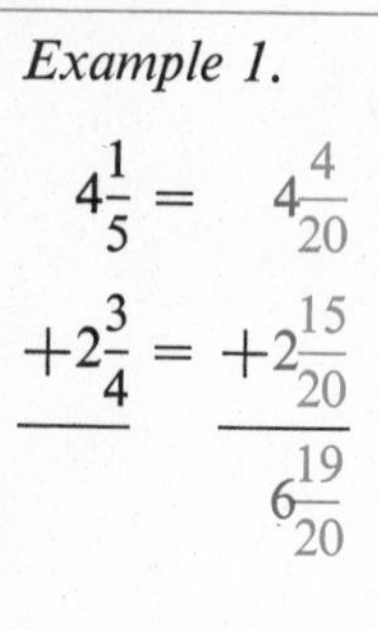

$$4\frac{1}{5} = 4\frac{4}{20}$$
$$+2\frac{3}{4} = +2\frac{15}{20}$$
$$6\frac{19}{20}$$

First change to equivalent fractions with like denominators. Add the fractional numbers and then add the whole numbers.

Example 2.

$$3\frac{3}{4} = \overset{1}{3}\frac{9}{12}$$
$$+5\frac{2}{3} = +5\frac{8}{12}$$
$$9\frac{5}{12}$$

When the sum of the fractional numbers is equal to or greater than 1, you will need to regroup. Here 17/12 was regrouped to 1 5/12.

These examples show how to subtract with mixed numerals.

Example 1.

$$9\frac{5}{8} = 9\frac{5}{8}$$
$$-6\frac{1}{2} = -6\frac{4}{8}$$
$$3\frac{1}{8}$$

First change to equivalent fractions with like denominators. Subtract the fractional numbers and then subtract the whole numbers.

Example 2.

$$12\frac{1}{4} = 12\frac{3}{12} = 11\frac{15}{12}$$
$$-3\frac{5}{6} = -3\frac{10}{12} = -3\frac{10}{12}$$
$$4\frac{5}{12}$$

Sometimes you will need to regroup. In this example 12 3/12 was regrouped to 11 15/12.

EXERCISES

Add. Give the fraction part in lowest terms.

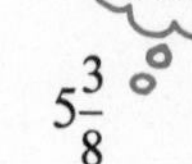

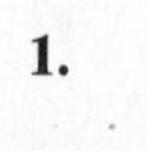

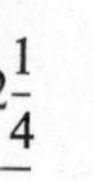
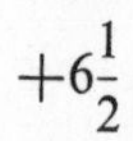
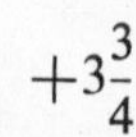

1. $3\frac{1}{2} + 2\frac{1}{4}$ **2.** $9\frac{3}{8} + 6\frac{1}{2}$ **3.** $11\frac{1}{6} + 3\frac{3}{4}$ **4.** $8\frac{3}{5} + 7\frac{1}{4}$ **5.** $5\frac{3}{8} + 18\frac{3}{4}$ **6.** $8\frac{2}{3} + 6\frac{1}{2}$

Subtract. Give the fraction part in lowest terms.

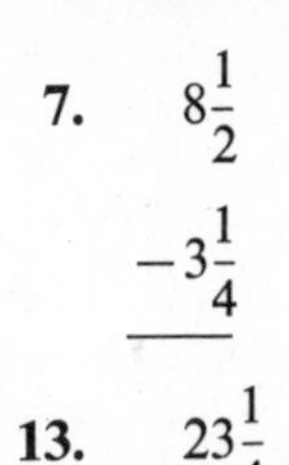

Regroup!

7. $8\frac{1}{2} - 3\frac{1}{4}$	**8.** $9\frac{3}{5} - 2\frac{1}{2}$	**9.** $12\frac{3}{4} - 4\frac{2}{3}$	**10.** $16\frac{7}{8} - 9\frac{2}{3}$	**11.** $18\frac{1}{2} - 9\frac{3}{4}$	**12.** $15\frac{3}{8} - 7\frac{2}{3}$
13. $23\frac{1}{4} - 14\frac{1}{2}$	**14.** $18 - 12\frac{3}{4}$	**15.** $21\frac{1}{3} - 19\frac{2}{3}$	**16.** $26\frac{1}{3} - 14\frac{5}{6}$	**17.** $32\frac{9}{10} - 23\frac{2}{5}$	**18.** $35 - 26\frac{5}{8}$

This time sheet shows the number of hours that the part-time help worked at The Pizza House during one week.

Hours Worked

Employee	Mon	Tues	Wed	Thur	Fri	Sat
Allan	$1\frac{3}{4}$	$2\frac{1}{2}$	$3\frac{1}{4}$	$1\frac{3}{4}$	$2\frac{3}{4}$	
Becker	2	$3\frac{1}{2}$		$2\frac{3}{4}$		$6\frac{1}{2}$
Davis	$2\frac{3}{4}$		3	$2\frac{1}{4}$	$1\frac{3}{4}$	5
Folder		$3\frac{1}{4}$	$2\frac{1}{4}$		$2\frac{1}{2}$	$7\frac{1}{2}$
Logan	$2\frac{1}{4}$	2	3	$2\frac{3}{4}$	$3\frac{1}{4}$	
Monroe	$1\frac{3}{4}$	$3\frac{1}{4}$		$2\frac{3}{4}$		8
Rogers	$2\frac{1}{2}$		$3\frac{1}{2}$	4	$5\frac{1}{2}$	$6\frac{1}{4}$
Sanchez		$2\frac{3}{4}$	$3\frac{1}{4}$		$4\frac{1}{4}$	$5\frac{3}{4}$

19. Who worked the most hours on Saturday?

20. On which day did Allan work the most hours?

21. How many hours did Rogers work during the week?

22. Who worked more hours, Folder or Sanchez? How many more?

23. How many hours of part-time help were used on Thursday?

24. Were more hours of part-time help used on Wednesday or Thursday? How many more?

Project

Daily stock prices are given in most newspapers. They are given in dollars and eighths of dollars. (An eighth of a dollar is 12.5¢ or \$.125.) Choose a common stock that is listed on the New York or American Stock Exchange and keep a line graph of its performance for a few weeks.

EXCURSION

If the sum of the factors of a whole number is greater than twice the whole number, it is called an *abundant number*.

Example.

12 (1, 2, 3, 4, 6, 12)

$$1 + 2 + 3 + 4 + 6 + 12 > 24$$

So, 12 is an abundant number. How many abundant numbers are there between 1 and 41?

Supplementary Exercises, Set 23, page 380

KEEPING SKILLS SHARP

Simplify.

1. $2^3 + 1$
2. $3^2 + 1$
3. $(2 + 1)^3$
4. $2 + 1^3$
5. $3^2 - (2 \times 4)$
6. $(5 + 1)^2 - 10$
7. $(8 - 6)^4$
8. $5^2 - 5^0$

Solve each equation.

9. $3a - 9 = 3$
10. $4b + 2 = 34$
11. $3(x + 4) = 21$
12. $14 - 2y = 0$
13. $\frac{2w}{3} = 10$
14. $\frac{3y + 1}{2} = 11$
15. $\frac{16 - 5k}{8} = 2$
16. $\frac{2(y + 4)}{5} = 4$

Round to the nearest .01.

17. .748
18. .396
19. .525
20. .301
21. .196
22. .5843
23. .2974
24. .6355
25. 2.893
26. 4.995

Add.

27. $\begin{array}{r} 783 \\ +609 \\ \hline \end{array}$
28. $\begin{array}{r} 536 \\ +295 \\ \hline \end{array}$
29. $\begin{array}{r} .739 \\ +.569 \\ \hline \end{array}$
30. $\begin{array}{r} 4.06 \\ +.98 \\ \hline \end{array}$
31. $\begin{array}{r} .299 \\ .704 \\ +3.92 \\ \hline \end{array}$
32. $\begin{array}{r} 56.3 \\ 82.7 \\ +1.05 \\ \hline \end{array}$

Subtract.

33. $\begin{array}{r} 365 \\ -218 \\ \hline \end{array}$
34. $\begin{array}{r} 437 \\ -159 \\ \hline \end{array}$
35. $\begin{array}{r} 2.63 \\ -1.78 \\ \hline \end{array}$
36. $\begin{array}{r} 3.4 \\ -2.96 \\ \hline \end{array}$
37. $\begin{array}{r} 12.03 \\ -7.84 \\ \hline \end{array}$
38. $\begin{array}{r} 8.001 \\ -3.456 \\ \hline \end{array}$

Multiply.

39. $\begin{array}{r} 381 \\ \times 2 \\ \hline \end{array}$
40. $\begin{array}{r} 743 \\ \times 10 \\ \hline \end{array}$
41. $\begin{array}{r} 9.84 \\ \times 6 \\ \hline \end{array}$
42. $\begin{array}{r} 37.5 \\ \times 21 \\ \hline \end{array}$
43. $\begin{array}{r} 80.6 \\ \times 3.9 \\ \hline \end{array}$
44. $\begin{array}{r} 7.64 \\ \times 1.84 \\ \hline \end{array}$

Divide.

45. $3\overline{)8418}$
46. $11\overline{)493.9}$
47. $.9\overline{)65.88}$
48. $.38\overline{)1.748}$
49. $12.7\overline{)4.826}$

Mathematics and science

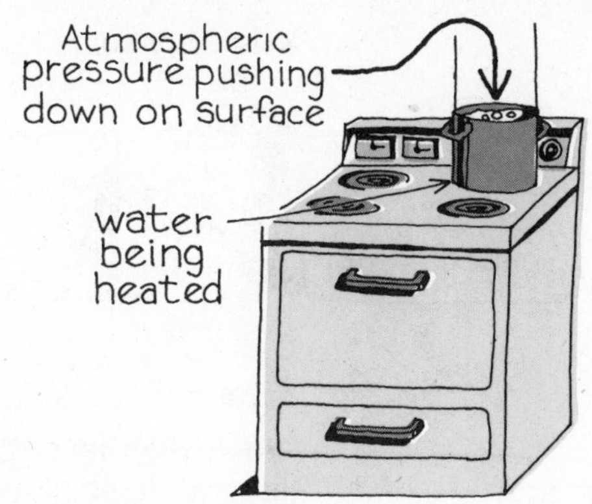

The boiling point of a liquid is the temperature at which the liquid bubbles and turns into a vapor.

For a liquid to boil, it must overcome the atmospheric pressure pushing down on its surface. At sea level, water boils at 100° Celsius.

Since atmospheric pressure is less at a higher altitude, water boils at a lower temperature. The boiling point of water decreases 1 degree Celsius for each 300 meters the altitude is increased.

EXERCISES

What is the boiling point of water at these altitudes? Round your answer to the nearest degree.

1. 600 m above sea level
2. 2100 m above sea level
3. 5000 m above sea level
4. Mount Everest is the highest mountain in the world. It is 8848 meters high. At what temperature does water boil atop Mount Everest?
5. If water boils at 97°C at a given place, what is the altitude of that place?
6. Oxygen boils at ⁻183° Celsius. Gold boils at 2600° Celsius. What is the difference between these boiling points?
7. The temperature at which chromium boils is twice the boiling point of calcium. If calcium boils at 1240°C, at what temperature does chromium boil?
8. The boiling point of lead is $\frac{54}{100}$ of the boiling point of iron. If iron boils at 3000°C, at what temperature does lead boil?

Skill Maintenance, Set 30, page 405

Multiplying fractional numbers

Below are some examples of multiplying fractional numbers.

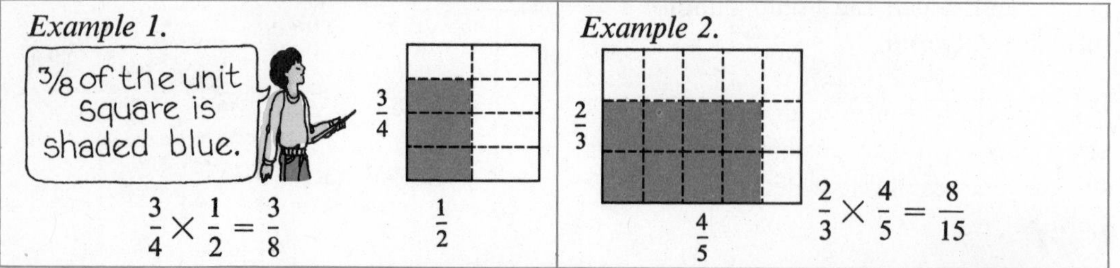

Notice that the product of the numerators gives the number of parts that are shaded blue and the product of the denominators gives the total number of parts.

> To multiply two fractional numbers, multiply the numerators to get the numerator of the product and multiply the denominators to get the denominator of the product.

Examples.

$\frac{3}{5} \times \frac{2}{7} = \frac{6}{35}$	$\frac{1}{5} \times 8 = \frac{8}{5}$ (thought: $\frac{8}{1}$)	$\frac{5}{2} \times \frac{2}{5} = \frac{10}{10} = 1$

In the last example the product is 1. If the product of two numbers is 1, then the numbers are called **reciprocals**, or multiplicative inverses. So, $\frac{5}{2}$ is the reciprocal of $\frac{2}{5}$ and $\frac{2}{5}$ is the reciprocal of $\frac{5}{2}$. What is the reciprocal of $\frac{2}{3}$? Of 4?

EXERCISES

Multiply. Give each product in lowest terms.

1. $\frac{1}{2} \times \frac{1}{3}$ **2.** $\frac{2}{3} \times \frac{4}{5}$ **3.** $\frac{3}{8} \times \frac{4}{5}$ **4.** $\frac{1}{6} \times \frac{2}{9}$ **5.** $\frac{3}{7} \times \frac{5}{3}$

6. $\frac{6}{5} \times \frac{51}{9}$ **7.** $\frac{12}{4} \times \frac{4}{3}$ **8.** $8 \times \frac{1}{2}$ **9.** $\frac{3}{5} \times \frac{0}{2}$ **10.** $6 \times \frac{2}{3}$

11. $\frac{2}{3} \times \frac{0}{5}$ **12.** $\frac{4}{3} \times 5$ **13.** $\frac{2}{3} \times \frac{3}{2}$ **14.** $\frac{5}{4} \times \frac{4}{5}$ **15.** $\frac{6}{7} \times \frac{7}{6}$

16. $\frac{8}{3} \times \frac{3}{8}$ **17.** $\frac{3}{8} \times \frac{3}{3}$ **18.** $\frac{5}{4} \times \frac{5}{5}$ **19.** $\frac{2}{3} \times \frac{4}{4}$ **20.** $\frac{6}{7} \times \frac{2}{2}$

Copy and complete the multiplication boxes. Give each product or factor in lowest terms.

21.

$\frac{1}{3}$	$\frac{2}{3}$	
$\frac{3}{4}$	$\frac{1}{4}$	

22.

$\frac{3}{8}$	$\frac{1}{3}$	
$\frac{3}{5}$	$\frac{5}{9}$	

23.

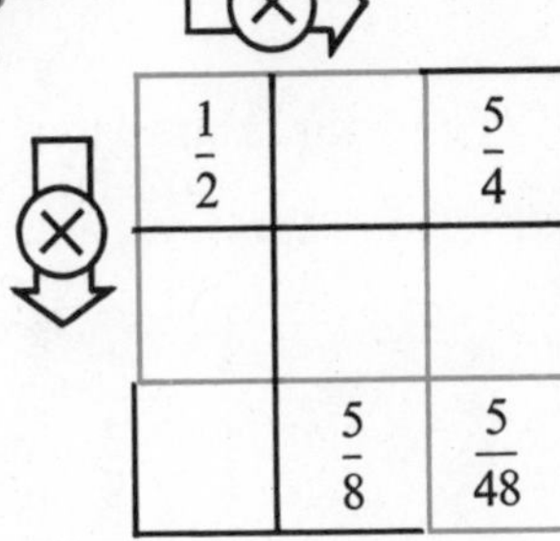

$\frac{1}{2}$		$\frac{5}{4}$
	$\frac{5}{8}$	$\frac{5}{48}$

Solve each equation.

24. $\frac{1}{2} \times y = \frac{1}{4}$

25. $\frac{3}{5} \times y = \frac{12}{5}$

26. $\frac{2}{3} \times y = \frac{8}{15}$

27. $\frac{8}{3} \times \frac{3}{8} = y$

28. $\frac{3}{4} \times \frac{4}{3} = y$

29. $\frac{5}{9} \times \frac{9}{5} = y$

30. $\frac{5}{7} \times y = 1$

31. $\frac{2}{3} \times y = 1$

32. $\frac{6}{5} \times y = 1$

True or false?

33. If both factors are less than 1, then their product is less than 1.

34. If both factors are greater than 1, then the product is greater than 1.

35. If one factor is less than 1 and the other is greater than 1, then the product equals 1.

36. One number is its own reciprocal.

37. Every number has a reciprocal.

Solve.

38. A cookie recipe calls for $\frac{3}{4}$ of a cup of flour. How much flour would be needed to make $\frac{2}{3}$ of a recipe?

39. Sue lives $\frac{5}{2}$ miles from her school. She rides the bus $\frac{4}{5}$ of the way to school. How far does she live from the bus stop?

CHECKUP
for pages 108–111

Give each sum in lowest terms.

1. $\frac{3}{8} + \frac{1}{2}$

2. $\frac{5}{3} + \frac{3}{4}$

3. $\frac{5}{6} + \frac{2}{3}$

4. $\frac{0}{8} + \frac{3}{4}$

5. $3 + \frac{5}{6}$

6. $\frac{5}{16} + \frac{3}{8}$

Give each difference in lowest terms.

7. $\frac{5}{8} - \frac{1}{2}$

8. $\frac{3}{4} - \frac{2}{3}$

9. $\frac{4}{7} - \frac{0}{3}$

10. $\frac{3}{2} - \frac{7}{8}$

11. $\frac{7}{6} - 1$

12. $\frac{7}{12} - \frac{3}{8}$

Answers on page 426.

Supplementary Exercises, Set 24, page 380

Dividing fractional numbers

Below are some examples of dividing fractional numbers.

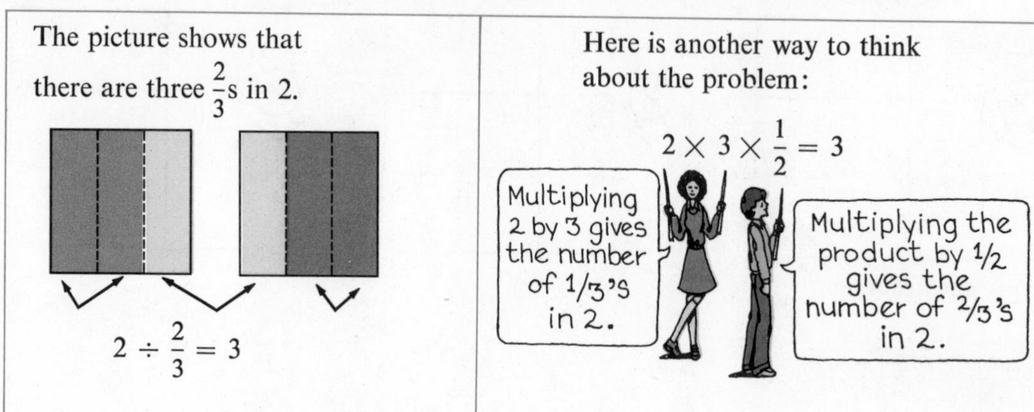

Multiplying by 3 and then by $\frac{1}{2}$ is the same as multiplying by $\frac{3}{2}$. Therefore, $2 \div \frac{2}{3} = 2 \times \frac{3}{2}$. Notice that dividing by $\frac{2}{3}$ is the same as multiplying by its reciprocal, $\frac{3}{2}$.

> To divide by a fractional number, multiply by its reciprocal, or multiplicative inverse.

Here are some examples.

Reciprocals	Reciprocals	Reciprocals
$2 \div \frac{1}{2} = 2 \times 2$	$\frac{3}{4} \div \frac{1}{4} = \frac{3}{4} \times \frac{4}{1}$	$\frac{3}{8} \div \frac{5}{3} = \frac{3}{8} \times \frac{3}{5}$
$= 4$	$= \frac{12}{4} = 3$	$= \frac{9}{40}$

EXERCISES

Complete.

1. To divide by 2 you can multiply by _?_.
2. To divide by $\frac{4}{5}$ you can multiply by _?_.
3. Dividing by $\frac{2}{3}$ is the same as multiplying by _?_.
4. Multiplying by $\frac{3}{8}$ is the same as dividing by _?_.

Divide. Give quotients in lowest terms.

5. $\frac{3}{8} \div \frac{1}{8}$
6. $2 \div \frac{1}{4}$
7. $3 \div \frac{1}{3}$
8. $\frac{3}{5} \div \frac{1}{5}$

9. $\frac{5}{9} \div \frac{1}{9}$
10. $\frac{8}{9} \div \frac{2}{9}$
11. $\frac{3}{5} \div \frac{1}{2}$
12. $\frac{4}{7} \div \frac{4}{3}$

13. $\frac{3}{5} \div 6$
14. $\frac{3}{8} \div \frac{5}{6}$
15. $\frac{3}{5} \div \frac{3}{2}$
16. $\frac{7}{4} \div 2$

17. $5 \div \frac{2}{3}$
18. $\frac{0}{6} \div \frac{2}{9}$
19. $3 \div \frac{1}{4}$
20. $\frac{5}{12} \div \frac{5}{3}$

21. $\frac{5}{3} \div \frac{3}{2}$
22. $\frac{2}{3} \div 8$
23. $\frac{4}{5} \div \frac{6}{10}$
24. $\frac{7}{8} \div \frac{5}{4}$

**True or false? Assume $a \neq 0$.**

25. If $a < b$, then $\frac{3}{4} \div a < \frac{3}{4} \div b$.

26. If $a < b$, then $\frac{3}{4} \times a < \frac{3}{4} \times b$.

27. If $a < b$, then $\frac{3}{4} + a < \frac{3}{4} + b$.

28. If $a < b$, then $\frac{3}{4} - a < \frac{3}{4} - b$.

Simplify.

29. $\left(\frac{1}{2} + \frac{1}{4}\right) \div \frac{1}{8}$

30. $\left(\frac{3}{8} \times \frac{8}{3}\right) \div \frac{1}{2}$

31. $\left(\frac{2}{5} - \frac{1}{4}\right) + \frac{1}{4}$

32. $\left(\frac{3}{5} \div \frac{3}{4}\right) \times \frac{2}{3}$

33. $\left(\frac{5}{4} + \frac{3}{5}\right) - \frac{5}{8}$

34. $\frac{7}{12} \times \left(\frac{3}{5} - \frac{3}{5}\right)$

Solve.

35. Miss Ramsey made $\frac{7}{2}$ pounds of fudge. She wants to give it to her friends in $\frac{1}{4}$-pound packages. How many friends can she give fudge to?

36. Samuel has $\frac{5}{2}$ cups of flour. If a full recipe of cookies calls for $\frac{4}{3}$ cups, how many recipes can he make?

**37.** Mr. Boyd had $\frac{3}{4}$ of a gallon of window trim paint. To paint one window, he used $\frac{2}{3}$ of a cup of paint. How many *more* windows of that size could he paint?

EXCURSION

Draw some evenly spaced dots on the sides of a square. Connect the dots as shown.

Supplementary Exercises, Set 25, page 380

Multiplying and dividing with mixed numerals

To multiply with mixed numerals, change each mixed numeral to an equivalent fraction and multiply.

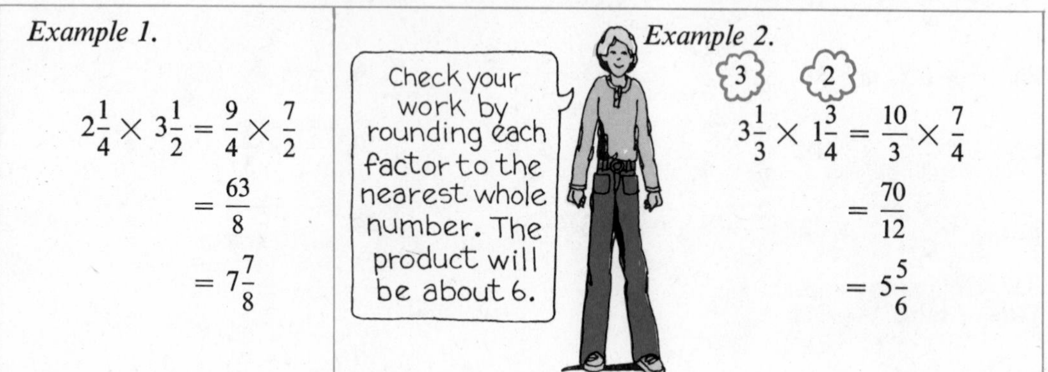

Example 1.

$$2\frac{1}{4} \times 3\frac{1}{2} = \frac{9}{4} \times \frac{7}{2} = \frac{63}{8} = 7\frac{7}{8}$$

Example 2.

$$3\frac{1}{3} \times 1\frac{3}{4} = \frac{10}{3} \times \frac{7}{4} = \frac{70}{12} = 5\frac{5}{6}$$

To divide with mixed numerals, change each mixed numeral to an equivalent fraction and divide.

Example 1.

$$5\frac{3}{4} \div 2\frac{1}{6} = \frac{23}{4} \div \frac{13}{6} = \frac{23}{4} \times \frac{6}{13} = \frac{138}{52} = 2\frac{17}{26}$$

Example 2.

$$6\frac{1}{8} \div 2\frac{3}{4} = \frac{49}{8} \div \frac{11}{4} = \frac{49}{8} \times \frac{4}{11} = \frac{196}{88} = 2\frac{5}{22}$$

EXERCISES

Estimate and then multiply.

1. $1\frac{1}{2} \times 1\frac{3}{4}$	**2.** $1\frac{1}{2} \times 2$	**3.** $1\frac{1}{3} \times 3\frac{1}{2}$	**4.** $2\frac{2}{3} \times 3\frac{1}{3}$
5. $4 \times 6\frac{1}{2}$	**6.** $1\frac{1}{4} \times 2\frac{2}{3}$	**7.** $1\frac{3}{8} \times 2\frac{3}{4}$	**8.** $3\frac{1}{4} \times 3$
9. $2\frac{1}{2} \times 5\frac{1}{4}$	**10.** $2\frac{1}{3} \times 3\frac{1}{5}$	**11.** $2\frac{1}{4} \times 2\frac{3}{8}$	**12.** $3\frac{1}{3} \times 2\frac{5}{8}$
13. $1\frac{2}{3} \times 5\frac{3}{4}$	**14.** $8 \times 4\frac{1}{8}$	**15.** $3\frac{2}{3} \times 1\frac{5}{8}$	**16.** $5\frac{1}{2} \times 3\frac{3}{4}$

Estimate and then divide.

17. $4 \div 1\frac{1}{2}$ **18.** $4\frac{1}{2} \div 1\frac{1}{2}$ **19.** $8\frac{3}{4} \div 2\frac{1}{3}$ **20.** $6\frac{3}{8} \div 3$

21. $9\frac{2}{3} \div 3\frac{3}{4}$ **22.** $8\frac{1}{2} \div 3\frac{2}{5}$ **23.** $9\frac{1}{4} \div 1\frac{1}{3}$ **24.** $10 \div 3\frac{1}{3}$

25. $9\frac{1}{2} \div 2$ **26.** $8 \div 2\frac{1}{4}$ **27.** $16 \div 2\frac{1}{2}$ **28.** $12\frac{1}{5} \div 8\frac{3}{4}$

29. $6\frac{7}{8} \div 1\frac{3}{4}$ **30.** $8\frac{2}{3} \div 8\frac{2}{3}$ **31.** $14\frac{1}{2} \div 3\frac{7}{8}$ **32.** $6\frac{1}{4} \div 5$

Solve.

Salt-Water Taffy

2 cups granulated sugar
1 cup light corn syrup
$1\frac{1}{2}$ teaspoons salt
$2\frac{1}{2}$ tablespoons butter
$\frac{1}{4}$ teaspoon oil of peppermint
5 drops food coloring

33. How many cups of sugar are needed for $\frac{2}{3}$ of a recipe?

34. How many teaspoons of salt are needed for 3 recipes?

35. How many recipes could be made with $7\frac{1}{2}$ cups of sugar?

36. Miss Adams has $8\frac{1}{3}$ tablespoons of butter. If she uses all the butter, how much salt should she use?

Solve.

37. What is the price of $2\frac{1}{3}$ dozen apples? Round the answer to the nearest cent.

38. Allison works $2\frac{1}{2}$ hours a day for 5 days a week. How much does she earn in a week if her hourly wage is $2.85?

39. A youth club planned a $12\frac{3}{4}$ mile hike. They planned to average $3\frac{1}{2}$ miles per hour. How many hours should the hike take them? How many minutes?

CHECKUP
for pages 118–121

Multiply. Give products in lowest terms.

1. $\frac{3}{8} \times \frac{8}{3}$ **2.** $6 \times \frac{2}{7}$ **3.** $\frac{5}{9} \times 4$

4. $\frac{4}{5} \times \frac{5}{4}$ **5.** $\frac{5}{9} \times \frac{3}{3}$ **6.** $\frac{2}{5} \times \frac{5}{3}$

Divide. Give quotients in lowest terms.

7. $8 \div \frac{1}{3}$ **8.** $\frac{2}{3} \div 2$ **9.** $\frac{5}{9} \div \frac{2}{3}$

10. $\frac{7}{4} \div \frac{7}{9}$ **11.** $\frac{0}{4} \div \frac{5}{4}$ **12.** $\frac{3}{2} \div \frac{2}{3}$

Answers on page 426.

Supplementary Exercises, Set 26, page 381

The cancellation shortcut

Below is an example of a shortcut that can often be used when *multiplying* fractional numbers. The shortcut, called **canceling**, is to divide both a numerator and a denominator by a common factor before multiplying.

Long method	Canceling shortcut
Multiply and then divide by a common factor.	Divide by a common factor and then multiply.
$\frac{3}{8} \times \frac{5}{24} = \frac{15}{192} = \frac{5}{64}$	$\frac{\overset{1}{\cancel{3}}}{8} \times \frac{5}{\underset{8}{\cancel{24}}} = \frac{5}{64}$

Notice that when the shortcut is used, smaller numbers are multiplied. Here are some more examples of canceling. Notice that in some examples the numerators and denominators were divided by more than one common factor.

$\frac{\overset{1}{\cancel{7}}}{\underset{4}{\cancel{12}}} \times \frac{\overset{1}{\cancel{3}}}{\underset{2}{\cancel{14}}} = \frac{1}{8}$	$\frac{\overset{1}{\cancel{9}}}{\underset{8}{\cancel{32}}} \times \frac{\overset{1}{\cancel{4}}}{\underset{2}{\cancel{18}}} = \frac{1}{16}$	$2\frac{1}{2} \times 1\frac{3}{10} = \frac{\overset{1}{\cancel{5}}}{2} \times \frac{13}{\underset{2}{\cancel{10}}}$ $= \frac{13}{4} = 3\frac{1}{4}$
$\frac{5}{8} \div \frac{3}{4} = \frac{5}{\underset{2}{\cancel{8}}} \times \frac{\overset{1}{\cancel{4}}}{3}$ $= \frac{5}{6}$	$\frac{5}{9} \div \frac{20}{21} = \frac{\overset{1}{\cancel{5}}}{\underset{3}{\cancel{9}}} \times \frac{\overset{7}{\cancel{21}}}{\underset{4}{\cancel{20}}}$ $= \frac{7}{12}$	$3\frac{1}{2} \div 2\frac{5}{6} = \frac{7}{2} \div \frac{17}{6}$ $= \frac{7}{\underset{1}{\cancel{2}}} \times \frac{\overset{3}{\cancel{6}}}{17}$ $= \frac{21}{17} = 1\frac{4}{17}$

EXERCISES

Use canceling to give each product in lowest terms.

1. $\frac{3}{9} \times \frac{5}{4}$ **2.** $\frac{9}{2} \times \frac{8}{21}$ **3.** $\frac{7}{2} \times \frac{8}{12}$ **4.** $\frac{4}{14} \times \frac{21}{6}$

5. $\frac{18}{3} \times \frac{15}{27}$ **6.** $\frac{12}{16} \times \frac{20}{21}$ **7.** $\frac{24}{18} \times \frac{5}{12}$ **8.** $\frac{36}{15} \times \frac{25}{12}$

9. $3\frac{3}{4} \times 3\frac{1}{5}$ **10.** $3\frac{1}{8} \times 1\frac{1}{5}$ **11.** $2\frac{4}{9} \times 2\frac{1}{4}$ **12.** $6\frac{3}{4} \times 2\frac{2}{3}$

Give each quotient in lowest terms. (*Hint*: Write as a product and cancel.)

13. $\frac{3}{8} \div \frac{3}{5}$
14. $\frac{3}{7} \div \frac{5}{14}$
15. $\frac{9}{2} \div \frac{3}{4}$
16. $\frac{15}{8} \div \frac{12}{6}$
17. $\frac{14}{9} \div \frac{21}{12}$
18. $\frac{24}{6} \div \frac{8}{3}$
19. $\frac{9}{8} \div \frac{3}{3}$
20. $\frac{16}{9} \div \frac{18}{36}$
21. $3\frac{1}{4} \div 2\frac{1}{2}$
22. $5\frac{2}{3} \div 1\frac{1}{6}$
23. $3\frac{3}{8} \div 6\frac{3}{4}$
24. $6\frac{3}{4} \div 3\frac{3}{8}$

Solve.

25. **Round each answer to the nearest cent.**
    a. What is the price of $2\frac{1}{2}$ yd of red ribbon?
    b. What is the price of $3\frac{3}{4}$ yd of blue ribbon?
    c. What is the total price of $1\frac{2}{3}$ yd of red ribbon and $2\frac{1}{2}$ yd of blue ribbon?

26. **Round each answer to the nearest cent.**
    a. What is the price of $\frac{3}{4}$ lb of chocolates?
    b. What is the price of 8 oz of chocolates?
    c. What is the price of $2\frac{1}{2}$ lb of chocolates?

27. Miss Davis bought $3\frac{1}{3}$ dozen oranges for $3.12. How much did they cost per dozen? Give the answer to the nearest cent.

28. Mr. Johnson averaged 58 kilometers an hour on a $2\frac{1}{2}$-hour trip. How many kilometers was the trip?

29. A certain blouse pattern calls for $1\frac{1}{4}$ yards of material. How many blouses can be made from $6\frac{1}{3}$ yards of material? How much material will be left over?

30. Mrs. Alexander bought $1\frac{3}{4}$ dozen sweet corn for $2.20. At that price how much would $2\frac{1}{2}$ dozen cost? Round the answer to the nearest cent.

EXCURSION

Construct this design with a compass. (*Hint:* Use just one compass setting.)

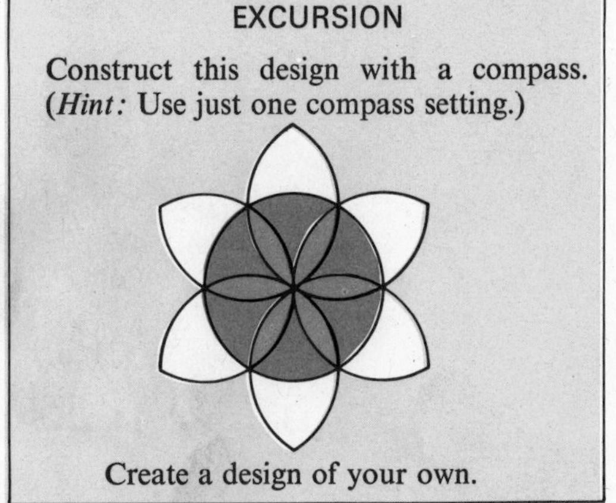

Create a design of your own.

Skill Maintenance, Set 31, page 405

Complex fractions

A fraction can be used to express the quotient of two whole numbers. Here are some examples:

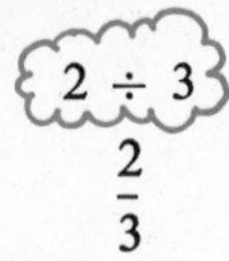

$\frac{2}{3}$

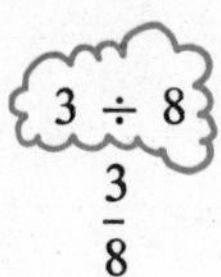

$\frac{3}{8}$

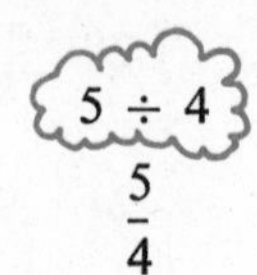

$\frac{5}{4}$

A complex fraction can be used to express the quotient of two fractional numbers. Here are some examples:

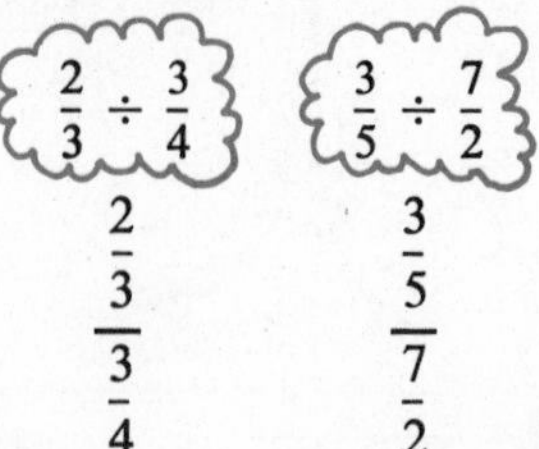

$$\frac{\frac{2}{3}}{\frac{3}{4}} \qquad \frac{\frac{3}{5}}{\frac{7}{2}}$$

Notice that you can think of the fraction bar as indicating division. Every complex fraction is equivalent to a fraction.
Here are some examples:

$\frac{\frac{3}{5}}{\frac{2}{5}} = \frac{3}{5} \div \frac{2}{5}$ $= \frac{3}{\cancel{5}_{1}} \times \frac{\cancel{5}^{1}}{2}$ $= \frac{3}{2}$	$\frac{\frac{3}{2}}{\frac{15}{8}} = \frac{3}{2} \div \frac{15}{8}$ $= \frac{\cancel{3}^{1}}{\cancel{2}} \times \frac{\cancel{8}}{\cancel{15}_{5}}$ $= \frac{4}{5}$	$\frac{5}{\frac{10}{3}} = 5 \div \frac{10}{3}$ $= \cancel{5}^{1} \times \frac{3}{\cancel{10}_{2}}$ $= \frac{3}{2}$

EXERCISES

Give each quotient in lowest terms.

1. $\frac{\frac{4}{3}}{\frac{2}{3}}$ **2.** $\frac{\frac{3}{8}}{\frac{3}{4}}$ **3.** $\frac{\frac{5}{2}}{\frac{7}{4}}$ **4.** $\frac{\frac{9}{2}}{\frac{3}{8}}$ **5.** $\frac{\frac{3}{10}}{\frac{4}{5}}$ **6.** $\frac{\frac{4}{9}}{\frac{2}{3}}$

7. $\frac{\frac{5}{8}}{\frac{3}{4}}$ **8.** $\frac{\frac{5}{6}}{\frac{2}{3}}$ **9.** $\frac{3}{\frac{1}{8}}$ **10.** $\frac{\frac{3}{5}}{4}$ **11.** $\frac{\frac{2}{7}}{\frac{3}{8}}$ **12.** $\frac{\frac{1}{9}}{\frac{7}{8}}$

13. $\frac{\frac{4}{3}}{\frac{12}{15}}$ **14.** $\frac{\frac{9}{16}}{\frac{3}{8}}$ **15.** $\frac{\frac{7}{3}}{\frac{14}{5}}$ **16.** $\frac{\frac{9}{4}}{\frac{4}{9}}$ **17.** $\frac{\frac{5}{8}}{6}$ **18.** $\frac{10}{\frac{5}{4}}$

Solve. Round the answers to the nearest cent.

JACKSON'S GROCERY—PART-TIME EVENING EMPLOYEES													
		Monday		Tuesday		Wednesday		Thursday		Friday		Saturday	
		Time		Time		Time		Time		Time		Time	
Employee	Hourly rate	In	Out	In	Out	In	Out	In	Out	In	Out	In	Out
Brown	$2.80	3:00	7:30	3:00	7:30	3:00	7:30			3:00	7:30	5:00	9:00
Johnson	3.10	2:30	4:45	2:30	4:45	2:30	4:45	2:30	4:45	2:30	4:45		
Martinez	2.90			4:00	7:15	4:00	7:15	4:00	7:15	4:00	7:15	4:00	7:15
Newberg	3.25	4:45	9:00	4:45	9:00	4:45	9:00	4:45	9:00	4:45	9:00	4:45	7:00
Randell	2.75	2:30	5:30			2:30	5:30	2:30	5:30	2:30	5:30	2:30	4:00
Tate	3.05	3:15	6:00	3:15	6:00			3:15	6:00	3:15	6:00	3:15	6:00

19. How many hours did Brown work during the week?

20. How much did Brown earn during the week?

21. Who worked fewer hours, Randell or Tate?

22. How much more did Newberg earn than Martinez?

23. Which employee worked the most hours on Saturday?

24. How much was spent for part-time help on Monday?

Solve.

25. A gallon of gasoline weighs about 5.66 pounds. The gasoline tank in a certain automobile holds 21.5 gallons. How much weight is added to the automobile when the tank is filled?

26. Jerry bought five records priced at $4.39, $3.99, $5.69, $4.59, and $4.99. What was the average price of a record?

27. Cindy is going on a 50-mile bike trip. She plans to average 9 miles per hour. How many hours and minutes will the trip take? Round your answer to the nearest minute.

CHECKUP

for pages 122–123

Give each product as a mixed numeral.

1. $2\frac{1}{4} \times 1\frac{1}{2}$

2. $7\frac{2}{3} \times 6\frac{1}{3}$

3. $4\frac{3}{4} \times 5$

4. $3\frac{3}{4} \times 5\frac{1}{8}$

5. $4\frac{2}{5} \times 5\frac{5}{8}$

6. $7 \times 9\frac{1}{2}$

Give each quotient as a mixed numeral.

1. $8\frac{1}{2} \div 4\frac{1}{8}$

2. $7 \div 5\frac{2}{3}$

3. $10\frac{3}{5} \div 1\frac{4}{5}$

4. $12\frac{3}{4} \div 2\frac{1}{3}$

5. $9\frac{7}{8} \div 3\frac{1}{4}$

6. $14\frac{5}{9} \div 3\frac{2}{3}$

Answers on page 426.

Skill Maintenance, Set 32, page 405

Practice exercises

Add. When possible, give answers as mixed numerals.

1. $\frac{3}{5} + \frac{2}{3}$
2. $\frac{1}{4} + \frac{5}{8}$
3. $\frac{8}{3} + \frac{5}{9}$
4. $\frac{3}{5} + \frac{5}{6}$
5. $\frac{5}{12} + \frac{3}{8}$
6. $\frac{5}{7} + \frac{2}{3}$
7. $2 + 3\frac{3}{4}$
8. $1\frac{3}{5} + 5\frac{1}{10}$
9. $7\frac{1}{3} + 8\frac{5}{6}$
10. $9\frac{7}{8} + 6\frac{3}{4}$
11. $3\frac{5}{9} + 5\frac{5}{6}$
12. $9\frac{3}{4} + 11\frac{3}{4}$

Subtract. When possible, give answers as mixed numerals.

13. $\frac{7}{8} - \frac{1}{2}$
14. $\frac{7}{9} - \frac{2}{3}$
15. $\frac{9}{10} - \frac{2}{5}$
16. $\frac{6}{7} - \frac{2}{3}$
17. $\frac{11}{12} - \frac{3}{4}$
18. $\frac{13}{16} - \frac{2}{3}$
19. $8\frac{1}{2} - 6$
20. $9\frac{3}{4} - 2\frac{3}{8}$
21. $11 - 4\frac{5}{6}$
22. $13\frac{1}{2} - 8\frac{7}{8}$
23. $16\frac{5}{12} - 7\frac{2}{3}$
24. $18\frac{3}{5} - 6\frac{7}{10}$

Simplify.

25. $\left(\frac{1}{2} \div \frac{3}{4}\right) \times \frac{0}{8}$
26. $\frac{2}{3} + \left(\frac{1}{3} + \frac{3}{8}\right)$
27. $\frac{0}{3} \times \left(\frac{5}{8} \div \frac{3}{4}\right)$
28. $\left(\frac{6}{5} \times \frac{5}{6}\right) \times \frac{5}{9}$
29. $\left(\frac{5}{4} \div \frac{2}{2}\right) + \frac{1}{4}$
30. $\left(\frac{5}{9} - \frac{1}{3}\right) \times \frac{9}{2}$
31. $\left(\frac{5}{6} \div \frac{1}{3}\right) + \left(\frac{3}{8} \times \frac{8}{3}\right)$
32. $\left(\frac{6}{7} + \frac{1}{3}\right) \times \left(\frac{13}{8} + 1\right)$
33. $\left(\frac{7}{4} - \frac{1}{2}\right) \div \left(\frac{3}{5} + \frac{2}{3}\right)$
34. $\left(2\frac{1}{2} \div 1\frac{3}{4}\right) + 1\frac{1}{2}$
35. $\left(8\frac{3}{5} \div 2\right) - 1\frac{7}{10}$
36. $\left(4\frac{3}{8} \times 6\frac{1}{5}\right) + 2\frac{3}{4}$
37. Follow the path to find the ending number.

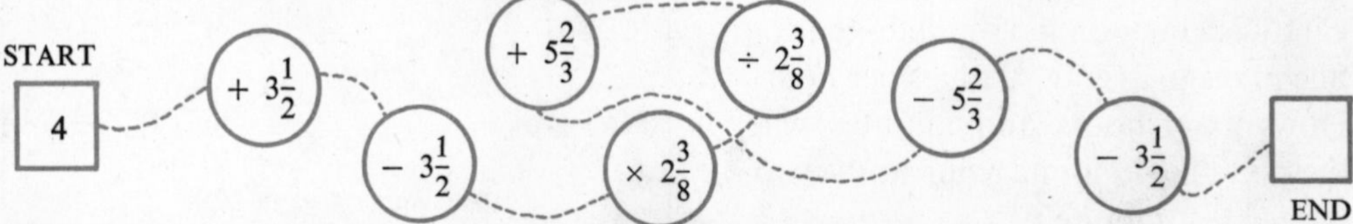

This game may be played between two players or between two teams of players. Draw a 4-by-4 grid like this:

The cells of the grid will be filled with 16 of these fractions:

$\frac{1}{2}, \frac{2}{2}$

$\frac{1}{3}, \frac{2}{3}, \frac{3}{3}$

$\frac{1}{4}, \frac{2}{4}, \frac{3}{4}, \frac{4}{4}$

$\frac{1}{6}, \frac{2}{6}, \frac{3}{6}, \frac{4}{6}, \frac{5}{6}, \frac{6}{6}$

$\frac{1}{8}, \frac{2}{8}, \frac{3}{8}, \frac{4}{8}, \frac{5}{8}, \frac{6}{8}, \frac{7}{8}, \frac{8}{8}$

No fraction may be used more than once in a game.

The teams take turns filling in the cells with fractions.

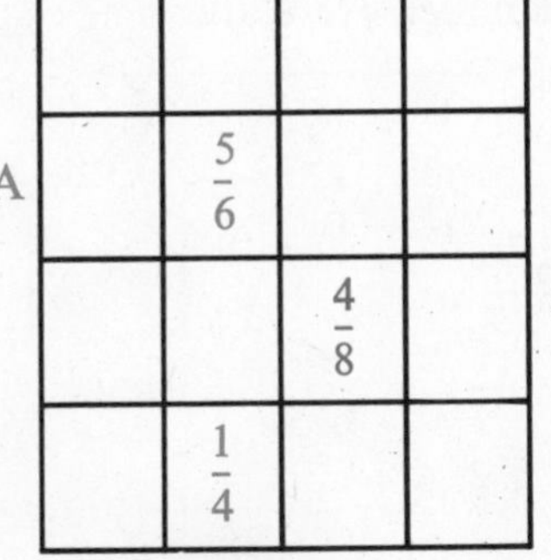

Play continues until all cells have been filled in.

$\frac{7}{8}$	$\frac{8}{8}$	$\frac{1}{6}$	$\frac{1}{8}$
$\frac{4}{6}$	$\frac{5}{6}$	$\frac{3}{8}$	$\frac{2}{8}$
$\frac{6}{8}$	$\frac{6}{6}$	$\frac{4}{8}$	$\frac{2}{6}$
$\frac{2}{4}$	$\frac{1}{4}$	$\frac{5}{8}$	$\frac{3}{6}$

Each team that completed four or more connecting squares adds the numbers in those squares. The team getting the greater sum wins the game.

$$\frac{4}{6} + \frac{5}{6} + \frac{6}{6} + \frac{1}{4} + \frac{2}{4} = 3\frac{1}{4}$$

$$\frac{1}{8} + \frac{2}{8} + \frac{3}{8} + \frac{4}{8} + \frac{5}{8} = 1\frac{7}{8}$$

Later you may wish to change the game to a multiplication game, that is, multiply the numbers in four or more connecting squares. The team getting the greater product wins the game.

Skill Maintenance, Set 33, page 406

Solving equations

The two equations are equivalent. That is, if you substitute the same number for x in both equations, either *both* will be true or *both* will be false.

$$x + \frac{1}{4} = \frac{3}{8}$$

$$x + \frac{1}{4} - \frac{1}{4} = \frac{3}{8} - \frac{1}{4}$$

An equivalent equation can be obtained by:

Adding the same number to both sides.	Subtracting the same number from both sides.
$n + 6 = 9$ $n + 6 + 4 = 9 + 4$	$n + 6 = 9$ $n + 6 - 5 = 9 - 5$
Multiplying both sides by the same number (not 0).	Dividing both sides by the same number (not 0).
$n + 6 = 9$ $2(n + 6) = 2 \times 9$	$n + 6 = 9$ $\frac{n + 6}{3} = \frac{9}{3}$

Check to see whether the equations in each pair have the same solution.

Equations can be solved by adding, subtracting, multiplying, or dividing both sides by the same number. Here are some examples:

$$2x + \frac{1}{4} = \frac{5}{8}$$

$$2x + \frac{1}{4} - \frac{1}{4} = \frac{5}{8} - \frac{1}{4} \quad \left[\text{subtract } \frac{1}{4}\right]$$

$$2x = \frac{3}{8} \quad \text{[simplify]}$$

$$\frac{2x}{2} = \frac{\frac{3}{8}}{2} \quad \text{[divide by 2]}$$

$$x = \frac{3}{16} \quad \text{[simplify]}$$

Check by substituting $\frac{3}{16}$ for x in the first equation.

$$2\left(\frac{3}{16}\right) + \frac{1}{4} = \frac{6}{16} + \frac{4}{16} = \frac{10}{16} = \frac{5}{8}$$

$$\frac{2}{3}y - \frac{1}{6} = \frac{3}{4}$$

$$\frac{2}{3}y - \frac{1}{6} + \frac{1}{6} = \frac{3}{4} + \frac{1}{6} \quad \left[\text{add } \frac{1}{6}\right]$$

$$\frac{2}{3}y = \frac{11}{12} \quad \text{[simplify]}$$

$$\frac{3}{2} \times \frac{2}{3}y = \frac{3}{2} \times \frac{11}{12} \quad \left[\text{multiply by } \frac{3}{2}\right]$$

$$y = \frac{11}{8} \quad \text{[simplify]}$$

Multiply by the reciprocal of 2/3 to get the y alone.

Check:

$$\frac{2}{3}\left(\frac{11}{8}\right) - \frac{1}{6} = \frac{11}{12} - \frac{2}{12} = \frac{9}{12} = \frac{3}{4}$$

Copy and complete.

1. $3x - \frac{1}{2} = \frac{7}{4}$

   $3x - \frac{1}{2} + \frac{1}{2} = \frac{7}{4} + \frac{1}{2}$ [add ?]

   $3x = ?$ [simplify]

   $\frac{3x}{3} = \frac{\frac{9}{4}}{?}$ [divide by 3]

   $x = ?$

2. $\frac{2}{5}y + \frac{2}{3} = 3$

   $\frac{2}{5}y + \frac{2}{3} - ? = 3 - ?$ $\left[\text{subtract } \frac{2}{3}\right]$

   $\frac{2}{5}y = ?$ [simplify]

   $\frac{5}{2} \times \frac{2}{5}y = \frac{5}{2} \times ?$ $\left[\text{multiply by } \frac{5}{2}\right]$

   $y = ?$

3. $\frac{1}{4}w - \frac{3}{8} = \frac{5}{6}$

   $\frac{1}{4}w - \frac{3}{8} + \frac{3}{8} = \frac{5}{6} + ?$

   $\frac{1}{4}w = ?$

   $4 \times \frac{1}{4}w = 4 \times ?$

   $w = ?$

4. $\frac{3}{2}n + \frac{2}{3} = 1$

   $\frac{3}{2}n + \frac{2}{3} - ? = 1 - ?$

   $\frac{3}{2}n = ?$

   $\frac{2}{3} \times \frac{3}{2}n = \frac{2}{3} \times ?$

   $n = ?$

5. $\frac{5}{8}t + \frac{3}{5} = \frac{4}{3}$

   $\frac{5}{8}t + \frac{3}{5} - \frac{3}{5} = \frac{4}{3} - ?$

   $\frac{5}{8}t = ?$

   $? \times \frac{5}{8}t = ? \times \frac{11}{15}$

   $t = ?$

Solve, and check your solution.

6. $3x + \frac{2}{3} = \frac{3}{2}$

7. $2x - \frac{1}{3} = \frac{3}{8}$

8. $5x + \frac{2}{9} = \frac{2}{3}$

9. $\frac{3}{4}x = \frac{1}{2}$

10. $\frac{3}{5}x - \frac{1}{4} = \frac{1}{2}$

11. $2x - \frac{5}{8} = \frac{7}{4}$

12. $\frac{5}{9}x + \frac{3}{4} = \frac{3}{4}$

13. $\frac{7}{3}x + \frac{1}{2} = \frac{7}{4}$

14. $\frac{3}{5}x - \frac{5}{6} = 2$

15. $\frac{5}{8}x - \frac{1}{5} = \frac{1}{2}$

16. $\frac{3}{7}x + \frac{2}{3} = \frac{9}{2}$

17. $\frac{5}{9}x + 2\frac{1}{2} = 3\frac{1}{4}$

18. $\frac{3}{4}x - 1\frac{1}{8} = 1\frac{1}{2}$

19. $\frac{4}{7}x - 1\frac{1}{3} = 2\frac{1}{3}$

20. $\frac{6}{5}x + 2\frac{3}{4} = 3\frac{1}{2}$

21. Give 12 equations that have the solution $\frac{1}{2}$.

22. Give 12 equations that have the same solution as

$$\frac{7}{8}w - \frac{1}{4} = 1\frac{1}{3}.$$

EXCURSION

The sheet metal is to be cut into two pieces that are the same size and shape.

2 in.

15 in.

The pieces are then used to make a cover for the box.

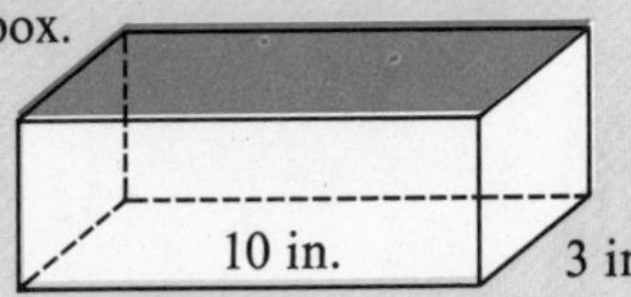

How can the sheet metal be cut?

Supplementary Exercises, Set 27, page 381

Basic properties of fractional numbers

Earlier you studied the basic properties of whole numbers. Listed below are some properties of fractional numbers.

ADDITION PROPERTIES	MULTIPLICATION PROPERTIES
Commutative Property of Addition $\frac{a}{b}+\frac{c}{d}=\frac{c}{d}+\frac{a}{b} \quad b \neq 0, d \neq 0$ $\frac{3}{5}+\frac{2}{7}=\frac{2}{7}+\frac{3}{5}$	Commutative Property of Multiplication $\frac{a}{b}\times\frac{c}{d}=\frac{c}{d}\times\frac{a}{b} \quad b \neq 0, d \neq 0$ $\frac{3}{5}\times\frac{2}{7}=\frac{2}{7}\times\frac{3}{5}$
Associative Property of Addition $\left(\frac{a}{b}+\frac{c}{d}\right)+\frac{e}{f}=\frac{a}{b}+\left(\frac{c}{d}+\frac{e}{f}\right)$ $b \neq 0, d \neq 0, f \neq 0$ $\left(\frac{1}{2}+\frac{3}{4}\right)+\frac{2}{3}=\frac{1}{2}+\left(\frac{3}{4}+\frac{2}{3}\right)$	Associative Property of Multiplication $\left(\frac{a}{b}\times\frac{c}{d}\right)\times\frac{e}{f}=\frac{a}{b}\times\left(\frac{c}{d}\times\frac{e}{f}\right)$ $b \neq 0, d \neq 0, f \neq 0$ $\left(\frac{1}{2}\times\frac{3}{4}\right)\times\frac{2}{3}=\frac{1}{2}\times\left(\frac{3}{4}\times\frac{2}{3}\right)$
Identity Property of Addition $\frac{a}{b}+0=\frac{a}{b} \quad b \neq 0$ $\frac{2}{3}+0=\frac{2}{3}$	Identity Property of Multiplication $\frac{a}{b}\times 1=\frac{a}{b} \quad b \neq 0$ $\frac{2}{3}\times 1=\frac{2}{3}$
	Multiplicative Inverse Property $\frac{a}{b}\times\frac{b}{a}=1 \quad a \neq 0, b \neq 0$

Distributive Property of Multiplication over Addition

$$\frac{a}{b}\left(\frac{c}{d}+\frac{e}{f}\right)=\frac{a}{b}\times\frac{c}{d}+\frac{a}{b}\times\frac{e}{f} \quad b \neq 0, d \neq 0, f \neq 0$$

$$\frac{1}{2}\left(\frac{2}{3}+\frac{5}{6}\right)=\frac{1}{2}\times\frac{2}{3}+\frac{1}{2}\times\frac{5}{6}$$

EXERCISES

Match each property with its example.

1. Associative property of multiplication
2. Distributive property of multiplication over addition
3. Commutative property of addition
4. Identity property of multiplication
5. Associative property of addition
6. Multiplicative inverse property
7. Commutative property of multiplication
8. Identity property of addition

a. $\frac{5}{8} \times \frac{2}{3} = \frac{2}{3} \times \frac{5}{8}$

b. $\left(\frac{3}{4} \times \frac{1}{3}\right) \times \frac{3}{7} = \frac{3}{4} \times \left(\frac{1}{3} \times \frac{3}{7}\right)$

c. $\frac{3}{8} + 0 = \frac{3}{8}$

d. $\frac{1}{5} + \frac{2}{3} = \frac{2}{3} + \frac{1}{5}$

e. $\frac{1}{8}\left(\frac{3}{4} + \frac{5}{9}\right) = \frac{1}{8} \times \frac{3}{4} + \frac{1}{8} \times \frac{5}{9}$

f. $\frac{5}{9} \times 1 = \frac{5}{9}$

g. $\left(\frac{3}{4} + \frac{2}{3}\right) + \frac{1}{5} = \frac{3}{4} + \left(\frac{2}{3} + \frac{1}{5}\right)$

h. $\frac{4}{5} \times \frac{5}{4} = 1$

Give the property.

9. When adding two fractional numbers you can change the order of the addends without changing the sum.
10. The sum of any fractional number and zero is that fractional number.
11. When multiplying three fractional numbers you can change the grouping of the factors without changing the product.
12. When multiplying two fractional numbers you can change the order of the factors without changing the product.
13. The product of any fractional number and 1 is that fractional number.

Prove that the following are not properties of fractional numbers. (*Hint:* Find a counterexample. That is, give an example of each "property" that is false.)

14. Commutative property of division
15. Commutative property of subtraction
16. Associative property of subtraction
17. Associative property of division

> **CHECKUP**
> for pages 130–131
>
> **Solve each equation.**
>
> **1.** $4y + \frac{2}{3} = \frac{5}{4}$ **2.** $3y - \frac{5}{3} = 1\frac{1}{4}$
>
> **3.** $\frac{3}{5}y - \frac{1}{8} = \frac{3}{4}$ **4.** $\frac{4}{7}y + \frac{3}{7} = 1\frac{1}{3}$
>
> **5.** $\frac{5}{2}y + \frac{5}{8} = 2$ **6.** $\frac{9}{4}y - \frac{4}{3} = 2\frac{3}{4}$
>
> Answers on page 426.

Skill Maintenance, Set 34, page 406

Mathematics in careers

Carpenters are skilled craftsmen who construct and repair structures made of wood. In house construction, carpenters called *framing carpenters* construct the structural framework of a house.

The structural part of a wall is made up of plates and studs. Plates and studs are made from 2 × 4s (lumber of a standard size).

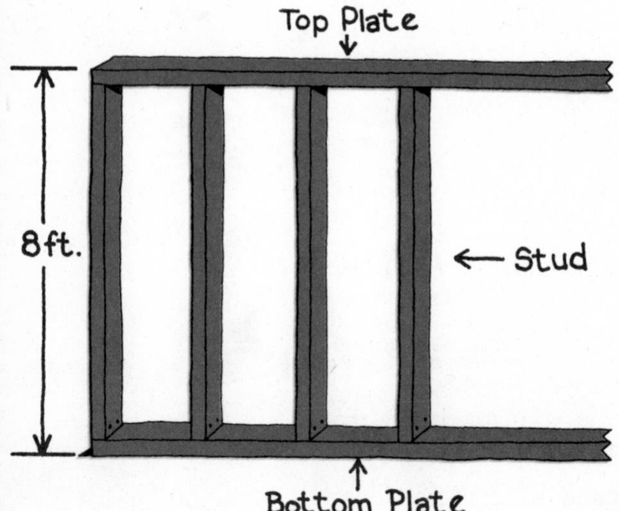

In the drawing, notice that the plates are the horizontal pieces and the studs are the vertical pieces.

Since most material used for covering the inside wall comes in 4-foot widths, the studs are "on 16-inch centers" (16 inches from the center of one stud to the center of the next). Carpenters start at one end of a wall and nail a stud to the plates every 16 inches. Any "remainder" that is less than 16 inches will be between the last two studs.

EXERCISES

Two-by-fours can be purchased in lengths of even numbers of feet (2 ft, 4 ft, etc.). If each plate must be a single 2 × 4 and if the studs are cut from 8-foot 2 × 4s, what material should be ordered for walls of these lengths?

1. 8 feet

2. 10 feet

3. 12 feet

4. $15\frac{1}{2}$ feet

5. $20\frac{3}{4}$ feet

6. $22\frac{2}{3}$ feet

CHAPTER CHECKUP

Reduce to lowest terms. [*page 100*]

1. $\frac{6}{8}$ **2.** $\frac{5}{10}$ **3.** $\frac{3}{9}$ **4.** $\frac{18}{10}$ **5.** $\frac{16}{28}$ **6.** $\frac{3}{12}$ **7.** $\frac{15}{12}$ **8.** $\frac{42}{36}$

Change to a decimal. [*page 102*]

9. $\frac{1}{2}$ **10.** $\frac{3}{8}$ **11.** $\frac{1}{6}$ **12.** $\frac{3}{4}$ **13.** $\frac{8}{5}$ **14.** $\frac{5}{6}$ **15.** $\frac{8}{6}$ **16.** $\frac{4}{3}$

Give each sum as a mixed numeral or a fraction in lowest terms. [*pages 108, 112*]

17. $\frac{3}{8}+\frac{1}{4}$ **18.** $\frac{5}{9}+\frac{2}{3}$ **19.** $\frac{7}{8}+\frac{3}{4}$ **20.** $\frac{0}{4}+\frac{5}{7}$

21. $2\frac{1}{2}+3$ **22.** $4\frac{2}{3}+1\frac{2}{3}$ **23.** $3\frac{3}{8}+2\frac{3}{4}$ **24.** $6\frac{2}{5}+3\frac{7}{10}$

Give each difference as a mixed numeral or a fraction in lowest terms. [*pages 110, 112*]

25. $\frac{5}{9}-\frac{1}{3}$ **26.** $\frac{3}{4}-\frac{3}{5}$ **27.** $2-\frac{3}{4}$ **28.** $1-\frac{7}{10}$

29. $2\frac{1}{2}-1$ **30.** $5-3\frac{1}{4}$ **31.** $3\frac{2}{5}-1\frac{1}{4}$ **32.** $5\frac{1}{3}-3\frac{7}{8}$

Give each product as a mixed numeral or a fraction in lowest terms. [*page 118*]

33. $\frac{3}{4}\times\frac{3}{2}$ **34.** $\frac{4}{7}\times\frac{7}{8}$ **35.** $\frac{5}{9}\times\frac{9}{5}$ **36.** $\frac{3}{8}\times\frac{2}{3}$

37. $2\times 1\frac{1}{3}$ **38.** $4\frac{1}{3}\times 5$ **39.** $2\frac{1}{4}\times 3\frac{3}{8}$ **40.** $3\frac{2}{5}\times 4\frac{3}{5}$

Give each quotient as a mixed numeral or a fraction in lowest terms. [*page 120*]

41. $\frac{3}{8}\div 2$ **42.** $6\div\frac{4}{5}$ **43.** $\frac{5}{9}\div\frac{7}{3}$ **44.** $\frac{5}{6}\div\frac{10}{9}$

45. $8\div 2\frac{1}{4}$ **46.** $5\div 1\frac{5}{8}$ **47.** $2\frac{1}{2}\div 3\frac{3}{8}$ **48.** $4\frac{1}{6}\div 2\frac{2}{3}$

Solve each equation. [*page 130*]

49. $5y+\frac{2}{3}=1$ **50.** $3y-\frac{2}{7}=1\frac{1}{2}$ **51.** $4y+\frac{3}{8}=\frac{5}{6}$

52. $\frac{3}{2}y-\frac{1}{2}=\frac{3}{4}$ **53.** $\frac{3}{4}y+\frac{2}{3}=2$ **54.** $\frac{2}{5}y+1\frac{1}{2}=3\frac{2}{3}$

MAJOR CHECKUP

Substitute and simplify. [*page 3*]

a	b	A	r	x
1	3	2	5	4

1. b^A **2.** A^b **3.** $rx - A$ **4.** $Ar + b$

5. $\frac{rx}{A}$ **6.** $r(b + A)$ **7.** $b(x - A)$ **8.** $\frac{br - r}{aA}$

Solve each equation. [*page 18*]

9. $3x + 9 = 30$ **10.** $5(x + 3) = 35$ **11.** $9(8 - x) = 0$

12. $4x - 10 = 34$ **13.** $\frac{8x + 4}{7} = 4$ **14.** $\frac{5(x + 2)}{4} = 10$

15. Copy and complete this table. [*page 40*]

Number	Rounded to the nearest				
	ten	one	tenth	hundredth	thousandth
58.6253					
94.7829					
369.4213					
279.0935					

Give each sum or difference. [*page 42*]

16. $367 + 594$ **17.** $27.49 + 28.35$ **18.** $.7346 + .2951$ **19.** $3.874 + 16.059$ **20.** $58.2 + 37.5 + 29.1$ **21.** $3.64 + 2.95 + 3.83$

22. $725 - 389$ **23.** $507 - 259$ **24.** $32.6 - 19.8$ **25.** $30.05 - 9.36$ **26.** $5.8 - 2.93$ **27.** $.7206 - .3817$

Give each product. [*pages 68, 74, 78*]

28. 321×8 **29.** 506×12 **30.** 34.2×7 **31.** 7.48×26 **32.** $.319 \times 8.3$ **33.** 4.07×13.9

Give each quotient. [*pages 82, 86*]

34. $2\overline{)594}$ **35.** $18\overline{)6.66}$ **36.** $.3\overline{)7.86}$ **37.** $5.3\overline{)254.4}$ **38.** $2.48\overline{)13.144}$

Project

The facts are about the common stock of Alcoa.

The year's high was $\$51\frac{3}{4}$ a share.

The year's low was $\$38\frac{3}{4}$ a share.

Today's high was $\$47\frac{7}{8}$ a share.

Today's low was $47 a share.

When the market closed, the stock was selling at $\$47\frac{7}{8}$ a share.

STOCK QUOTATIONS													
Year's High	Year's Low	Stocks and Dividends in Dollars	Today's High	Today's Low	Today's Last	Year's High	Year's Low	Stocks and Dividends in Dollars	Today's High	Today's Low	Today's Last
$9\frac{5}{8}$	$5\frac{7}{8}$	AllenGrp .40	$6\frac{1}{4}$	6	6	$10\frac{3}{4}$	$7\frac{1}{2}$	Allis Chal .26	$8\frac{5}{8}$	$8\frac{1}{4}$	$8\frac{3}{8}$
$54\frac{1}{4}$	$33\frac{1}{4}$	AlldCh 1.50	$37\frac{1}{4}$	$35\frac{1}{2}$	37	$17\frac{3}{8}$	$11\frac{5}{8}$	Alpha Pl .72	$11\frac{7}{8}$	$11\frac{7}{8}$	$11\frac{7}{8}$
$22\frac{5}{8}$	$12\frac{1}{4}$	AlldMnt .48	$15\frac{1}{2}$	$15\frac{1}{8}$	$15\frac{3}{8}$	$51\frac{3}{4}$	$38\frac{3}{4}$	Alcoa 1.34	$47\frac{7}{8}$	47	$47\frac{7}{8}$
$17\frac{1}{2}$	$12\frac{7}{8}$	AlldPd .80	15	$14\frac{5}{8}$	$14\frac{7}{8}$	$28\frac{1}{2}$	$21\frac{1}{2}$	A Sug 1.60a	23	$22\frac{3}{4}$	23
$25\frac{5}{8}$	20	AlldStr 1.50	$21\frac{5}{8}$	$21\frac{1}{4}$	$21\frac{1}{4}$	$52\frac{7}{8}$	$35\frac{5}{8}$	Amax 1.65	$38\frac{1}{2}$	$37\frac{1}{2}$	$37\frac{1}{2}$
$4\frac{7}{8}$	$2\frac{1}{4}$	Alld Supmkt	$2\frac{7}{8}$	$2\frac{3}{4}$	$2\frac{7}{8}$	129	88	Amax pf 5.25	$93\frac{3}{8}$	$92\frac{1}{4}$	$92\frac{1}{4}$

1. Find the stock quotations in a newspaper. Pretend that you buy $1000 worth of one stock and $1000 worth of another. Pretend also that you pay the "Today's Low" price.

Example. You want to buy a stock selling at $\$25\frac{1}{2}$.

$$1000 \div 25\frac{1}{2} = 1000 \div \frac{51}{2}$$
$$= 1000 \times \frac{2}{51}$$
$$= \frac{2000}{51}$$
$$= 19\frac{31}{51}$$

So, 19 shares could be purchased with $1000.

2. Show the daily value of your stock (use today's low) on a line graph like this:

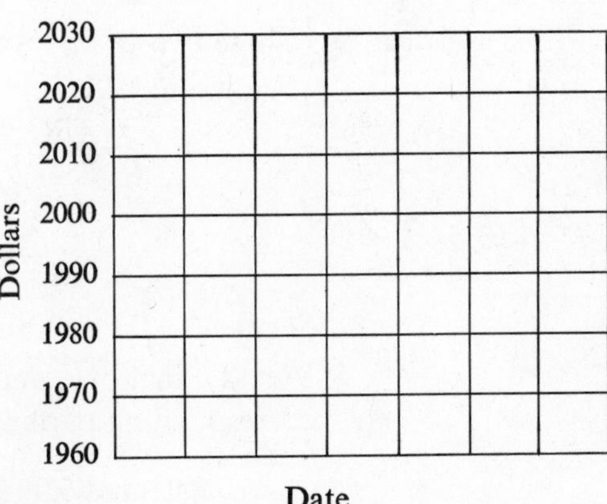

5 Geometry-Congruence and Symmetry

Congruent figures

The blue figure is an **image** of the red figure. A tracing of the red figure fits the blue figure.

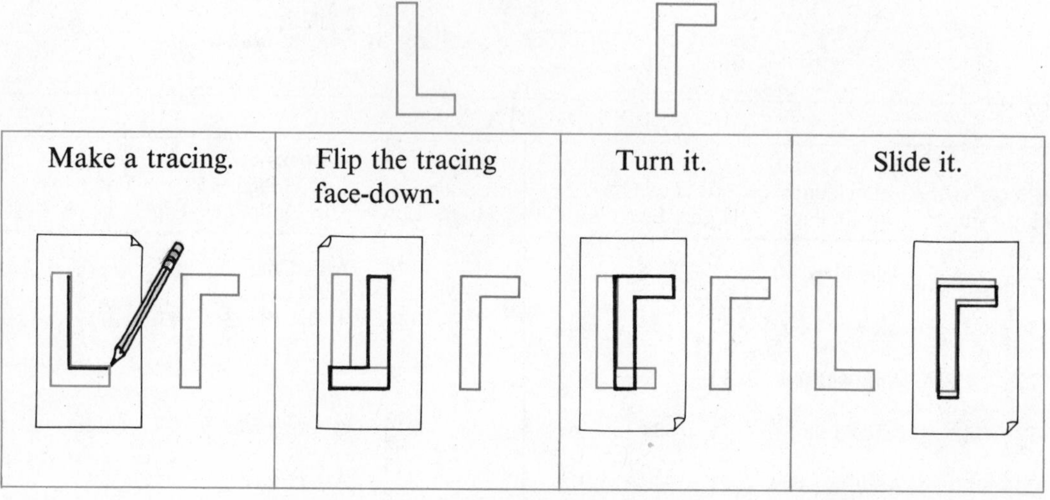

Obviously, the red figure is also an image of the blue figure. Because the figures are the same size and shape we say that they are **congruent.**

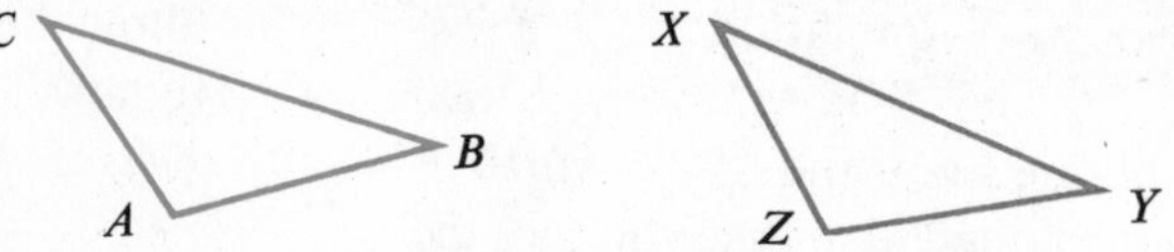

These two triangles are congruent.
We write:

$$\triangle ABC \cong \triangle ZYX$$

Segment AC ($\overline{AC}$) and segment ZX ($\overline{ZX}$) are images of each other. We say that $\overline{AC}$ and $\overline{ZX}$ are **corresponding parts**. Other pairs of corresponding parts are:

$\overline{AB}$ and $\overline{ZY}$	angle A ($\angle A$) and angle Z ($\angle Z$)
$\overline{BC}$ and $\overline{YX}$	$\angle B$ and $\angle Y$
	$\angle C$ and $\angle X$

EXERCISES

Are the blue figure and the red figure congruent? Use a tracing if you need to.

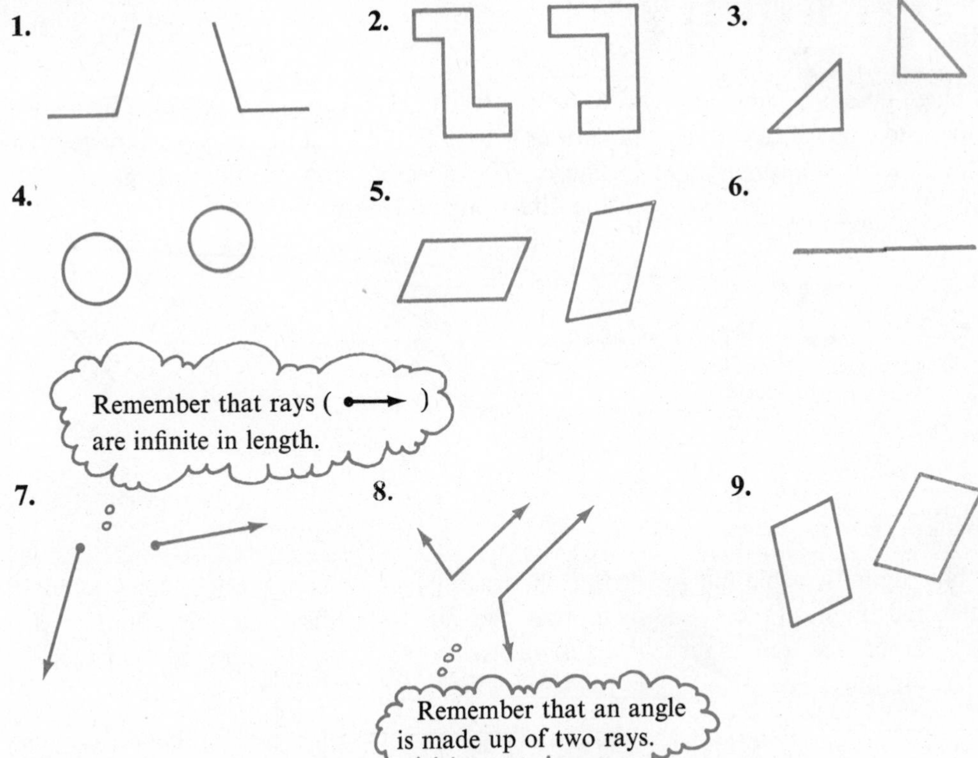

The red figure is congruent to the blue figure. List the corresponding sides and the corresponding angles.

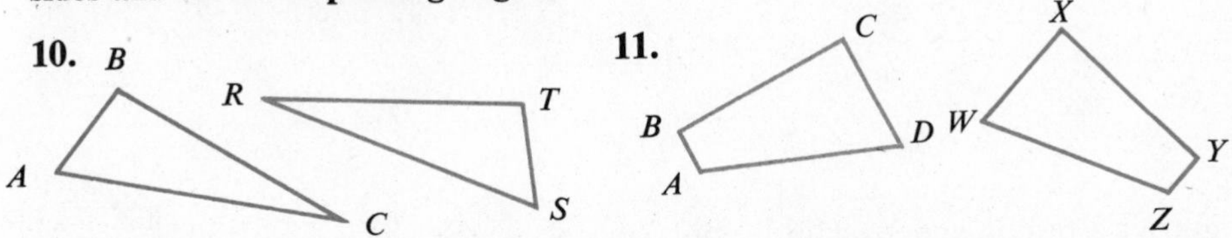

12. These two congruent triangles can be fitted together in two different ways. This means that there are two sets of corresponding parts, one for each fitting. List the two sets of corresponding parts.

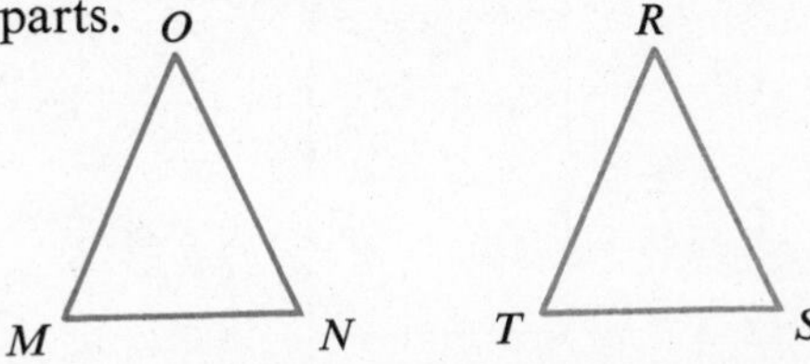

Supplementary Exercises, Set 28, page 381

Slides, flips, and turns

In this lesson you will study the three single motions: slides, flips, and turns.

Slide Images

The blue figure is a **slide image** of the red figure (and vice versa). Trace the red figure.

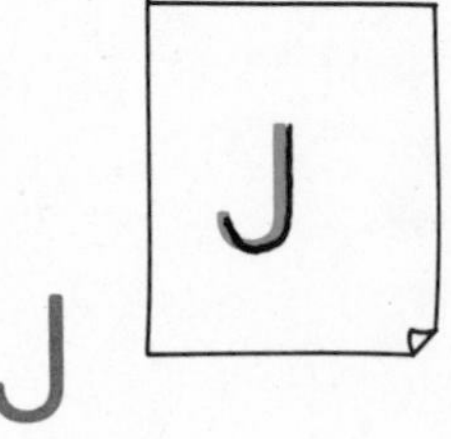

Slide the tracing (without turning) to fit the blue figure. The arrows show the direction and length of the slide.

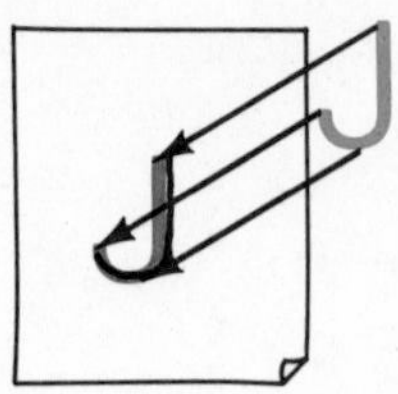

Each blue figure is a slide image of the red figure.

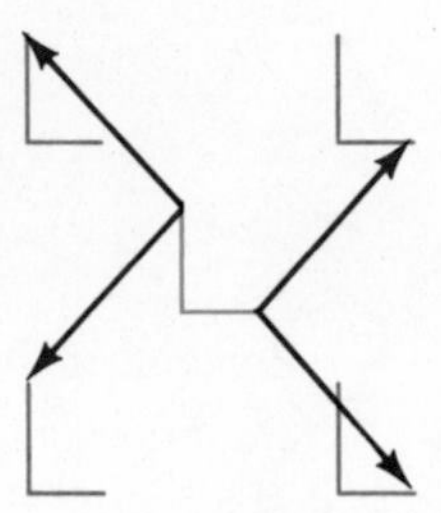

Flip Images

The blue figure is a **flip image** of the red figure (and vice versa). Trace the red figure and the flip line.

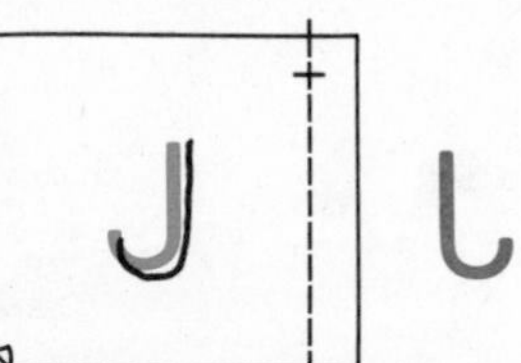

Flip the tracing face-down so that the flip line falls back on itself.

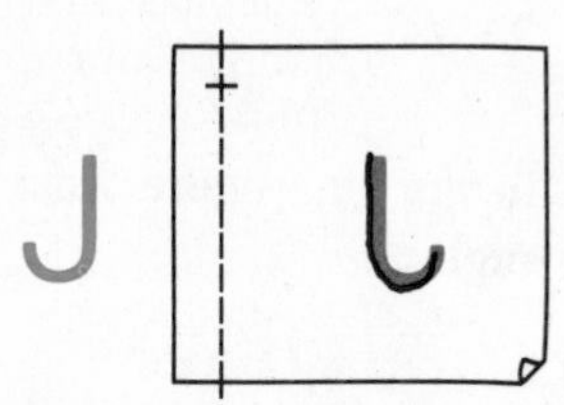

Each blue figure is a flip image of the red figure.

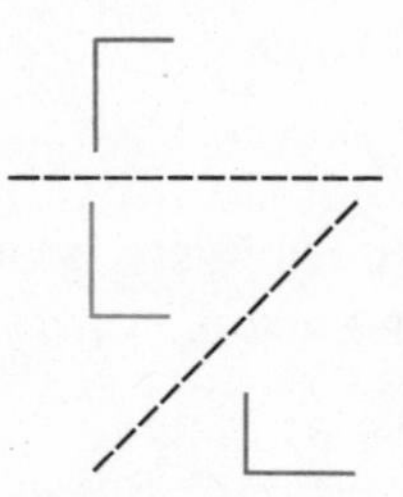

Turn Images

The blue figure is a **turn image** of the red figure (and vice versa). Trace the red figure and the turn center.

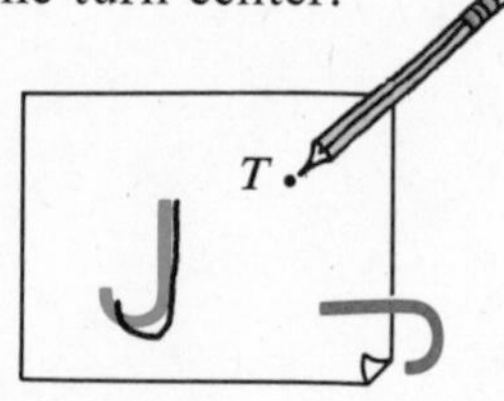

Hold your pencil at the turn center and turn the tracing about that point. The arrow shows the turn.

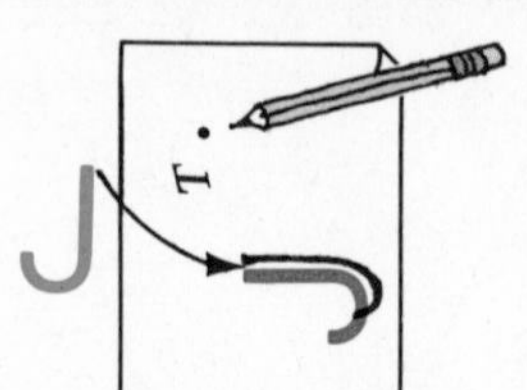

Each blue figure is a turn image of the red figure.

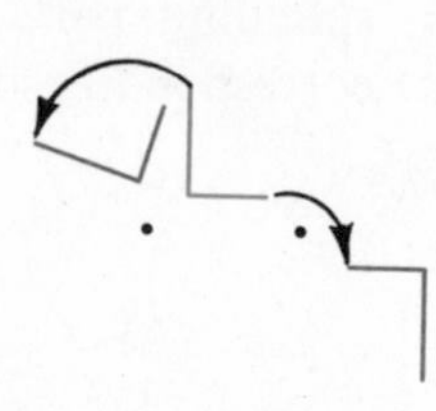

EXERCISES

In each exercise the blue figure is either a slide image, a flip image, or a turn image of the red figure. Tell which kind.

1.

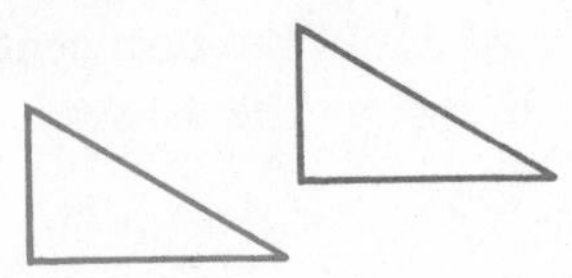

2.

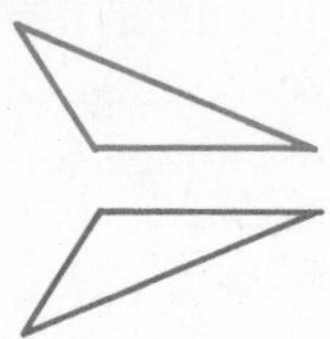

3.

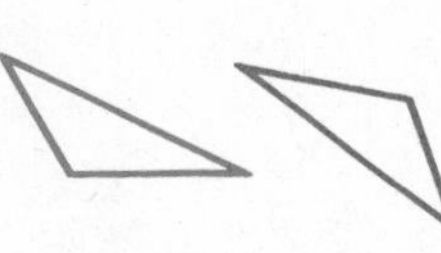

4.

5.

6.

7.

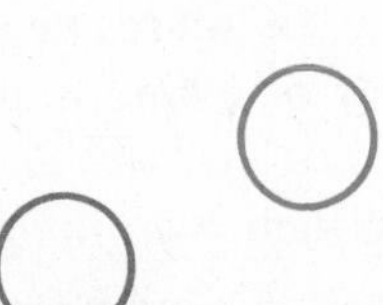

8.

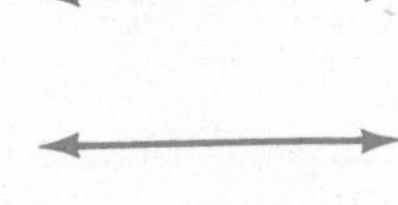

9.

10. Trace each pair of figures in exercises 1–9.

a. Draw an arrow to show the slide if they are slide images.

b. Draw the flip line if they are flip images.

c. Draw the turn center if they are turn images.

Is the red ray the flip image of the blue ray for a flip about the dashed line?

11.

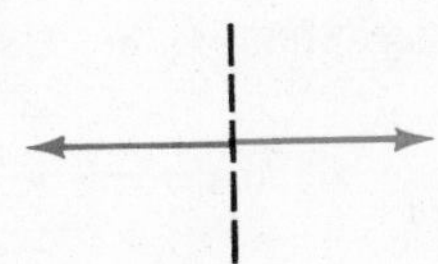

12.

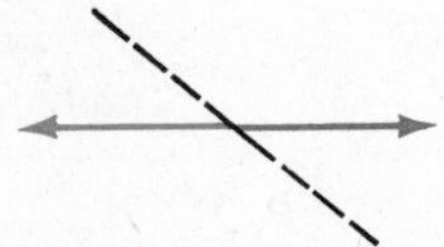

13.

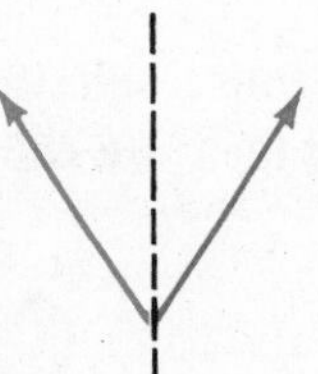

Is the red line a slide image of the blue line?

14.

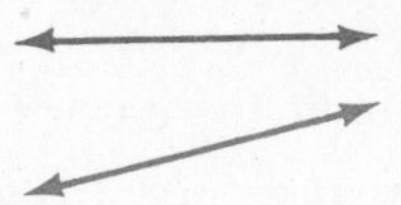

15.

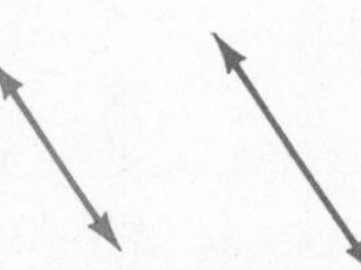

Supplementary Exercises, Set 29, page 382

Self-images

Some figures are their own images for a single motion. For example, the triangle below fits itself for a flip about the dashed line. The parallelogram is its own image for a half-turn about the turn center, and the line is its own image for the slide shown by the arrow.

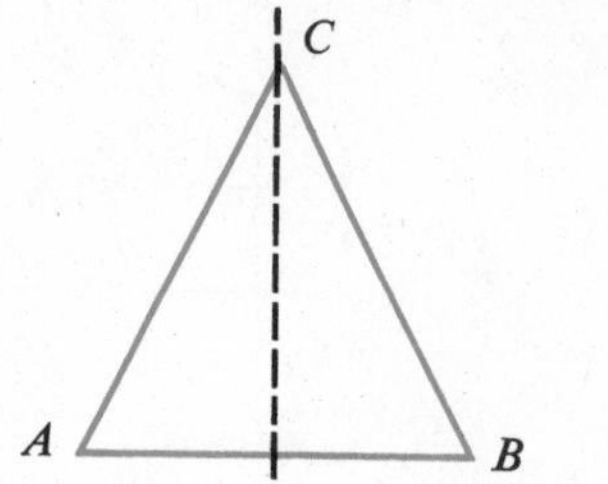

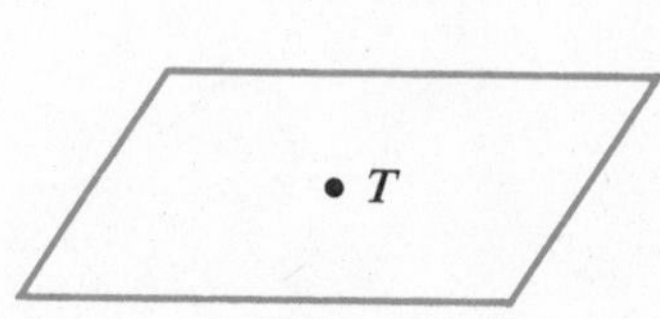

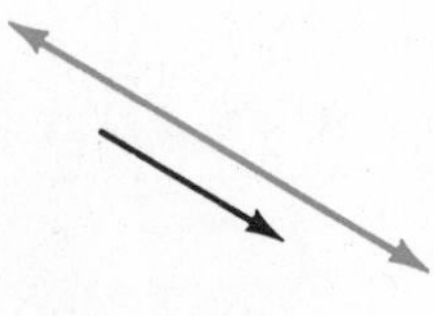

In the triangle, $\overline{AC}$ and $\overline{BC}$ are images of each other and are congruent. Tell what other facts you know about the figures because parts are images of each other. What properties of a line make it its own slide image?

Here are some special cases of figures being their own images.

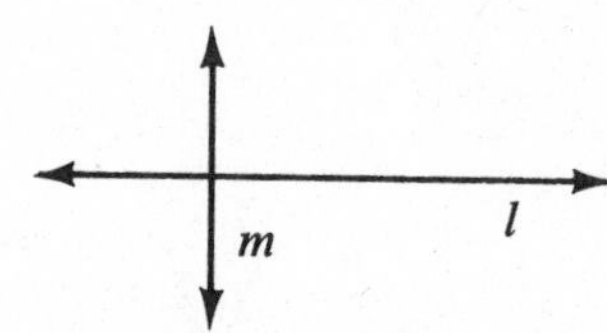

Line *l* is its own image for a flip about line *m*. This means that line *m* is **perpendicular** to line *l*. We write:

$m \perp l$ Line m is perpendicular to line l.

The four angles formed by perpendicular lines are called **right angles.**

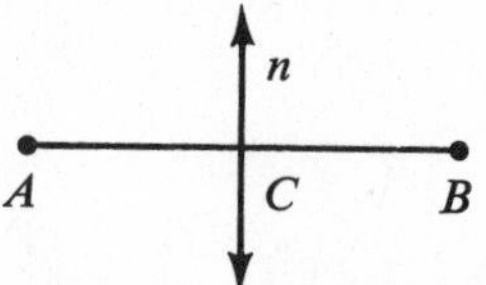

Segment *AB* is its own image for a flip about line *n*. This means that line *n* is the **perpendicular bisector** of $\overline{AB}$. *Bisect* means "cut in half." $\overline{AB}$ is bisected by line *n* because $\overline{AC} \cong \overline{CB}$. We say that *C* is the **midpoint** of *AB*.

Point B is the vertex of the angle.

Angle *ABC* is its own image for a flip about the dashed line. This means that $\angle ABD \cong \angle CBD$. We say that ray *BD* ($\overrightarrow{BD}$) **bisects** the angle. $\overrightarrow{BD}$ is called the **angle bisector.**

EXERCISES

Is the figure its own image for a single motion? If it is, trace the figure and draw the flip line(s), the turn center, or an arrow to show the slide. Careful! Some figures are self-images for more than one motion.

1

S

2.

3.

4.

J

5.

6.

7.

8.

G

9.

10.

11.

True or false?

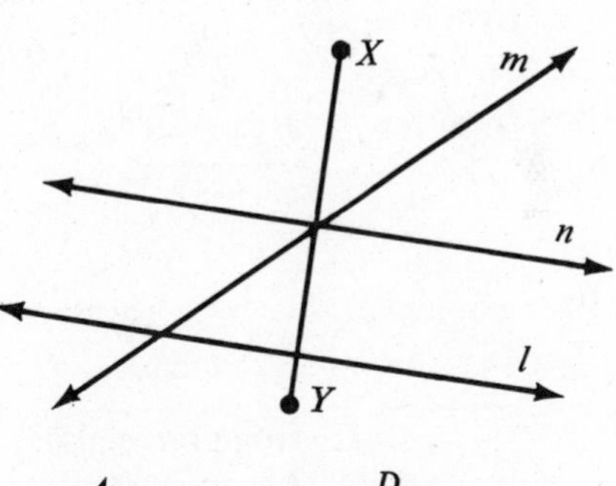

12. $m \perp \overline{XY}$.

13. $l \perp \overline{XY}$.

14. m bisects $\overline{XY}$.

15. n bisects $\overline{XY}$.

16. n is the perpendicular bisector of $\overline{XY}$.

17. l bisects $\overline{XY}$.

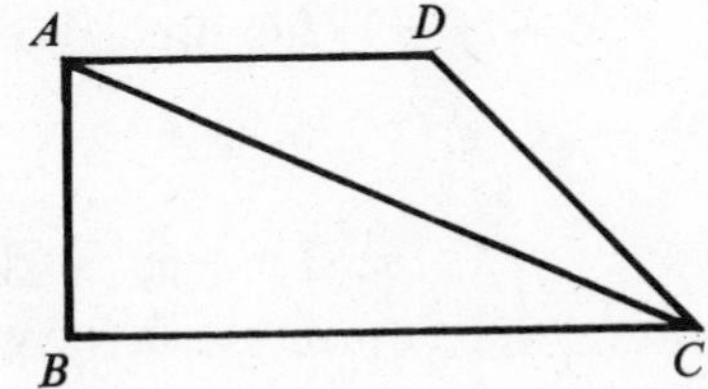

18. $\angle D$ is a right angle.

19. $\angle B$ is a right angle.

20. $\angle DAB$ is a right angle.

21. Ray CA bisects $\angle DCB$.

22. Find examples in your school of perpendicular lines, right angles, and bisectors.

Skill Maintenance, Set 35, page 406

Parallel lines

Two lines are parallel if one is a slide image of the other.

The arrow shows one slide that fits the red line to the blue line. Draw two parallel lines and show at least 5 slides that fit one to the other.

Notice that two parallel lines never meet. They are always the same distance apart.

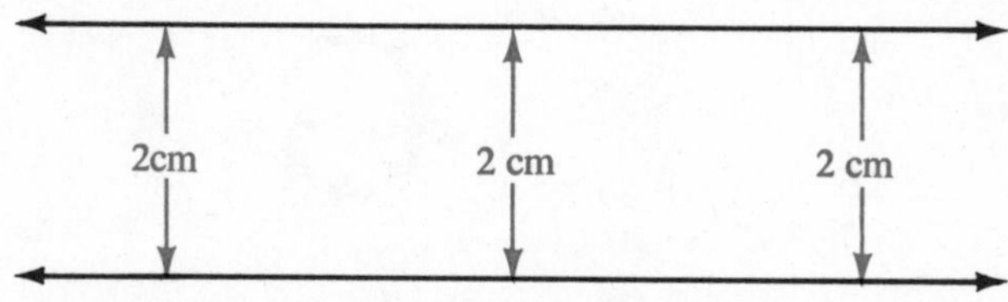

EXERCISES

The picture shows two parallel lines and a third line that crosses them (a *transversal*). Eight angles are pictured. They have been numbered to make them easy to write about. Point *B* is the midpoint of $\overline{AC}$.

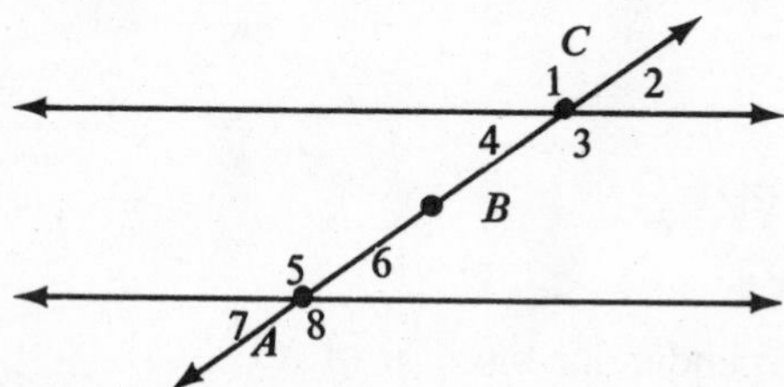

1. Imagine making a half-turn about point *B*. The whole figure fits itself. What is the image of:

   a. $\angle 4$? **b.** $\angle 3$? **c.** $\angle 1$? **d.** $\angle 2$?

2. Imagine a slide that fits the upper line to the lower line in such a way that *C* is the image of *A*. What is the image of:

   a. $\angle 4$? **b.** $\angle 3$? **c.** $\angle 2$? **d.** $\angle 1$?

Imagine making a half-turn about the turn center. Are the two segments images of each other? Are they congruent? Are they parallel?

3. **4.** **5.**

6. What must be true if two segments are images for a half-turn?
7. The blue line is the perpendicular bisector of $\overline{XY}$. Tell whether each of the labeled points is nearer to X, nearer to Y, or the same distance from X and Y.

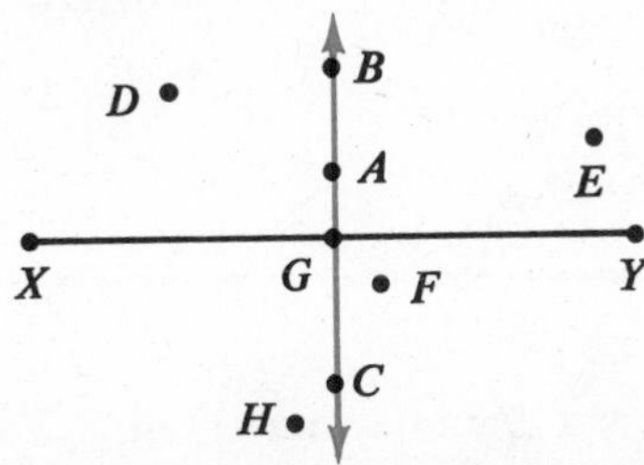

8. Look at your answers to exercise 7. Can you state a rule about all points that are the same distance from two given points?

This figure is its own image for a flip about the dashed line. Trace it and the flip line.

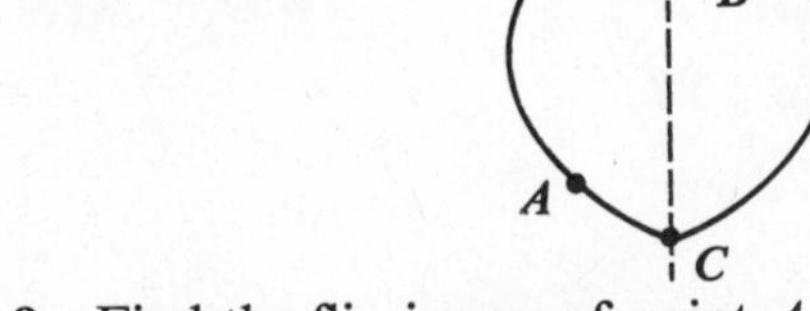

9. Find the flip image of point A.
10. Draw the segment that joins A with its image.
11. How is the flip line related to the segment of exercise 10?
12. Repeat exercises 9–11 with point B.
13. Pick a point of your own on the figure and repeat exercises 9–11.
14. Can you state a rule?
15. Repeat exercises 9–11 with point C.
16. Do you have to change your rule for exercise 15?

EXCURSION

An **acute angle** is smaller than a right angle.

An **obtuse angle** is larger than a right angle.

Draw segments to divide this triangular region into triangular regions that do *not* have any obtuse angles or right angles.

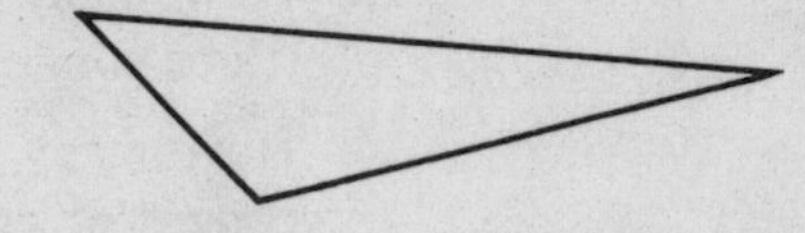

Skill Maintenance, Set 36, page 406

Line of symmetry

Notice that triangle ABC is its own image for a flip about the dashed line. We say that the dashed line is a **line of symmetry** of the triangle.

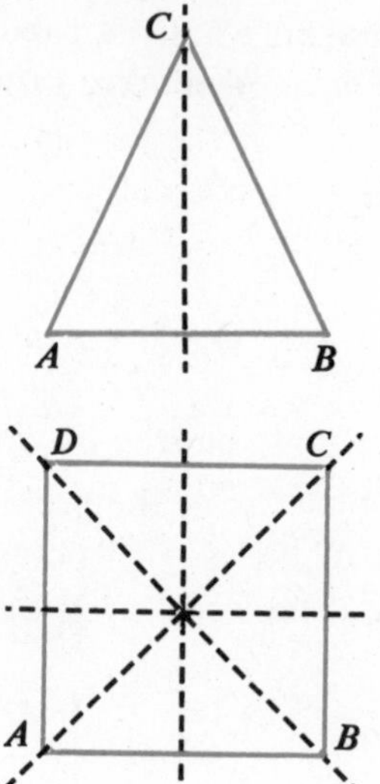

This square has four lines of symmetry. You may wish to trace the square and actually flip it about each of the lines to see that for every flip the square is its own image.

EXERCISES

The dashed line is a line of symmetry of $\triangle XYZ$.

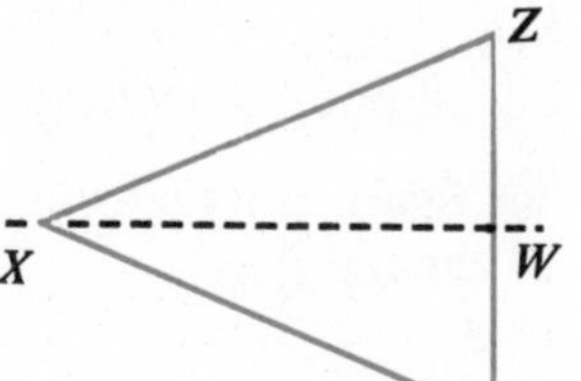

1. What is the flip image of point Z?
2. What is the flip image of point X?
3. What is the flip image of point W?
4. What is the flip image of $\overline{XY}$?
5. What segment is congruent to $\overline{XY}$?
6. What is the flip image of $\angle Y$?
7. What angle is congruent to $\angle Y$?
8. What is the flip image of $\overline{YW}$?
9. What segment is congruent to $\overline{YW}$?
10. Is W the midpoint of $\overline{YZ}$?
11. What is the image of $\angle ZWX$?
12. Is line XW the perpendicular bisector of $\overline{YZ}$?
13. Is ray XW the bisector of $\angle YXZ$?
14. $\triangle XYZ$ has 2 congruent sides. What is the name given to such a triangle?
15. How many lines of symmetry does an equilateral triangle (three congruent sides) have?
16. How many lines of symmetry does a scalene triangle (no congruent sides) have?

True or false?

17. If a line of symmetry of a polygon goes through a side of the polygon, it is the perpendicular bisector of that side.
18. If a line of symmetry of a polygon goes through the vertex of an angle of the polygon, it bisects the angle.

Each of the four dashed lines, *m*, *n*, *o*, and *p*, is a line of symmetry of the square. Answer each question.

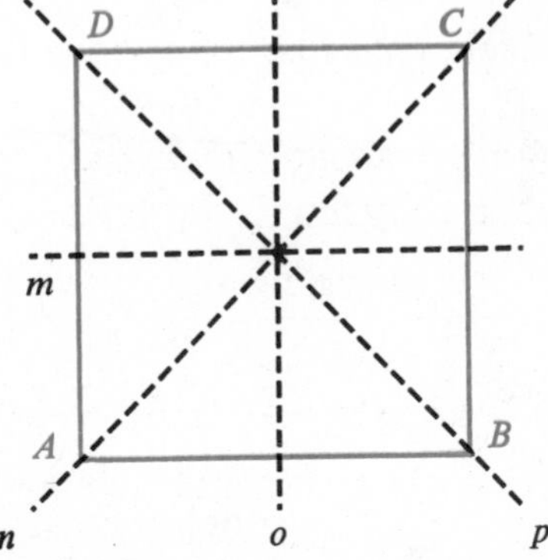

19. What is the image of $\overline{AD}$ for a flip about line o? For a flip about line n? For a flip about line p? For a flip about line m?
20. What can you say about the four sides?
21. What is the image of $\angle CBA$ for a flip about line o? Line n? Line m? Line p?
22. What can you say about the four angles?
23. For a square, two of the lines of symmetry pass through vertices and two of them pass through midpoints of sides. Draw a four-sided polygon with just one line of symmetry that goes through vertices.
24. Draw a four-sided polygon with:
    a. just one line of symmetry going through midpoints of sides.
    b. just two lines of symmetry going through vertices.
    c. just two lines of symmetry going through midpoints of sides.
25. What are the names of the figures in exercises 23 and 24?
26. Tell what you can about each of the figures in exercises 23 and 24.

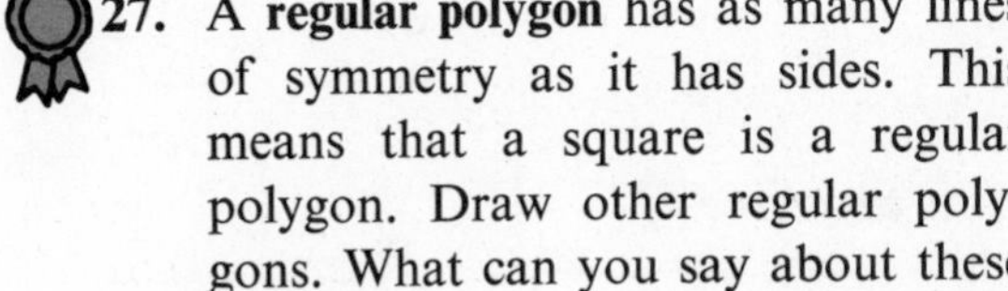

27. A **regular polygon** has as many lines of symmetry as it has sides. This means that a square is a regular polygon. Draw other regular polygons. What can you say about these figures?

EXCURSION

1. Multiply your age by 10.
2. Multiply 9 by any 1-digit whole number.
3. Subtract the product in step 2 from the product in step 1.
4. If your answer in step 3 has two digits, add them. This will be your age.
   Example. 10×11 (age) $= 110$
   $9 \times 6 = 54$
   $110 - 54 = 56$
   The sum of 5 and 6 is 11 (age).
5. If your answer in step 3 has 3 digits, your age is the sum of the first two digits and the third.
   Example. 10×17 (age) $= 170$
   $9 \times 3 = 27$
   $170 - 27 = 143$
   The sum of 14 and 3 is 17 (age).
   Repeat with other numbers.

Supplementary Exercises, Set 30, page 382

Point of symmetry

Some figures are self-images for half-turns about a point. That point is called a **point of symmetry** of the figure. Point T is a point of symmetry for this parallelogram.

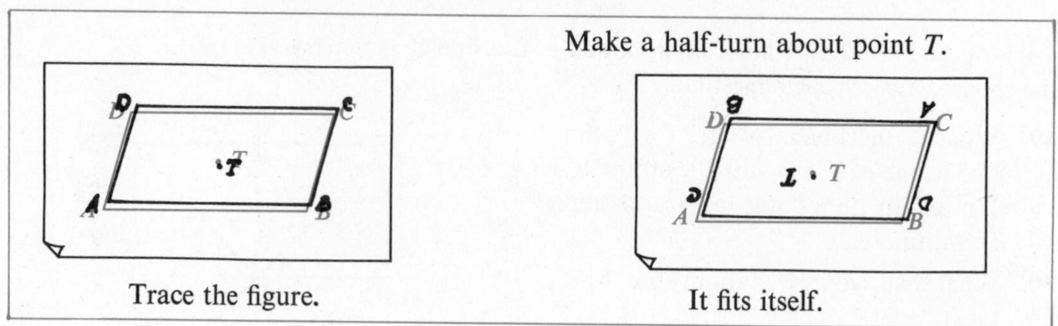

$\overline{AB}$ and $\overline{CD}$ are half-turn images of each other. This means that they are parallel and congruent. $\overline{AD}$ and $\overline{BC}$ are also parallel and congruent, and $\angle A \cong \angle C$ and $\angle B \cong \angle D$.

This triangle does not have a point of symmetry. It is its own image for a $\frac{1}{3}$-turn and a $\frac{2}{3}$-turn but not for a half-turn.

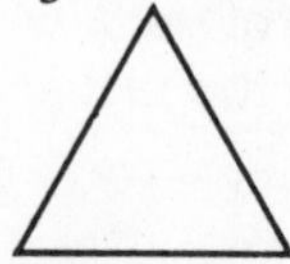

EXERCISES

Is the black point a point of symmetry of the figure?

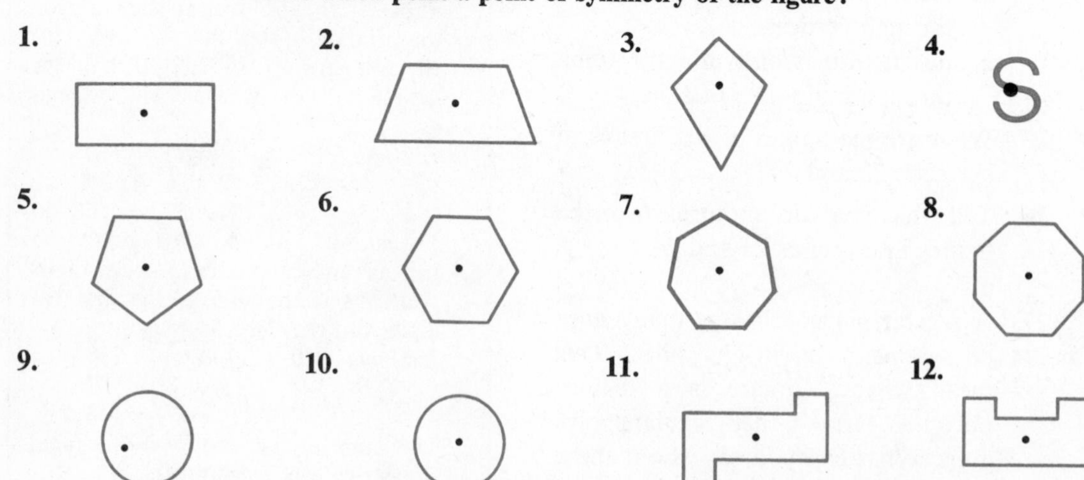

13. Look at exercises 5–8. Can a polygon with an odd number of sides have a point of symmetry? Why or why not?

14. Can a polygon with an even number of sides have a point of symmetry?

15. Draw a 6-sided polygon that does not have a point of symmetry.

16. Nancy thinks that point T is the point of symmetry of this polygon. Prove that she is wrong.

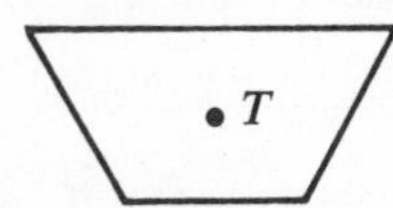

In each exercise half the figure is covered. In some of the figures there is a dashed line, which is a line of symmetry of the figure. In others there is a point *T*, which is a point of symmetry. Trace and complete each figure.

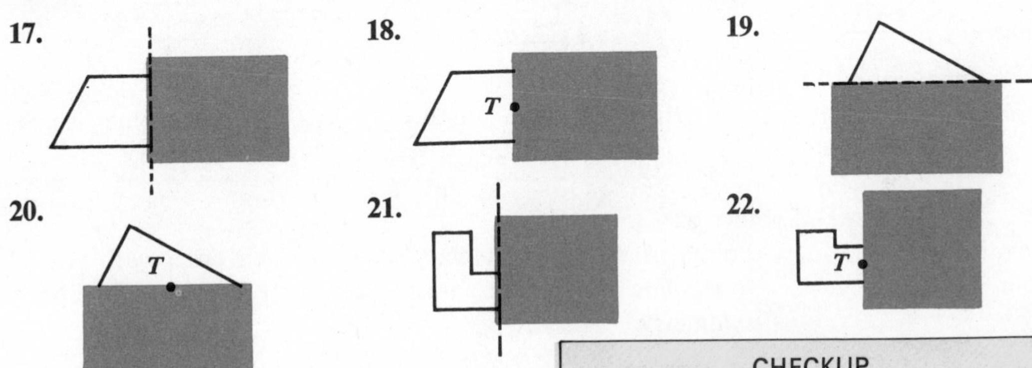

Trace this figure and its point of symmetry.

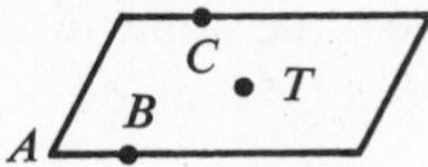

23. Locate the turn image of A.

24. Draw the segment that joins A with its turn image.

25. How is the point of symmetry related to the segment you drew for exercise 24?

26. Repeat exercises 23–25 for point B. For point C.

27. Can you state a rule?

28. Pick any other point of the figure and repeat exercises 23–25.

29. Does your rule still work?

CHECKUP

for pages 138–142

1. **Which figure is congruent to $\triangle ABC$?**

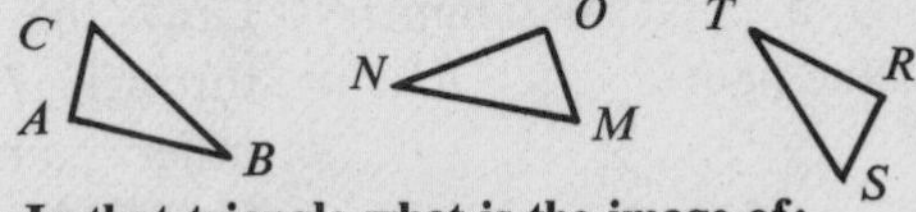

In that triangle what is the image of:

2. $\overline{AB}$?

3. $\angle A$?

4. Which figure is a slide image of the black figure?

5. Which line is parallel to line l?

6. Which line is perpendicular to line l?

Answers on page 426.

Supplementary Exercises, Set 31, page 382

Symmetry

Exercises 9–16 on page 145 gives us a different way of testing to see whether a line is a line of symmetry of a figure. Here is the test.

Is the blue line a line of symmetry of the figure?  Pick any point of the figure not on the blue line. Call it A.	Draw the segment from A that is perpendicular to the blue line and ends at another point of the figure. Call that point B.  Does the blue line bisect segment AB? Yes.	Does the same thing happen for all points of the figure (except those points that are *on* the blue line)? 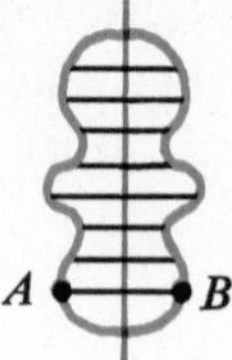 Yes. Then the blue line *is* a line of symmetry.

Another way to say this:

Points of the figure directly opposite each other with respect to the line of symmetry are the same distance from the line of symmetry.

Exercises 23–29 on page 149 suggest a similar test for a point of symmetry. Here is the test.

Is T a point of symmetry of the figure? 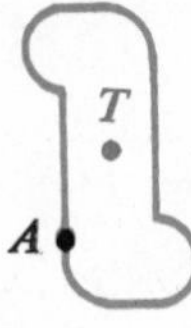 Pick any point of the figure. Call it A.	Draw the segment from A through T ending at another point of the figure. Call that point B. 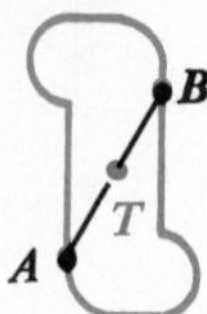 Is T the midpoint of segment AB? Yes.	Does the same thing happen for all points of the figure? 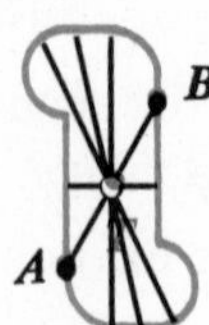 Yes. So T *is* a point of symmetry.

This means:

Points of the figure directly opposite each other with respect to the point of symmetry are the same distance from the point of symmetry.

EXERCISES

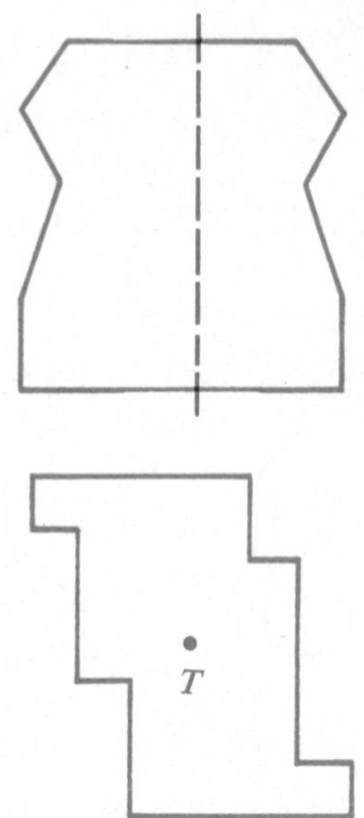

1. The blue line is not a line of symmetry of the red figure. Use the method of testing given on page 150 to tell why not.

2. Point T is not a point of symmetry of the red figure. Use the method of testing given on page 150 to tell why not.

3. Draw a 4-sided figure that has a line of symmetry but does not have a point of symmetry.

4. Draw a 4-sided figure that has a point of symmetry but does not have a line of symmetry.

5. Draw a 6-sided figure that does not have a line of symmetry but does have a point of symmetry.

6. Draw a 6-sided figure that has a line of symmetry but does not have a point of symmetry.

EXCURSION

Notice that there are two data lines in this computer program. When the computer has read the last piece of data from the first line, it will go on to the second line. The computer will use the first piece of data for A, the second for B, the third for C, and then continue with the program. Then it will return to line 10 and use the next three pieces of data for A, B, and C. When all data have been used, the computer will stop. Follow this program.

```
10  READ A,B,C
20  LET D = (A + B)*C
30  IF D < 50 THEN 60
40  LET E = D + 5.9
50  PRINT E
55  GØ TØ 10
60  PRINT D
65  GØ TØ 10
70  DATA 5.6, 3.9, 2.7, 4.8,
      9.7, 10.4, 12.6
80  DATA 15.9, 20.5
90  END
```

Supplementary Exercises, Set 32, page 382

KEEPING SKILLS SHARP

Add.

1. $\begin{array}{r} 7.820 \\ 4.387 \\ +.666 \\ \hline \end{array}$
2. $\begin{array}{r} .4395 \\ .0177 \\ +.985 \\ \hline \end{array}$
3. $\begin{array}{r} 21.99 \\ 3.46 \\ +.017 \\ \hline \end{array}$
4. $4.36 + .08 + 23$
5. $.0038 + .217 + 5.87$

Subtract.

6. $\begin{array}{r} 5.63 \\ -1.82 \\ \hline \end{array}$
7. $\begin{array}{r} .734 \\ -.591 \\ \hline \end{array}$
8. $\begin{array}{r} 4.3 \\ -2.69 \\ \hline \end{array}$
9. $\begin{array}{r} 21.04 \\ -7.48 \\ \hline \end{array}$
10. $\begin{array}{r} 3.001 \\ -.465 \\ \hline \end{array}$

Multiply.

11. $\begin{array}{r} 8.49 \\ \times 7 \\ \hline \end{array}$
12. $\begin{array}{r} 73.5 \\ \times 36 \\ \hline \end{array}$
13. $\begin{array}{r} 60.8 \\ \times 9.3 \\ \hline \end{array}$
14. $\begin{array}{r} 46.7 \\ \times .148 \\ \hline \end{array}$
15. $\begin{array}{r} .376 \\ \times .09 \\ \hline \end{array}$

Divide. Round each quotient so that it has at most 3 digits.

16. $3.7\overline{)5.92}$
17. $.8\overline{)73}$
18. $.12\overline{)117.4}$
19. $3.04\overline{)67.2}$
20. $.9\overline{)10}$

Add or subtract.

21. $\frac{5}{8} + \frac{3}{4}$
22. $\frac{7}{9} + \frac{2}{3}$
23. $3\frac{3}{5} + \frac{5}{6}$
24. $2\frac{3}{8} + 1\frac{3}{10}$
25. $\frac{5}{6} - \frac{1}{4}$
26. $\frac{5}{9} - \frac{1}{2}$
27. $2\frac{2}{5} - \frac{1}{3}$
28. $3\frac{1}{8} - 1\frac{5}{6}$

Multiply or divide.

29. $\frac{3}{8} \times \frac{1}{4}$
30. $\frac{2}{3} \times \frac{3}{4}$
31. $1\frac{3}{8} \times \frac{2}{3}$
32. $2\frac{2}{3} \times \frac{9}{10}$
33. $\frac{5}{8} \div \frac{3}{8}$
34. $\frac{3}{2} \div \frac{2}{3}$
35. $7\frac{3}{4} \div 1\frac{1}{3}$
36. $8 \div 2\frac{1}{8}$

Solve.

37. $5(x + 10) = 80$
38. $5x + 10 = 80$
39. $\frac{e + 8}{2} = 9$
40. $\frac{a}{2} + 8 = 9$
41. $\frac{5}{8} = \frac{x}{9}$
42. $\frac{12}{15} = \frac{6}{g}$
43. $\frac{53}{100} = \frac{c}{827}$
44. $\frac{7}{100} = \frac{h}{300}$

Follow the flow chart.

45.

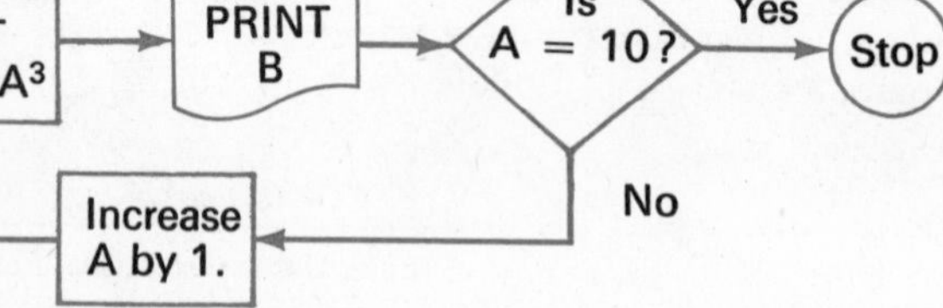

Problem solving

1. Solve this problem to review the problem-solving skills we discussed on pages 54–57.

What is the sum of the first 50 odd numbers?

a. Collect data by thinking of similar problems with fewer numbers.

Sum of first 5 odd numbers:
$1 + 3 + 5 + 7 + 9 = ?$

Sum of first 2 odd numbers:
$1 + 3 = ?$

Sum of first 4 odd numbers:
$1 + 3 + 5 + 7 = ?$

b. Organize the data.

$1 + 3 = ?$ $1 + 3 + 5 = ?$ $1 + 3 + 5 + 7 = ?$

c. Analyze the data.

I think I see a pattern.

d. State a hypothesis (a possible rule).

The sum of the first ***n*** odd numbers is . . . .

e. Test your hypothesis.

Does the rule work for the sum of the first 8 odd numbers?

f. Revise it if necessary.

g. Use your rule to answer the question.

2. Solve this problem.

What is the sum of the first 50 whole numbers?

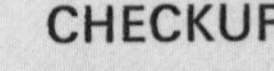

CHECKUP

for pages 146–149

The blue line is a line of symmetry. Point *T* is a point of symmetry. Sketch the whole figure.

1.

2.

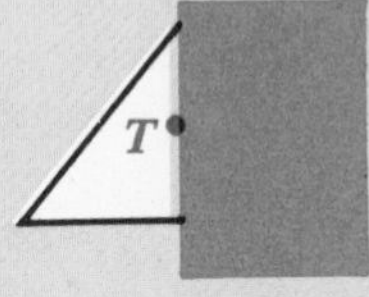

3.

The blue line is a line of symmetry and point *T* is a point of symmetry.

Suppose that segment *AH* is 5 cm long, segment *RT* is 4 cm long, and segment *TG* is 7 cm long.

How long are these segments?

4. $\overline{TY}$

5. $\overline{HC}$

6. $\overline{AG}$

7. $\overline{RY}$

Answers on page 426.

Skill Maintenance, Set 37, page 407

Planes of symmetry

The plane shown is a **plane of symmetry** of the 3-dimensional figure.

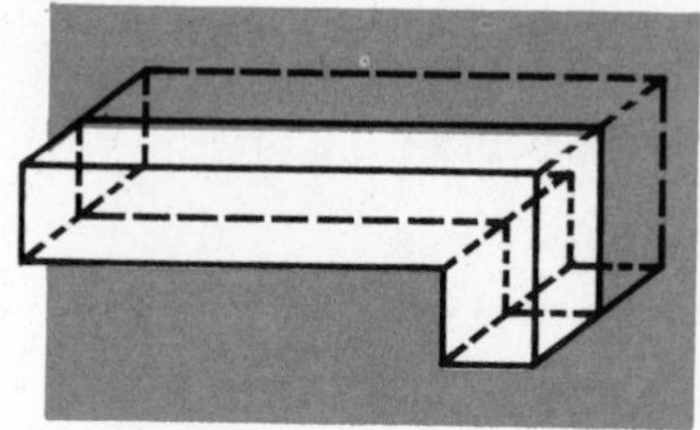

The plane separates the figure into two parts.

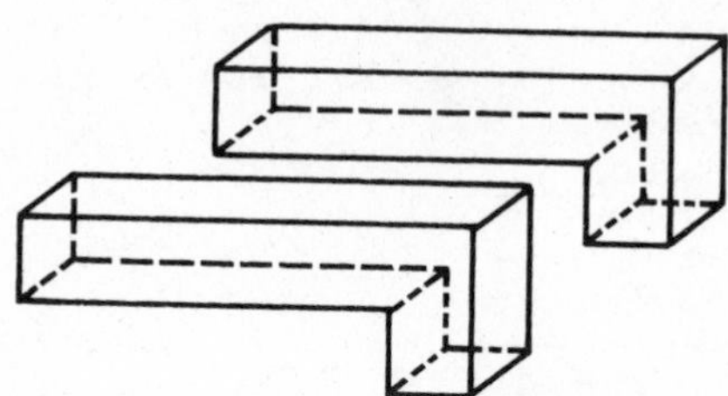

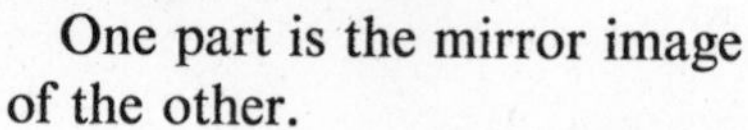

One part is the mirror image of the other.

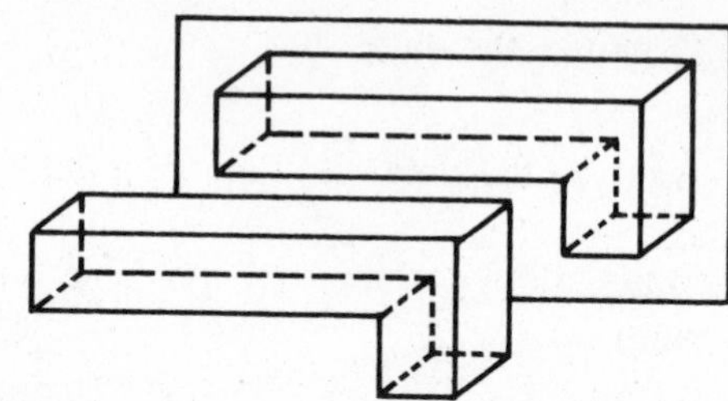

Here is another way of testing to see whether a plane is a plane of symmetry of a figure.

Is the plane a plane of symmetry of the figure?

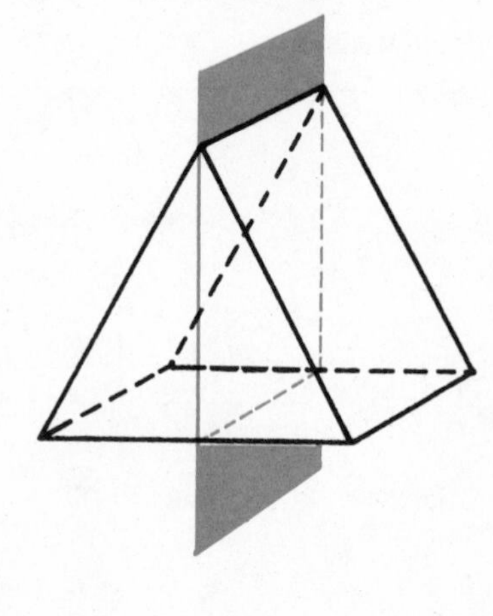

Think about segments that join two points of the figure *and* are perpendicular to the plane.

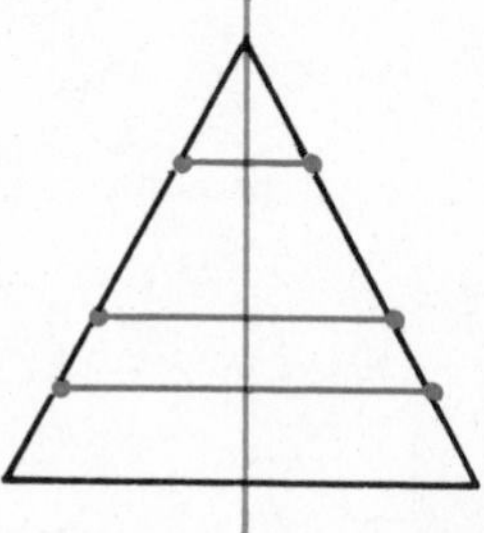

Does the plane bisect all of them? Yes! Then the plane is a plane of symmetry.

If points opposite each other (with respect to the plane) are the same distance from the plane, then the plane is a plane of symmetry.

This picture shows all three planes of symmetry of a **rectangular solid.**

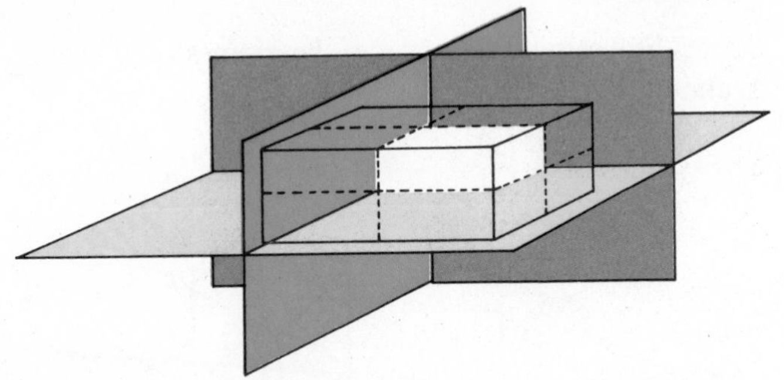

EXERCISES

How many planes of symmetry?

1. 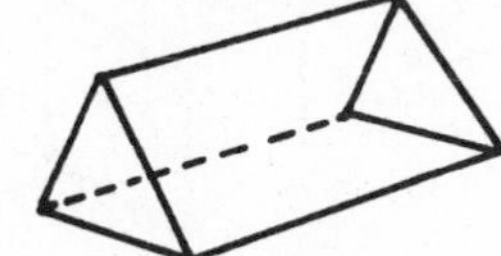

2. 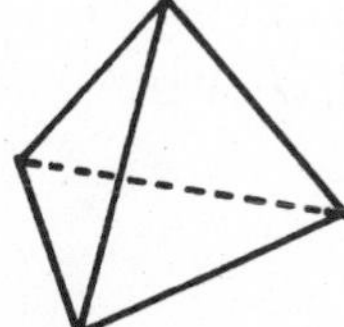

3. 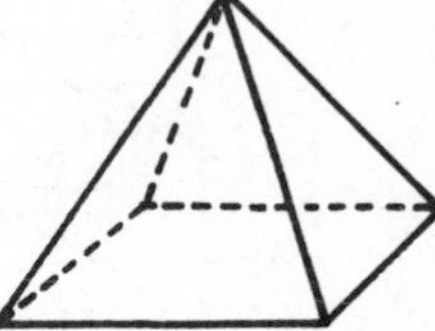

4. 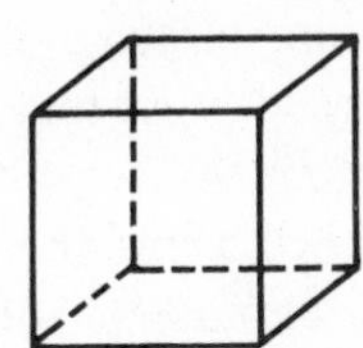

5. 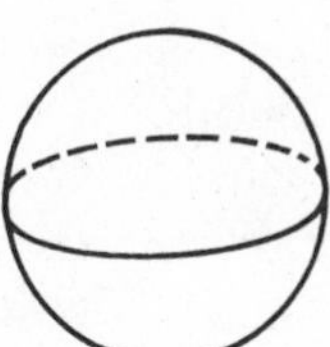

6. 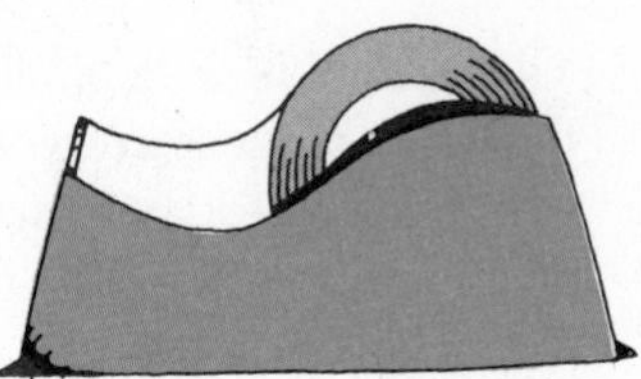

Project

1. Find physical objects that have planes of symmetry.

2. Tape cardboard to the objects to show planes of symmetry.

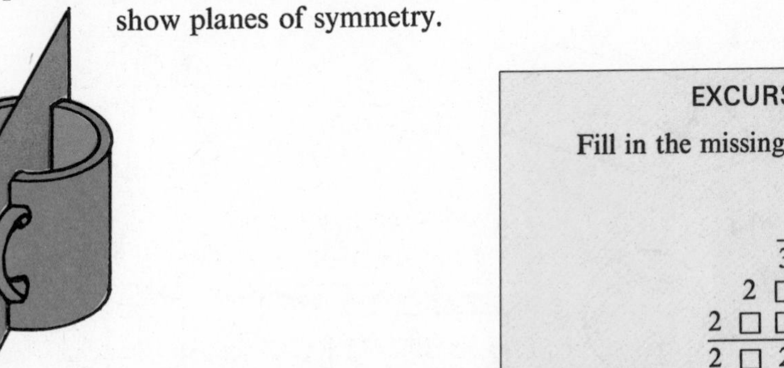

EXCURSION

Fill in the missing digits.

```
         3 □ □ 6
       × □ 8 □
       ---------
       3 □ □ 0 4
     2 □ 6 □ 8 0
   2 □ □ 9 2 0 0
   -------------
   2 □ 2 □ □ 8 4
```

Skill Maintenance, Set 38, page 407

Lines and points of symmetry

Three-dimensional figures may have lines of symmetry or points of symmetry.

The blue line is a line of symmetry.

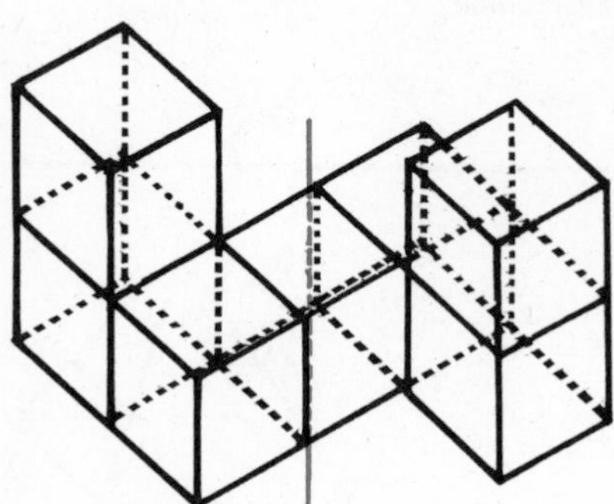

The blue line is a line of symmetry of the figure because every segment that joins two points of the figure *and* is perpendicular to the blue line is bisected by the blue line. This means that points of the figure that are opposite each other with respect to the line of symmetry are the same distance from the line of symmetry.

The blue point is a point of symmetry.

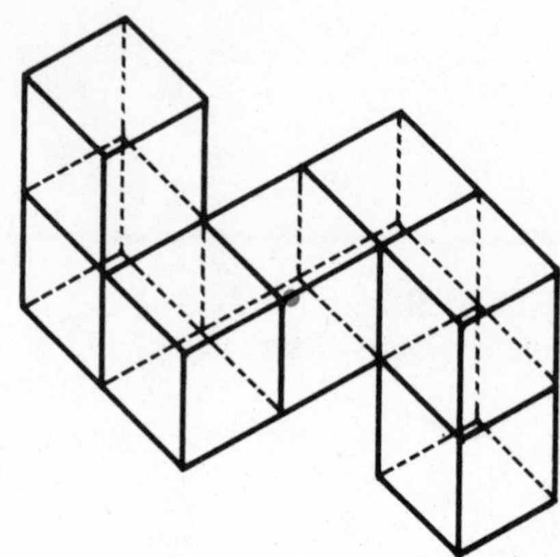

The blue point is a point of symmetry of the figure because every segment that joins two points of the figure *and* passes through the blue point is bisected by the blue point. This means that points of the figure that are opposite each other with respect to the point of symmetry are the same distance from the point of symmetry.

EXERCISES

Tell how many planes of symmetry, how many lines of symmetry, and how many points of symmetry.

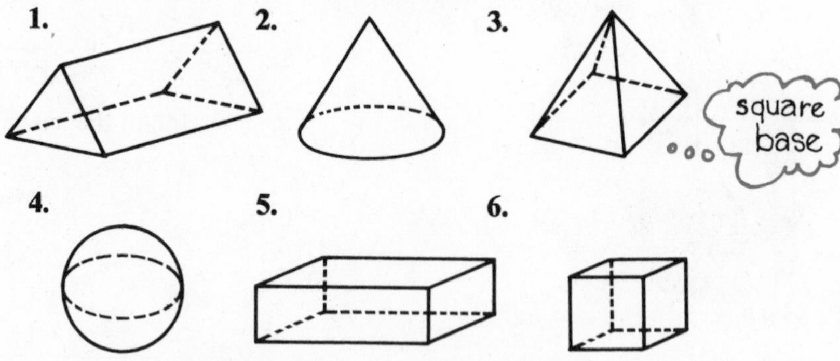

This figure is a rectangular solid. It has 3 planes of symmetry.

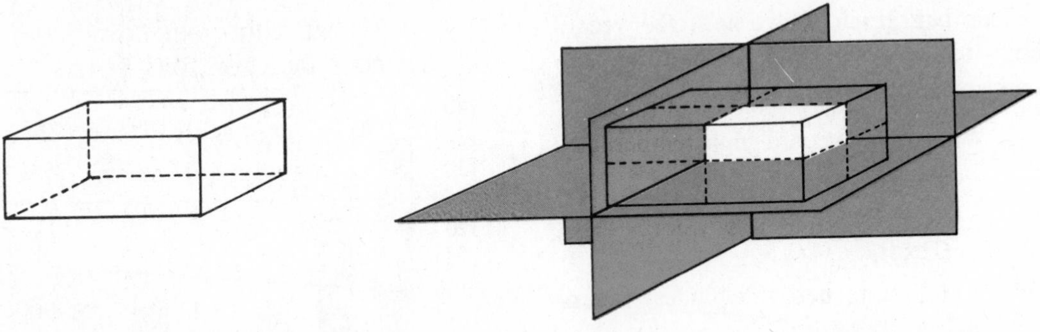

7. How many lines of symmetry does the figure have?
8. How are the lines of symmetry related to the planes of symmetry?
9. How many points of symmetry does the figure have?
10. How are the points of symmetry related to the planes and lines of symmetry?
11. Look at the figures in exercises 1–4 and 6. How are the points, lines, and planes of symmetry related?
12. Try to make a 3-dimensional figure that has a plane of symmetry but no lines or points of symmetry.
13. Try to make a 3-dimensional figure that has a line of symmetry but no planes or points of symmetry.
14. Try to make a 3-dimensional figure that has a point of symmetry but no planes or lines of symmetry.
15. Draw a 3-dimensional figure with no symmetry.

Collect objects and pictures of objects with planes, lines, and points of symmetry.

EXCURSION

Make a row of 7 squares and put 3 pennies at one end and 3 nickels at the other end, as shown.

Now try to move the coins to the opposite ends of the row of squares.

The rules are:

1. One coin is moved at a time.
2. You may move a coin to an empty square next to the coin.
3. You may move a coin by jumping over 1 coin onto an empty square.
4. Move pennies only to the right and nickels only to the left.

Skill Maintenance, Set 39, page 407

Graphs

This bar graph shows both the record high temperatures and the record low temperatures for some states.

1. What is the record high temperature for Michigan?
2. What is the record low temperature for Texas?
3. Which state had the highest record high temperature?
4. Which state had the lowest record low temperature?
5. Which state had the lowest record high?
6. Which state had the highest record low?
7. Which state had the greatest difference between the record high and the record low?

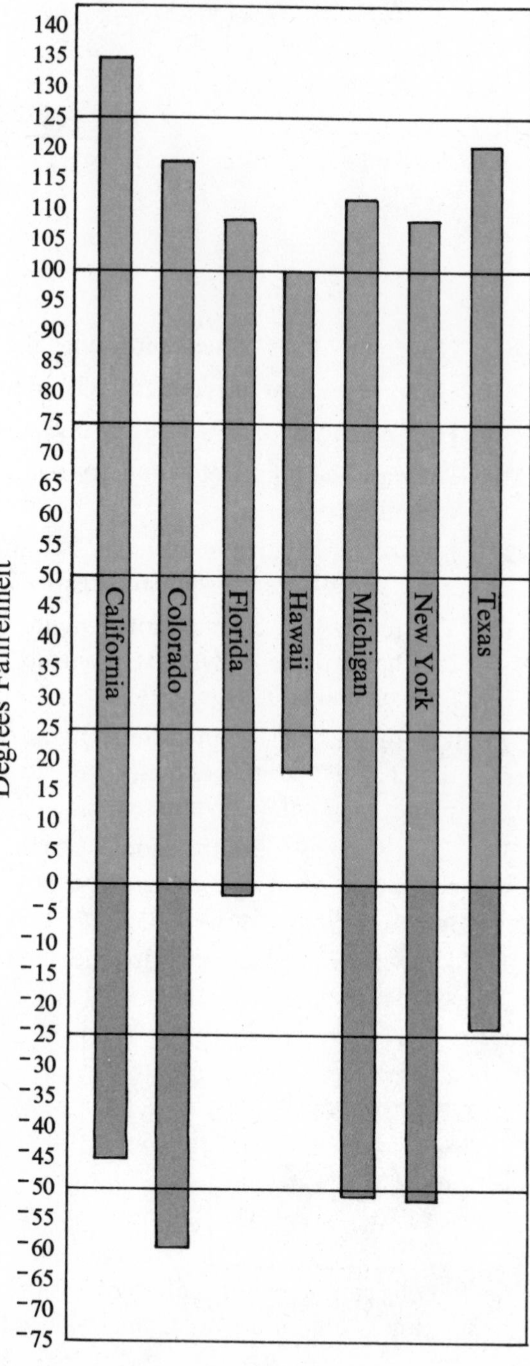

8. Here are record temperature data for some other states. Make a similar bar graph.

State	*High*	*Low*
Alaska	100°	−76°
Georgia	112°	−17°
Illinois	117°	−35°
Minnesota	114°	−59°
North Carolina	109°	−26°

9. Find some other data that can be graphed in the same manner. Make a graph.

CHAPTER CHECKUP

Are the two figures congruent? [*page 138*]

1. 

2. 

3. 

Look at the figures. What is the image of each of the following parts? [*page 138*]

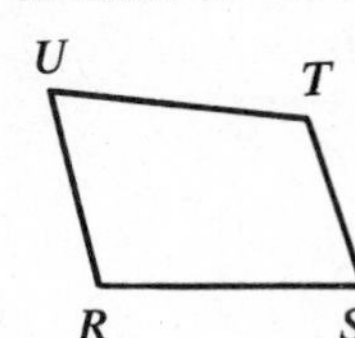

4. $\overline{AB}$ **5.** $\angle T$ **6.** $\overline{RU}$ **7.** $\angle C$ **8.** $\overline{AC}$

The blue figure is a single-motion image of the red figure. Tell whether the motion is a slide, a flip, or a turn. [*page 140*]

9. 

10. 

11. 

This figure is its own image for a flip about the dashed line. What is the image of each of these parts? [*page 146*]

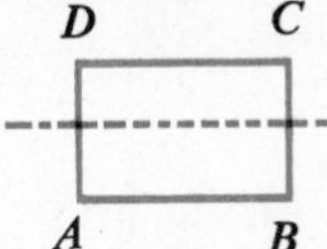

12. $\overline{AB}$ **13.** $\angle D$

14. $\angle C$ **15.** $\overline{AD}$

This figure is its own image for a half-turn about point *T*. What is the image of each of these parts? [*page 148*]

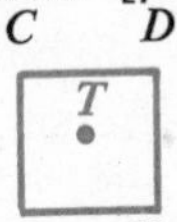

16. $\overline{AB}$ **17.** $\angle D$

18. $\angle C$ **19.** $\overline{AD}$

How many lines of symmetry for each figure? How many points of symmetry? [*page 150*]

20. 

21. 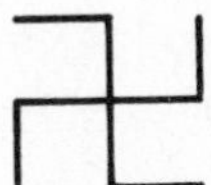

22. 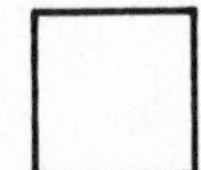

23. 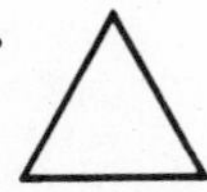

24. The blue line is a line of symmetry of the figure. Sketch the whole figure.

25. The point *T* is a point of symmetry of the figure. Sketch the whole figure.

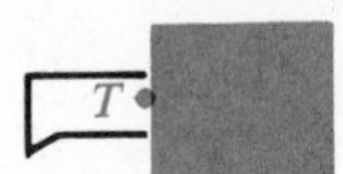

26. How many planes of symmetry? [*page 154*]

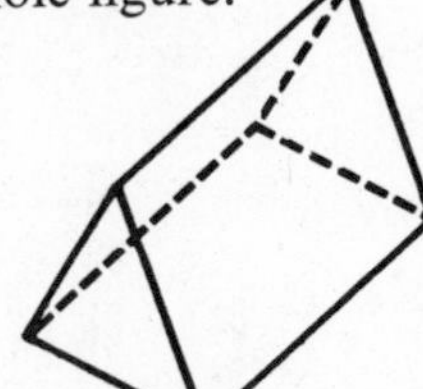

MAJOR CHECKUP

Solve. [*pages 16–19*]

1. $2y + 1 = 9$ **2.** $2x - 1 = 9$ **3.** $4a + 6 = 6$ **4.** $4b - 6 = 6$

5. $\frac{d}{5} = 0$ **6.** $\frac{e - 1}{5} = 0$ **7.** $\frac{2F}{3} = 0$ **8.** $\frac{2g - 6}{3} = 0$

Multiple choice.
Which number is nearest to the number given in red? [*pages 40–41*]

9. 17 **a.** .204 **b.** 2.04 **c.** 20.4 **d.** 204

10. 102 **a.** 1.06 **b.** 10.6 **c.** 106 **d.** 1060

11. 205 **a.** 1.962 **b.** 19.62 **c.** 196.2 **d.** 1962

12. .05 **a.** .0041 **b.** .041 **c.** .41 **d.** 4.1

13. Follow the flow chart. [*pages 46–49*]

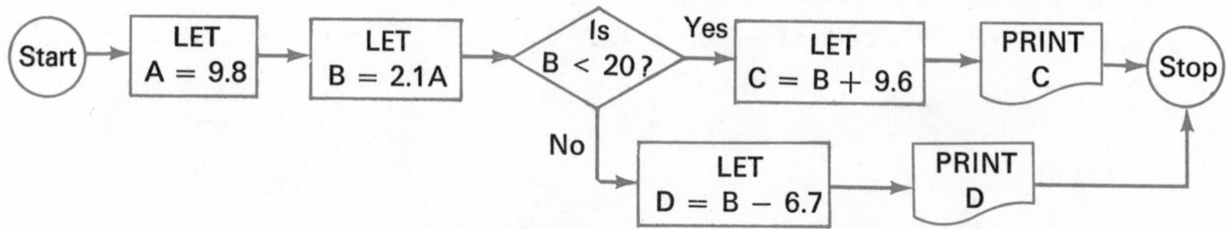

Write a flow chart for this problem. [*pages 50–53*]

14. Clair worked 15.5 hours at $2.36 per hour; $7.39 was taken out of her earnings for social security and withholding tax. How much money did she receive?

Copy the quotient digits and place the decimal point in the proper place. [*pages 82–87, 90–91*]

15. $6.14 \div 2 = 307$ **16.** $6.14 \div .2 = 307$

17. $6.14 \div 20 = 307$ **18.** $6.14 \div .02 = 307$

Complete. [*pages 42, 78, 90, 114, 118–123*]

19. **a.** $.4 + .02$ **b.** $.4 - .02$ **c.** $.4 \times .02$ **d.** $.4 \div .02$

20. **a.** $3 + .6$ **b.** $3 - .6$ **c.** $3 \times .6$ **d.** $3 \div .6$

21. **a.** $1\frac{3}{5} + \frac{2}{5}$ **b.** $1\frac{3}{5} - \frac{2}{5}$ **c.** $1\frac{3}{5} \times \frac{2}{5}$ **d.** $1\frac{3}{5} \div \frac{2}{5}$

22. **a.** $2 + \frac{1}{3}$ **b.** $2 - \frac{1}{3}$ **c.** $2 \times \frac{1}{3}$ **d.** $2 \div \frac{1}{3}$

City geometry

Each grid represents streets in a city and shows where two houses are located. For each grid, use graph paper to mark all the points that are the same number of blocks from the two houses.

I. *A* *B*

II. *F* *E*

III. *D* *C*

IV. *L* *K*

V. *G* *H*

Can you locate the point that is the same number of blocks from the three houses *X*, *Y*, and *Z*?

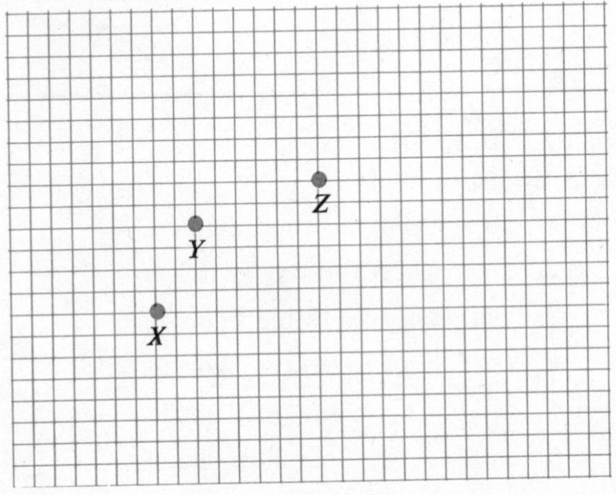

6 Ratios, Proportions, and Percent

Ratios

A ratio compares two numbers. The ratio of the number of straws to the number of sodas is 6 to 3. Here are three ways to express the ratio.

6 to 3 6:3

$\frac{6}{3}$

From the picture above we see that there are 2 straws for 1 soda, 4 straws for 2 sodas, and 6 straws for 3 sodas. The picture suggests these equivalent ratios:

$$\frac{2}{1} = \frac{4}{2} = \frac{6}{3}$$

You can find equivalent ratios by thinking about equivalent fractions. What are some other ratios that are equivalent to the ratios above? Remember that order is important when working with ratios. For example, the ratio of sodas to straws is:

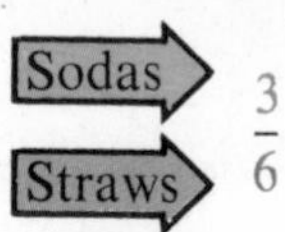

$\frac{3}{6}$

The ratio of straws to sodas is:

$\frac{6}{3}$

EXERCISES

Give the ratio of:

1. large figures to small figures.
2. green figures to red figures.
3. yellow figures to red figures.
4. red figures to yellow figures.
5. red circles to squares.
6. small figures to yellow squares.

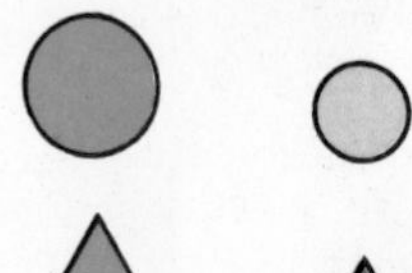

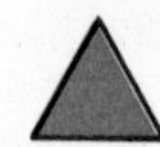

Solve these ratio equations. (***Hint:*** **Think about equivalent fractions.)**

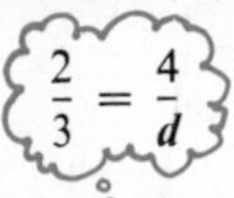

$\frac{3}{4} = \frac{c}{8}$

7. $2:3 = 4:d$
8. $1:2 = 3:d$
9. $3:4 = c:8$
10. $5:9 = c:27$
11. $3:b = 15:20$
12. $3:b = 12:28$
13. $a:9 = 6:18$
14. $a:16 = 5:4$
15. $a:3 = 10:30$
16. $12:b = 24:22$
17. $7:9 = c:36$
18. $3:1 = 300:d$

Give each ratio as a fraction in lowest terms.

19. 9:6
20. $\frac{8}{6}$
21. 21 to 14
22. $\frac{14}{21}$
23. 36 to 24
24. 18 inches to 12 inches
25. 12 ounces to 20 ounces
26. 12 hours to 16 hours
27. 32 kilograms to 18 kilograms
28. 24 minutes to 18 minutes
29. 14 quarts to 8 quarts

Solve.

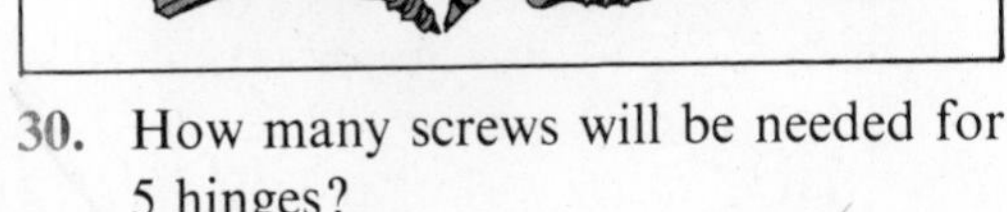

30. How many screws will be needed for 5 hinges?
31. What would they pay for 18 bottles?

32. To get gray paint, Ms. Adams mixed 3 quarts of white paint with 1 quart of black paint. How much of each color would she need to mix 3 gallons?

1. Measure your height to the nearest centimeter.
2. Measure the distance that you can long-jump to the nearest centimeter.
3. What is your height-to-long-jump ratio? Divide and express the ratio as a decimal and round to the nearest tenth.
4. Show your ratio and those of your classmates on a bar graph.

EXCURSION

Two cubes and one screw weigh as much as eight nails. One cube weighs as much as one screw and one nail. How many nails weigh as much as one cube?

Skill Maintenance, Set 40, page 408

Proportions

An equation stating that two ratios are equal is called a **proportion**. Here are some examples.

Each proportion has a related multiplication equation: The product of the means equals the product of the extremes.

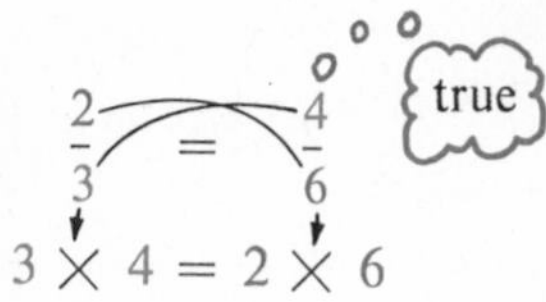

$\frac{2}{3} = \frac{4}{6}$ (true) — $3 \times 4 = 2 \times 6$

$\frac{21}{14} = \frac{3}{2}$ (true) — $14 \times 3 = 21 \times 2$

$\frac{4}{5} = \frac{5}{6}$ (false) — $5 \times 5 = 4 \times 6$

A proportion and its related multiplication equation (cross product = cross product) are either both true or both false. A proportion that has a placeholder can be solved by solving its related multiplication equation. Here are some examples.

$\frac{5}{6} = \frac{c}{8}$ [proportion]	$\frac{y}{5} = \frac{9}{8}$ [proportion]
$6c = 40$ [cross products]	$45 = 8y$ [cross products]
$\frac{6c}{6} = \frac{40}{6}$ [divide by 6]	$\frac{45}{8} = \frac{8y}{8}$ [divide by 8]
$c = 6\frac{2}{3}$ [simplify] ($\frac{40}{6} = \frac{20}{3} = 6\frac{2}{3}$)	$5\frac{5}{8} = y$ [simplify]
The solution is $6\frac{2}{3}$.	The solution is $5\frac{5}{8}$.

EXERCISES

True or false?

1. a. $\frac{2}{4} = \frac{1}{2}$
b. $4 \times 1 = 2 \times 2$

2. a. $\frac{3}{4} = \frac{8}{12}$
b. $4 \times 8 = 3 \times 12$

3. a. $\frac{6}{4} = \frac{3}{2}$
b. $4 \times 3 = 6 \times 2$

4. a. $\frac{3}{3} = \frac{4}{4}$
b. $4 \times 3 = 3 \times 4$

5. a. $\frac{15}{12} = \frac{5}{3}$
b. $12 \times 5 = 15 \times 3$

6. a. $\frac{18}{15} = \frac{12}{10}$
b. $15 \times 12 = 18 \times 10$

Give the solution as a mixed numeral.

7. $\frac{5}{9} = \frac{x}{3}$ [proportion]

$9x = 15$ [cross products]

$\frac{9x}{9} = \frac{15}{9}$ [divide by 9]

$x = ?$ [simplify]

8. $\frac{7}{4} = \frac{9}{x}$ [proportion]

$36 = 7x$ [cross products]

$\frac{36}{7} = \frac{7x}{7}$ [divide by 7]

$? = x$ [simplify]

Copy and complete.

9. $\frac{x}{7} = \frac{10}{3}$ [proportion]

___?___ [cross products]

___?___ [divide by 3]

___?___ [simplify]

10. $\frac{8}{x} = \frac{9}{5}$ [proportion]

___?___ [cross products]

___?___ [divide by 9]

___?___ [simplify]

Solve each proportion.

11. $\frac{2}{3} = \frac{a}{7}$ 12. $\frac{3}{4} = \frac{11}{b}$ 13. $\frac{5}{8} = \frac{8}{d}$ 14. $\frac{3}{2} = \frac{c}{9}$

15. $\frac{r}{7} = \frac{4}{5}$ 16. $\frac{7}{2} = \frac{3}{s}$ 17. $\frac{12}{t} = \frac{4}{3}$ 18. $\frac{v}{6} = \frac{9}{10}$

19. $\frac{8}{5} = \frac{z}{9}$ 20. $\frac{6}{1} = \frac{8}{x}$ 21. $\frac{w}{9} = \frac{5}{3}$ 22. $\frac{21}{v} = \frac{7}{8}$

Do not solve these proportions. Use the clue to estimate the solution to the nearest whole number.

23. $\frac{5}{9} = \frac{x}{19}$

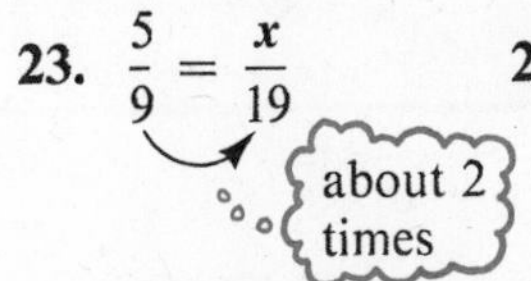

24. $\frac{3}{8} = \frac{x}{3}$

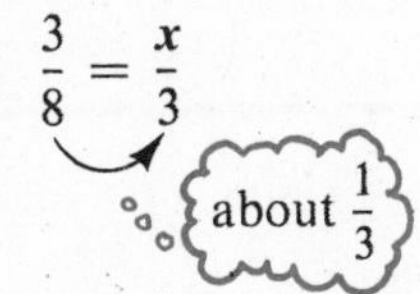

Answer. about 10

25. $\frac{7}{4} = \frac{29}{w}$

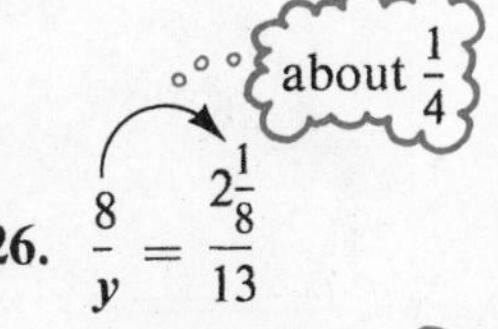

26. $\frac{8}{y} = \frac{2\frac{1}{8}}{13}$

27. $\frac{n}{100} = \frac{19}{48}$

about $\frac{1}{2}$

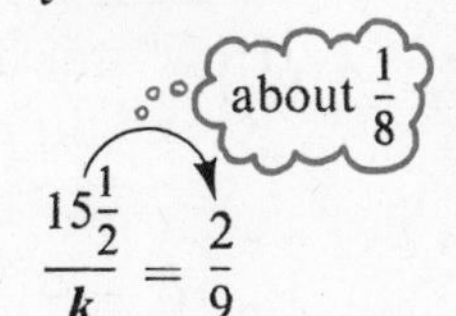

28. $\frac{15\frac{1}{2}}{k} = \frac{2}{9}$

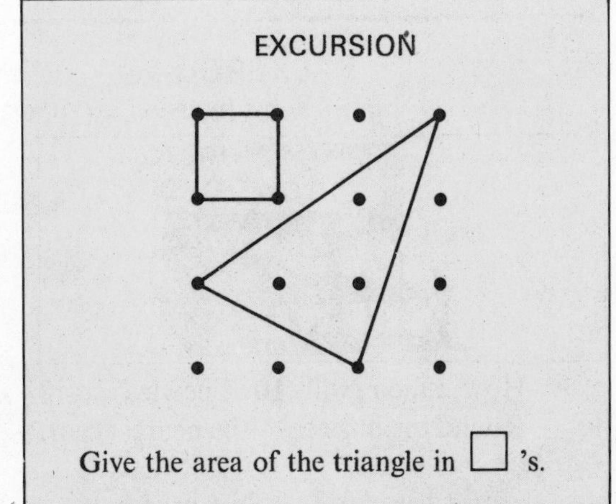

Supplementary Exercises, Set 33, page 383

Rates

A rate is a ratio of two quantities.
Here are some examples.

Rate: $\frac{14 \text{ kilometers}}{1 \text{ hour}}$

Rate: $\frac{\$1.35}{1 \text{ dozen}}$

A proportion may be used to solve a rate problem.

Example.

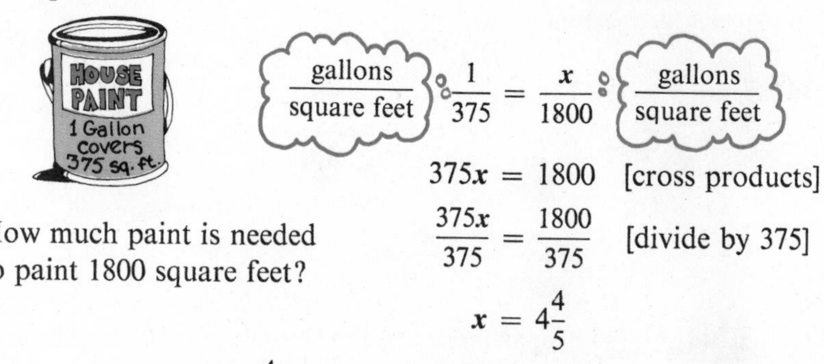

$$\frac{1}{375} = \frac{x}{1800}$$

$$375x = 1800 \quad \text{[cross products]}$$

$$\frac{375x}{375} = \frac{1800}{375} \quad \text{[divide by 375]}$$

$$x = 4\frac{4}{5}$$

How much paint is needed to paint 1800 square feet?

So, $4\frac{4}{5}$ gallons of paint are needed.

EXERCISES

Solve by using a proportion.

1. How much will 10 Chewies cost? Round the answer to the nearest cent.

   Chewies/cents $\frac{3}{5} = \frac{?}{?}$ Chewies/cents

2. How much will 20 cookies cost? Round the answer to the nearest cent.

   cents/cookies $\frac{65}{12} = \frac{?}{?}$ cents/cookies

3. Mrs. Allan drove 138 miles in 3 hours. At that rate, how long would it take her to drive 214 miles?

4. If 12 pencils cost 42¢, how much would 9 pencils cost? Round the answer to the nearest cent.

5. John hit 5 home runs in 84 times at bat. At that rate, how many times at bat would he need to hit 7 home runs? Round the answer to the nearest whole number.

6. Mr. Jackson's automobile used 12.5 gallons of gasoline in 175 miles. At that rate, how much gasoline would be needed for a 285-mile trip? Round the answer to the nearest tenth gallon.

7. A certain recipe calls for 2 teaspoons of vanilla and 5 tablespoons of butter. How much vanilla is needed for 12 tablespoons of butter?

8. A certain machine can print 8000 leaflets in an hour. At that rate, how many minutes would it take to print 1750 leaflets?

9. Donna earned $5.75 for 4 hours of baby-sitting. At that rate, what should she charge for 3 hours of baby-sitting? Round the answer to the nearest cent.

10. George hiked $13\frac{1}{2}$ miles in 4 hours. At that rate, how many miles could he hike in $6\frac{1}{2}$ hours?

1. Decide which television program is your favorite.
2. Take a survey to determine the ratio of students in your school who watch the program.
3. Solve a proportion to estimate how many students in your school watch the program.

EXCURSION

Copy and fill in the missing digits.

```
     4 8
   × □ □
   -----
   □ □ □
 □ □ □
 -------
 □ □ □ 0
```

Skill Maintenance, Set 41, page 408

Problem solving

Many problems can be solved by using a proportion. When "setting up" a proportion for a problem you must be careful that the ratios are in the same order. Here is an example.

An airplane flew 1156 miles in $2\frac{1}{4}$ hours. At that rate, how far would the airplane fly in $3\frac{1}{2}$ hours?

0 miles	1156 miles	x miles
0 hours	$2\frac{1}{4}$ hours	$3\frac{1}{2}$ hours

Any of these proportions could be used to solve the problem.

shorter distance / shorter time $\quad \frac{1156}{2\frac{1}{4}} = \frac{x}{3\frac{1}{2}} \quad$ longer distance / longer time

shorter time / shorter distance $\quad \frac{2\frac{1}{4}}{1156} = \frac{3\frac{1}{2}}{x} \quad$ longer time / longer distance

shorter time / longer time $\quad \frac{2\frac{1}{4}}{3\frac{1}{2}} = \frac{1156}{x} \quad$ shorter distance / longer distance

longer time / shorter time $\quad \frac{3\frac{1}{2}}{2\frac{1}{4}} = \frac{x}{1156} \quad$ longer distance / shorter distance

Check to see if all four proportions have the same solution.

EXERCISES

Study the picture. Then use a proportion to solve the problem.

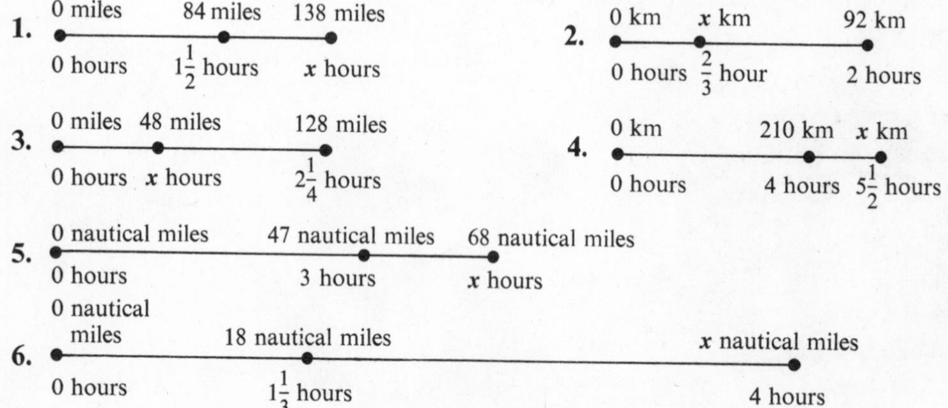

Solve by solving a proportion.

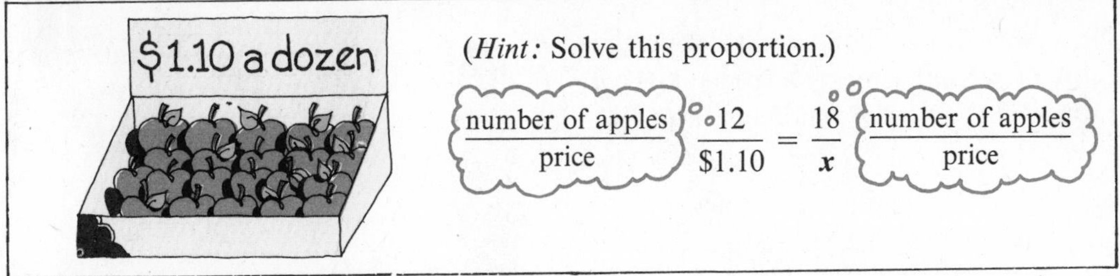

(*Hint:* Solve this proportion.)

$$\frac{\text{number of apples}}{\text{price}} \quad \frac{12}{\$1.10} = \frac{18}{x} \quad \frac{\text{number of apples}}{\text{price}}$$

7. What is the price of 18 apples? Round the answer to the nearest cent.

8. What is the price of $2\frac{3}{4}$ pounds of candy? Round the answer to the nearest cent.

9. If you drove at the speed limit for $3\frac{1}{4}$ hours, how far would you travel?

10. Paul read 32 pages in $\frac{3}{4}$ of an hour. At that rate, how many pages could he read in $2\frac{1}{2}$ hours?

11. Mr. O'Brien drove 236 miles in 5 hours. At that rate, how long would it take him to drive 200 miles?

12. Alice hiked 13 miles in 4 hours. At that rate, how long would it take her to hike 16 miles?

13. Beth typed 127 words in 3 minutes. At that rate, how many words could she type in 12 minutes?

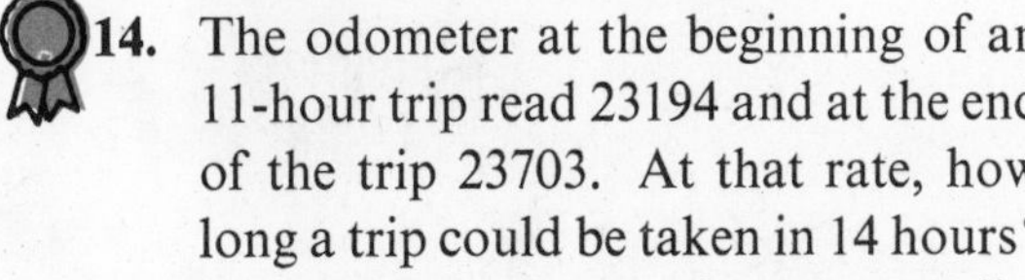

14. The odometer at the beginning of an 11-hour trip read 23194 and at the end of the trip 23703. At that rate, how long a trip could be taken in 14 hours? Round the answer to the nearest mile.

CHECK UP
for pages 162–163

Give each ratio as a fraction in lowest terms.

1. 2:4	**2.** 3:12	**3.** 5:10
4. 24:15	**5.** 3:9	**6.** 36:27
7. 21:30	**8.** 40:24	**9.** 15:25
10. 18 to 12		**11.** 3 to 6
12. 5 to 15		**13.** 4 to 12
14. 5 to 20		**15.** 10 to 45
16. 15 to 9		**17.** 80 to 30
18. 4 to 8		

Answers on page 426.

Skill Maintenance, Set 42, page 408

Changing a fraction to a percent

"Percent" means "hundredths." You can think of percent as being a special kind of ratio—one that has a denominator of 100.

$$\frac{27}{100} = 27\%$$

fraction   percent

Fractions that are equivalent to a fraction having a denominator of 100 are easy to change to a percent. Here are some examples.

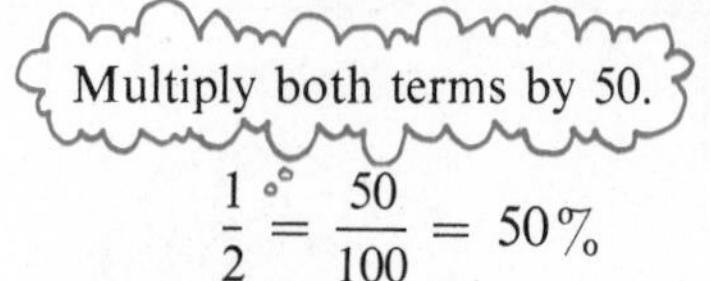

$$\frac{1}{2} = \frac{50}{100} = 50\% \qquad \frac{1}{4} = \frac{25}{100} = 25\% \qquad \frac{7}{2} = \frac{350}{100} = 350\%$$

Any fraction can be changed to a percent by solving a proportion. Here are some examples.

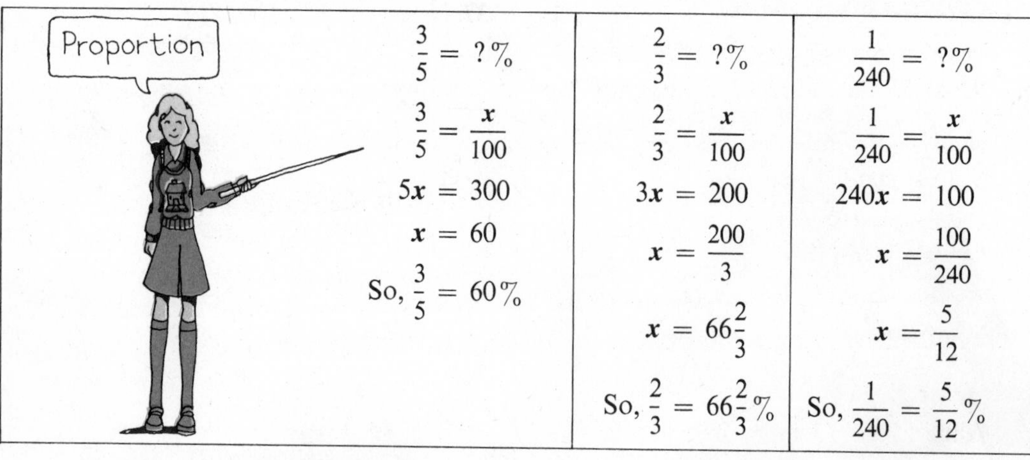

$$\frac{3}{5} = ?\% \qquad \frac{3}{5} = \frac{x}{100} \qquad 5x = 300 \qquad x = 60 \qquad \text{So, } \frac{3}{5} = 60\%$$

$$\frac{2}{3} = ?\% \qquad \frac{2}{3} = \frac{x}{100} \qquad 3x = 200 \qquad x = \frac{200}{3} \qquad x = 66\frac{2}{3} \qquad \text{So, } \frac{2}{3} = 66\frac{2}{3}\%$$

$$\frac{1}{240} = ?\% \qquad \frac{1}{240} = \frac{x}{100} \qquad 240x = 100 \qquad x = \frac{100}{240} \qquad x = \frac{5}{12} \qquad \text{So, } \frac{1}{240} = \frac{5}{12}\%$$

EXERCISES

Change to a percent.

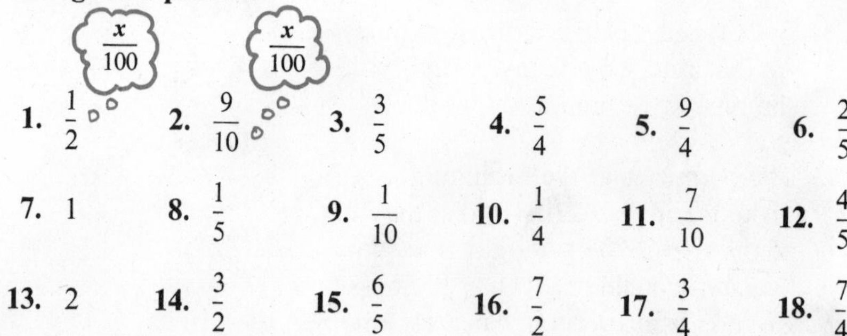

1. $\frac{1}{2}$ **2.** $\frac{9}{10}$ **3.** $\frac{3}{5}$ **4.** $\frac{5}{4}$ **5.** $\frac{9}{4}$ **6.** $\frac{2}{5}$

7. 1 **8.** $\frac{1}{5}$ **9.** $\frac{1}{10}$ **10.** $\frac{1}{4}$ **11.** $\frac{7}{10}$ **12.** $\frac{4}{5}$

13. 2 **14.** $\frac{3}{2}$ **15.** $\frac{6}{5}$ **16.** $\frac{7}{2}$ **17.** $\frac{3}{4}$ **18.** $\frac{7}{4}$

Change to a percent by solving a proportion.

19. $\frac{1}{3}$ $\left(\frac{1}{3} = \frac{x}{100}\right)$ 20. $\frac{3}{8}$ $\left(\frac{3}{8} = \frac{x}{100}\right)$ 21. $\frac{5}{9}$ $\left(\frac{5}{9} = \frac{x}{100}\right)$

22. $\frac{3}{7}$ 23. $\frac{4}{9}$ 24. $\frac{1}{6}$ 25. $\frac{1}{500}$ 26. $\frac{1}{300}$ 27. $\frac{1}{275}$

Complete.

28. If $\frac{1}{8} = 12\frac{1}{2}\%$, then $\frac{2}{8} = \underline{?}\,\%$.

29. If $\frac{1}{9} = 11\frac{1}{9}\%$, then $\frac{2}{9} = \underline{?}\,\%$.

30. If $\frac{1}{9} = 11\frac{1}{9}\%$, then $\frac{5}{9} = \underline{?}\,\%$.

31. If $\frac{1}{7} = 14\frac{2}{7}\%$, then $\frac{2}{7} = \underline{?}\,\%$.

32. If $\frac{1}{11} = 9\frac{1}{11}\%$, then $\frac{3}{11} = \underline{?}\,\%$.

33. If $\frac{1}{11} = 9\frac{1}{11}\%$, then $\frac{8}{11} = \underline{?}\,\%$.

34. If $\frac{1}{6} = 16\frac{2}{3}\%$, then $\frac{2}{6} = \underline{?}\,\%$.

35. If $\frac{1}{3} = 33\frac{1}{3}\%$, then $\frac{2}{3} = \underline{?}\,\%$.

36. If $\frac{1}{100} = 1\%$, then $\frac{1}{200} = \underline{?}\,\%$.

37. If $\frac{1}{100} = 1\%$, then $\frac{1}{400} = \underline{?}\,\%$.

Solve.

38. What percent of the windowpanes are broken?

39. What percent of the marbles are red? Are green? Are blue?

40. There were 750 tickets printed for a school play. Thus far 235 tickets have been sold. What percent of the tickets have been sold?

41. Beth wants to buy a radio that costs \$34.95. She has \$22.50. What percent of the money needed does she have?

Take a survey to find out what percent of your schoolmates walk to school.

EXCURSION

Construct this figure with a compass and straightedge.

Use a compass and straightedge to construct a figure of your own.

Supplementary Exercises, Set 34, page 383

Changing a percent to a fraction

To change a percent to a fraction, express the percent as a fraction having a denominator of 100. Then reduce to lowest terms. Here are some examples.

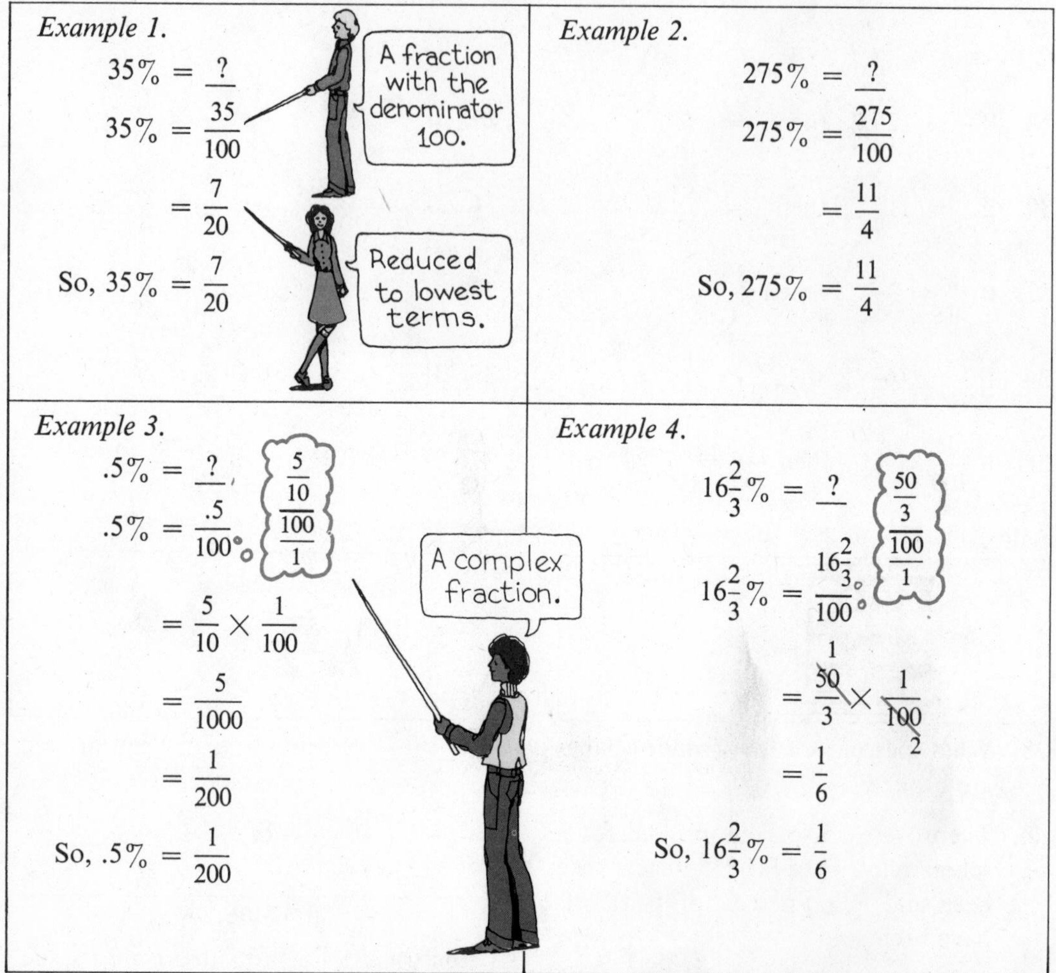

Example 1.

$35\% = \frac{?}{}$

$35\% = \frac{35}{100}$

$= \frac{7}{20}$

So, $35\% = \frac{7}{20}$

Example 2.

$275\% = \frac{?}{}$

$275\% = \frac{275}{100}$

$= \frac{11}{4}$

So, $275\% = \frac{11}{4}$

Example 3.

$.5\% = \frac{?}{}$

$.5\% = \frac{.5}{100}$ $\left(\frac{\frac{5}{10}}{\frac{100}{1}}\right)$

$= \frac{5}{10} \times \frac{1}{100}$

$= \frac{5}{1000}$

$= \frac{1}{200}$

So, $.5\% = \frac{1}{200}$

Example 4.

$16\frac{2}{3}\% = \frac{?}{}$

$16\frac{2}{3}\% = \frac{16\frac{2}{3}}{100}$ $\left(\frac{\frac{50}{3}}{\frac{100}{1}}\right)$

$= \frac{\cancel{50}^{1}}{3} \times \frac{1}{\cancel{100}_{2}}$

$= \frac{1}{6}$

So, $16\frac{2}{3}\% = \frac{1}{6}$

EXERCISES

Change each percent to a fraction.

1. 25%	**2.** 50%	**3.** 75%	**4.** 100%	**5.** 10%	**6.** 65%
7. 175%	**8.** 300%	**9.** $12\frac{1}{2}\%$	**10.** $33\frac{1}{3}\%$	**11.** .2%	**12.** 2.5%
13. $66\frac{2}{3}\%$	**14.** $87\frac{1}{2}\%$	**15.** .8%	**16.** $6\frac{1}{4}\%$	**17.** $37\frac{1}{2}\%$	**18.** $111\frac{1}{9}\%$

Complete.

19. If $6\frac{1}{4}\% = \frac{1}{16}$, then $18\frac{3}{4}\% = \underline{?}$.

20. If $\frac{1}{10} = 10\%$, then $\frac{11}{10} = \underline{?}\,\%$.

21. If $11\frac{1}{9}\% = \frac{1}{9}$, then $22\frac{2}{9}\% = \underline{?}$.

22. If $8\frac{1}{3}\% = \frac{1}{12}$, then $41\frac{2}{3}\% = \underline{?}$.

23. If $\frac{1}{5} = 20\%$, then $\frac{3}{5} = \underline{?}\,\%$.

24. If $16\frac{2}{3}\% = \frac{1}{6}$, then $83\frac{1}{3}\% = \underline{?}$.

<, =, or >?

25. $\frac{4}{5}$ ● 80%

26. $\frac{3}{20}$ ● 15%

27. 250% ● $\frac{5}{2}$

28. $\frac{1}{11}$ ● 10%

29. $\frac{9}{8}$ ● 115%

30. $\frac{5}{8}$ ● 60%

31. $\frac{5}{9}$ ● 58%

32. .6% ● $\frac{1}{200}$

The results of a mathematics test are shown on the bar graph.

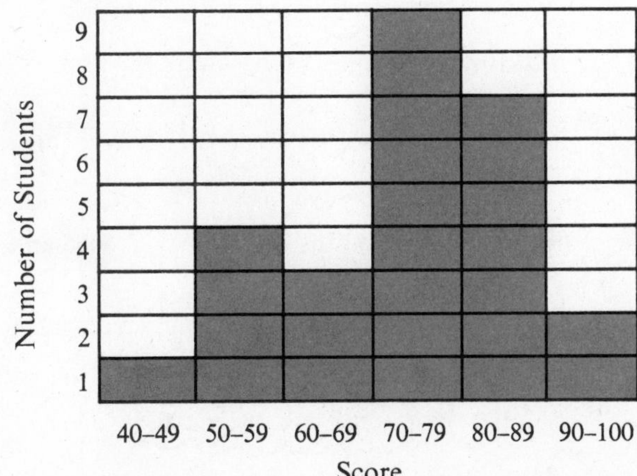

33. How many students took the test?
34. What percent of the students got a test score in the eighties?
35. What percent scored below 70?
36. What percent scored 80 or above?
37. What fraction of the students scored below 60?
38. What fraction scored in the sixties?

CHECKUP
for pages 164–165

Solve each proportion.

1. $\frac{x}{3} = \frac{5}{8}$
2. $\frac{9}{4} = \frac{x}{7}$
3. $\frac{2}{5} = \frac{3}{x}$
4. $\frac{9}{x} = \frac{6}{11}$
5. $\frac{x}{3} = \frac{7}{6}$
6. $\frac{8}{x} = \frac{4}{9}$
7. $\frac{5}{2} = \frac{x}{1}$
8. $\frac{3}{8} = \frac{x}{7}$
9. $\frac{8}{x} = \frac{6}{5}$
10. $\frac{2}{15} = \frac{9}{x}$
11. $\frac{12}{19} = \frac{x}{16}$
12. $\frac{18}{11} = \frac{13}{x}$

Answers on page 427.

Supplementary Exercises, Set 35, page 383

Decimals and percents

In an earlier chapter you learned that a fraction is equivalent to either a terminating decimal or a repeating decimal.

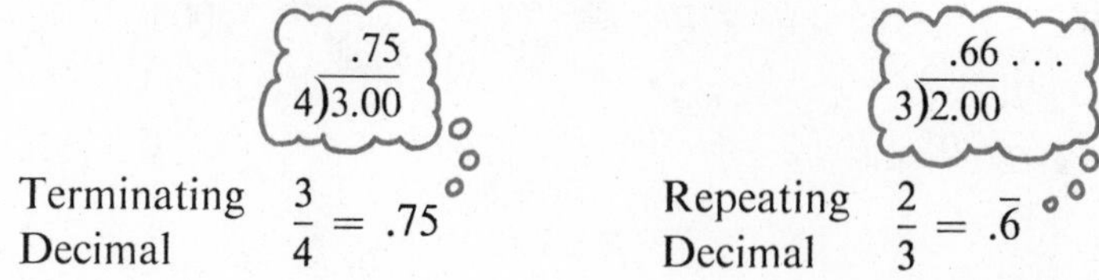

Terminating Decimal $\frac{3}{4} = .75$ Repeating Decimal $\frac{2}{3} = .\overline{6}$

Sometimes decimals are written as mixed decimals.

$\frac{2}{3} = ?$

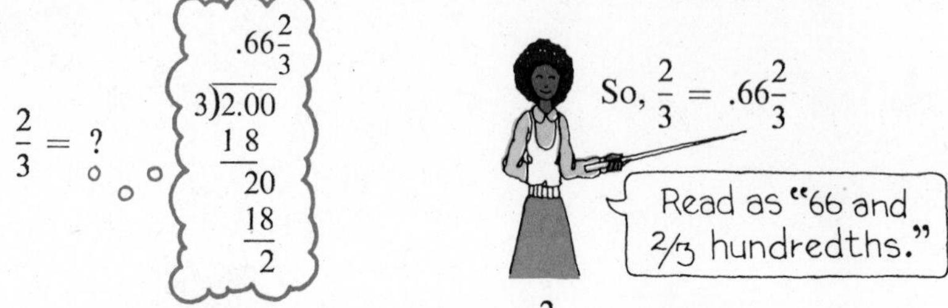

Here are some other mixed decimals for $\frac{2}{3}$.

$.6\frac{2}{3}$ $.666\frac{2}{3}$ $.6666\frac{2}{3}$

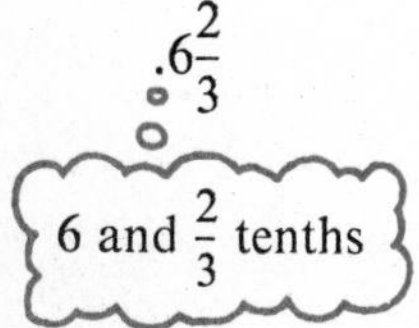

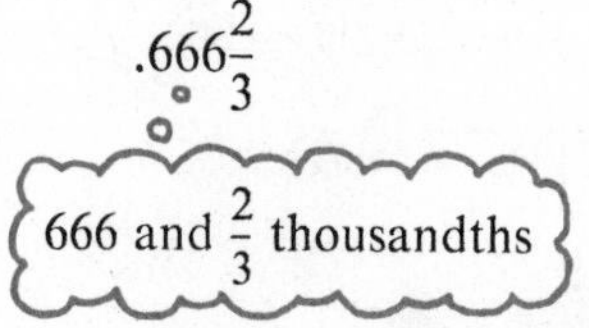

Here are some examples of changing a decimal to a percent.

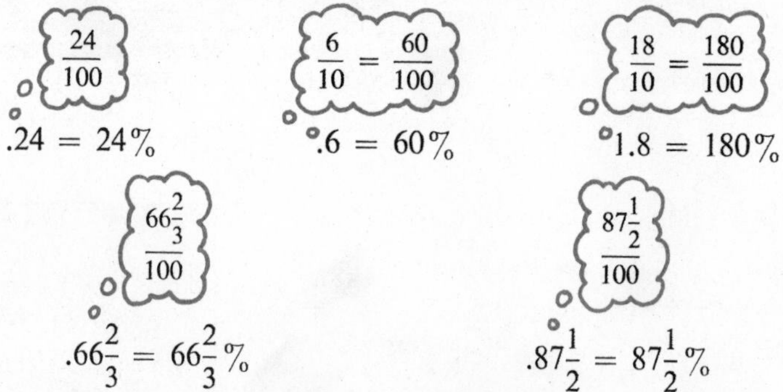

$.24 = 24\%$ $.6 = 60\%$ $1.8 = 180\%$

$.66\frac{2}{3} = 66\frac{2}{3}\%$ $.87\frac{1}{2} = 87\frac{1}{2}\%$

Notice that a decimal can be changed to a percent by moving the decimal point two places to the *right* and annexing the percent sign. Notice also that a percent can be changed to a decimal by moving the decimal point two places to the *left* and omitting the percent sign.

Examples. $38\% = .38$ $33\frac{1}{3}\% = .33\frac{1}{3}$ $.8\% = .008$

EXERCISES

Change to a percent.

1. .17 **2.** .82 **3.** 2.57 **4.** 1.4 **5.** .2 **6.** 5

7. $.87\frac{1}{2}$ **8.** .06 **9.** $.06\frac{1}{4}$ **10.** .003 **11.** $.16\frac{2}{3}$ **12.** $.62\frac{1}{2}$

Change to a decimal.

13. 15% **14.** 9% **15.** 300% **16.** $12\frac{1}{2}\%$ **17.** 560% **18.** 62.5%

19. $16\frac{2}{3}\%$ **20.** $37\frac{1}{2}\%$ **21.** 87.5% **22.** $83\frac{1}{3}\%$ **23.** .9% **24.** .06%

Copy and complete.

	25.	26.	27.	28.	29.	30.	31.	32.	33.	34.
Fraction	$\frac{1}{2}$	?	?	$\frac{5}{6}$	?	?	?	$\frac{8}{3}$	?	?
Decimal	?	.8	?	?	.06	?	1.2	?	$.22\frac{2}{9}$	?
Percent	?	?	75%	?	?	175%	?	?	?	.9%

Solve.

35. In a recent United States census the male population was estimated to be 95,356,000 and the female population was estimated to be 102,858,000. What percent of the population was female? Male?

36. In another census it was found that 203,184,772 people lived in the United States. Of this number, 19,953,134 lived in California. What percent of the population lived in California?

Take a traffic survey and compute the percent of automobiles having the driver as the only passenger.

EXCURSION

Take three pennies and place them like this on your desk:

Can you get three "heads-up" by turning over two coins at a time? Can you give an argument for your answer?

Supplementary Exercises, Set 36, page 383

KEEPING SKILLS SHARP

Substitute and simplify.

w	x	Y	z
8	6	9	4

1. $w(x + z)$ **2.** $wx + wz$ **3.** $(Y - x)(w + z)$ **4.** $(w - x)(Y - z)$

5. $wx + Y$ **6.** $\frac{wx}{z}$ **7.** $\frac{wx + z}{z}$ **8.** x^z

Round to the nearest .1.

9. 6.85 **10.** .95 **11.** .708 **12.** 6.99 **13.** 59.97

Multiply.

14. 58×5 **15.** 39×46 **16.** 7.46×58 **17.** 25.8×6.7 **18.** $9.341 \times .67$ **19.** 58.26×3.48

Divide.

20. $9\overline{)7857}$ **21.** $15\overline{)3600}$ **22.** $4.2\overline{)12.18}$ **23.** $.68\overline{)6.46}$ **24.** $18.2\overline{)82.992}$

Give each sum in lowest terms.

25. $\frac{1}{5} + \frac{3}{5}$ **26.** $\frac{2}{3} + \frac{1}{6}$ **27.** $\frac{5}{8} + \frac{3}{4}$ **28.** $\frac{5}{6} + \frac{4}{9}$

Give each difference in lowest terms.

29. $\frac{5}{9} - \frac{2}{9}$ **30.** $\frac{7}{8} - \frac{1}{4}$ **31.** $1 - \frac{3}{8}$ **32.** $\frac{3}{2} - \frac{2}{3}$

Give each product in lowest terms.

33. $\frac{3}{5} \times 4$ **34.** $\frac{1}{6} \times \frac{3}{4}$ **35.** $\frac{5}{3} \times \frac{9}{10}$ **36.** $\frac{5}{8} \times \frac{8}{5}$

Give each quotient in lowest terms.

37. $1 \div \frac{1}{2}$ **38.** $\frac{5}{3} \div \frac{1}{3}$ **39.** $\frac{7}{8} \div \frac{3}{4}$ **40.** $\frac{5}{2} \div \frac{15}{4}$

Mathematics and science

In 1787, Jacques Charles first studied the relationship between gas temperature and gas volume. He found that the volume of a sample of air at 0° C would double when heated to 273° C, provided that the pressure on the gas remained the same.

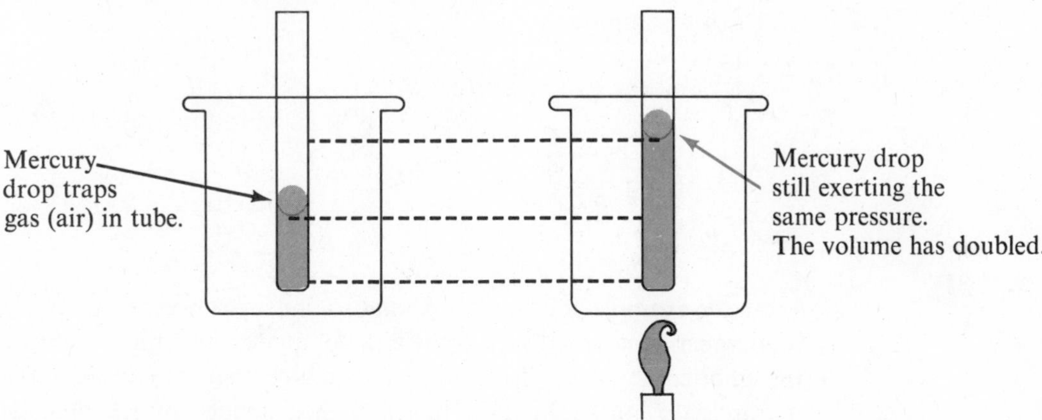

It was found that for each degree the temperature was increased or decreased from 0° C, the volume would increase or decrease $\frac{1}{273}$ of the volume at 0° C.

1. Copy and complete this table.
Round answers to the nearest hundredth.

Volume of air	?	?	?	?	1 (liter)	?	?	?	?
Temperature of air	−250	−120	−80	−50	0(°C)	100	150	220	250

Charles' law states that the volume of a gas is directly related to the temperature of the gas when the pressure remains the same. The law might be stated like this:

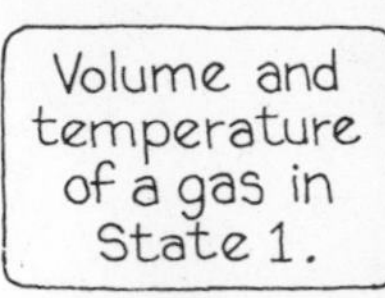

$$\frac{V_1}{T_1} = \frac{V_2}{T_2}$$

2. The volume of a gas at 18° C is 1.3 liters. If the pressure remains the same, what is the volume of the gas at 83° C? Round the answer to the nearest hundredth.

3. The volume of a gas at 42° C is 2.5 liters. If the pressure is to remain the same, what temperature is needed to increase the volume by 1.8 liters?

Skill Maintenance, Set 43, page 408

Finding a fraction or percent of a number

You have probably heard expressions involving fractions or percents like these:

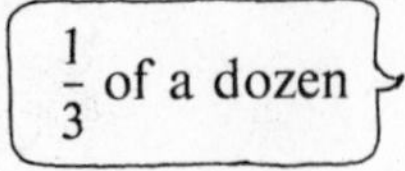

$\frac{3}{4}$ of a mile

20% of the class

Study this example.

$\frac{2}{3}$ of 15 marbles = m marbles

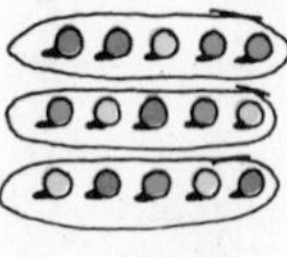

Divide the marbles equally into 3 sets and count the marbles in 2 of the sets.

$m = 10$

From the example you should see that to find a fraction of a quantity or number you can divide by the denominator and then multiply the quotient by the numerator. Also notice that you could have multiplied by the numerator first and then divided by the denominator.

The same method can be used to solve an equation like this:

$\frac{3}{4}$

75% of 36 = x First think of an equivalent fraction. Then divide by the denominator and multiply by the numerator.

So, 75% of 36 = 27

EXERCISES

Solve each equation.

1. $\frac{1}{2}$ of \$18 = \$$k$

2. $\frac{1}{3}$ of 21¢ = f¢

3. 25% of 32 in. = c in.

4. 20% of 30 lb = r lb

5. $\frac{5}{2}$ of 18 oz = t oz

6. $\frac{9}{4}$ of 36 ft = u ft

7. 60% of 35 = g

8. 125% of 36 = b

9. $\frac{5}{3}$ of 27 = n

10. $\frac{1}{3}$ of 21 = s

11. 50% of 52 = v

12. $\frac{2}{3}$ of 24 = j

13. $\frac{7}{8}$ of 5.6 = a

14. $\frac{3}{2}$ of .84 = m

15. $\frac{1}{3}$ of 7.2 = d

16. $\frac{9}{8}$ of 9.6 = q

17. $\frac{4}{5}$ of 8.5 = h

18. $\frac{5}{8}$ of .64 = p

Solve. Round each answer to the nearest cent.

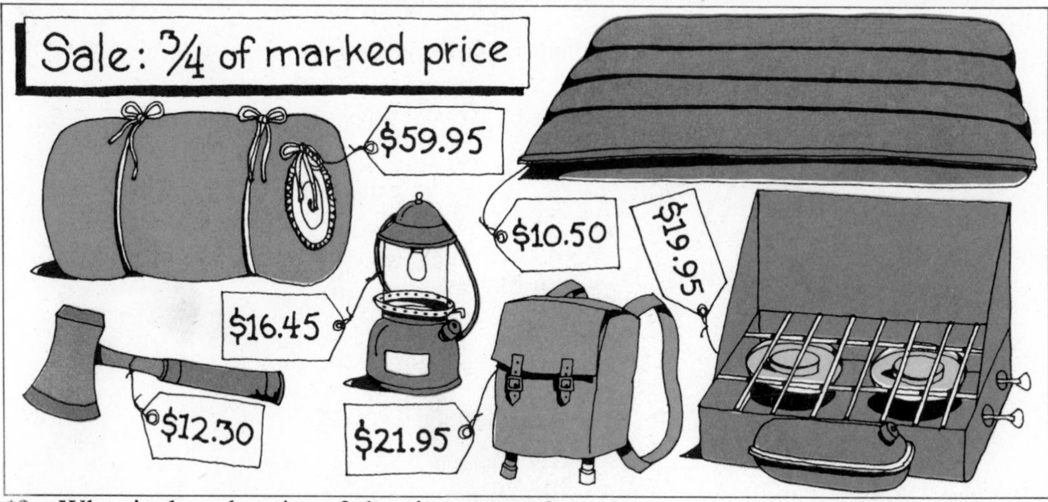

19. What is the sale price of the air mattress?
20. What is the sale price of the sleeping bag?
21. How much can be saved by buying the lantern on sale?
22. What is the total sale price of the ax and stove?
23. Gerry has $13.60. How much more money does he need for the pack?
24. How much money would be saved by buying an air mattress and sleeping bag on sale?

Solve.

25. A gallon of a certain kind of paint will cover 425 square feet. How many square feet will $\frac{2}{3}$ of a gallon cover? Round the answer to the nearest whole number.
26. The Drama Society is putting on a play. They hope to sell 400 tickets. One team is to sell $\frac{3}{8}$ of the tickets. How many tickets is that?
27. In a survey of 560 workers, 40% of those surveyed commute more than 10 miles to their jobs. How many workers live within 10 miles of their work?

CHECKUP
for pages 162–163

Reduce to lowest terms.

1. $\frac{2}{4}$	**2.** $\frac{3}{9}$	**3.** $\frac{6}{8}$
4. $\frac{12}{15}$	**5.** $\frac{20}{4}$	**6.** $\frac{9}{6}$
7. $\frac{8}{6}$	**8.** $\frac{24}{16}$	**9.** $\frac{15}{20}$
10. $\frac{14}{12}$	**11.** $\frac{3}{6}$	**12.** $\frac{49}{35}$
13. $\frac{18}{24}$	**14.** $\frac{30}{5}$	**15.** $\frac{64}{48}$
16. $\frac{42}{7}$	**17.** $\frac{9}{27}$	**18.** $\frac{10}{20}$

Answers on page 427.

Supplementary Exercises, Set 37, page 384

Solving percent equations

Most percent problems involve finding a percent of a number. Here is an example.

What would the raise be for a miner earning \$9800?

Equation: 12% of \$9800 = x

Here are three methods that can be used to find the solution of the equation.

Method 1. Solve by multiplying fractional numbers.

$$\frac{12}{100} \text{ of } \$9800 = \frac{12}{\cancel{100}_1} \times \overset{98}{\cancel{\$9800}} = \$1176$$

Method 2. Solve by multiplying by the equivalent decimal.

$$\begin{array}{r} \$9800 \\ \times .12 \\ \hline 196\,00 \\ 980\,0 \\ \hline \$1176.00 \end{array}$$

Method 3. Solve by solving a proportion.

$$\frac{12}{100} = \frac{x}{9800}$$

$$100x = 12 \times 9800$$

$$100x = 117{,}600$$

$$x = 1176$$

So, the raise would be \$1176.

You should use whichever method is easiest for a particular problem. Here are some examples.

$\frac{1}{2}$ 50% of 348 = ?

Method 1 is probably the easiest, since all you would really do is divide by 2.

$$\frac{1}{\cancel{2}_1} \times \overset{174}{\cancel{348}} = 174$$

23% of 97 = ?

Method 2 is probably the easiest.

$$\begin{array}{r} 97 \\ \times .23 \\ \hline 2\,91 \\ 19\,4 \\ \hline 22.31 \end{array}$$

$8\frac{1}{4}$% of 153 = ?

Method 3 is probably the easiest.

$$\frac{8\frac{1}{4}}{100} = \frac{x}{153}$$

$$100x = 8\frac{1}{4} \times 153$$

$$100x = \frac{5049}{4}$$

$$x = \frac{5049}{400}$$

$$x = 12\frac{249}{400}$$

EXERCISES

Solve each equation.

1. 8% of $50 = m$
2. 25% of $64 = s$
3. $33\frac{1}{3}\%$ of $78 = p$
4. 20% of $25 = u$
5. 200% of $18 = w$
6. 40% of $56 = r$
7. $87\frac{1}{2}\%$ of $64 = x$
8. $112\frac{1}{2}\%$ of $100 = q$
9. $.5\%$ of $70 = v$
10. $66\frac{2}{3}\%$ of $96 = t$
11. $37\frac{1}{2}\%$ of $140 = y$
12. 150% of $66 = n$

The scores in red are the number of exercises out of 60 that were done correctly. Give the percent of exercises that were done correctly by:

13. Adams
14. Dennis
15. Jones
16. Marston
17. Mathews
18. Thomas
19. Copy and complete this table. Round to the nearest tenth.

Basketball Statistics			
Player	Shots attempted	Shots made	Percent made
Allen	186	82	?
Becker	153	59	?
Elsworth	193	93	?
Fernandez	170	81	?
Meeker	174	79	?
Reyes	132	53	?
Smith	156	70	?
Towns	143	61	?
Victor	125	53	?
Williams	192	83	?

20. What player in exercise 19 had the best shooting percentage?

EXCURSION

Draw a square and cut it up as shown by the dotted lines.

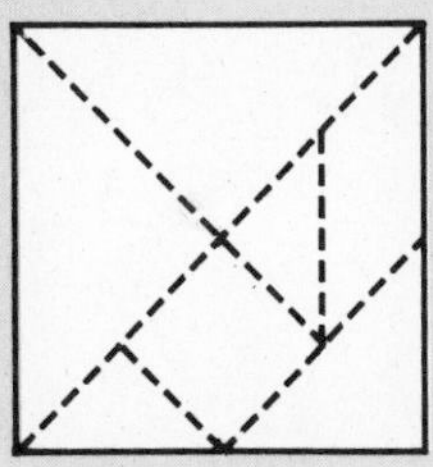

See if you can use all seven pieces to make a triangle.
To make a rectangle.

Supplementary Exercises, Set 38, page 384

Finding the whole

You have solved fraction or percent equations like this:

$$\frac{2}{3} \text{ of } 12 = x$$

Now let's think about solving an equation to find the number when a fraction of the number is given.

To solve this fraction equation, I can think about dividing up objects.

Example.

$$\frac{3}{4} \text{ of } x = 15$$

I know that 3/4 of the objects is 15. So, I divide 15 by 3 to find the number of objects in 1 set. Then I multiply by 4 to find the total number of objects.

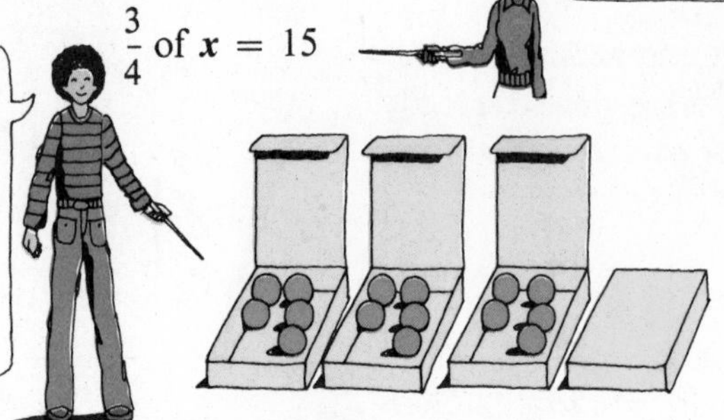

$$\frac{3}{4} \text{ of } 20 = 15$$

Another way to solve the equation is to multiply by the reciprocal of 3/4.

$$\frac{3}{4} \times x = 15$$

$$\frac{4}{3} \times \frac{3}{4} \times x = \frac{4}{3} \times 15 \quad \left[\text{multiply by } \frac{4}{3}\right]$$

$$x = 20$$

EXERCISES

Solve each fraction equation.

1. $\frac{1}{4}$ of $c = 16$ **2.** $\frac{3}{2}$ of $f = 21$ **3.** $\frac{1}{3}$ of $j = 9$

4. $\frac{5}{4}$ of $p = 35$ **5.** $\frac{5}{6}$ of $n = 25$ **6.** 20% of $t = 7$

7. $\frac{2}{3}$ of $s = 16$ **8.** $\frac{5}{8}$ of $a = 15$ **9.** $\frac{3}{5}$ of $b = 12$

10. $\frac{3}{8}$ of $g = 18$ **11.** 50% of $k = 19$ **12.** 120% of $r = 36$

13. 40% of $v = 10$ **14.** 75% of $e = 36$ **15.** 80% of $m = 24$

16. $\frac{9}{2}$ of $q = 36$ **17.** $\frac{4}{3}$ of $h = 32$ **18.** $\frac{7}{8}$ of $d = 35$

Solve.

19. What is the regular price of the belt?
20. What is the regular price of the jacket?
21. How much is saved by buying the tennis shoes on sale?
22. How much is saved by buying the belt on sale?
23. Greg has $12.65. How much more money does he need to buy a belt and jacket?
24. Sally bought a pair of tennis shoes and 3 pairs of socks. How much did she save by buying the items on sale?

Solve.

25. A youth club has raised 40% of the money needed for a club trip. If they have raised $48, how much more money do they need to raise?
26. At the beginning of a trip the odometer on Mr. Rose's car read 356 miles. At the end of the trip the odometer read 571 miles. If his car used 16.3 gallons of gasoline, how many miles per gallon did his car average?
27. If ground beef sells for $1.36 per pound, how much will 2 lb 12 oz cost?

EXCURSION

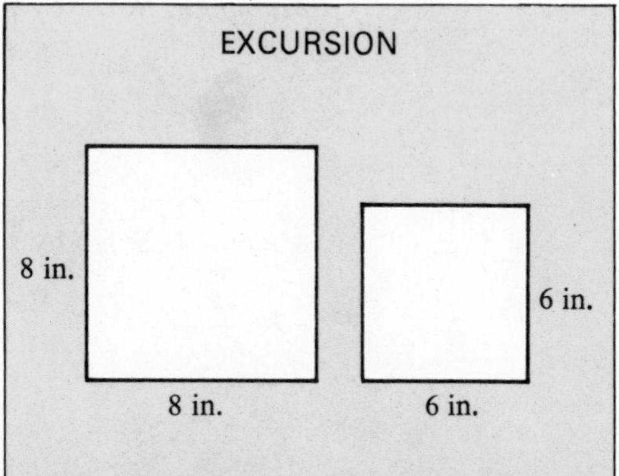

Make an 8-inch square and a 6-inch square out of paper. Cut each square into 2 pieces so that the 4 pieces fit together to form a 10-inch square.

Supplementary Exercises, Set 39, page 384

More on solving percent equations

What was the regular price of the radio?

Equation: 60% of y = \$36

Below are three methods that can be used to find the solution of the equation.

Method 1. Solve by solving a fraction equation.

$$60\% \times y = \$36$$

$$\frac{60}{100} \times y = \$36$$

$$\frac{100}{60} \times \frac{60}{100} y = \frac{100}{60} \times \$36 \quad \left[\text{multiply by } \frac{100}{60}\right]$$

$$y = \frac{\overset{10}{\cancel{100}}}{\underset{\underset{1}{\cancel{6}}}{\cancel{60}}} \times \overset{6}{\cancel{\$36}} \quad \text{[simplify]}$$

$$y = \boxed{\$60}$$

Method 2. Solve by dividing by the equivalent decimal.

$$.60 \times y = \$36$$

$$\frac{.60y}{.60} = \frac{\$36}{.60} \qquad .60\overline{)\$36.00} = \boxed{\$60}$$

Method 3. Solve by solving a proportion.

$$\begin{matrix}\text{part} \rightarrow \\ \text{total} \rightarrow\end{matrix} \frac{60}{100} = \frac{\$36}{y} \begin{matrix}\leftarrow \text{part price} \\ \leftarrow \text{total price}\end{matrix}$$

$$\$3600 = 60y$$

$$\frac{\$3600}{60} = \frac{60y}{60}$$

$$\boxed{\$60} = y$$

You should use whichever method is easiest for a particular problem.

EXERCISES

Solve each equation.

1. 50% of $x = 17$
2. 75% of $x = 18$
3. 20% of $x = 35$
4. 120% of $x = 42$
5. 43% of $x = 19$
6. $33\frac{1}{3}\%$ of $x = 18$
7. $37\frac{1}{2}\%$ of $x = 48$
8. $.8\%$ of $x = 20$
9. $.1\%$ of $x = 60$
10. $66\frac{2}{3}\%$ of $x = 44$
11. $44\frac{4}{9}\%$ of $x = 64$
12. $112\frac{1}{2}\%$ of $x = 54$

Solve.

13. \$672 car
    $33\frac{1}{3}\%$ down payment
    How much is the down payment?

14. \$9135 yearly budget
    25% for housing
    How much for housing?

15. 350 pages in book
    Read 40% of it
    How many pages left to read?

16. Bought bicycle for \$126.90
    Sold for $66\frac{2}{3}\%$ of cost
    What was the selling price?

17. 256 times at bat
    Hit 25% of the time
    How many hits?

18. \$380 spent for utilities
    12% of yearly budget for utilities
    How much is the yearly budget?

19. 25% down payment
    \$120 paid down
    What was the total price?

20. Read 80% of a book
    Read 288 pages
    How many pages in the book?

21. 824 students
    $37\frac{1}{2}\%$ ride bus
    How many ride bus to school?

22. 80% of class members walk to school
    24 walk to school
    How many class members?

23. Hit 39% of times at bat
    43 hits
    How many times at bat?

24. Sold camera for \$18.50
    Sold for 60% of cost
    How much did camera cost?

EXCURSION

Remember that in a magic square the sum of the numbers in any row, column, or diagonal is the same. Copy and complete this magic square.

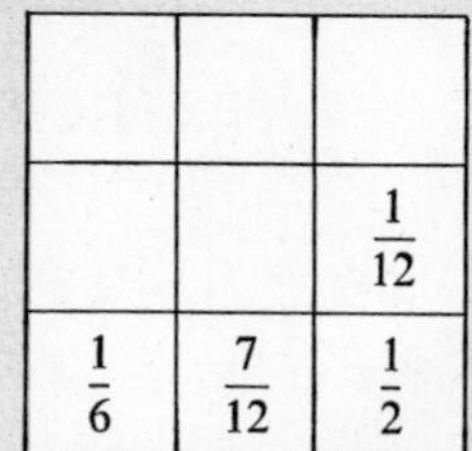

		$\frac{1}{12}$
$\frac{1}{6}$	$\frac{7}{12}$	$\frac{1}{2}$

Supplementary Exercises, Set 40, page 385

Finding a percent

In a basketball game Anita made 12 baskets out of 42 shots. What percent of her shots did she make?

Method 1. Use a proportion.

$$\begin{array}{r} \text{shots made} \rightarrow \\ \text{total shots} \rightarrow \end{array} \frac{21}{42} = \frac{x}{100} \begin{array}{l} \leftarrow \text{part} \\ \leftarrow \text{total} \end{array}$$

$$42x = 12 \times 100$$

$$x = \frac{\overset{200}{\cancel{1200}}}{\underset{7}{\cancel{42}}}$$

$$x = 28\frac{4}{7}$$

Method 2.

$$12 = x\% \text{ of } 42$$

$$12 = \frac{x}{100} \times 42$$

$$\frac{100 \times 12}{42} = x \quad \text{[divide by 42 and multiply by 100]}$$

$$28\frac{4}{7} = x$$

So, Anita made $28\frac{4}{7}\%$ of her shots.

Mr. Rader's annual salary was \$12,400. After a raise, his salary was \$14,000. What percent was his salary increased?

amount of increase = \$14,000 − \$12,400 = \$1600

Method 1.

$$\begin{array}{r} \text{increase} \rightarrow \\ \text{base salary} \rightarrow \end{array} \frac{1600}{12{,}400} = \frac{x}{100}$$

$$12{,}400x = 160{,}000$$

$$x = \frac{160{,}000}{12{,}400}$$

$$x = 12\frac{28}{31}$$

Method 2.

$$1600 = x\% \text{ of } 12{,}400$$

$$1600 = \frac{x}{100} \times 12{,}400$$

$$\frac{1600 \times 100}{12{,}400} = x \quad \text{[divide by 12,400 and multiply by 100]}$$

$$12\frac{28}{31} = x$$

So, his salary was increased $12\frac{28}{31}\%$.

EXERCISES

Solve the equations.

1. $a\%$ of $18 = 12$ (total: 18; part: 12)
2. $x\%$ of $32 = 16$
3. $z\%$ of $16 = 10$
4. $y\%$ of $15 = 20$
5. $c\%$ of $38 = 30$
6. $x\%$ of $45 = 21$

Solve.

City	Population in Census Year		
	1950	1960	1970
New York City	7,891,957	7,781,984	7,894,862
Chicago	3,620,962	3,550,404	3,369,359
Los Angeles	1,970,358	2,479,015	2,809,596
Philadelphia	2,071,605	2,002,512	1,950,098
Detroit	1,849,568	1,670,144	1,513,601
Houston	596,163	938,219	1,232,802
Baltimore	949,708	939,024	905,759
Dallas	434,462	679,684	844,401
Washington, D.C.	802,178	763,956	756,510

7. **a.** Which cities had a decrease in population from 1950 to 1960? From 1960 to 1970?

   b. Which cities had an increase in population from 1950 to 1960? From 1960 to 1970?

8. **a.** How much did the population of Detroit decrease from 1960 to 1970?

   b. What was the percent of decrease? Round answer to the nearest tenth percent.

9. **a.** How much did the population of Dallas increase from 1960 to 1970?

   b. What was the percent of increase? Round to the nearest tenth percent.

10. By what percent did the population of Houston increase from 1950 to 1960?

11. A clothing-store manager bought a suit for \$63.75 and sold it for \$85.00. What was his percent of "markup"? Give the answer to the nearest tenth percent.

12. One week Mr. Johnson's car averaged 16 miles per gallon of gasoline. After a tune-up it averaged 20 miles per gallon. By what percent did the mileage improve?

13. A certain storm-window company claims that a fuel bill can be reduced 20% by installing its storm windows. If so, how much could have been saved on a fuel bill of \$372?

14. Ms. Hargrave bought a house for \$27,500 and sold it 5 years later for \$42,000. By what percent did the price increase?

CHECKUP
for pages 180–183

Solve.

1. 50% of $y = 17$
2. 30% of $153 = y$
3. 160% of $96 = y$
4. $33\frac{1}{3}\%$ of $y = 26$
5. $87\frac{1}{2}\%$ of $y = 182$
6. 39% of $68 = y$
7. 15% of $450 = y$
8. $66\frac{2}{3}\%$ of $y = 54$
9. $116\frac{2}{3}\%$ of $84 = y$
10. $.8\%$ of $y = 16$
11. 67% of $72 = y$
12. 19% of $y = 45$

Answers on page 427.

Skill Maintenance, Set 44, page 409

Mathematics in careers

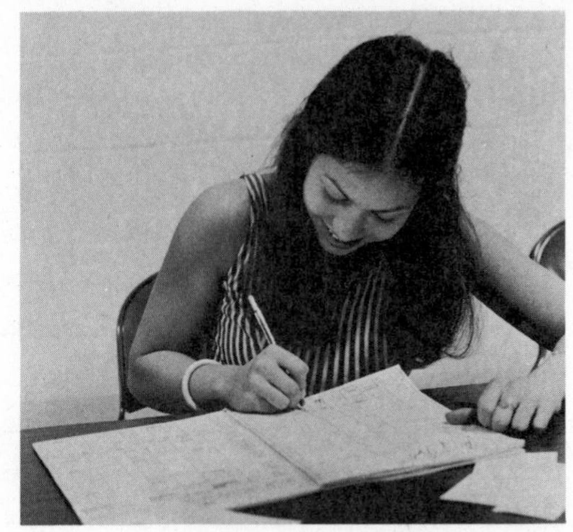

Professional ball teams hire people to keep mathematical records of individual and team performance.

For example, the batting average of each professional baseball player is computed. The batting average is the following ratio:

$$\frac{\text{Number of hits}}{\text{Number of times at bat}}$$

It is expressed as a decimal rounded to the nearest thousandth.

Example. In his professional career Babe Ruth got 2873 hits in 8399 times at bat. What was his lifetime batting average?

$$\frac{2873}{8399} = ?$$

```
            .3420
8399)2873.0000
      2519 7
       353 30
       335 96
        17 340
        16 798
           5420
```

So, his lifetime batting average was .342.

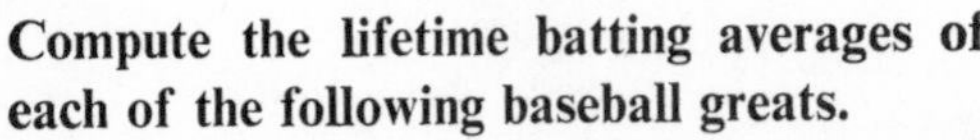

Compute the lifetime batting averages of each of the following baseball greats.

Name	Number of times at bat	Number of hits	Av.
Ty Cobb	11,429	4,191	
Joe DiMaggio	6,821	2,214	
Lou Gehrig	8,001	2,721	
Rogers Hornsby	8,173	2,930	
Stan Musial	10,972	3,630	
Jackie Robinson	4,877	1,518	
Ted Williams	7,706	2,654	

CHAPTER CHECKUP

Solve each proportion. [*page 164*]

1. $\frac{5}{8} = \frac{x}{24}$ **2.** $\frac{3}{2} = \frac{5}{y}$ **3.** $\frac{w}{9} = \frac{5}{17}$ **4.** $\frac{23}{8} = \frac{d}{19}$

Solve. [*pages 166, 168*]

5. A speedboat traveled 93 nautical miles in $2\frac{1}{2}$ hours. At that rate, how far did it travel in $1\frac{1}{2}$ hours?

6. Randy earned $9 for working $3\frac{1}{2}$ hours. At that rate how much would he earn for working $5\frac{3}{4}$ hours?

Change to a percent. [*page 170*]

7. $\frac{3}{10}$ **8.** $\frac{1}{5}$ **9.** $\frac{1}{3}$ **10.** $\frac{7}{4}$ **11.** $\frac{5}{8}$ **12.** $\frac{15}{16}$

Change to a fraction. [*page 172*]

13. 50% **14.** 120% **15.** $33\frac{1}{3}\%$ **16.** $55\frac{5}{9}\%$ **17.** 1.2% **18.** 5.6%

Copy and complete. [*page 174*]

	19.	**20.**	**21.**	**22.**	**23.**	**24.**
Decimal	.59	.3	2.4			
Percent				$37\frac{1}{2}\%$	183%	.9%

Solve each equation. [*pages 178, 180*]

25. 16% of 54 = y **26.** $66\frac{2}{3}\%$ of 171 = w **27.** 105% of 1240 = z

28. $6\frac{1}{4}\%$ of 256 = b **29.** 87.5% of 584 = g **30.** .6% of 1240 = d

Solve each equation. [*pages 182, 184*]

31. 30% of r = 18 **32.** 75% of u = 54 **33.** 110% of t = 22

34. a% of 57 = 19 **35.** x% of 40 = 6 **36.** 112.5% of v = 54

Solve. [*page 184*]

37. What percent was the price decreased?

PRICE REDUCED
~~$625~~ $550

MAJOR CHECKUP

Match. [*pages 8–9*]

1. commutative property of addition
2. associative property of multiplication
3. adding 0 property
4. commutative property of multiplication
5. multiplying by 1 property
6. associative property of addition
7. distributive property

a. $a + 0 = a$
b. $a \times b = b \times a$
c. $a \times (b + c) = (a \times b) + (a \times c)$
d. $(a + b) + c = a + (b + c)$
e. $(a \times b) \times c = a \times (b \times c)$
f. $a \times 1 = a$
g. $a + b = b + a$

Complete. [*pages 24–27*]

8. If $f(x) = 3x - 7$, then $f(8) = ?$
9. If $g(x) = 4x + 5$, then $g(0) = ?$
10. If $h(x) = x^2 - 1$, then $h(7) = ?$
11. If $j(x) = \frac{x + 7}{2}$, then $j(9) = ?$

Multiply. [*pages 68, 74, 78*]

12. 76.3×9
13. 8.96×15
14. 36.8×2.4
15. 2.56×4.2
16. 5.97×1.03

Divide. Round each quotient to the nearest tenth. [*pages 82, 86, 90*]

17. $9\overline{)211}$
18. $6\overline{)70.5}$
19. $2.4\overline{)9.06}$
20. $.45\overline{)3.906}$
21. $.106\overline{)73.51}$

Add. Reduce answers to lowest terms. [*pages 108, 114*]

22. $\frac{2}{3} + \frac{1}{6}$
23. $\frac{5}{6} + \frac{3}{4}$
24. $2\frac{1}{2} + 3\frac{1}{4}$
25. $5\frac{2}{3} + 3\frac{5}{8}$

Subtract. Reduce answers to lowest terms. [*pages 110, 114*]

26. $\frac{5}{9} - \frac{1}{3}$
27. $\frac{7}{8} - \frac{3}{5}$
28. $4\frac{1}{2} - 3\frac{1}{8}$
29. $5\frac{1}{3} - 3\frac{3}{8}$

Multiply. Reduce answers to lowest terms. [*pages 118, 122*]

30. $\frac{3}{8} \times \frac{8}{3}$
31. $\frac{5}{9} \times \frac{4}{4}$
32. $2\frac{1}{3} \times 5$
33. $1\frac{2}{5} \times 2\frac{3}{5}$

Divide. Reduce answers to lowest terms. [*pages 120, 122*]

34. $\frac{5}{8} \div \frac{5}{2}$
35. $\frac{5}{9} \div \frac{2}{3}$
36. $3 \div 2\frac{3}{8}$
37. $4\frac{2}{3} \div 3\frac{1}{2}$

1. Get a copy of a local newspaper. How many columns wide is each page? How many inches long is a full column?
2. Pick a page that has both advertising and news. What percent of the page is advertising?
3. What percent of the whole newspaper is advertising?
4. What percent of the whole paper is sports news?

Get a magazine and find out what percent of it is advertising.

1. Pick a 3-hour period during prime TV time. What percent of that time is advertising?
2. Pick a different 3-hour period of TV time. What percent of that time is advertising?
3. Look at the percents of advertising in these projects. Which is greatest?

MIDYEAR TEST

Name____________________

Substitute and simplify. [*Chapter 1*]

A	a	b	c
2	5	3	6

1. $15 - a - b$ **2.** $15 - (a - b)$ **3.** $12 \div c \div A$ **4.** $12 \div (c \div A)$

5. a^3 **6.** b^5 **7.** $a(b + c)$ **8.** Aa^2

Match. [*Chapter 1*]

9. $6(3 + 4) = 6 \times 3 + 6 \times 4$

10. $6 \times 1 = 6$

11. $6 \times 0 = 0 \times 6$

12. $6 \times (1 \times 0) = (6 \times 1) \times 0$

a. associative property of multiplication

b. multiplying by 1 property

c. commutative property of multiplication

d. distributive property

Solve. [*Chapter 1*]

13. $a + 15 = 62$ **14.** $54 - 3g = 6$ **15.** $\frac{a + 7}{5} = 12$

Give the GCF and the LCM of each pair of numbers. Use prime factors. [*Chapter 1*]

16. 35, 56 **17.** 72, 120 **18.** 225, 315

Here are two functions.

$$f(x) = 5x + 3 \qquad g(x) = 3x^2$$

Complete the following statements. [*Chapter 1*]

19. $f(6) =$ __?__ **20.** $g(6) =$ __?__ **21.** $f($_?_$) = 53$ **22.** $g($_?_$) = 27$

Complete, using decimals. [*Chapter 2*]

23. 1 year = __?__ century **24.** 9 years = __?__ century

25. 74 years = __?__ century **26.** 436 years = __?__ centuries

27. .53 century = __?__ years **28.** 1.41 centuries = __?__ years

29. Round 14.732 to the nearest tenth.

30. Round 297.5 to the nearest unit.

31. Round 47.85 to the nearest tenth.

32. Round 47.75 to the nearest tenth.

Tell how you would estimate in each exercise. [*Chapter 2*]

33. 78 + 64 **34.** 91.7 − 59.8 **35.** 6.59 + 2.16

Add or subtract. [*Chapter 2*]

36. $\begin{array}{r} 7.26 \\ +10.58 \\ \hline \end{array}$ **37.** $\begin{array}{r} .800 \\ -.395 \\ \hline \end{array}$ **38.** $\begin{array}{r} 63.01 \\ -9.57 \\ \hline \end{array}$

Follow this flow chart. [*Chapter 2*]

39.

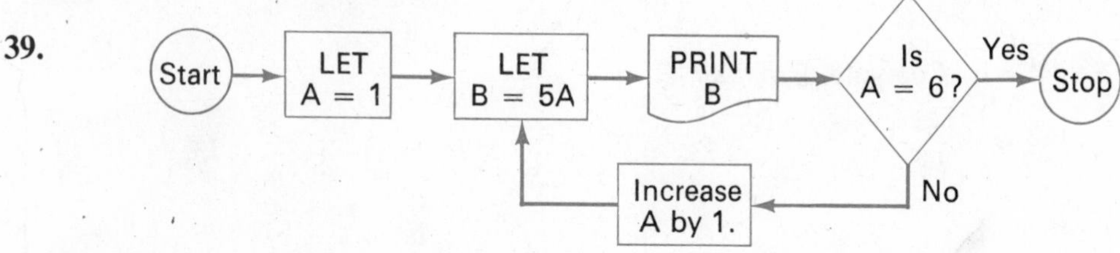

Write a flow chart that tells how to solve this problem. [*Chapter 2*]

40. Carol bought 2 shirts for \$4.45 each and a pair of pants for \$10.98. What change would she get from a \$20 bill?

41. Solve the problem of exercise 40.

Multiply. [*Chapter 3*]

42. $\begin{array}{r} 4.2 \\ \times 3 \\ \hline \end{array}$ **43.** $\begin{array}{r} 5.71 \\ \times 10 \\ \hline \end{array}$ **44.** $\begin{array}{r} 62.9 \\ \times 100 \\ \hline \end{array}$ **45.** $\begin{array}{r} 35.6 \\ \times 17 \\ \hline \end{array}$

Copy the "product" and place the decimal point. You may need to write extra zeros. [*Chapter 3*]

46. 3.8 × 5.6 = 2128 **47.** 5.13 × 8.2 = 42066 **48.** .03 × .02 = 6

Multiply. [*Chapter 3*]

49. $\begin{array}{r} 3.6 \\ \times 2.4 \\ \hline \end{array}$ **50.** $\begin{array}{r} 2.01 \\ \times 6.3 \\ \hline \end{array}$ **51.** $\begin{array}{r} .04 \\ \times .06 \\ \hline \end{array}$

Divide. [*Chapter 3*]

52. $6\overline{)3.24}$ **53.** $5\overline{)2.7}$ **54.** $25\overline{)1.75}$

Divide. Round quotients to the nearest hundredth. [*Chapter 3*]

55. $.6\overline{)3.51}$ **56.** $.29\overline{)6.41}$ **57.** $5.2\overline{)92.44}$

Change to decimals. [*Chapter 4*]

58. $\frac{3}{10}$ **59.** $\frac{1}{2}$ **60.** $\frac{3}{4}$ **61.** $\frac{2}{3}$ **62.** $\frac{1}{11}$ **63.** $\frac{3}{8}$

Change to fractions. [*Chapter 4*]

64. .7 **65.** .09 **66.** .16 **67.** .007

Copy and write the correct sign, $<$, $=$, or $>$. [*Chapter 4*]

68. $\frac{3}{7} \bullet \frac{3}{8}$ **69.** $\frac{5}{8} \bullet \frac{6}{8}$ **70.** $\frac{3}{4} \bullet \frac{5}{6}$ **71.** $\frac{3}{5} \bullet \frac{4}{7}$

Compute. [*Chapter 4*]

72. **a.** $\frac{5}{8}+\frac{3}{8}$ **b.** $\frac{5}{8}-\frac{3}{8}$ **c.** $\frac{5}{8}\times\frac{3}{8}$ **d.** $\frac{5}{8}\div\frac{3}{8}$

73. **a.** $\frac{4}{5}+\frac{1}{2}$ **b.** $\frac{4}{5}-\frac{1}{2}$ **c.** $\frac{4}{5}\times\frac{1}{2}$ **d.** $\frac{4}{5}\div\frac{1}{2}$

74. **a.** $5\frac{1}{2}+3\frac{1}{4}$ **b.** $5\frac{1}{2}-3\frac{1}{4}$ **c.** $5\frac{1}{2}\times 3\frac{1}{4}$ **d.** $5\frac{1}{2}\div 3\frac{1}{4}$

75. **a.** $6\frac{1}{2}+3\frac{2}{3}$ **b.** $6\frac{1}{2}-3\frac{2}{3}$ **c.** $6\frac{1}{2}\times 3\frac{2}{3}$ **d.** $6\frac{1}{2}\div 3\frac{2}{3}$

Solve. [*Chapter 4*]

76. $2x+\frac{3}{4}=\frac{3}{2}$ **77.** $\frac{1}{2}g-\frac{1}{3}=\frac{3}{8}$

Answer each question. [*Chapter 5*]

78. Which figure is the slide image of the black figure?

79. Which is the flip image of the black figure?

80. Which is the turn image of the black figure?

Are the two figures congruent? [*Chapter 5*]

81. **82.** **83.** **84.**

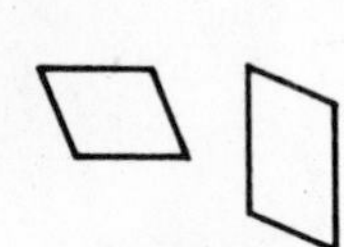

Is the dashed line a line of symmetry? [*Chapter 5*]

85.

86.

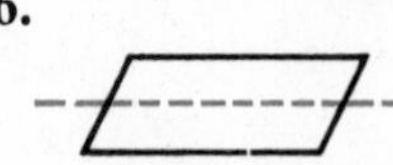

87.

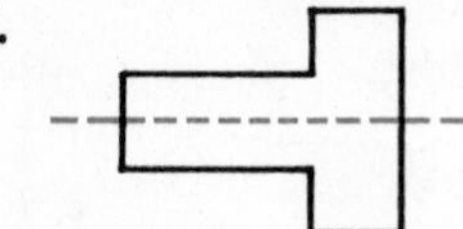

The dashed line is a line of symmetry and the red point is a point of symmetry. Sketch the whole figure. [*Chapter 5*]

88. 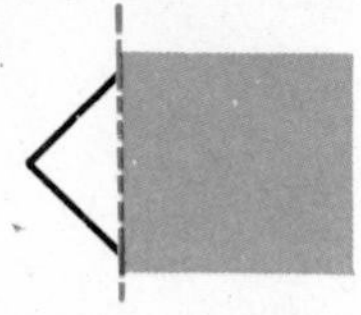

89. 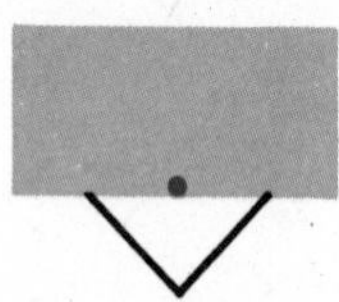

90. 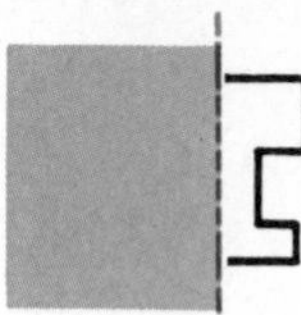

How many planes of symmetry? [*Chapter 5*]

91. 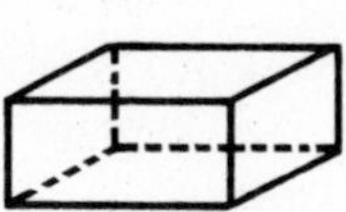

92. 

93. 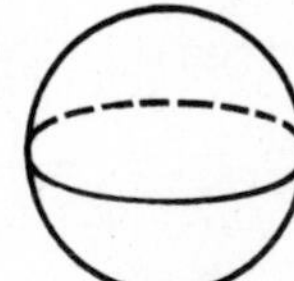

Give the ratios. [*Chapter 6*]

94. Squares to circles.

95. Red to blue.

96. Red to all figures.

Solve each proportion.

97. $\frac{3}{8} = \frac{9}{x}$

98. $\frac{5}{6} = \frac{a}{15}$

99. $\frac{3}{4} = \frac{g}{13}$

Solve. [*Chapter 6*]

100. 12 oranges cost 84¢. How much will 15 oranges cost?

101. Jerry read 24 pages in $\frac{2}{3}$ hour. At that rate how many pages could he read in $1\frac{1}{2}$ hours?

Change to percents. [*Chapter 6*]

102. $\frac{1}{2}$

103. $\frac{3}{5}$

104. $\frac{2}{3}$

105. .17

106. 1.86

Change to fractions. [*Chapter 6*]

107. 50%

108. 75%

109. $33\frac{1}{3}\%$

110. 150%

111. 100%

Complete. [*Chapter 6*]

112. 75% of 24 = ___?___

113. 16% of 43 = ___?___

114. 120% of 12 = ___?___

115. ___?___% of 16 = 8

116. ___?___% of 15 = 10

117. ___?___% of 20 = 25

118. 10% of ___?___ = 6

119. 50% of ___?___ = 8

120. 150% of ___?___ = 12

7 Measurement

Measuring length in the metric system

The meter (m) is the basic unit of length in the metric system.

Metric Units of Length
1 millimeter (mm) = .001 meter
1 centimeter (cm) = .01 meter
1 decimeter (dm) = .1 meter
1 meter (m) = 1 meter
1 dekameter (dam) = 10 meters
1 hectometer (hm) = 100 meters
1 kilometer (km) = 1000 meters

The table shows units of length that are used in the metric system.

The metric system, like our numeration system, is based on the number 10. That is, 10 of a unit is equal to 1 of the next larger unit.

Examples. 10 mm = 1 cm 10 cm = 1 dm 10 dm = 1 m

Below are some ways that the length of the pencil can be recorded.

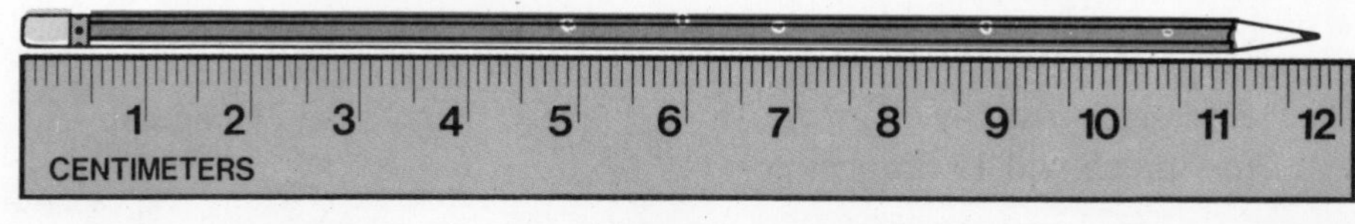

118 mm 11.8 cm 1.18 dm

Since the metric system is based on the number 10, you can change from one unit to another by "moving the decimal point" and changing the unit name. For example, the length of the pencil is

118 mm = 11.8 cm = 1.18 dm = .118 m = .0118 dam

How many hectometers long is the pencil? How many kilometers? These examples should help you remember which way to move the decimal point.

5.63 m = ___?___ cm

Changing to two units smaller. The number of units will be greater. So, move the decimal point 2 places to the right.

807 mm = ___?___ m

Changing to three units greater. The number of units will be smaller. So, move the decimal point 3 places to the left.

EXERCISES

Get a ruler that is marked off in millimeters. Draw segments of these lengths.

1. 7 cm	**2.** 1 dm	**3.** 1.3 dm	**4.** 49 mm	**5.** 5.6 cm
6. 109 mm	**7.** 9.3 cm	**8.** 78 mm	**9.** 7.8 cm	**10.** .78 dm

Complete.

11. 3 km = ___?___ m	**12.** 2 km = ___?___ dam	**13.** 1 km = ___?___ hm
14. 3 km = ___?___ mm	**15.** 5.2 km = ___?___ hm	**16.** 16.9 m = ___?___ dm
17. 9.59 m = ___?___ cm	**18.** 43.9 m = ___?___ mm	**19.** 68.2 dm = ___?___ m
20. 68.2 dm = ___?___ cm	**21.** 68.2 dm = ___?___ mm	**22.** 68.2 dm = ___?___ dam
23. 59.3 cm = ___?___ m	**24.** 7.46 mm = ___?___ cm	**25.** 5.06 m = ___?___ hm
26. 74.3 km = ___?___ m		

27. Arrange these lengths in order from shortest to longest. (*Hint:* Change to a common unit.)

830 mm	8 m	.799 dam	8.1 dm	79 dm	804 cm	8.03 m	83.7 cm

1. Measure the length of a school corridor to the nearest meter.
2. Measure the height of your desk to the nearest centimeter.
3. Measure the length of a pencil to the nearest millimeter.
4. Measure the width of your classroom to the nearest decimeter.

Select a convenient path around your school grounds. What is its length in meters? Convert your measurement to kilometers.

EXCURSION

Copy and continue this pattern of numbers.

1
1 1
1 2 1
1 3 3 1
1 4 6 4 1
* * * * * *
* * * * * * *
* * * * * * * *

Add the numbers in each horizontal row. What do you notice about the sums?

Supplementary Exercises, Set 41, page 385

Converting units

Here are some units of measure in the English system.

Units of Length	Units of Capacity
12 inches (in. or ″) = 1 foot (ft or ′) 3 feet (ft) = 1 yard (yd) 1760 yards (yd) = 1 mile (mi) (or 5280 ft)	3 teaspoons (tsp) = 1 tablespoon (tbsp) 16 tablespoons = 1 cup (c) 2 cups = 1 pint (pt) 2 pints = 1 quart (qt) 4 quarts = 1 gallon (gal)
Units of Weight	**Units of Dry Measure**
16 ounces (oz) = 1 pound (lb) 2000 pounds (lb) = 1 ton (t)	2 pints (pt) = 1 quart (qt) 8 quarts = 1 peck (pk) 4 pecks = 1 bushel (bu)

Example 1. Convert 4 feet to inches.

$$4 \text{ ft} = 4 \text{ ft} \times \frac{12 \text{ in.}}{1 \text{ ft}}$$

$$= 4 \cancel{\text{ft}} \times \frac{12 \text{ in.}}{1 \cancel{\text{ft}}}$$

$$= 48 \text{ in.}$$

Example 2. Convert 18 pints to gallons.

$$18 \text{ pt} = 18 \text{ pt} \cdot \frac{1 \text{ gal}}{8 \text{ pt}}$$

$$= \overset{9}{\cancel{18}} \cancel{\text{pt}} \cdot \frac{1 \text{ gal}}{\underset{4}{\cancel{8}} \cancel{\text{pt}}}$$

$$= 2\frac{1}{4} \text{ gal}$$

Or, we can make the same conversion by using two conversion fractions.

$$18 \text{ pt} = 18 \text{ pt} \cdot \frac{1 \text{ qt}}{2 \text{ pt}} \cdot \frac{1 \text{ gal}}{4 \text{ qt}}$$

$$= \overset{9}{\cancel{18}} \cancel{\text{pt}} \cdot \frac{1 \cancel{\text{qt}}}{\underset{1}{\cancel{2}} \cancel{\text{pt}}} \cdot \frac{1 \text{ gal}}{4 \cancel{\text{qt}}}$$

$$= \frac{9}{4} \text{ gal} = 2\frac{1}{4} \text{ gal}$$

Notice that the numerator of the conversion fraction contains the unit you are converting to and the denominator contains the unit you are converting from.

EXERCISES

Copy and complete each of these conversion fractions.

1. $\frac{1 \text{ ft}}{? \text{ in.}}$ **2.** $\frac{? \text{ lb}}{16 \text{ oz}}$ **3.** $\frac{1 \text{ ton}}{? \text{ lb}}$ **4.** $\frac{1 \text{ mi}}{? \text{ yd}}$ **5.** $\frac{? \text{ ft}}{1 \text{ yd}}$

6. $\frac{1 \text{ bu}}{4 \ ?}$ **7.** $\frac{1 \text{ m}}{100 \ ?}$ **8.** $\frac{4 \ ?}{1 \text{ gal}}$ **9.** $\frac{8 \text{ qt}}{1 \ ?}$ **10.** $\frac{4 \text{ c}}{? \text{ qt}}$

Use the method shown in this lesson to convert the following.

11. 28 yd to ft **12.** 5.4 cm to m **13.** 20 pt to gal

14. .4 km to m **15.** 8 qt to cups **16.** 4 cups to tbsp

17. 108 in. to yd **18.** 18 gal to qt **19.** 5 bu to qt

20. 2640 yd to mi **21.** 2640 ft to mi **22.** 2 mi to yd

Solve.

23. The length of sea routes is generally given in nautical miles. A nautical mile is 1.852 kilometers. Convert each distance to kilometers.

Sea route	Nautical miles	Kilo-meters
New York–Liverpool	3079	?
San Francisco–Yokohama	4536	?
Los Angeles–Panama	2913	?

1. Have a classmate use a stopwatch and time you running the 50-yard dash.
2. Convert yards per second to miles per hour.

Hint: Use these conversion fractions:

$\frac{1 \text{ mi}}{1760 \text{ yd}}$ $\frac{3600 \text{ sec}}{1 \text{ hr}}$

EXCURSION

The steps below show how to bisect an angle.

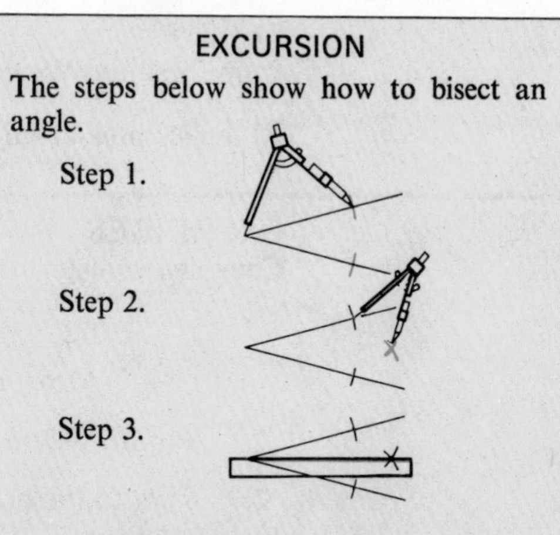

Draw some triangles. Bisect the three angles of each triangle. What do you notice about the three angle bisectors of each triangle?

Supplementary Exercises, Set 42, page 385

Error of measurement

The pin is 1 dm long when measured to the nearest decimeter.

8 cm to the nearest cm.

83 mm to the nearest mm.

Of course, no measurement is exact. The precision of a measurement depends on the size of the unit used. Here is an example:

In each case there was some error in the measurement. The error of measurement is the difference between the exact length and the measured length. Notice that the error of measurement is less when a smaller unit is used. The greatest possible error (g.p.e.) is always $\frac{1}{2}$ of the unit used in a measurement. For example, suppose the length of a segment is 2 inches measured to the nearest half inch. The measurement by itself tells us that the exact length is closer to 2 inches than to $1\frac{1}{2}$ inches or $2\frac{1}{2}$ inches. The exact length must fall

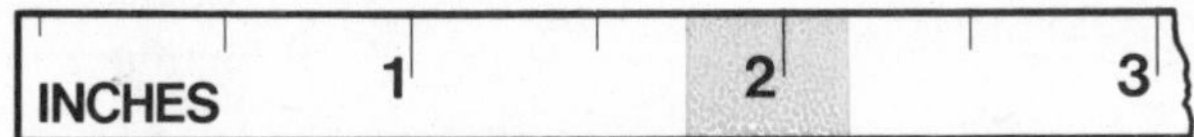

somewhere in the "yellow range." The greatest possible error is $\frac{1}{4}$ inch. That is, the exact length cannot differ more than $\frac{1}{4}$ inch from 2 inches. We can express this length as 2 in. $\pm \frac{1}{4}$ in. (Read as "2 inches plus or minus $\frac{1}{4}$ inch").

EXERCISES

Copy and complete this table.

	Measurement	Greatest possible error	Range for exact length
1.	8 in. to the nearest in.	?	? ± ?
2.	6 cm to the nearest cm	?	? ± ?
3.	$3\frac{1}{2}$ in. to the nearest $\frac{1}{2}$ in.	?	? ± ?
4.	98 m to the nearest m	?	? ± ?

Copy and complete this table.

	Measurement	Greatest possible error	Range for exact length
5.	8.2 m to the nearest .1 m	?	___?___ ± ___?___
6.	4.05 m to the nearest .01 m	?	___?___ ± ___?___
7.	$8\frac{1}{3}$ yd to the nearest $\frac{1}{3}$ yd	?	___?___ ± ___?___
8.	$10\frac{3}{8}$ in. to the nearest $\frac{1}{8}$ in.	?	___?___ ± ___?___

9. Which unit will give the most precise measurement?

a. a centimeter, a dekameter, a decimeter

b. a yard, an inch, a foot

c. a ton, an ounce, a pound

d. a day, an hour, a second, a minute

e. a quart, a cup, a gallon, a pint

Measure each segment to the nearest inch, $\frac{1}{2}$ inch, and $\frac{1}{4}$ inch. Then give the range for the exact length.

10. ________________

11. ______________________________

12. ________________________________

13. ________________

14. ________________________

15. ____________________

16. ____________________________

Here are some measurements. Give the greatest possible exact length and the least possible exact length.

17. $9\frac{1}{4}$ in. $\pm \frac{1}{8}$ in.

18. 8 cm ± .5 cm

19. $6\frac{1}{2}$ yd $\pm \frac{1}{4}$ yd

20. 15.4 km ± .05 km

21. $13\frac{1}{2}$ ft $\pm \frac{1}{4}$ ft

22. 18.5 m ± .05 m

23. John measured two segments. One was 1 cm to the nearest cm and the other was 500 cm to the nearest cm. What was the g.p.e. in each measurement? Do you think one measurement was better than the other?

CHECKUP

for pages 196–197

Complete.

1. 13 m = ___?___ dm

2. 568 mm = ___?___ cm

3. 32 cm = ___?___ mm

4. 1.5 m = ___?___ mm

5. 6 m = ___?___ mm

6. 25 hm = ___?___ km

7. 46 m = ___?___ dam

8. 82 cm = ___?___ m

9. 354 mm = ___?___ dm

10. 23 m = ___?___ cm

11. 18 km = ___?___ hm

12. 1.3 km = ___?___ m

Answers on page 427.

Skill Maintenance, Set 45, page 409

Relative error

Below are pictured two dowels and their measures.

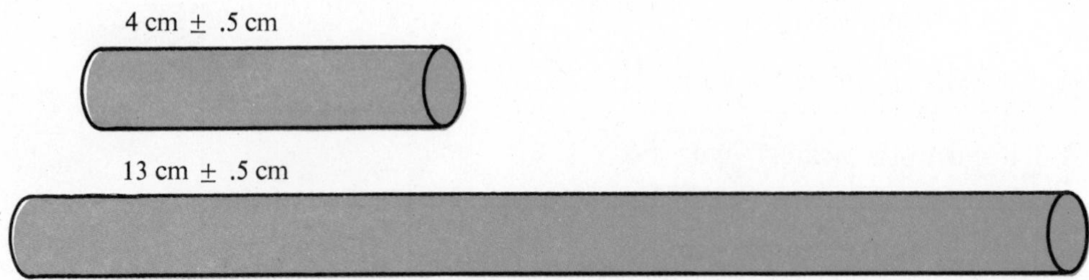

The exact length of the shorter dowel is within .5 cm of 4 cm. So it is possible to have an error of measurement of .5 cm in 4 cm. This is called the **relative error** of the measurement and is expressed as a ratio:

greatest possible error / measurement → $\frac{.5\text{ cm}}{4\text{ cm}} = \frac{5}{40} = \frac{1}{8}$ ← relative error

What is the relative error of the measurement of the longer dowel? Do you see that the greater the measurement compared with the error the less the relative error will be? Often the relative error ratio is expressed as a percent and is called the **percent of error**. Since the relative error of the measurement of the shorter dowel is $\frac{1}{8}$, the percent of error can be found by changing $\frac{1}{8}$ to a percent.

Compute the percent of error for the measurement of the longer dowel. Is it less than the percent of error for the measurement of the shorter dowel? Provided that you measure with the same unit, should the percent of error be less for a longer measurement? Should it be greater for a shorter measurement? Why or why not?

EXERCISES

Copy and complete this table.

	Measurement	Greatest possible error	Relative error (common fraction)	Percent of error
1.	6 in. $\pm \frac{1}{2}$ in.	$\frac{1}{2}$ in.	$\frac{.5}{6} =$?	?
2.	15 cm $\pm$ .5 cm	?	?	?
3.	$8\frac{1}{2}$ ft $\pm \frac{1}{4}$ ft	?	?	?
4.	24 ft $\pm \frac{1}{4}$ ft	?	?	?
5.	18 m $\pm$ .5 m	?	?	?
6.	46.3 m $\pm$ .05 m	?	?	?

Solve.

7. Sarah threw a softball 72 feet, measured to the nearest foot. What was the relative error of the measurement?

8. The capacity of a container is 15.6 liters, measured to the nearest .1 liter. What is the relative error?

9. A package of meat weighs 2.54 pounds, measured to the nearest hundredth pound. What is the percent of error?

10. José ran the 100-meter dash in 13.5 seconds. If the time was measured to the nearest .1 second, what was the percent of error?

Measure your height to the nearest centimeter. Compute the percent of error of your measurement.

Measure your weight to the nearest pound. Compute the percent of error of your measurement.

EXCURSION

Copy and complete this magic square.

1	?	$\frac{1}{2}$
?	$1\frac{1}{4}$	?
2	?	?

Supplementary Exercises, Set 43, page 386

Measuring angles

The **degree** is the standard unit used for measuring angles. Pictured here is a 1° angle.

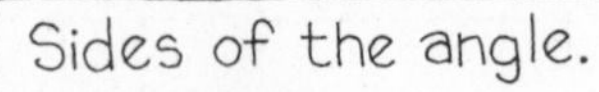

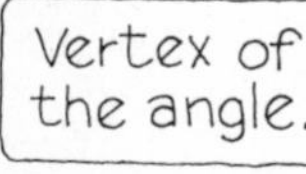

If you divide a degree into sixty parts, each part is called a **minute**. If you divide a minute into sixty parts, each part is called a **second**. What fraction of a degree is a minute? What fraction of a minute is a second? What fraction of a degree is a second?

A protractor is used to measure angles. To measure an angle, place the vertex of the angle at the center of the protractor and one side of the angle at the 0° mark.

The measure of the angle is 20°. Read "20°" as "twenty degrees."

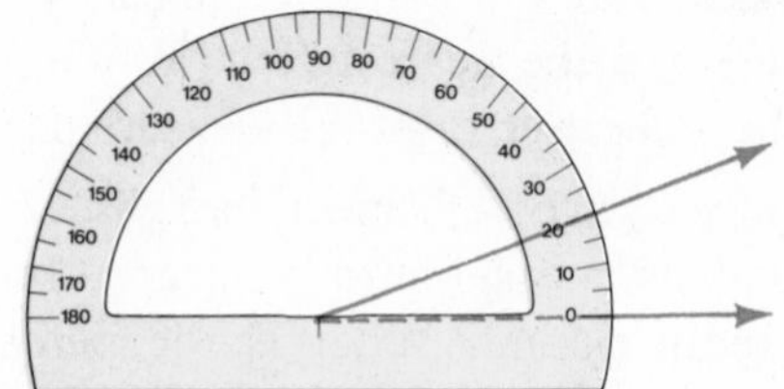

The measurement was made to the nearest degree. Suppose that the angle was measured to the nearest second with a very precise instrument and was found to measure 20 degrees, 18 minutes, and 37 seconds.

Remember that an angle whose measure is between 0° and 90° is called an acute angle, an angle whose measure is 90° is called a right angle, and an angle whose measure is between 90° and 180° is called an obtuse angle.

EXERCISES

Measure each angle to the nearest degree.

1. 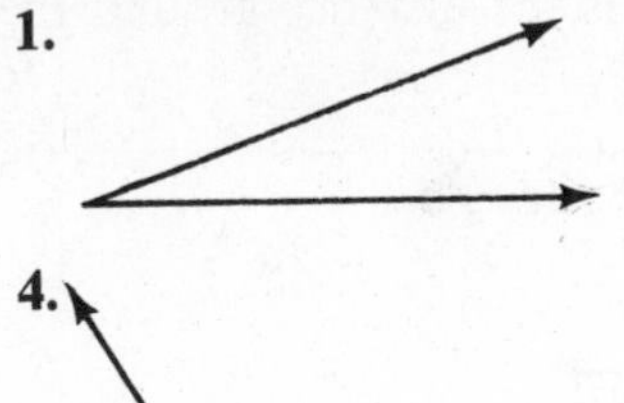

2. 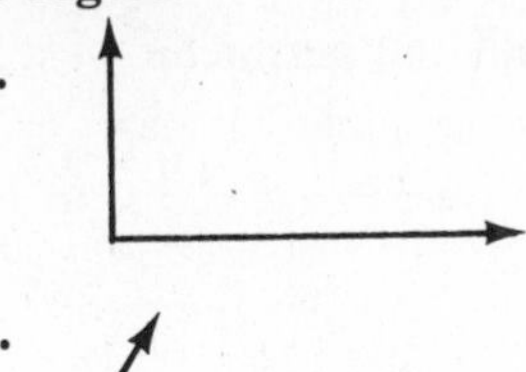

3. 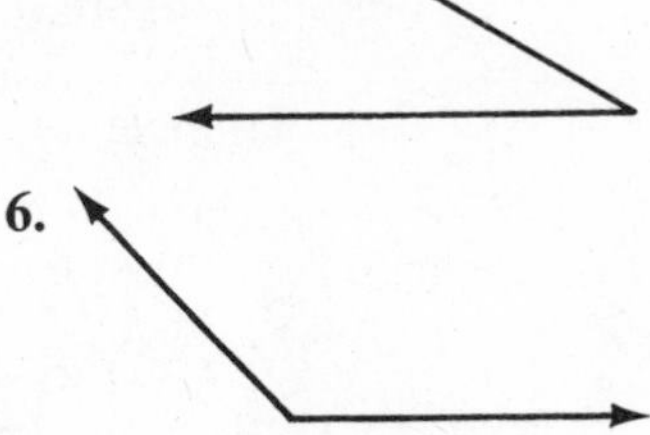

4.

5.

6.

7. a. Which of the angles in exercises 1–6 are acute angles?
b. Which are right angles? **c.** Which are obtuse angles?

Draw angles having these measures.

8. 8° **9.** 59° **10.** 115° **11.** 74° **12.** 90° **13.** 162°

Give each sum or difference.

Regroup 60′ for 1°.

14. 28° 15′ + 19° 17′

15. 64° 29′ + 30° 48′

16. 52° 42′ 27″ + 43° 23′ 54″

Regroup 1° for 60′.

17. 63° 42′ − 27° 15′

18. 48° 23′ − 12° 49′

19. 53° 19′ 41″ − 44° 24′ 52″

1. Draw a large triangle. Add the measures of the angles. Repeat with some other triangles. In each case you should have gotten 180° for the sum. This has been recorded in the table.

Number of sides	3	4	5
Sum of measures of angles	180°	?	?

2. Copy the table. Repeat step 1 for 4-sided figures and fill in your table.

3. Extend your table as far as you wish.

4. What would the sum of the angles for an n-sided figure be?

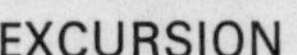

Remember that a prime number is a number having exactly 2 factors. For example, 2, 3, 5, 7, 11, . . . are prime numbers. Notice that 13 and 31 are both prime. What other pairs of two-digit prime numbers have the same digits?

Supplementary Exercises, Set 44, page 386

Perimeter

Remember that the **perimeter** of a figure is the distance around the figure.

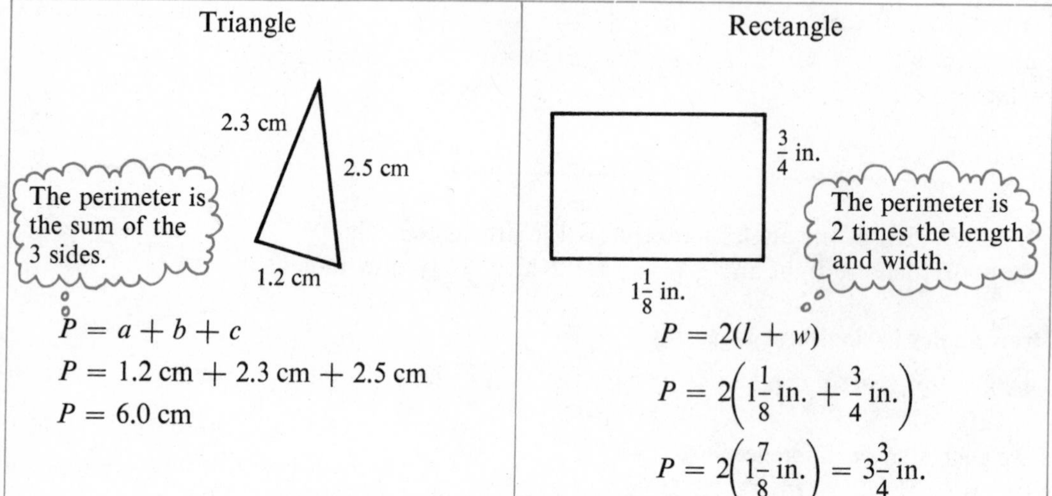

$P = a + b + c$

$P = 1.2\text{ cm} + 2.3\text{ cm} + 2.5\text{ cm}$

$P = 6.0\text{ cm}$

$P = 2(l + w)$

$P = 2\left(1\frac{1}{8}\text{ in.} + \frac{3}{4}\text{ in.}\right)$

$P = 2\left(1\frac{7}{8}\text{ in.}\right) = 3\frac{3}{4}\text{ in.}$

Generally, the perimeter of a figure is determined by measuring the sides of the figure and then adding those lengths. However, when this is done the error of measurement accumulates. For example, suppose that the perimeter of the plot of land pictured below is to be determined. The length of each side is first measured to the nearest .1 meter.

Then the measures are added like this:

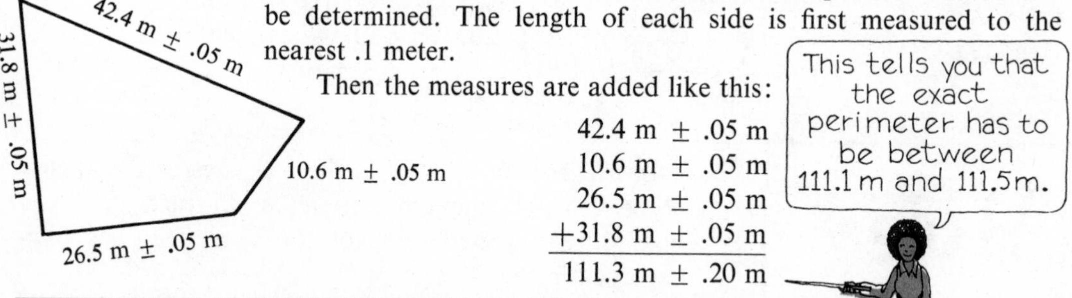

$$\begin{array}{r} 42.4\text{ m} \pm .05\text{ m} \\ 10.6\text{ m} \pm .05\text{ m} \\ 26.5\text{ m} \pm .05\text{ m} \\ +31.8\text{ m} \pm .05\text{ m} \\ \hline 111.3\text{ m} \pm .20\text{ m} \end{array}$$

EXERCISES

Compute each perimeter.

1. square, 3.5 m

2.

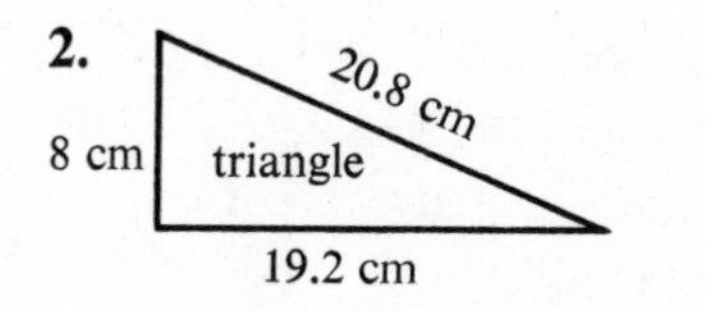

3.

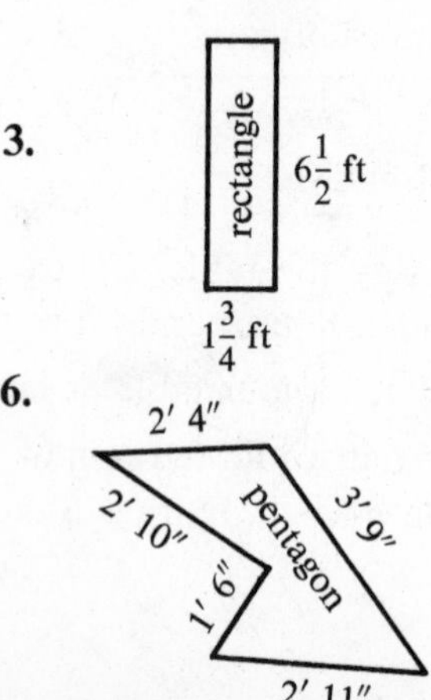

4.

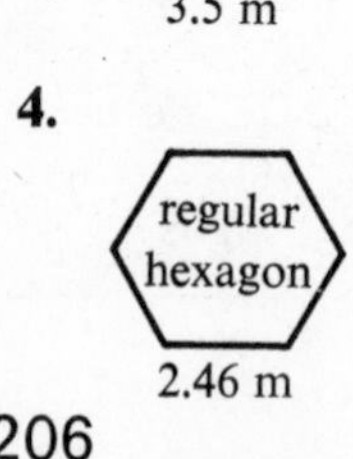

5.

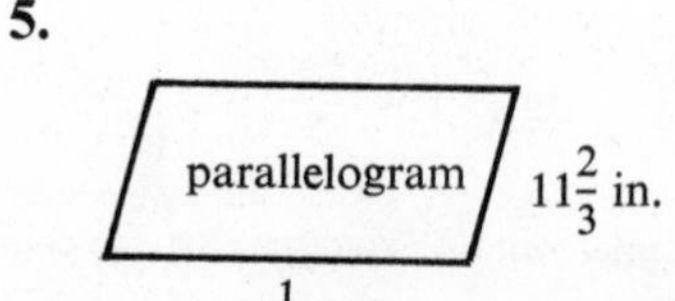

6. pentagon

7. 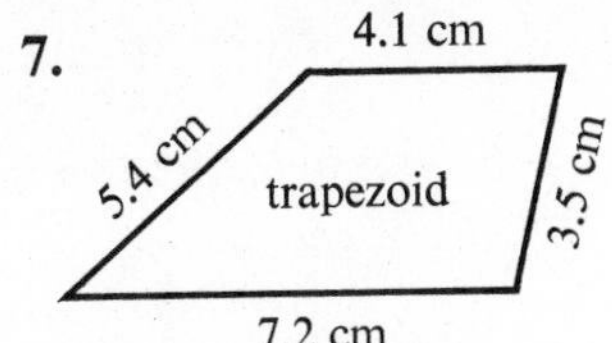

8. rhombus

2 yd 2 ft

9. 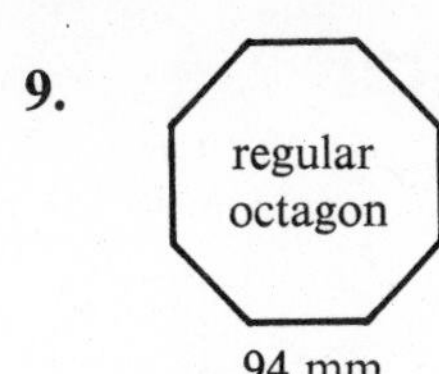

First measure each side to the nearest millimeter. Then compute the perimeter.

10. 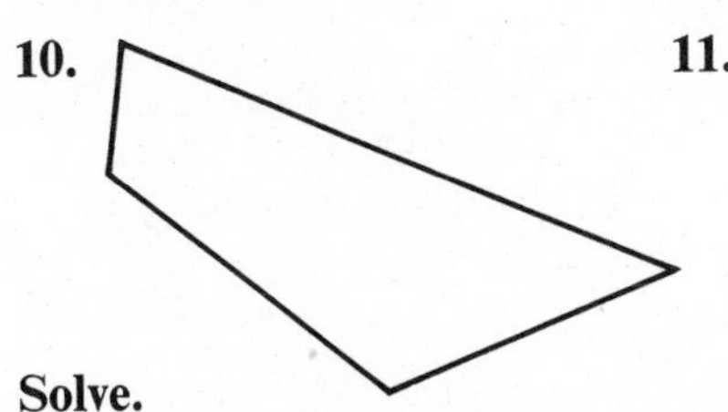

11.

12. 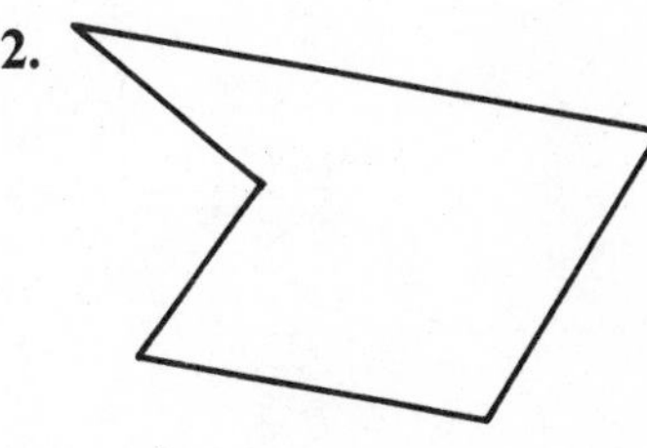

Solve.

13. A rectangular lot that measures 56 m by 120 m is to be fenced in with fencing that costs \$4.30 a running meter. How much will the fencing cost?

14. An $18\frac{1}{2}'$ by $28\frac{1}{4}'$ rectangular patio is to be edged with brick. If each brick is 8 inches long, how many bricks will it take to edge the patio?

15. The perimeter of a rectangular parking lot is 580 feet. The lot is 150 feet long. What is its width?

16. Give the dimensions of a square that has the same perimeter as an equilateral triangle with sides of 6.4 dm.

Measure the length and width of a rectangular room to the nearest decimeter. Compute the perimeter. Determine within what range the exact perimeter must be.

Get a geoboard or some dot paper. See how many polygons you can construct that have a perimeter of 12 units.

Example. 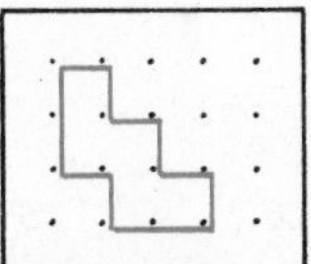

Keep a record of your polygons.

EXCURSION

Here is part of a multiplication table. Two patterns are shown in red. Find some other patterns.

×	0	1	2	3	4	5	6
0	0	0	0	0	0	0	0
1	0	1	2	3	4	5	6
2	0	2	4	6	8	10	12
3	0	3	6	9	12	15	18
4	0	4	8	12	16	20	24
5	0	5	10	15	20	25	30

One sum is always 1 greater than the other.

Skill Maintenance, Set 46, page 409

Area

Remember that the area of a region is the number of square units that it takes to cover the region.

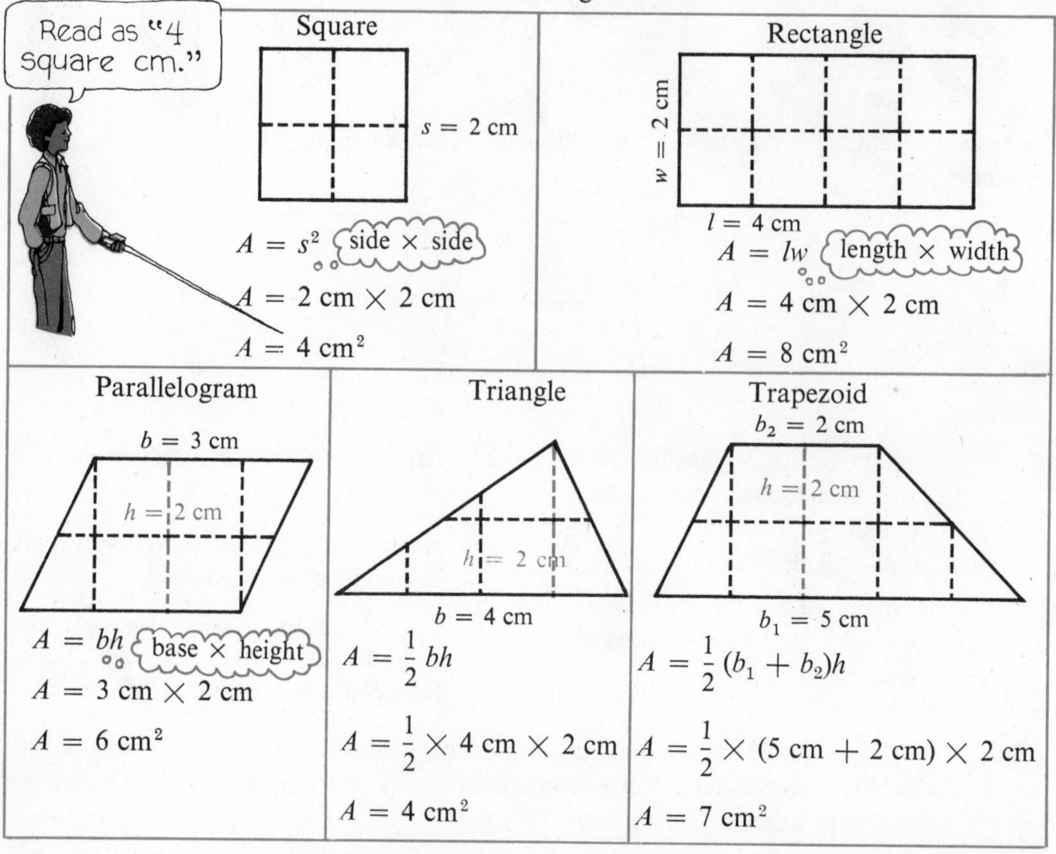

To convert from one square unit to another, you can use the method that you worked with earlier.

Example 1. Convert 2 yd² to square feet.

Method 1. Using 1 conversion fraction:	Method 2. Using 2 conversion fractions:
$2 \text{ yd}^2 = 2 \text{ yd}^2 \cdot \boxed{\dfrac{9 \text{ ft}^2}{1 \text{ yd}^2}}$ $= 18 \text{ ft}^2$	$2 \text{ yd}^2 = 2 \text{ yd}^2 \cdot \boxed{\dfrac{3 \text{ ft}}{1 \text{ yd}}} \cdot \boxed{\dfrac{3 \text{ ft}}{1 \text{ yd}}}$ $= 2 \times 9 \text{ ft}^2 = 18 \text{ ft}^2$

Example 2. Convert 224 dm² to square meters.

Method 1.	Method 2.
$224 \text{ dm}^2 = 224 \text{ dm}^2 \cdot \boxed{\dfrac{1 \text{ m}^2}{100 \text{ dm}^2}}$ $= 2.24 \text{ m}^2$	$224 \text{ dm}^2 = 224 \text{ dm}^2 \cdot \boxed{\dfrac{1 \text{ m}}{10 \text{ dm}}} \cdot \boxed{\dfrac{1 \text{ m}}{10 \text{ dm}}}$ $= 2.24 \text{ m}^2$

EXERCISES

Compute each area.

1. 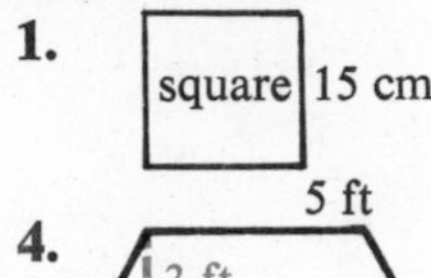

2. 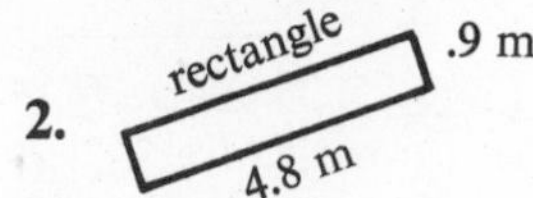

3. 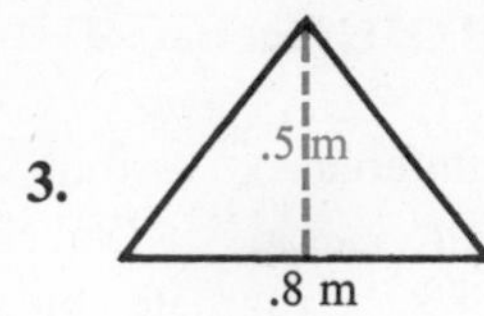

4. 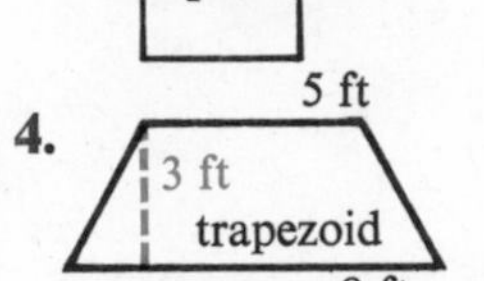

5. 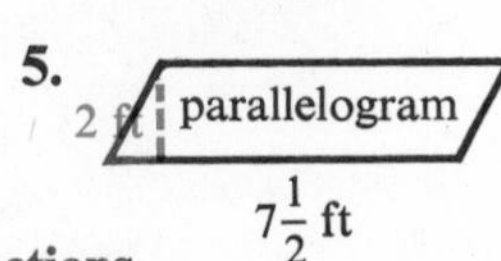

6. 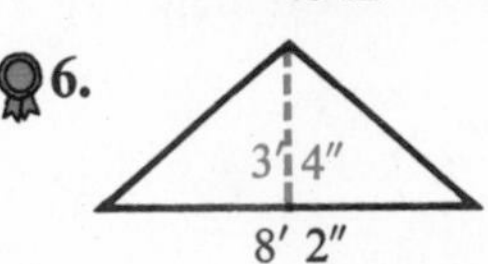

Convert by using conversion fractions.

7. 3 ft^2 to $in.^2$

8. 4 yd^2 to ft^2

9. 1 yd^2 to $in.^2$

10. 2.5 m^2 to dm^2

11. 12.8 cm^2 to mm^2

12. 1584 cm^2 to dm^2

13. $\frac{1}{4}$ mi^2 to yd^2

14. 1.5 km^2 to m^2

15. $\frac{1}{4}$ yd^2 to $in.^2$

Solve.

16. A rectangular room 6.2 m by 4.5 m is to be covered with carpet costing $14.75 a square meter. How much will the carpet cost? Round your answer to the nearest dollar.

17. A rectangular room is $15\frac{1}{2}$ feet by $23\frac{3}{4}$ feet. How many square yards of carpeting are needed to carpet the room?

18. A fence is $5\frac{1}{2}$ feet high and 406 feet long. How much paint is necessary for both sides if 1 gallon will cover 325 sq. ft? Round the answer "up" to the next gallon.

1. The **are** (a) is the metric unit used for measuring land area. A square 10 meters on a side has an area of 1 are: 1 a = 100 m^2. The other unit for measuring land area is the **hectare**: 1 hectare = 100 ares. Determine the land area of your school grounds in ares. In hectares.

2. On a geoboard or dot paper construct a square, a rectangle, a triangle, a trapezoid, and a parallelogram the same area.

CHECKUP
for pages 202–203

Give the percent of error of each measure. Round the answers to the nearest .1%.

1. 100 m ± .5 m **2.** 64 ft ± $\frac{1}{2}$ ft

3. 36 qt ± $\frac{1}{2}$ qt **4.** $20\frac{1}{2}$ gal ± $\frac{1}{4}$ gal

5. $42\frac{1}{4}$ in. ± $\frac{1}{8}$ in. **6.** 5 lb 8 oz ± $\frac{1}{2}$ oz

Answers on page 427.

Supplementary Exercises, Set 45, page 386

Circumference and area of a circle

The **circumference** of a circle is the distance around the circle. It can be found by multiplying the diameter by π (pi).

Formula $C = \pi d$

π is a number for which we will use an approximation of $3\frac{1}{7}$ or 3.14. So, the circumference of a circle is a little more than 3 times the diameter of the circle. To see that this is reasonable, you could do the following experiment.

1. Find a line marked on a playground or sidewalk.
2. Mark a starting point on a bicycle wheel.
3. Roll the wheel along the line one complete revolution and mark the stopping point.
4. Compare the diameter of the wheel with the distance traveled in one complete revolution (its circumference).

The area of a circle can be found by multiplying the square of the radius by π.

Formula $A = \pi r^2$

Again we will use $3\frac{1}{7}$ or 3.14 as an approximation for π. The following picture should verify the formula for you.

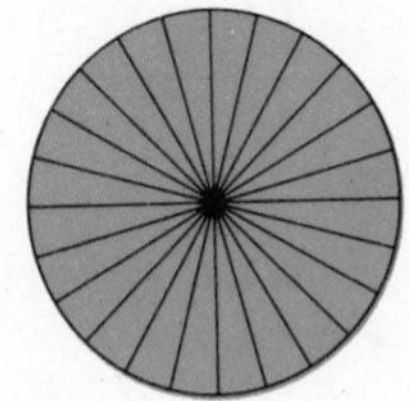

Take the circle apart and put it together like this.

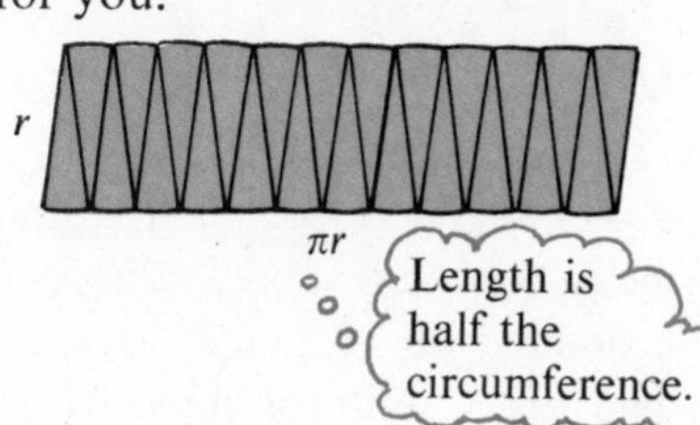

Example. Compute the circumference and area of the circle shown below. Use 3.14 as an approximation for π.

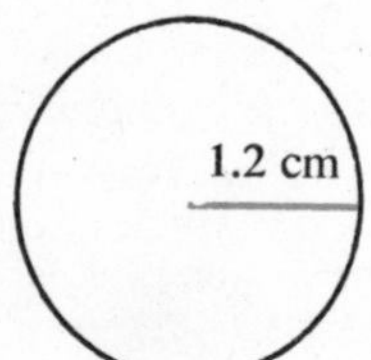

$C = \pi d$

$C = 3.14 \times 2.4 \text{ cm}$

$C = 75.36 \text{ cm}$

$A = \pi r^2$

$A = 3.14\ (1.2 \text{ cm})^2$

$A = 3.14\ (1.44 \text{ cm}^2)$

$A = 4.52 \text{ cm}^2$

Rounded to the nearest .01

EXERCISES

Give the circumference and area of each circle to the nearest .01. Use 3.14 as an approximation for π.

1.

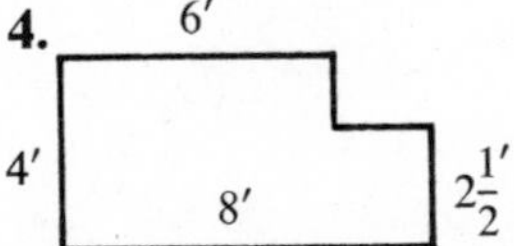

2.

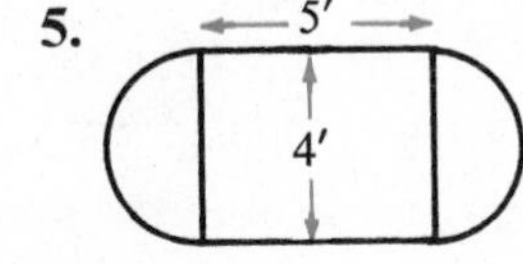

3.

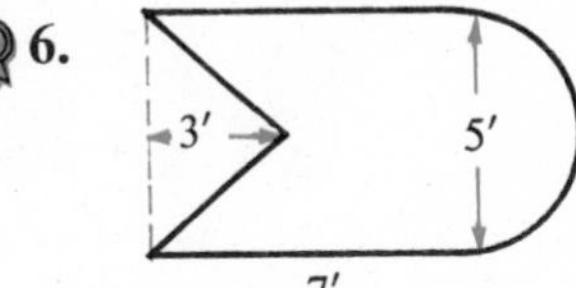

Give each area. Use $3\frac{1}{7}$ as an approximation for π.

(*Hint:* Find the area of each part and add.)

4. 6′, 4′, 8′, $2\frac{1}{2}$′

5. 5′, 4′

6. 3′, 5′, 7′

Solve. Use 3.14 as an approximation for π.

7. The circumference of a circle is 28.26 meters. What is its diameter?

8. What's the area of the largest circle that can be cut from a square measuring 6.8 cm on a side?

9. Four circular disks each 1.2 dm in diameter are to be stamped out of a square piece of sheet metal that measures 2.5 dm on a side. How much metal will be wasted? What percent of the metal will be wasted?

10. A 10-inch (diameter) pizza sells for \$1.90. At that rate how much should be charged for a 14-inch pizza?

Although π cannot be expressed as a terminating or repeating decimal, a decimal approximation to any degree of accuracy can be obtained. For example, 3.14159265 is the decimal approximation correct to 8 decimal places. Carefully carry out the experiment described on the preceding page, using circles of different sizes. Use as small a unit as possible when measuring. Record and average your approximations for π. To how many decimal places was your average correct?

EXCURSION

The steps below show how to construct the perpendicular bisector of a line segment.

Step 1.

Step 2.

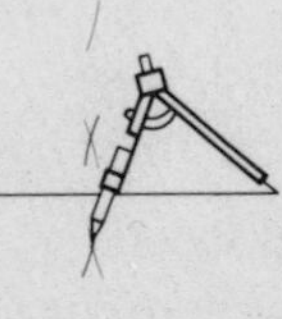

Step 3.

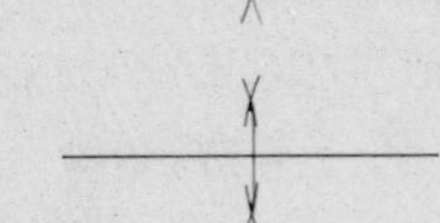

Draw some triangles. Construct the perpendicular bisectors of the three sides of each triangle. What do you notice about the perpendicular bisectors of the sides of each triangle?

Skill Maintenance, Set 47, page 410

Surface area—prism and cylinder

Pictured below are some **prisms.**
Notice that the lateral (yellow) faces of a prism are always rectangular. Also notice that the bases (blue faces) are congruent and are in parallel planes.

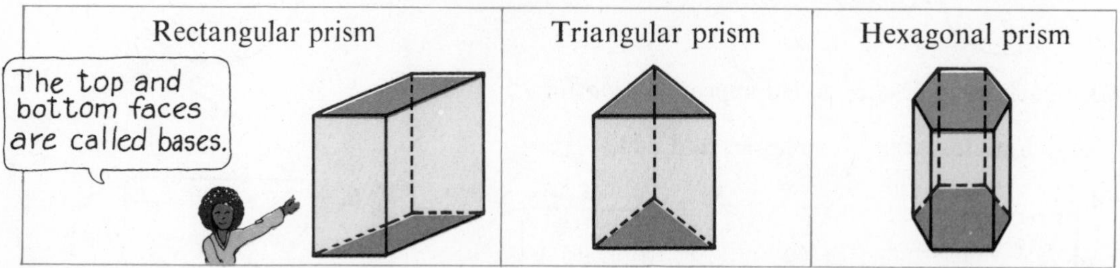

The surface area of a prism is the sum of the areas of all the faces.
Pictured here is a (right circular) cylinder.

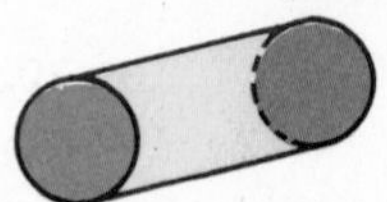

The bases are circular.

The surface area of a cylinder is the sum of the areas of the rounded surface and the bases.

Example 1.

Compute the surface area.

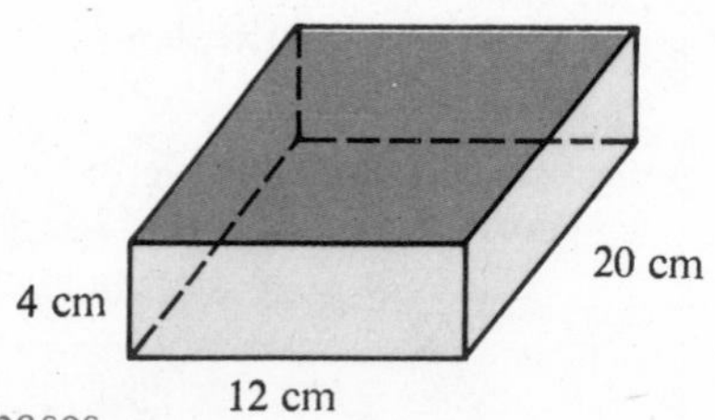

Area of bases

$2(12 \text{ cm} \cdot 20 \text{ cm}) = 480 \text{ cm}^2$

Area of lateral faces

$2(4 \text{ cm} \cdot 12 \text{ cm}) + 2(4 \text{ cm} \cdot 20 \text{ cm})$

$= 96 \text{ cm}^2 + 160 \text{ cm}^2$

$= 256 \text{ cm}^2$

Surface area $= 480 \text{ cm}^2 + 256 \text{ cm}^2$

$= 736 \text{ cm}^2$

Example 2.

Compute the surface area.
Use 3.14 as an approximation for π.

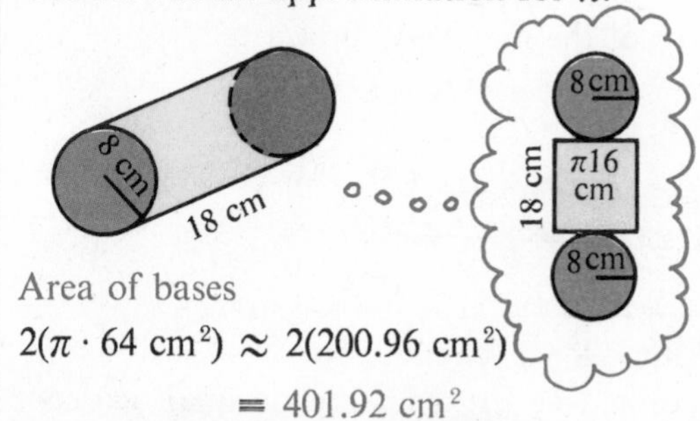

Area of bases

$2(\pi \cdot 64 \text{ cm}^2) \approx 2(200.96 \text{ cm}^2)$

$= 401.92 \text{ cm}^2$

Notice that the rounded surface can be thought of as a rectangle that has a width equal to the circumference of the circle.

Area of rounded surface

$18 \text{ cm} \cdot \pi \cdot 16 \text{ cm} = \pi \cdot 288 \text{ cm}^2$

$\approx 904.32 \text{ cm}^2$

Surface area $\approx 401.92 \text{ cm}^2 + 904.32 \text{ cm}^2$

$= 1306.24 \text{ cm}^2$

EXERCISES

Find the surface area. Use $3\frac{1}{7}$ as an approximation for π.

1. 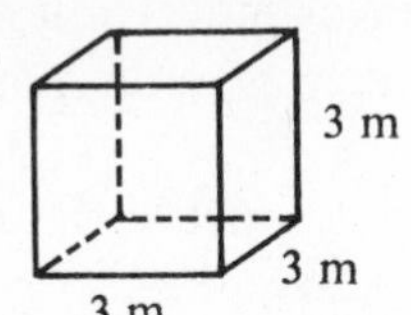

2. 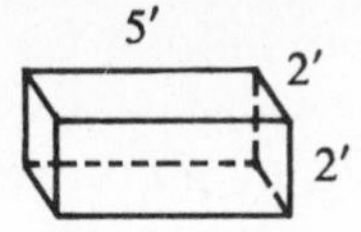

3. 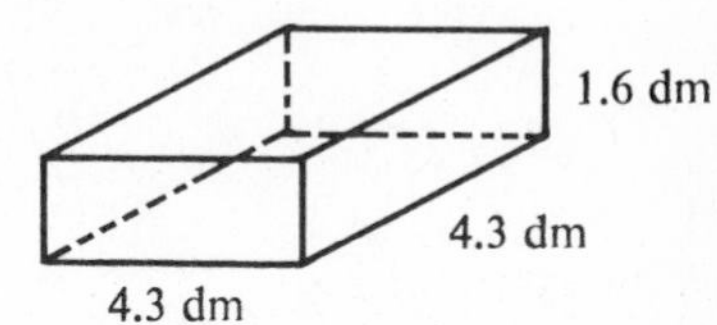

4. 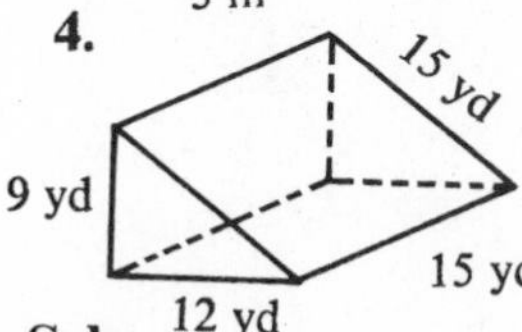

5. 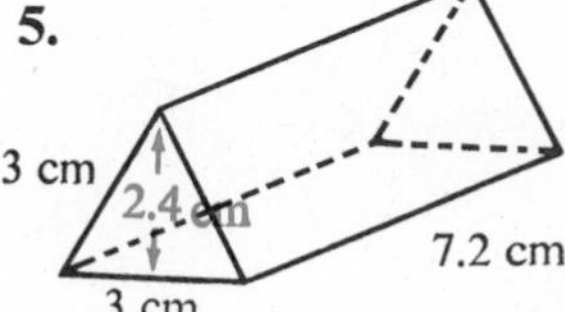

6. 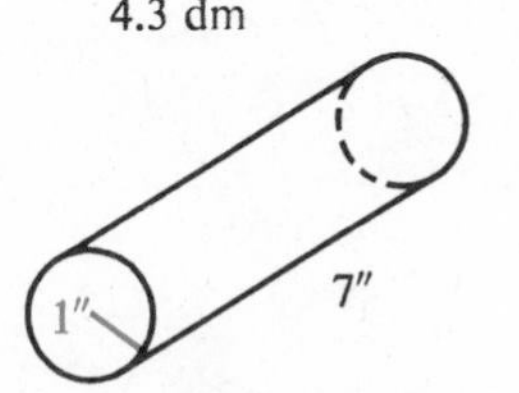

Solve.

7. An open cylinder is made from a square piece of sheet metal measuring 5.25 m on a side. What will be the radius of the cylinder? Use 3.14 for π. Round answer to the nearest .01 m.

8. A round silo has a height of 15.5 meters and a diameter of 4.2 meters. If 1 liter of paint covers 10 square meters, how many liters will be needed to paint the top and sides with 1 coat? Use 3.14 for π and round the answer up to the nearest liter.

9. The surface area of a cube is 216 cm^2. What are the dimensions of the cube?

10. A rectangular house 48 ft long by 26 ft wide needs to be painted. The house has ten 3′ × 4′ windows, two 2′ × 3′ windows, and two 3′ × $6\frac{1}{2}$′ doors. If the walls are $10\frac{1}{2}$′ high, how many ft^2 of surface is to be painted?

A rectangular prism has been built with 64 blocks. The surface area is 160 square units.

Determine how the blocks can be stacked to get a rectangular prism having the least surface area.

EXCURSION

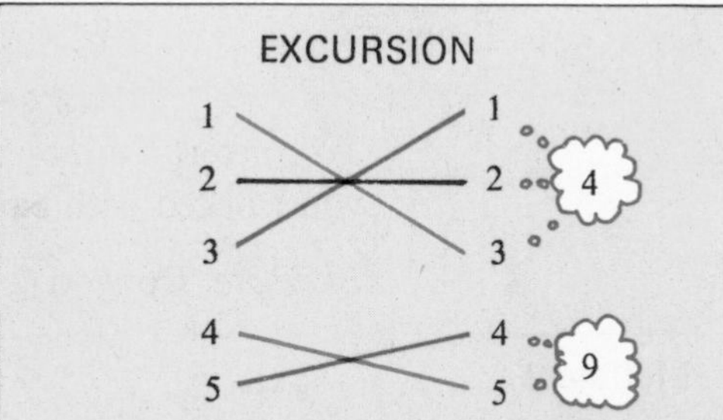

Here are two columns of numbers. The numbers have been paired so that each sum is a square number. Make two columns of numbers from 1 through 10. Pair the numbers so that each sum is a square number.

Skill Maintenance, Set 48, page 410

Volume—prism and cylinder

Remember that to find the volume of a prism (or cylinder) you pick a unit volume (a cube) and determine the number of units that it will take to fill the prism (or cylinder).

The volume of a prism or cylinder is equal to the product of the area of the base (B) and the height (h). Here are some examples:

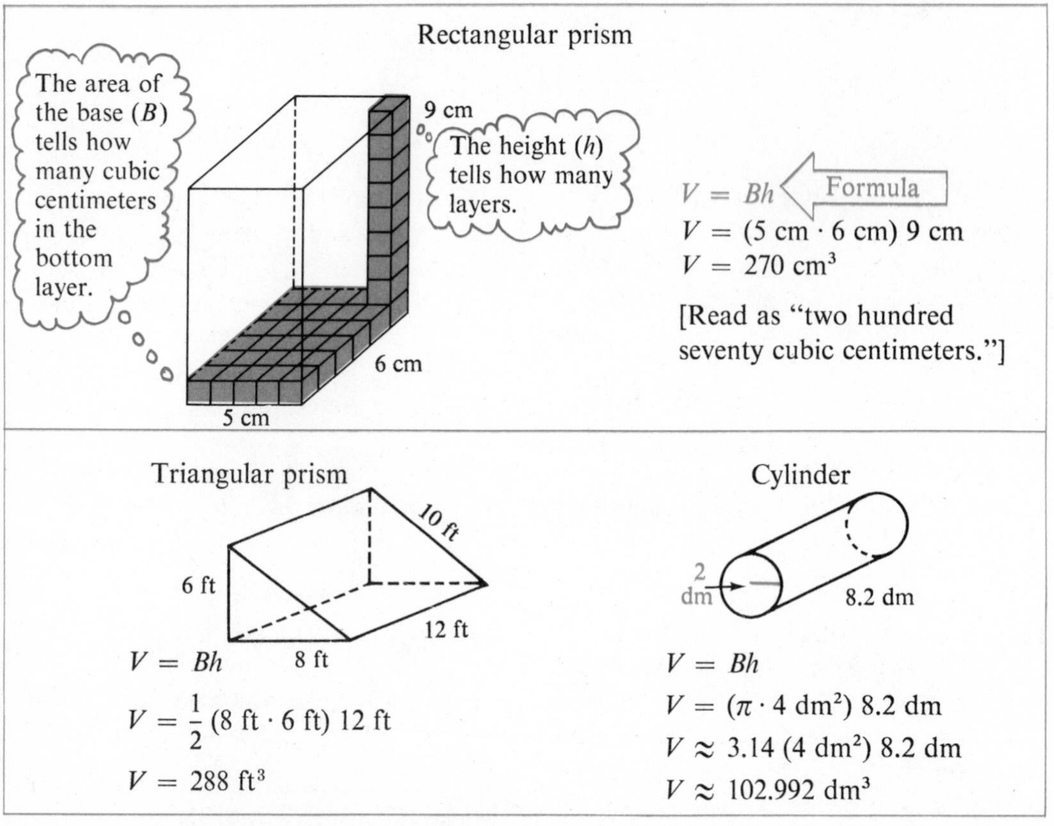

To convert from one unit of volume to another, use the method that you worked with earlier.

Example. Convert 2 yd³ to ft³.

Method 1.	Method 2.
Using 1 conversion fraction:	Using 3 conversion fractions:
$2\text{ yd}^3 = 2\text{ yd}^3 \cdot \boxed{\frac{27\text{ ft}^3}{1\text{ yd}^3}}$	$2\text{ yd}^3 = 2\text{ yd}^3 \cdot \boxed{\frac{3\text{ ft}}{1\text{ yd}}} \cdot \boxed{\frac{3\text{ ft}}{1\text{ yd}}} \cdot \boxed{\frac{3\text{ ft}}{1\text{ yd}}}$
$= 54\text{ ft}^3$	$= 54\text{ ft}^3$

EXERCISES

Compute each volume. Use $3\frac{1}{7}$ as an approximation for π.

1.

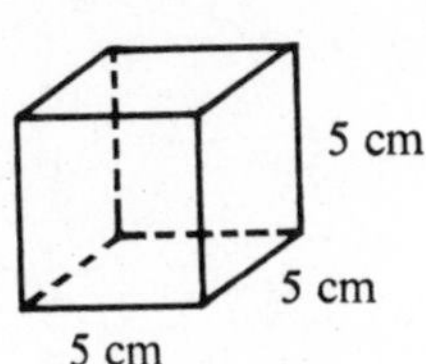

2.

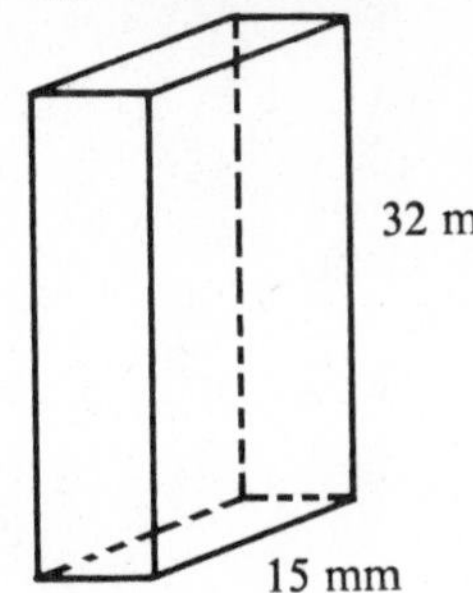

3.

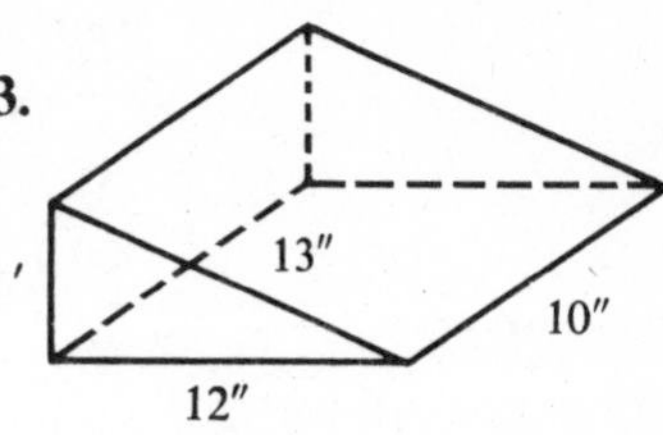

4.

5.

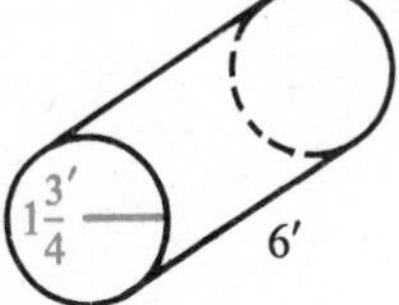

 **6.**

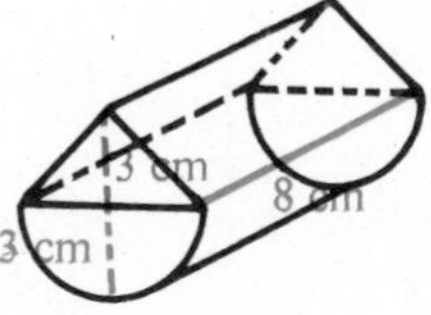

Convert by using conversion fractions.

7. 4 yd^3 to ft^3 **8.** 2 ft^3 to $in.^3$ **9.** 3 cm^3 to mm^3

10. 6 m^3 to dm^3 **11.** 3.6 dm^3 to cm^3 **12.** 368 mm^3 to cm^3

13. 63.84 cm^3 to dm^3 **14.** $13\frac{1}{2}$ ft^3 to yd^3 **15.** 1256 $in.^3$ to ft^3

Solve.

16. A circular barrel has a diameter of 8.2 dm and a height of 12.4 dm. What is its volume? Use 3.14 for π, and round your answer to the nearest .1 dm^3.

17. A rectangular box is 2 ft by 3 ft by 6 ft. What is its volume in cubic feet? In cubic yards?

18. A rectangular swimming pool is 36 feet long, 20 feet wide, and $6\frac{1}{2}$ feet deep. How many cubic feet of water does the pool hold? If there are about 7.5 gallons per ft^3, about how many gallons does the pool hold?

19. A rectangular form that is 18 ft long, $1\frac{1}{2}$ ft wide, and 5 ft deep is to be filled with concrete. How many yd^3 of concrete are needed to fill the form?

EXCURSION

Copy and draw the path that will take you from the starting number to the ending number.

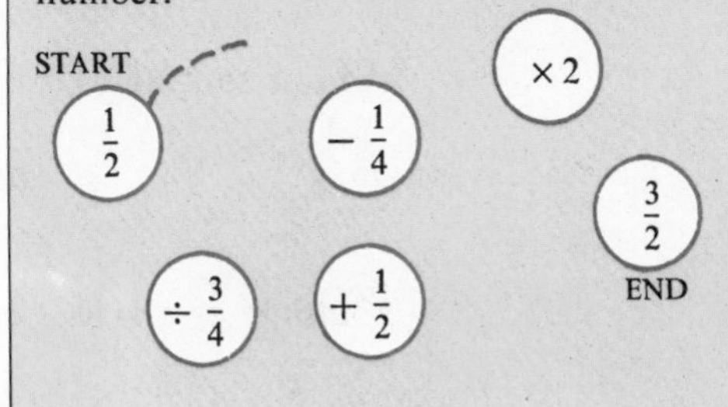

Skill Maintenance, Set 49, page 410

KEEPING SKILLS SHARP

Simplify.

1. 2^3 2. 3^2 3. 10^3 4. 2^6 5. $(2 + 3)^2$ 6. $2^2 + 3^2$

Solve each equation.

7. $5x + 7 = 22$ 8. $3x - 9 = 21$ 9. $8(x + 6) = 72$

10. $\frac{2x + 6}{2} = 18$ 11. $\frac{5x - 15}{3} = 10$ 12. $\frac{4(x - 5)}{6} = 4$

Multiply.

13. 274×8 14. 139.2×5 15. $26.34 \times .8$ 16. $36.74 \times .59$ 17. 946.3×58.6

Divide.

18. $5\overline{)385}$ 19. $9\overline{)46.08}$ 20. $2.5\overline{)78.75}$ 21. $6.3\overline{)308.7}$ 22. $2.54\overline{)14.732}$

Express each fraction as a decimal.

23. $\frac{1}{4}$ 24. $\frac{5}{8}$ 25. $\frac{2}{3}$ 26. $\frac{5}{9}$ 27. $\frac{5}{4}$ 28. $\frac{7}{6}$

Express each fraction as a percent.

29. $\frac{1}{6}$ 30. $\frac{3}{8}$ 31. $\frac{1}{3}$ 32. $\frac{1}{1}$ 33. $\frac{3}{5}$ 34. $\frac{5}{3}$

How many lines of symmetry does each figure have?

35. 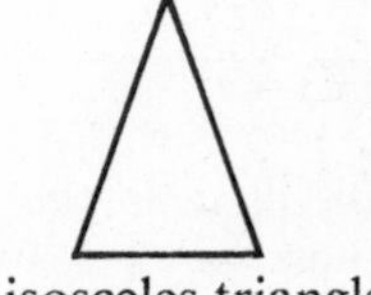
isosceles triangle

36. 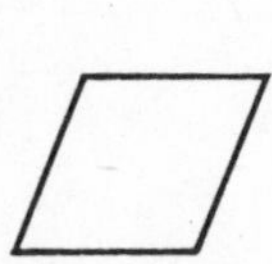
rhombus

37. 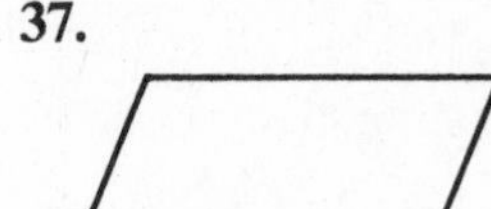
parallelogram

38. 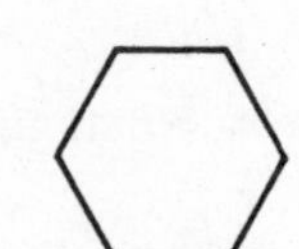
regular hexagon

Add or subtract. Give answers in lowest terms.

39. $\frac{3}{5} + \frac{1}{10}$ 40. $\frac{2}{3} + \frac{5}{8}$ 41. $\frac{3}{5} - \frac{1}{4}$ 42. $\frac{7}{8} - \frac{2}{3}$

Multiply or divide. Give answers in lowest terms.

43. $\frac{3}{5} \times \frac{5}{3}$ 44. $\frac{5}{9} \times \frac{4}{4}$ 45. $\frac{7}{8} \div \frac{3}{4}$ 46. $\frac{2}{5} \div \frac{2}{3}$

You have probably noticed that a brick is heavier than a piece of balsa wood the same size. We say that the brick is more *dense* than the balsa wood. The **density** of a substance is the ratio of its weight to its volume. Density in the English system is generally expressed in pounds per cubic foot (lb per ft^3). In the metric system density is generally expressed in grams per cubic centimeter. For example, the density of the wooden block shown here is 25 lb per ft^3.

$$\frac{50 \text{ lb}}{2 \text{ ft}^3} = \frac{25 \text{ lb}}{1 \text{ ft}^3}$$

EXERCISES

Compute the density of each of the substances shown below. Express each as a decimal rounded to the nearest .01.

1.

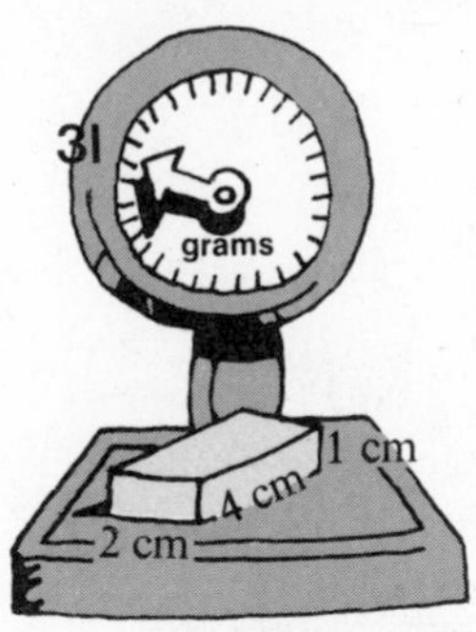

2.

3.

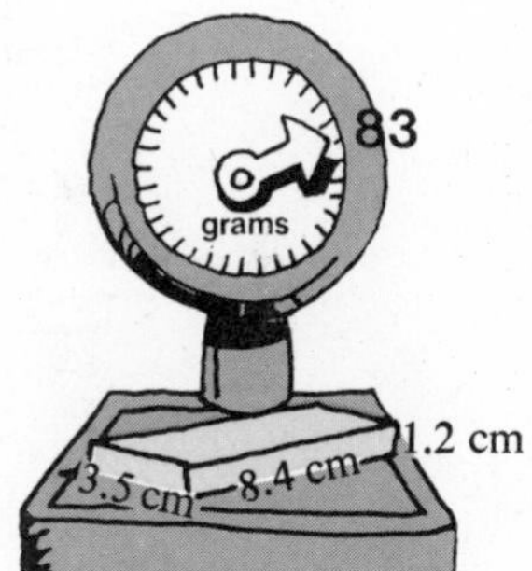

4. The density of balsa wood is 8.11 lb per ft^3. Gold is about 148.5 times as dense as balsa wood. Compute the density of gold to the nearest whole unit.

5. A cubic foot of water weighs 62.4 pounds. The average density of the earth is about 5.52 times the average density of water. What is the approximate average density of the earth?

Skill Maintenance, Set 50, page 410

Surface area—pyramid, cone, sphere

A **pyramid** has a base that is a polygonal region and **slant faces** that are triangular regions. (We will be concerned only with pyramids having congruent slant faces.)

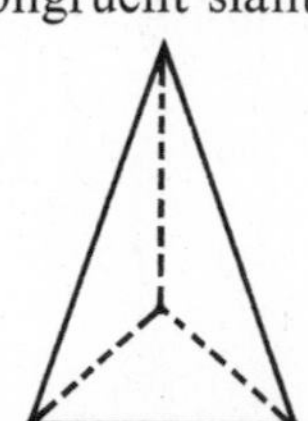

Triangular base

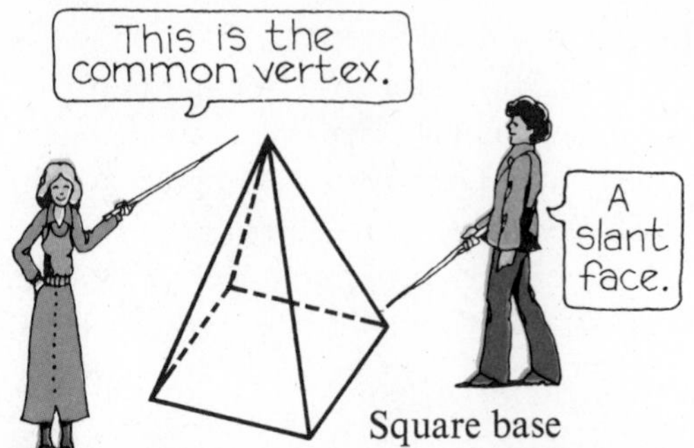

Square base

To find the surface area of a pyramid, add the area of the base and the areas of the slant faces.

Pictured here are some **cones.** (We will be concerned only with right circular cones. See the picture.)

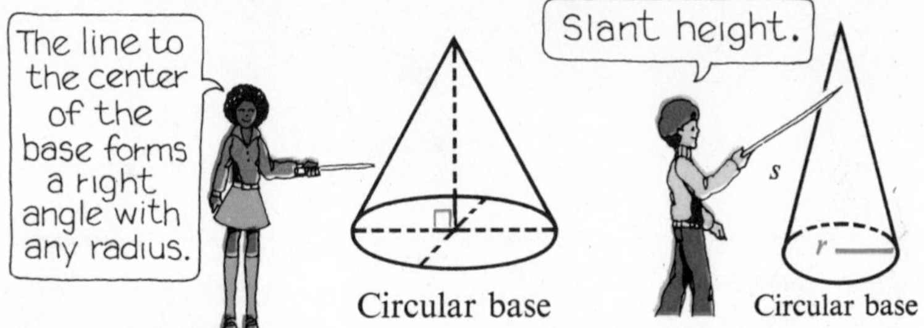

Circular base

Circular base

To find the surface area of a cone, add the area of the base, πr^2, and the area of the slant surface, πrs.

Example. Find the surface area. Use 3.14 for π.

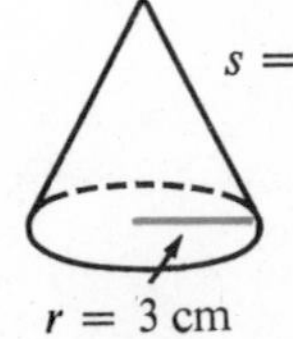

Base Area $= \pi(3\text{ cm})^2$
$\approx 3.14 \cdot 9\text{ cm}^2$
$= 28.26\text{ cm}^2$

Slant surface Area $= \pi(3\text{ cm})(12\text{ cm})$
$\approx 3.14 \cdot 36\text{ cm}^2$
$= 113.04\text{ cm}^2$

Surface Area $\approx 28.26\text{ cm}^2 + 113.04\text{ cm}^2$
$= 141.30\text{ cm}^2$

The surface area of a sphere can be found by using the formula

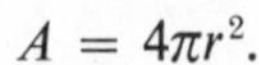

$$A = 4\pi r^2.$$

Example.
Find the surface area.
Use 3.14 for π.

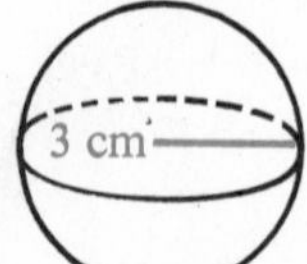

$$\begin{aligned} A &= 4\pi r^2 \\ &\approx 4(3.14)(3\text{ cm})^2 \\ &= 4(3.14)(9\text{ cm}^2) \\ &= 113.04\text{ cm}^2 \end{aligned}$$

EXERCISES

Give the surface area. Each pyramid has a square base.

1.

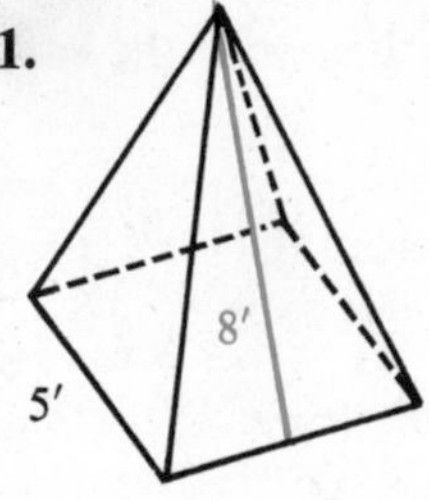

2.

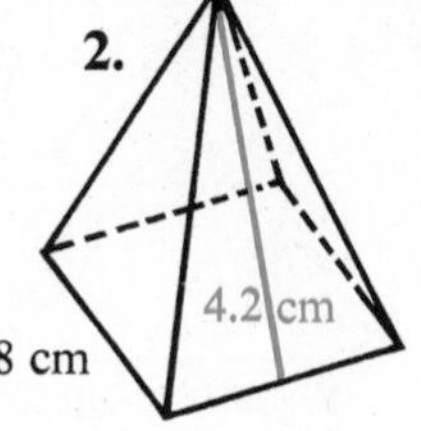

3.

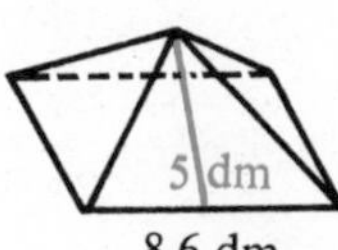

4.

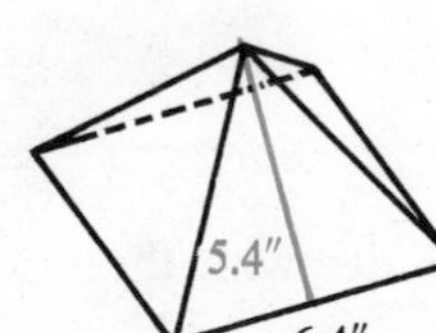

5.

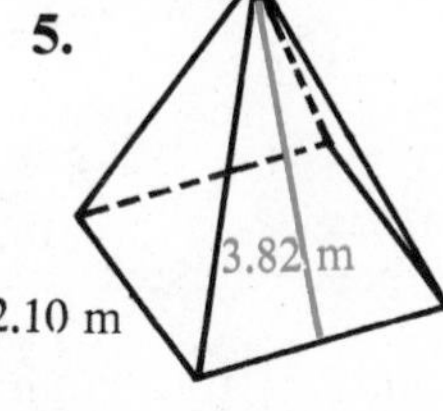

6.

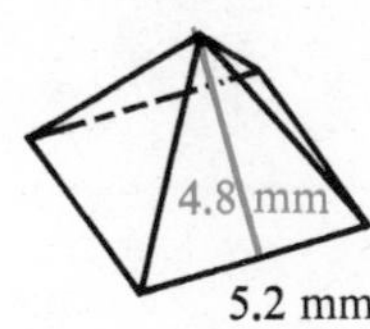

Give the surface area. Use 3.14 as an approximation for π.

7.

1.8 m

.6 m

8.

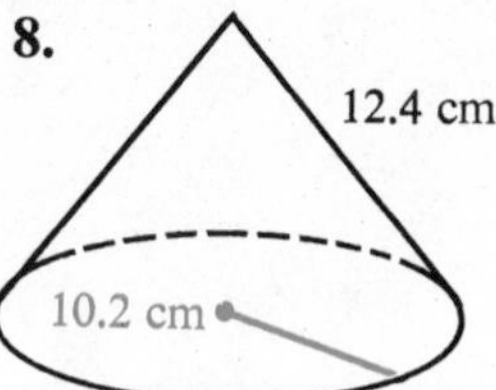

9.

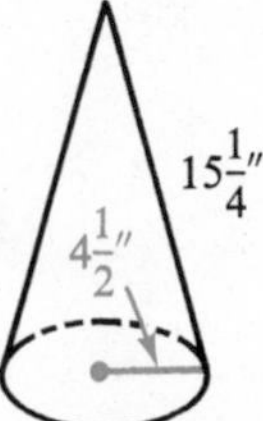

Give the surface area.
Use 3.14 as an approximation for π.

10.

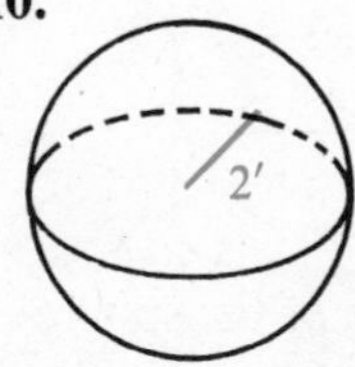

11.

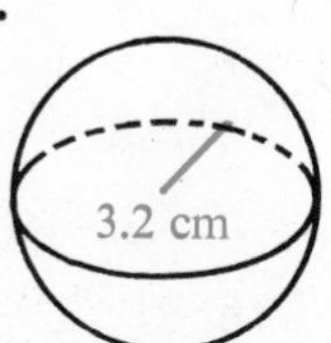

12.

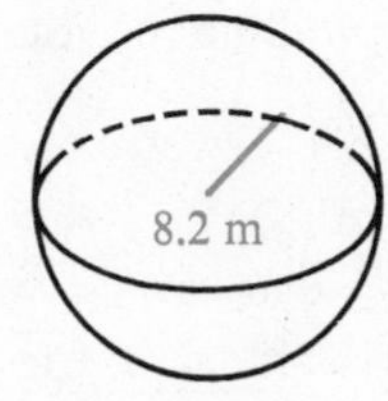

13.

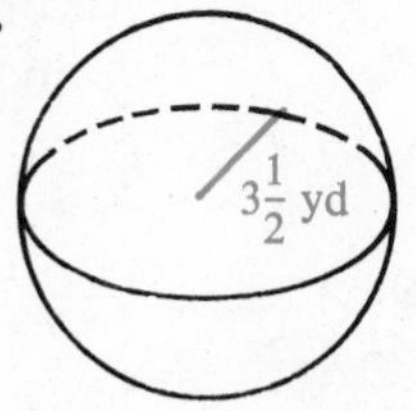

EXCURSION

Going along the paths in the direction of the arrows, how many routes are there from point *R* to point *S*?
From point *R* to point *T*?
From point *R* to point *U*?

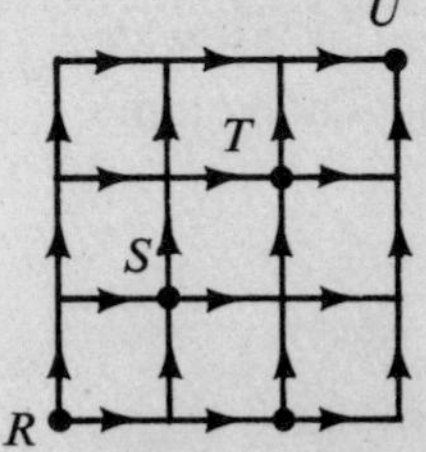

Skill Maintenance, Set 51, page 411

Volume—pyramid, cone, sphere

The volume of a pyramid is $\frac{1}{3}$ the volume of a prism with the same base and height.

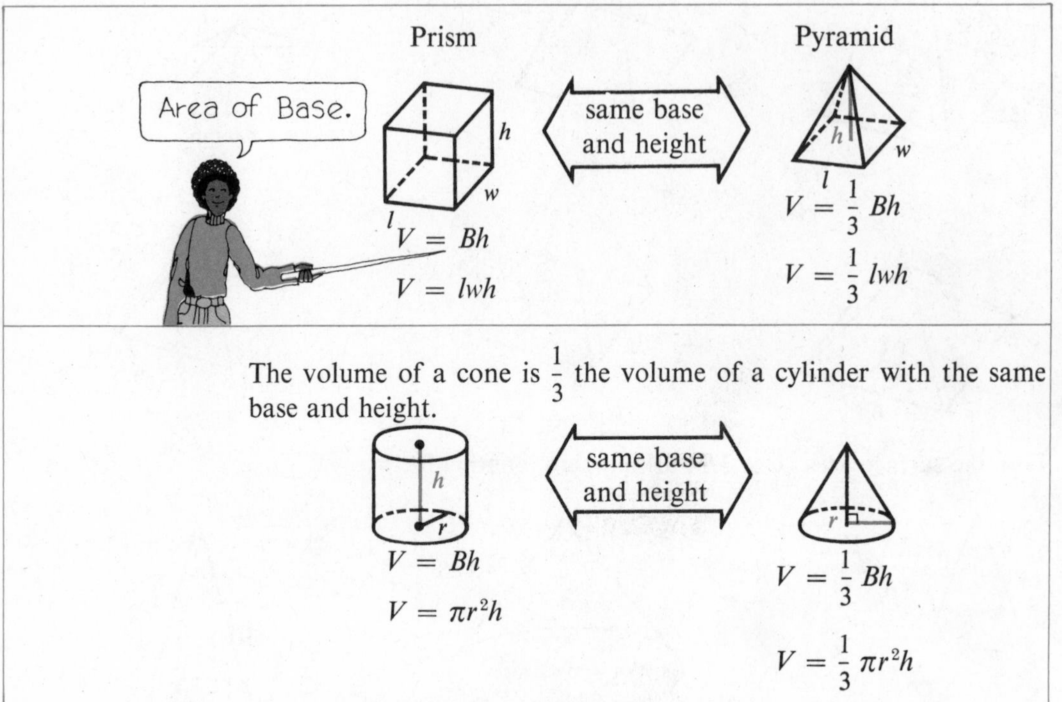

The volume of a cone is $\frac{1}{3}$ the volume of a cylinder with the same base and height.

To see that the formula for the volume of a sphere is reasonable, study the illustrations given below.

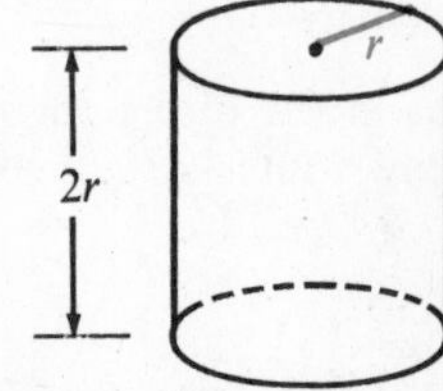

Find the volume of a cylinder that is as wide as it is high. The volume would be:

$$V = Bh$$
$$= \pi r^2(2r)$$
$$= 2\pi r^3 = \frac{6}{3} \pi r^3$$

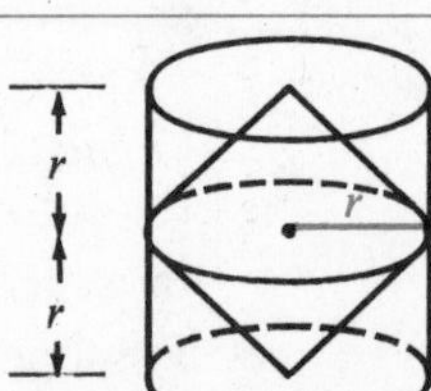

Find the volume of the two cones that are shown inside the cylinder.

$$V = 2\left[\frac{1}{3} Bh\right]$$
$$= 2\left[\frac{1}{3} \pi r^2 r\right] = \frac{2}{3} \pi r^3$$

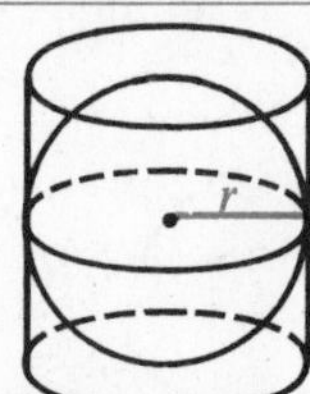

The volume of the sphere is midway between the volume of the cylinder and the volume of the two cones.

$$V = \frac{4}{3} \pi r^3$$

EXERCISES

Give each volume. Use 3.14 as an approximation for π.

1.

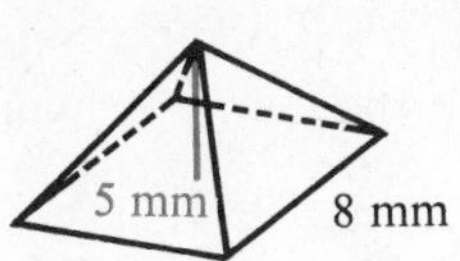

2.

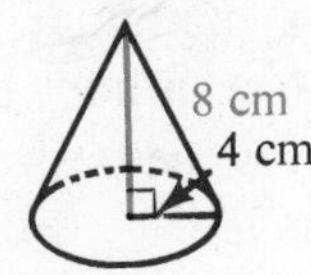

3.

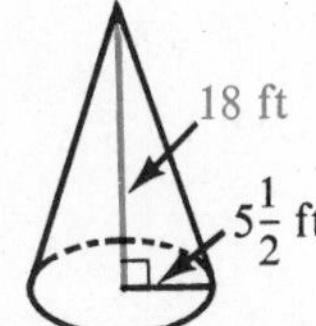

4.

5.

6.8 dm

5.4 dm

6.

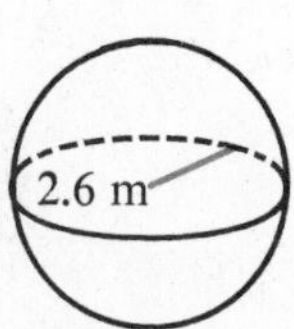

Solve. Use 3.14 as an approximation for π.

7. What is the volume of a spherical water tank that has a diameter of 48 feet? How many gallons of water will the tank hold if 1 cubic foot of water is 7.48 gallons? Round the answer to the nearest gallon.

8. A certain railroad tank car in the shape of a cylinder has a length of 19.8 m and a diameter of 2.4 m. What is its volume?

9. A baseball is about 7.4 cm in diameter. What are its surface area and volume?

10. A grain bin in the shape of a cylinder has a radius of 8 ft and a height of 18 ft. What is the volume of the bin? If there are about 1.24 ft^3 per bushel, about how many bushels of grain will the bin hold? Round the answer to the nearest bushel.

11. If the radius of a sphere is doubled, by how many times is the volume increased?

12. If you double the radius of a cone, by how many times is the volume increased?

1. Find the surface area and the volume of a basketball.

2. Find the volume of a circular wastebasket that has slanted sides. [*Hint:* Think of it as the lower part of a cone.]

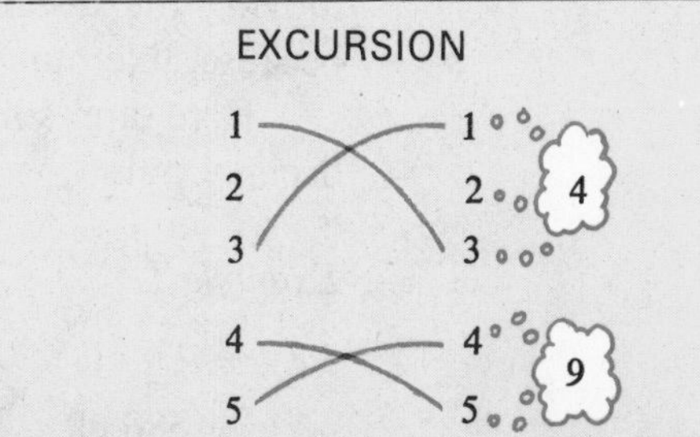

Here are two columns of numbers. The numbers have been paired so that each sum is a square number. Make two columns of numbers from 1 through 9. Pair the numbers so that each sum is a square number.

Supplementary Exercises, Set 46, page 386

Measuring capacity in the metric system

The capacity of a container is the same as its volume. It can be measured in cubic centimeters, cubic decimeters, or other similar units. The liter (*l*) is the basic unit of capacity in the metric system. A liter is the same as 1000 cm^3 or 1 dm^3.

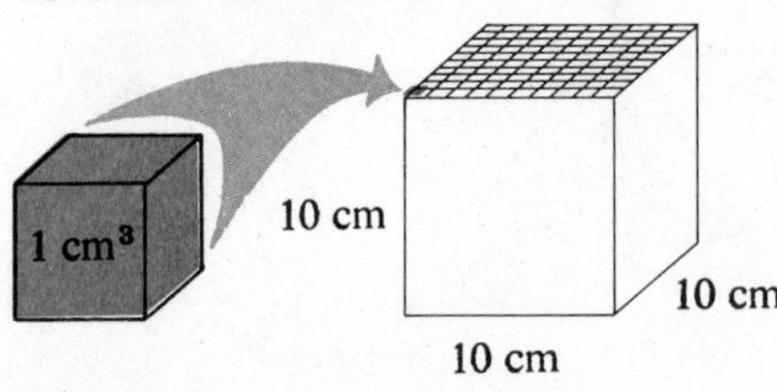

The metric units of capacity are shown in the table.

Metric Units of Capacity
1 milliliter (ml) = .001 liter
1 centiliter (cl) = .01 liter
1 deciliter (dl) = .1 liter
1 liter (*l*) = 1 liter
1 dekaliter (dal) = 10 liters
1 hectoliter (hl) = 100 liters
1 kiloliter (kl) = 1000 liters

A conversion fraction can be used to change from one unit of capacity to another.

Example. 56 dl = ? dal

Method 1.	Method 2.
$56 \text{ dl} = 56 \cancel{\text{dl}} \cdot \frac{1 \text{ dal}}{100 \cancel{\text{dl}}}$	$56 \text{ dl} = 56 \cancel{\text{dl}} \cdot \frac{1 \cancel{l}}{10 \cancel{\text{dl}}} \cdot \frac{1 \text{ dal}}{10 \cancel{l}}$
$= \frac{56}{100} \text{ dal}$	$= \frac{56}{100} \text{ dal}$
$= .56 \text{ dal}$	$= .56 \text{ dal}$

Notice that we could have changed from one unit to another by moving the decimal point. We can do this in the metric system because, like our numeration system, it is based on the number 10.

Here are some examples of changing units by moving the decimal point.

Example 1.

5.8 *l* = ? cl
= 580 cl

Since I'm converting to the second smaller unit, the number of units will be larger. So, I'll move the decimal point two places to the right.

Example 2.

36.52 hl = ? kl
= 3.652 kl

EXERCISES

Copy and complete each conversion fraction.

1. $\frac{1\ l}{?\ \text{cl}}$ 2. $\frac{1\ l}{?\ \text{ml}}$ 3. $\frac{?\ \text{dal}}{100\ \text{dl}}$ 4. $\frac{1\ \text{kl}}{?\ l}$

Copy and complete.

5. $3\ l = \underline{?}$ cl
6. $4.5\ l = \underline{?}$ cl
7. 5.4 dl $= \underline{?}$ cl
8. 3.86 dl $= \underline{?}$ ml
9. 48.2 cl $= \underline{?}\ l$
10. 386 dl $= \underline{?}$ dal
11. 34 kl $= \underline{?}$ hl
12. 5.3 kl $= \underline{?}\ l$
13. 63.8 hl $= \underline{?}\ l$
14. 74.83 kl $= \underline{?}$ dal
15. 3694 ml $= \underline{?}$ cl
16. 2438 ml $= \underline{?}\ l$

Complete.

A container having a volume of:

17. $1000\ \text{cm}^3$ has a capacity of $\underline{\quad ?\quad}\ l$.
18. $800\ \text{cm}^3$ has a capacity of $\underline{\quad ?\quad}\ l$.
19. $1\ \text{dm}^3$ has a capacity of $\underline{\quad ?\quad}\ l$.

20. $1.8\ \text{m}^3$ has a capacity of $\underline{\quad ?\quad}\ l$.

Solve.

21. What is the capacity in liters of this rectangular container?

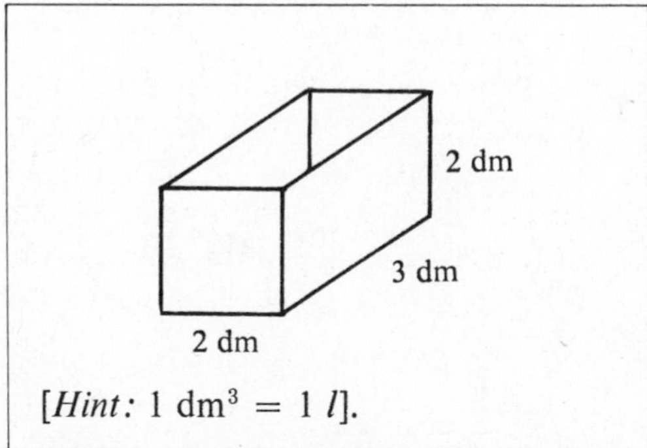

[*Hint:* $1\ \text{dm}^3 = 1\ l$].

22. What is the capacity in liters of this cylinder? Use 3.14 for π.

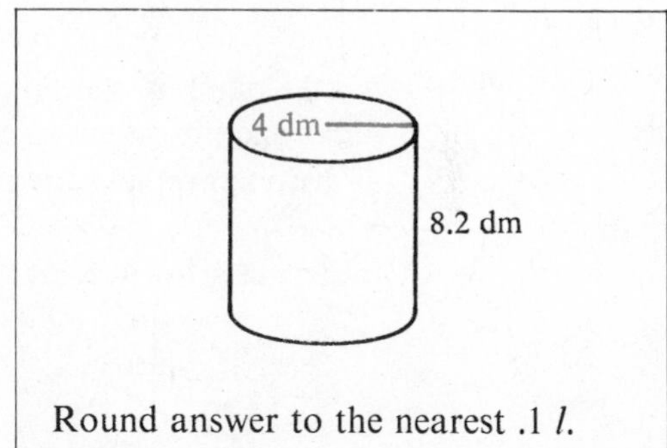

Round answer to the nearest .1 l.

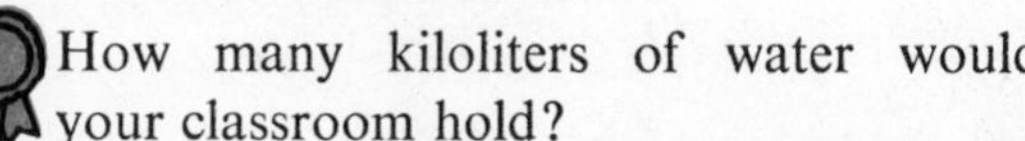

How many kiloliters of water would your classroom hold?

EXCURSION

Find 3 different values for a, b, and c so that the equation will be true.

$$\frac{1}{a} + \frac{1}{b} + \frac{1}{c} = 1$$

Supplementary Exercises, Set 47, page 387

Computing capacity

Often you will wish to find the capacity of a container in liters when the dimensions are given in units of length. This example shows you how to do this.

Problem:

What is the capacity of this rectangular container in liters?

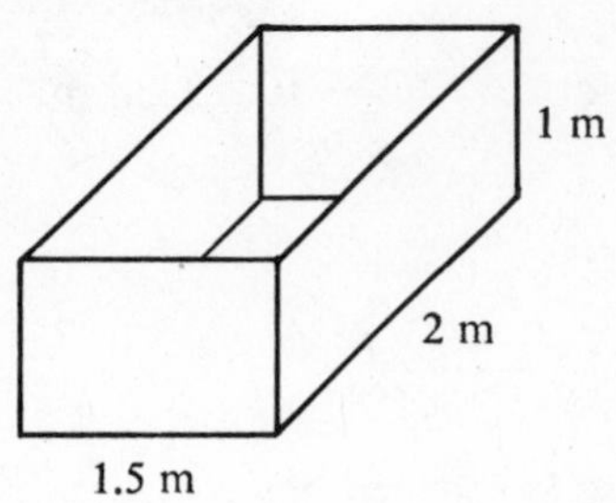

Solution:

The volume is 3 m³. Now we need to convert to liters. Since 1 dm³ equals 1 *l*, we will first convert m³ to dm³.

$$\begin{aligned} 3\text{ m}^3 &= 3\not{\text{m}^3}\cdot\frac{10\text{ dm}}{1\not{\text{m}}}\cdot\frac{10\text{ dm}}{1\not{\text{m}}}\cdot\frac{10\text{ dm}}{1\not{\text{m}}} \\ &= 3000\not{\text{dm}^3}\cdot\boxed{\frac{1\ l}{1\not{\text{dm}^3}}} \\ &= 3000\ l \\ &= 3\text{ kl} \end{aligned}$$

From the problem you should see that 1 m³ equals 1 kl. If this fact had been used in a conversion fraction, the solution to the problem above would have been easier.

$$\begin{aligned} 3\text{ m}^3 &= 3\not{\text{m}^3}\cdot\boxed{\frac{1\text{ kl}}{\not{\text{m}^3}}} \\ &= 3\text{ kl} \end{aligned}$$

The point is that there are many ways of doing these problems, depending on what conversion fraction you work with. Here are three conversion fractions:

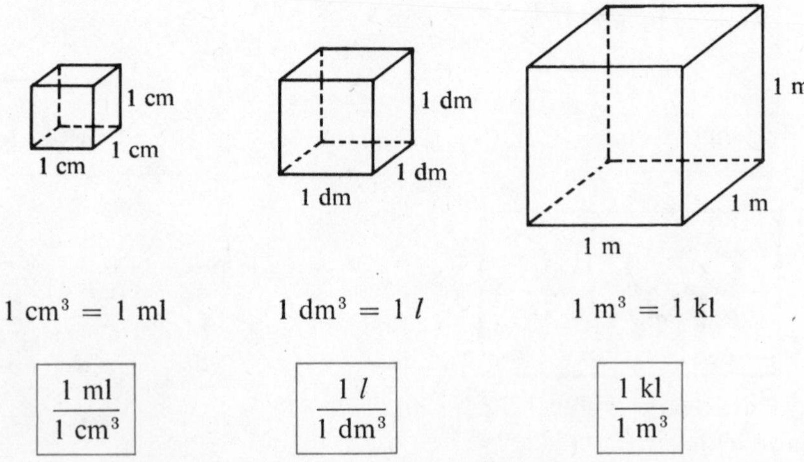

$1\text{ cm}^3 = 1\text{ ml}$ $\qquad$ $1\text{ dm}^3 = 1\ l$ $\qquad$ $1\text{ m}^3 = 1\text{ kl}$

$$\boxed{\frac{1\text{ ml}}{1\text{ cm}^3}} \qquad \boxed{\frac{1\ l}{1\text{ dm}^3}} \qquad \boxed{\frac{1\text{ kl}}{1\text{ m}^3}}$$

EXERCISES

Give the capacity of each container to the nearest liter. Use 3.14 as an approximation for π.

1. 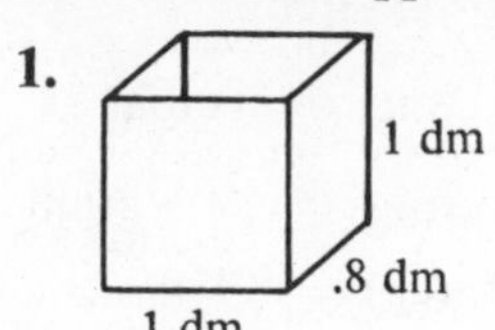

2. 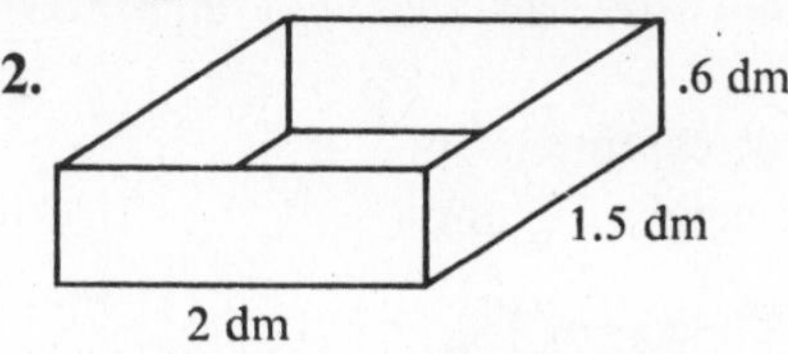

3. 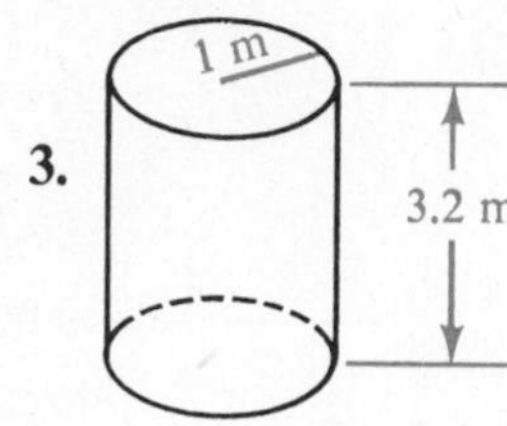

4. 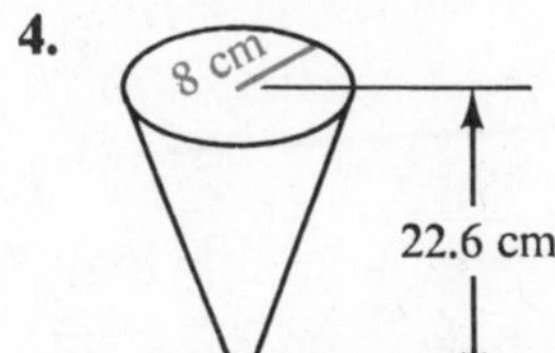

5. 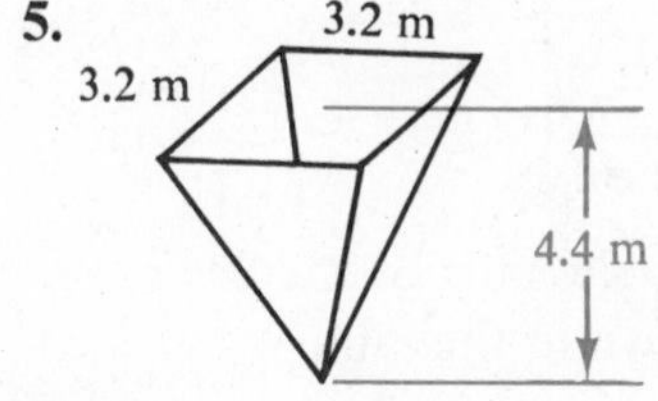

6. 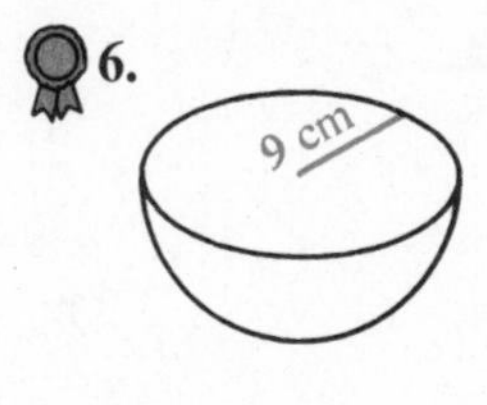

What is the capacity of the container in:

7. exercise 1 in dl?
8. exercise 2 in dal?
9. exercise 3 in kl?
10. exercise 4 in hl?
11. exercise 5 in ml?
12. exercise 6 in cl?

Solve.

13. A rectangular swimming pool is 12 m long, 5.2 m wide, and 2.3 m deep. How many kiloliters of water will it take to fill the pool?

14. A circular silo has a diameter of 4.6 m and a height of 18.2 m. How many kiloliters of silage will it hold? Use 3.1 as an approximation for π.

1. Measure to the nearest millimeter the dimensions of a quart milk container, as shown above.
2. Convert to liters to find about how many liters are in a quart.

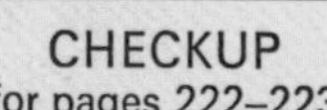

Copy and complete.

1. 3 *l* = __?__ dl
2. 4 *l* = __?__ cl
3. 19 *l* = __?__ dal
4. 34 cl = __?__ dl
5. 253 ml = __?__ cl
6. 584 cl = __?__ *l*
7. 2.6 kl = __?__ hl
8. 3.8 dl = __?__ dal
9. 23.4 dl = __?__ ml
10. 63.8 hl = __?__ *l*

Answers on page 427.

Skill Maintenance, Set 52, page 411

Measuring weight in the metric system

The **gram** is the basic unit of weight in the metric system.

A cubic centimeter of water weighs 1 gram.

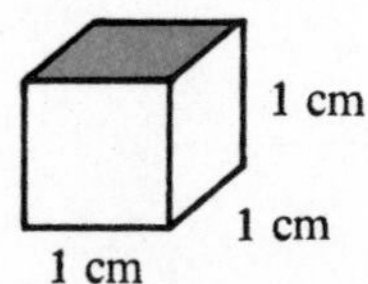

The metric units of weight are shown in the table.

Metric Units of Weight
1 milligram (mg) = .001 gram
1 centigram (cg) = .01 gram
1 decigram (dg) = .1 gram
1 gram (g) = 1 gram
1 dekagram (dag) = 10 grams
1 hectogram (hg) = 100 grams
1 kilogram (kg) = 1000 grams

Notice again how the metric system is based on the number 10.

To convert from 1 unit of weight to another, you can use a conversion fraction.

Example. 3.8 hg = ___?___ g

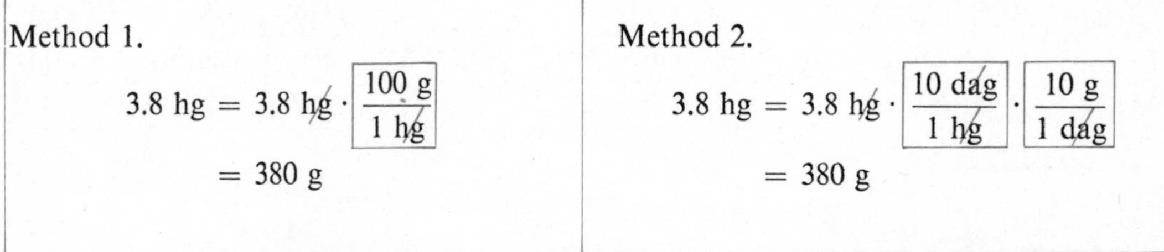

Method 1.

$$3.8 \text{ hg} = 3.8 \not{\text{hg}} \cdot \boxed{\frac{100 \text{ g}}{1 \not{\text{hg}}}}$$

$$= 380 \text{ g}$$

Method 2.

$$3.8 \text{ hg} = 3.8 \not{\text{hg}} \cdot \boxed{\frac{10 \not{\text{dag}}}{1 \not{\text{hg}}}} \cdot \boxed{\frac{10 \text{ g}}{1 \not{\text{dag}}}}$$

$$= 380 \text{ g}$$

Remember that you can also change units by moving the decimal point. Here are some examples:

EXERCISES

Copy and complete.

1. 5.68 g = ? dg

2. 5.68 g = ? cg

3. 5.68 g = ? mg

4. 37.4 cg = ? dg

5. 37.4 cg = ? g

6. 37.4 cg = ? dag

7. 58.3 mg = ? dg

8. .742 dg = ? mg

9. 5.61 dg = ? g

10. 38 mg = ? cg

11. .25 g = ? mg

12. 3.6 g = ? kg

Solve.

13. A backpacking club has 127.3 kilos (kilograms) of gear to be carried by its 13 members. How many kilos should each member carry?

14. If steak costs $4.20 a kilo, how much will 2.6 kilos of steak cost?

15. The table gives some facts about the starting lineup of a football team. Compute the average height to the nearest centimeter and the average weight to the nearest .1 kilogram.

Name	Allan	Pride	Dodds	Cohen	Jones	Weaver	Krantz	Mendez	Moore	Davis	Bursma
Position	LE	LT	LG	C	RG	RT	RE	QB	LHB	RHB	FB
Height (cm)	180	176	181	186	190	183	188	192	179	182	189
Weight (kg)	83	87	84	89	92	90	88	87	90	86	93

16. A rectangular aquarium measures 52 cm long, 26 cm wide, and 30 cm high. How many kilograms of water does it hold when completely filled? How many liters of water?

Remember that the density of a substance is the ratio of its weight to its volume. Density is usually expressed as grams per cubic centimeter in the metric system. Find the density of some substances.

EXCURSION

Copy, and fill in the missing digits.

```
          1 8
□ □ ) 5 9 □ □
      □ □
      2 7 7
      □ □ □
        □ □ □
        □ □ 2
          2 2
```

Supplementary Exercises, Set 48, page 387

More on conversions—metric and English systems

Sometimes you may wish to convert a measurement in the metric system to the English system or vice versa. Below is a table of metric-English "equivalent" measures. Actually they are close approximations.

Metric-English Equivalent Measures		
Length	Capacity	Weight
1 cm $\approx$ .39 in. 1 m $\approx$ 39 in. 1 m $\approx$ 3.3 ft 1 m $\approx$ 1.1 yd 1 km $\approx$ .62 mi	1 $l \approx$ 1.06 qt	1 kg $\approx$ 2.2 lb
1 in. $\approx$ 2.5 cm 1 ft $\approx$ 30.5 cm 1 ft $\approx$ .3 m 1 yd $\approx$ .9 m 1 mi $\approx$ 1.6 km	1 qt $\approx$ .944 l	1 oz $\approx$ 28.25 g 1 lb $\approx$ 453.6 g

Study these examples of converting from one system to the other. Notice that the unit in the denominator is the unit that we are converting from and the unit in the numerator is the unit we are converting to.

Example 1. 124 mi to km

$$124 \text{ mi} \approx 124 \not{\text{mi}} \cdot \boxed{\frac{1.6 \text{ km}}{1 \not{\text{mi}}}}$$
$$= 198.4 \text{ km}$$

Example 2. 320 oz to kg

$$320 \text{ oz} = 320 \not{\text{oz}} \cdot \boxed{\frac{1 \text{ lb}}{16 \not{\text{oz}}}} = 20 \text{ lb}$$
$$\approx 20 \not{\text{lb}} \cdot \frac{1 \text{ kg}}{2.2 \not{\text{lb}}} = 9.09 \text{ kg}$$

Notice that in example 2 we first converted from ounces to pounds and then from pounds to kilograms. What is another way to carry out the conversion?

Example 3. 138 m² to yd²

$$138 \text{ m}^2 \approx 138 \not{\text{m}}^2 \cdot \boxed{\frac{1.1 \text{ yd}}{1 \not{\text{m}}}} \cdot \boxed{\frac{1.1 \text{ yd}}{1 \not{\text{m}}}}$$
$$= 166.98 \text{ yd}^2$$

Example 4. 100 ft³ to m³

$$100 \text{ ft}^3 \approx 100 \not{\text{ft}}^3 \cdot \boxed{\frac{.3\text{m}}{1 \not{\text{ft}}}} \cdot \boxed{\frac{.3\text{m}}{1 \not{\text{ft}}}} \cdot \boxed{\frac{.3\text{m}}{1 \not{\text{ft}}}}$$
$$= 2.7 \text{ m}^3$$

Recall from the last two examples that you can work with units the same way as you work with numbers.

EXERCISES

Complete these conversion fractions.

1. $\boxed{\frac{1\ l}{?\ \text{qt}}}$ **2.** $\boxed{\frac{1\ \text{mi}}{?\ \text{km}}}$ **3.** $\boxed{\frac{2.2\ \text{lb}}{?\ \text{kg}}}$ **4.** $\boxed{\frac{1\ \text{in.}}{?\ \text{cm}}}$ **5.** $\boxed{\frac{1\ \text{lb}}{?\ \text{g}}}$

Carry out the following conversions. If the computation does not come out even, round to the nearest hundredth.

6. 13 qt to *l* **7.** 29 lb to kg **8.** 49 kg to lb

9. 15.2 *l* to qt **10.** 58 oz to g **11.** 153 g to oz

Convert these area units.

12. 240 cm^2 to in.^2 **13.** 40 m^2 to ft^2 **14.** 200 ft^2 to m^2

Convert these volume units.

15. 20 yd^3 to m^3 **16.** 160 ft^3 to m^3 **17.** 400 cm^3 to in.^3

Solve.

18. It is 345 miles from Chicago to Cleveland. How many kilometers is that?

19. The smallest state in the United States in area is Rhode Island. Its area is 1214 mi^2. What is its area in km^2?

20. A rectangular box is 12 in. long, 8 in. wide, and 6 in. high. What is its volume in cm^3?

21. The density of water is 62.4 lb per ft^3. Express the density of water in grams per cm^3.

Measure the length and width of your desk top with an inch ruler. Compute the area in square inches. Convert the area to square centimeters.

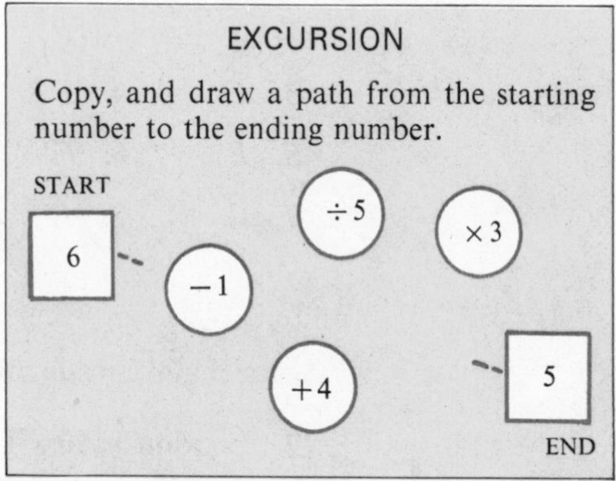

Supplementary Exercises, Set 49, page 387

Mathematics in careers

Navigators of ships and airplanes are responsible for knowing their location at all times. Today they use very precise instruments. A navigator locates the position of a ship or plane by two coordinates. The first coordinate is called **latitude**. Latitude tells the location of a point on the earth's surface relative to the equator.

The latitude of point P is 20° north. In fact, any point on the red circle has latitude 20° N. The latitude of point Q is 40° South. Any point on the green circle has latitude 40° S.

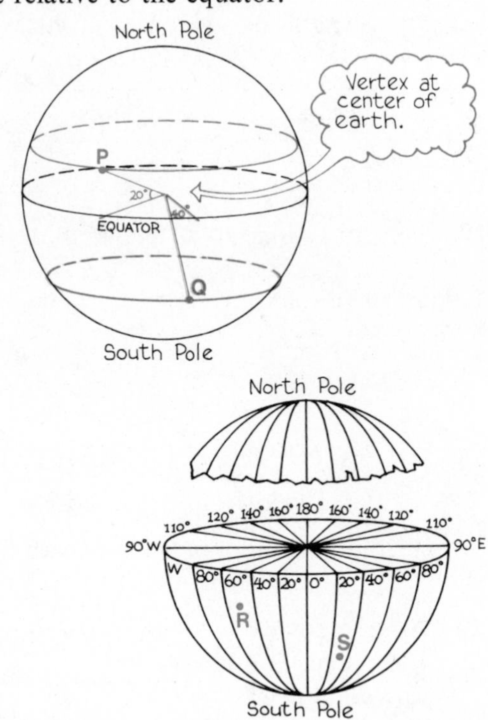

The second coordinate is called **longitude**. Longitude tells the location of a point on the earth's surface relative to a meridian (a circle passing through both poles) that passes through Greenwich, England.

The longitude of point R is 50° west. The longitude of point S is 30° east.

EXERCISES

Estimate the coordinates (latitude and longitude) of each of these points.

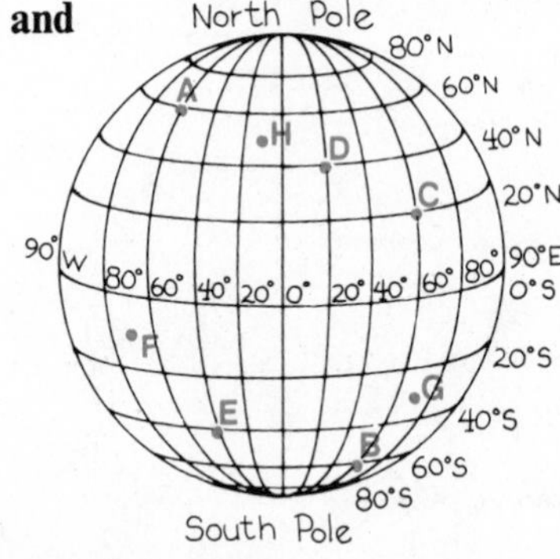

1. A
2. B
3. C
4. D
5. E
6. F
7. G
8. H

Using a globe, estimate the coordinates of these cities.

9. London
10. Tokyo
11. New York City
12. Honolulu

CHAPTER CHECKUP

Complete. *[page 196]*

1. 38.6 m = ___?___ dm **2.** 2.43 km = ___?___ dm

3. 56 cm = ___?___ mm **4.** 384 mm = ___?___ m

Complete this table. *[page 200]*

	Measurement	Greatest Possible Error	Range for Exact Length
5.	9 cm to the nearest cm		
6.	$5\frac{1}{2}$ in. to the nearest $\frac{1}{2}$ in.		

Solve. *[page 202]*

7. A stick measured to the nearest cm was found to be 24 cm long. What was the relative error of the measurement?

8. An angle when measured to the nearest degree was found to be 85°. What was the percent error of the measurement?

Compute the perimeter and area of each figure. *[pages 206, 208]*

9.

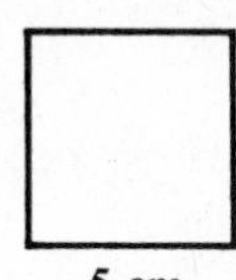

10.

12.4 m

3.2 m

11.

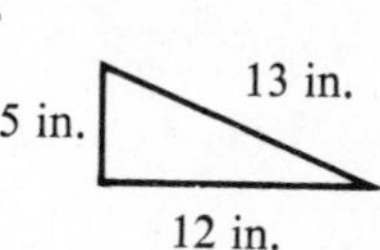

12.

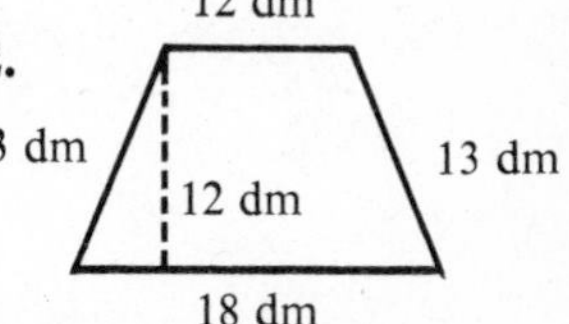

Compute the surface area and volume. Use 3.14 as an approximation for π. *[pages 212, 214]*

13.

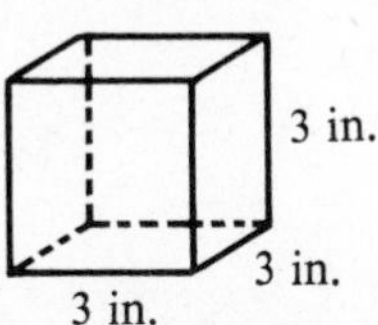

14.

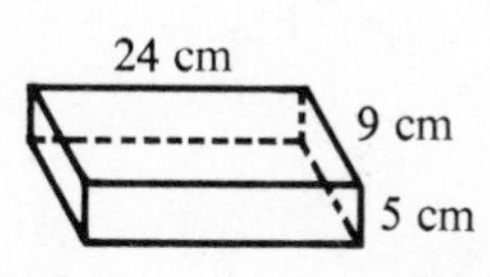

15.

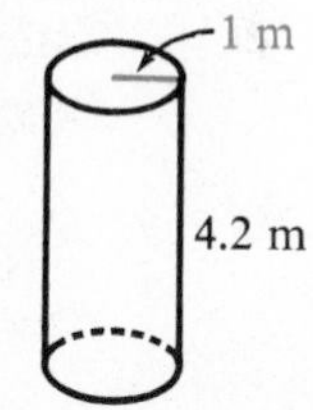

Give each volume. Use 3.14 as an approximation for π. *[page 220]*

16.

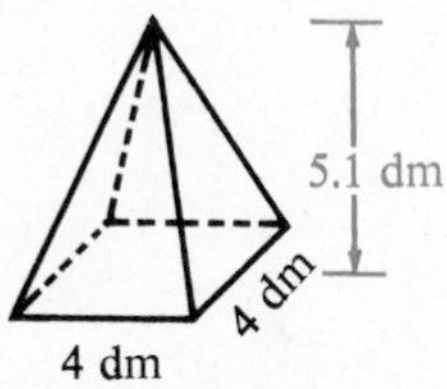

17.

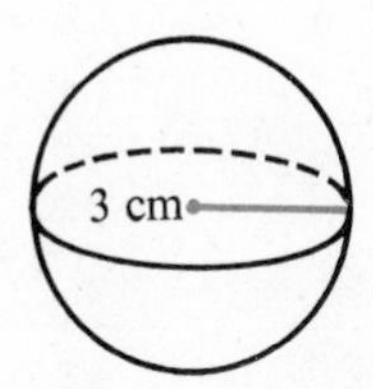

Copy and complete. *[page 222]*

18. 5.1 *l* = _?_ cl **19.** 3.82 dl = _?_ cl

20. 3.94 kl = _?_ hl

21. 8652 ml = _?_ *l*

22. 82 g = _?_ dg **23.** 3614 dg = _?_ cg

24. 3 kg = _?_ dag **25.** 237 mg = _?_ g

MAJOR CHECKUP

Complete. [*page 26*] $f(x) = 2x + \frac{1}{3}$

1. $f\left(\frac{1}{2}\right) = \underline{\ ?\ }$
2. $f(0) = \underline{\ ?\ }$
3. $f\left(\frac{3}{5}\right) = \underline{\ ?\ }$
4. $f\left(\frac{5}{3}\right) = \underline{\ ?\ }$

5. **Complete.** [*pages 46, 48*]

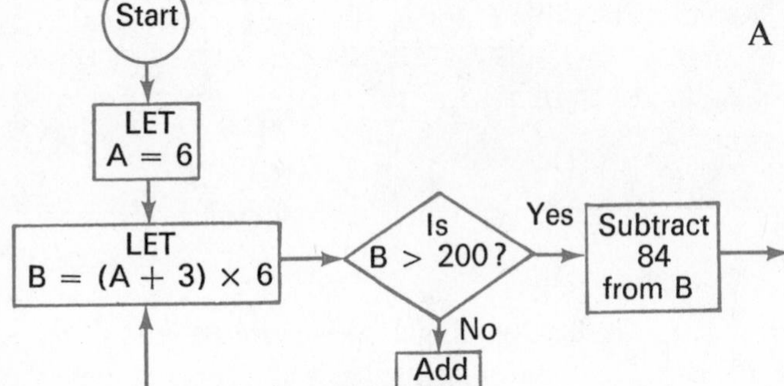

6. Follow the flow chart again but let $A = 5\frac{1}{6}$.

Multiply. [*pages 68, 74*]

7. $\begin{array}{r} 56.4 \\ \times 9 \\ \hline \end{array}$
8. $\begin{array}{r} 9.32 \\ \times 1.8 \\ \hline \end{array}$
9. $\begin{array}{r} 78.1 \\ \times 2.3 \\ \hline \end{array}$
10. $\begin{array}{r} 29.34 \\ \times .59 \\ \hline \end{array}$
11. $\begin{array}{r} 617.5 \\ \times .713 \\ \hline \end{array}$

Divide. Round the quotient to the nearest .01. [*pages 82, 86, 90*]

12. $7\overline{)838}$
13. $8\overline{)35.68}$
14. $.6\overline{)38.94}$
15. $4.3\overline{)1.246}$
16. $1.56\overline{)39.483}$

Give each sum or difference. [*pages 114–115*]

17. $\begin{array}{r} 5\frac{1}{2} \\ +3\frac{1}{4} \\ \hline \end{array}$
18. $\begin{array}{r} 18\frac{2}{3} \\ +5\frac{5}{6} \\ \hline \end{array}$
19. $\begin{array}{r} 18\frac{2}{3} \\ +6\frac{3}{4} \\ \hline \end{array}$
20. $\begin{array}{r} 28\frac{5}{8} \\ -13\frac{1}{4} \\ \hline \end{array}$
21. $\begin{array}{r} 6 \\ -5\frac{2}{5} \\ \hline \end{array}$
22. $\begin{array}{r} 49\frac{1}{3} \\ -15\frac{6}{8} \\ \hline \end{array}$

Copy and complete. [*pages 174–175*]

	23.	24.	25.	26.	27.	28.	29.	30.
Fraction	$\frac{1}{2}$	?	?	?	?	$\frac{7}{5}$	?	$\frac{5}{3}$
Decimal	?	.6	?	.375	?	?	.875	?
Percent	?	?	75%	?	130%	?	?	?

1. Cut out a rectangular region about the size of a postcard.

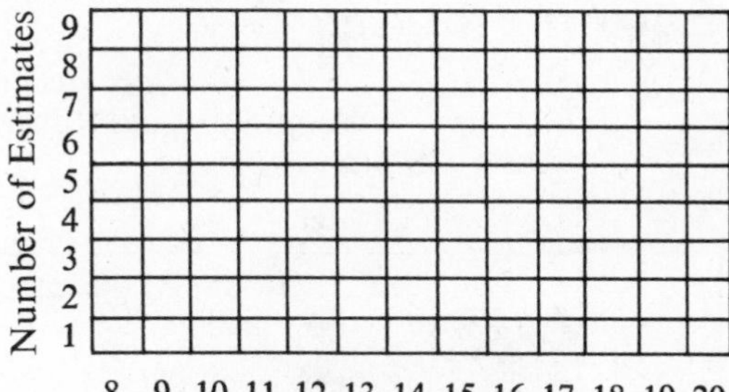

2. Have students estimate the area to the nearest square inch and record their estimates.
3. Show their estimates on a bar graph.
4. Measure and compute the area. Compare the computed area with the estimates. Did most estimates "cluster around" the computed area?

1. Collect some solid rectangular objects of different materials. Some possibilities are:
   a solid block of wood

   a solid brick

   a solid piece of concrete

   a solid piece of metal
2. Measure each object and carefully compute its volume to the nearest cm^3.
3. Weigh each object to the nearest gram.
4. Compute the density of each object.

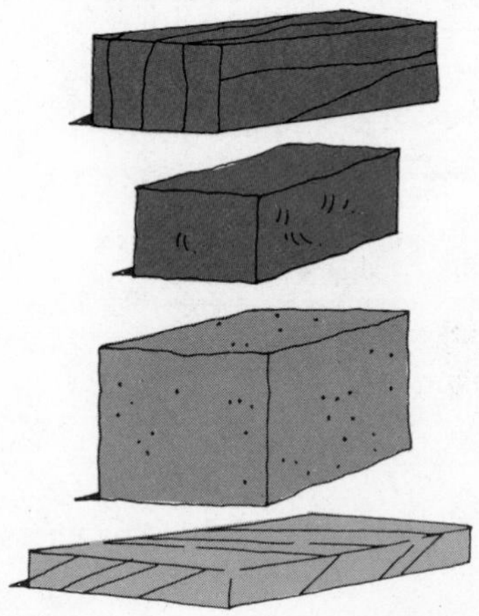

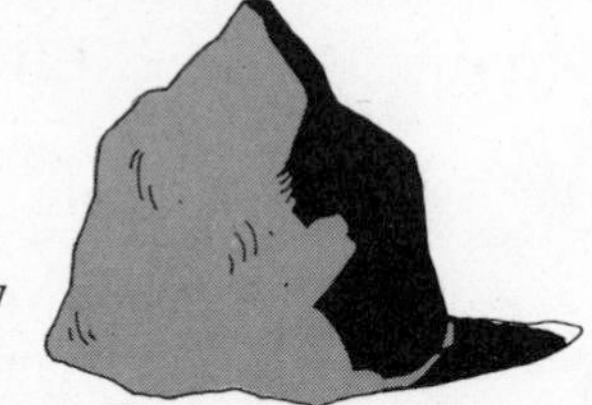

Project 3

Determine the density of an irregularly shaped rock.

8 Consumer Mathematics

Earning money

People are paid for their work in many ways. Here are some examples.

TEACHER	BARBER
 Paid an annual salary. *Example.* \$12,500 per year	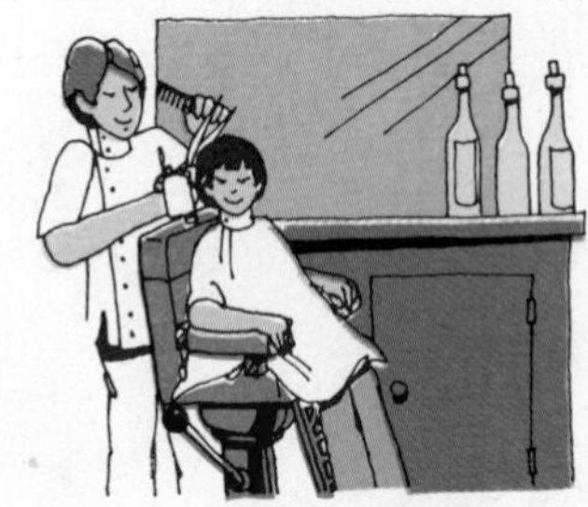 Paid a fee. *Example.* \$3.50 a haircut

SALESPERSON	CARPENTER
 Paid a commission *Example.* 10% of total sales	 Paid an hourly wage. *Example.* \$7.75 per hour.

The following exercises will help you learn about the ways people are paid.

EXERCISES

1. Joe often baby-sits for a neighbor. He is paid \$1.25 per hour. How much would he be paid for 6.5 hours?
2. Marcia is paid \$1.25 per hour for baby-sitting before midnight and \$1.75 per hour after midnight. How much would she earn for sitting from 8:30 P.M. to 2:00 A.M.?

3. George works in a factory. He is paid \$4.86 per hour for the first 40 hours plus time and a half for each hour over 40 he works in one week. ("Time and a half" means that he is paid $1\frac{1}{2}$ times the regular hourly wage.) How much will he earn if he works a 50-hour week?

4. Joan sells cookware. She is paid a commission of 17% of her total sales. One month she sold \$3428 worth of cookware. What was her commission?

5. Harvey works in a clothing store. He is paid \$175 per week plus a 5% commission on his total sales. One week his sales amounted to \$1425. What did he earn that week?

6. Jill sells textbooks to schools. She is paid \$12,000 per year plus a commission of 7.5% of all sales above her yearly quota of \$75,000. One year her sales were \$117,356. What did she earn that year?

7. Jack runs a lathe in a tractor factory. He is paid according to the number of pieces he completes in a day. This is called *piecework*. He is paid \$2.35 per piece. One day he turned out 27 pieces. How much did he earn?

8. Carol works in a beauty shop. She charges \$6.50 for each haircut. She gets half and the shop owner gets half. If she did 8 haircuts in one day, how much would she earn from them?

9. Mary Ellen works in a bank. She earns \$175 per week. How much does she earn in a year (52 weeks)?

10. Ken earns \$250 per week and a 6.5% commission on all sales over \$50,000 per year. If his year's sales were \$67,500, what did he earn?

Find as many occupations as you can that are paid by fees, by yearly salaries, and by commission.

EXCURSION

Use a geoboard or dot paper. Make a figure that has 4 boundary points and 1 interior point.

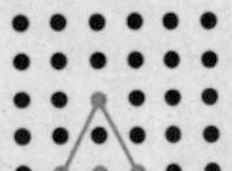

Make 3 other figures, each with 4 boundary points and 1 interior point.

Make a figure with:

1. 3 boundary points and

- **a.** 0 interior points
- **b.** 1 interior point
- **c.** 2 interior points

2. 4 boundary points and 0 interior points

Supplementary Exercises, Set 50, page 388

Payroll deductions

Carol has a job that pays $125 a week. This was her check for the first week:

CORNHURST INDUSTRIES 18753
8674 Mimosa Blvd.
Albany, New York July 17 1976

Pay to Carol Carpenter $ 91 11/100

Ninety-one and 11/100 Dollars

Harold R. Cornhurst

Notice that the pay she received was less than the $125 she earned. This is because her employer is required by law to **withhold** part of her earnings for federal income tax, state income tax, and social security. The employer then sends this money to the federal and state tax-collecting agencies.

With her check Carol received this statement:

CORNHURST INDUSTRIES					Carol Carpenter
	Deductions				
Gross Pay	Social Security	Federal Withholding	State Withholding	Miscellaneous	Net Pay
$125.00	$7.31	$20.70	$5.88		$91.11

EXERCISES

These questions refer to the example given above.

1. What is the total amount of the deductions?
2. Suppose that Carol worked for the same salary for 1 year (52 weeks).
   a. What were her total earnings?
   b. What was the total social security deduction?
   c. What was the total of the federal withholding?
   d. What was the total of the state withholding?
   e. About what percent of her earnings was withheld for social security? For federal withholding? For state withholding?

Tom studied welding at a vocational-technical school. After graduation he answered this newspaper ad and was hired.

HELP WANTED
Welder. Good working conditions. $5.68 per hr. Time and a half for over 40 hours. Benefits. Apply at . . .

3. How much did he earn in a 40-hour week?
4. Nineteen percent of his earnings was withheld for federal income tax. How much did this amount to?
5. One week he worked 50 hours. Twenty-two percent of his earnings was withheld for federal income tax. How much did he earn? What was the federal withholding?
6. During a regular 40-hour week, besides the federal withholding, he had deductions of $13.29 for social security, $5.84 for hospitalization insurance, and $5.00 for a savings plan. What was the total amount of the deductions?

Solve the problems.

7. Sarah drove a taxi. She was paid 50% of her total fares and also received tips from her passengers. One week when her fares totaled $504, her employer withheld 23% of her earnings for federal income tax and 5% for state income tax. She also received $51.25 in tips. What were her total earnings? What was the total amount of the deductions? What was her "take-home" pay?

8. Jim was a salesman. He was paid 15% of his total sales as a commission. Twenty-one percent of his earnings was deducted for federal withholding, 4% for state withholding, 9% for a company retirement plan, and $24.75 for hospitalization insurance. What was his take-home pay if his total sales one month were $12,000?

9. Sally had a choice of two jobs. Both paid $7200 per year. In the first she would get a $100 raise after each 6-month period. In the second she would get a $200 raise after each year. Which paid more over a 3-year period?

EXCURSION

Use a geoboard or dot paper. This square shows the area unit.

Make several figures with 3 boundary points and 0 interior points. What is the area of each?

Repeat for figures with 4 boundary points and 0 interior points. Repeat for figures with 5 boundary points and 0 interior points.

Can you make a rule that relates the area to the number of boundary points when there are no interior points?

Supplementary Exercises, Set 53, page 411

Income taxes

Almost every person who earns income must pay federal income tax. Not all of a taxpayer's income is taxed. For example, before computing the income tax the taxpayer may subtract $750 from total income for *each* dependent. A **dependent** is someone who is supported by the income—the taxpayer, the taxpayer's wife or husband, their children, and so on. The $750 is called an **exemption.** Here are two examples:

Example 1.

Mike Conrad supports himself and his parents. He claims three exemptions. The total amount exempted is $2250.

Example 2.

Martha Brown supports herself, her husband, and their two children. She claims four exemptions.

EXERCISES

Answer these questions.

1. Jerry has three dependents, excluding himself. How many exemptions can he claim? What amount of his income is exempted?

2. Carla has no dependents, excluding herself. How many exemptions can she claim? What amount is exempted?

3. Mr. Harold earns $10,000 per year. He claims four exemptions. What percent of his income is exempted?

4. Mrs. Hopewell earns $100,000 per year. She claims four exemptions. What percent of her income is exempted?

5. A taxpayer may claim another person as a dependent only if the taxpayer pays more than 50% of the money needed to support that person. May two taxpayers legally claim the same person as a dependent?

A taxpayer is also allowed to deduct from total income certain other expenses. These deductions include interest paid on loans, state and local taxes, some medical expenses, donations to charities, and some expenses related to the taxpayer's job. If the taxpayer wishes to claim these deductions, he must itemize (list) them on a tax form. Instead of itemizing deductions, the taxpayer may merely subtract a **standard deduction** of 15% of his income. This deduction cannot exceed $2000.

Answer these questions.

6. Mr. Halley claimed these deductions: $525.74 for interest on his home mortgage, $625 for real-estate tax, $106 for state sales tax, and $100 for money given to his church. What was the total amount of his deductions?
7. Mr. Halley's (exercise 6) income was $8000. Which would be better for him, the standard deduction or the itemized deductions?
8. Miss Hudson earns $15,000 per year. She uses the standard deduction. How much does the deduction amount to?

If a taxpayer's income is under $10,000 and she does not itemize deductions, she may find her income tax by simply looking at a table. No computation is needed. Here are parts of two tables:

One exemption

If the amount of your taxable income is At least	But less than	And you are— Single, not head of household: Your tax is—
$4,150	$4,200	$334
4,200	4,250	343
4,250	4,300	353
4,300	4,350	362
4,350	4,400	372
4,400	4,450	381
4,450	4,500	391
4,500	4,550	400

Three exemptions

If the amount of your taxable income is At least	But less than	And you are— Single, not head of household: Your tax is—
$4,100	$4,150	$81
4,150	4,200	89
4,200	4,250	96
4,250	4,300	104
4,300	4,350	111
4,350	4,400	119
4,400	4,450	126
4,450	4,500	134

9. After graduation Carol worked part of a year as a teacher. She earned $4437. She had no dependents except herself. She did not itemize deductions. What was her income tax? About what percent of her income did she pay in taxes?
10. Carl supported himself and his parents, who lived in another city. He earned $4437 and did not itemize deductions. What was his income tax? About what percent of his income did he pay in taxes?

EXCURSION

Use a geoboard or dot paper. This is the area unit:

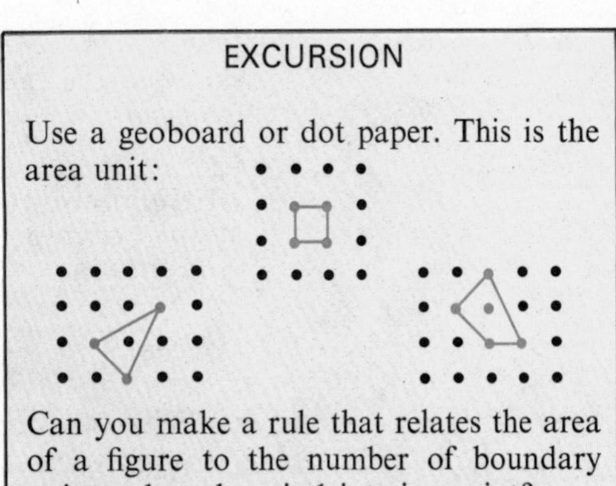

Can you make a rule that relates the area of a figure to the number of boundary points when there is 1 interior point?

Skill Maintenance, Set 54, page 411

Income taxes

A taxpayer who earns more than $10,000 cannot use the tables shown on page 239. He uses tables like these instead. People with incomes less than $10,000 who itemize deductions also use these tables.

Single Taxpayers

If the amount of your taxable income is / Your tax is

Not over $500 . . . 14% of your taxable income.

Over—	But not over—		of excess over—
$500	$1,000	$70 + 15%	$500
$1,000	$1,500	$145 + 16%	$1,000
$1,500	$2,000	$225 + 17%	$1,500
$2,000	$4,000	$310 + 19%	$2,000
$4,000	$6,000	$690 + 21%	$4,000
$6,000	$8,000	$1,110 + 24%	$6,000
$8,000	$10,000	$1,590 + 25%	$8,000
$10,000	$12,000	$2,090 + 27%	$10,000
$12,000	$14,000	$2,630 + 29%	$12,000
$14,000	$16,000	$3,210 + 31%	$14,000
$16,000	$18,000	$3,830 + 34%	$16,000
$18,000	$20,000	$4,510 + 36%	$18,000
$20,000	$22,000	$5,230 + 38%	$20,000
$90,000	$100,000	$46,190 + 69%	$90,000
$100,000	....	$53,090 + 70%	$100,000

Married Persons Filing Separate Returns

If the amount of your taxable income is / Your tax is

Not over $500 . . . 14% of your taxable income.

Over—	But not over—		of excess over—
$500	$1,000	$70 + 15%	$500
$1,000	$1,500	$145 + 16%	$1,000
$1,500	$2,000	$225 + 17%	$1,500
$2,000	$4,000	$310 + 19%	$2,000
$4,000	$6,000	$690 + 22%	$4,000
$6,000	$8,000	$1,130 + 25%	$6,000
$8,000	$10,000	$1,630 + 28%	$8,000
$10,000	$12,000	$2,190 + 32%	$10,000
$12,000	$14,000	$2,830 + 36%	$12,000
$14,000	$16,000	$3,550 + 39%	$14,000
$16,000	$18,000	$4,330 + 42%	$16,000
$18,000	$20,000	$5,170 + 45%	$18,000
$20,000	$22,000	$6,070 + 48%	$20,000
$90,000	$100,000	$48,590 + 69%	$90,000
$100,000	....	$55,490 + 70%	$100,000

EXERCISES

Answer these questions.

1. Jackie Colly had a taxable income of $7000. She was single, so she used the table on the left. This is the line of the table that she used:

If the amount of your taxable income is over—	But not over—	Your tax is	of excess over—
$6,000	$8,000	$1,110 + 24%	$6,000

a. What was the excess of her income over $6000?

b. What is 24% of that excess?

c. Her tax was $1110 plus the amount in part b. What was her tax?

2. Mildred Corry was single with a taxable income of $11,750. What was her income tax?

3. Jerry Stoker is married but he and his wife file separate returns. His taxable income is $9773. What is his tax?

4. George is single. His total income is $11,630.
   a. He takes the 15% standard deduction. How much is his deduction?
   b. He claims 1 dependent. What is the amount of his exemption?
   c. What is his taxable income (total less deductions and exemptions)?
   d. What is his tax?

5. Maynard is married but files a separate return. His total income was $17,651. He listed deductions totaling $3256 and claimed 3 exemptions. What was his tax?

6. Notice that the income tax is *graduated.* That is, the percent paid in taxes rises as income rises. Each interval on the tax table is called a *tax bracket* and is known by the percent of excess income paid. For example, a person whose taxable income is between $14,000 and $16,000 is said to be in the 31% tax bracket.
   a. What percent (single taxpayer) is paid on the first $500?
   b. In what tax bracket is a single taxpayer with income between $6000 and $8000? Between $10,000 and $12,000?
   c. Single Mr. Brooks has a taxable income of $100,000. What is his tax? How much of that $100,000 does he have left after taxes?

7. Mrs. Holt's taxable income was $200,000.
   a. What was her tax?
   b. How much did she have left after taxes?
   c. Suppose that she had given an extra $10,000 to charity. What would her taxable income have been?
   d. What would her tax have been?
   e. What would her income after taxes have been?
   f. Subtract **e** from **b** to see what her donation actually cost her.

8. Repeat exercise 7 for a married person who had a taxable income of $20,000.

CHECKUP

for pages 234–237

1. Karl earns $5.40 per hour for 40 hours per week and time and a half for over 40 hours. How much would he earn in a 50-hour week?
2. His payroll deductions include $20.16 for social security, $53.17 for withholding, and $4.21 for hospital insurance. What is his take-home pay?
3. Jean earned a commission of 15% of total sales. Her sales one month were $4500. What was her commission?

Answers on page 427.

Skill Maintenance, Set, 55 page 412

Other taxes

Besides the income tax, there are many other kinds of taxes. One of the most common is the sales tax.

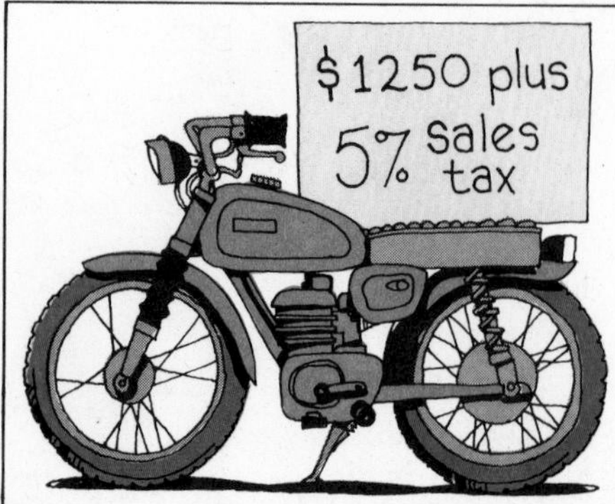

5% of \$1250 = .05 × \$1250 = \$62.50
sales tax

\$1250 + \$62.50 = \$1312.50
total cost

These exercises will tell you about sales taxes and other kinds of taxes.

EXERCISES

Compute the sales tax and the total price on these items.

1. \$79.95 bicycle
5% sales tax

2. \$19.98 jacket
4% sales tax

3. \$3024.50 car
4.5% sales tax

4. A house was valued at \$24,000 for tax purposes. The real-estate tax rate was \$3.50 per \$100 of the value of the house.
a. How many \$100s are there in \$24,000?
b. What is the tax?

5. A house was valued at \$18,750 and the tax rate was \$2.75 per \$100. What was the tax?

6. Real-estate tax rates are often given in mills. A mill is a thousandth of a dollar. (Notice the similarity between *mill* and the prefix *milli* used in the metric system.) What would be the tax on a house valued at \$21,000 if the tax rate was 37 mills per dollar? (37 mills = \$.037)

7. In an election the school board asked the voters to approve an increase of 8 mills per dollar in the school tax rate. How much would this increase the taxes on a \$30,000 house?

8. All states have a gasoline tax. If the tax on gasoline in a state is 8¢ per gallon, how much tax is paid on a purchase of 15 gallons?

9. Miss Heller drove her car 18,000 miles in one year. Her car averaged 15 miles per gallon of gasoline.
   a. How many gallons of gas did she buy?
   b. If the tax on gasoline in her state is 7.5¢ per gallon, how much tax did she pay in the year?

10.

John had his tank filled with 16.5 gallons of gasoline.
   a. How much did he pay in all?
   b. How much state tax did he pay?

11. Some states have an automobile excise tax. If you own a car you have to pay this tax annually. Suppose that the tax rate is $62.50 per thousand dollars of valuation. That means that on a car valued at $2000 you would have to pay $115. Compute the amount of tax owed on cars of the following valuations if the rate is $55.75 per thousand.
   a. $750 **b.** $2500 **c.** $1350 **d.** $3500

1. What is your state sales tax rate? Is the tax charged on all sales?
2. Use your state tax rate to compute the tax on a $3416.95 automobile.
3. How many different kinds of taxes can you find? What are the present rates?

EXCURSION

Use a geoboard or dot paper. Can you find a rule that relates the area of a figure to the number of boundary points when there are 2 interior points?

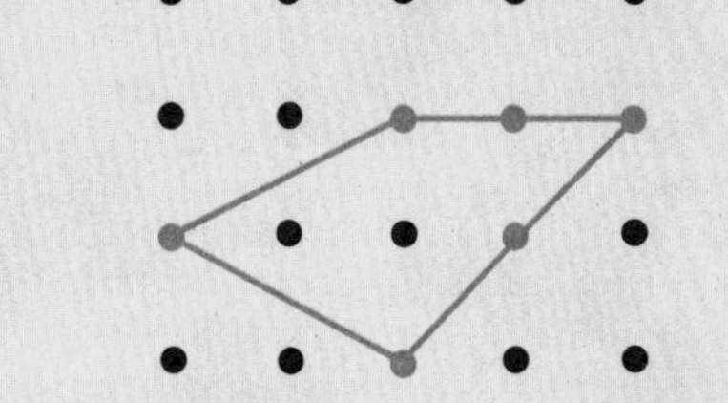

Supplementary Exercises, Set 51, page 388

Buying wisely

Once you have earned your money by hard work and paid your taxes, you ought to spend as wisely as possible to get the most for your money. The exercises on these pages suggest some ways of spending wisely.

EXERCISES

1. Records at the Hart Music Shop are selling at 50% off. How much would a record cost which usually sells for $5.98?
2. A record player was reduced from $190 to $140. What was the percent of reduction?
3. Eight-track tapes were reduced 25%. A tape is on sale for $4.20. What was the regular price?

4.

Mr. Wright and his neighbor wanted to paint their houses. They went together and bought 12 gallons of paint. How much did they save by buying together?

5. Karen works in a department store. All employees get 20% discount on all merchandise. If she bought these items, what would she pay?

a. b. c.

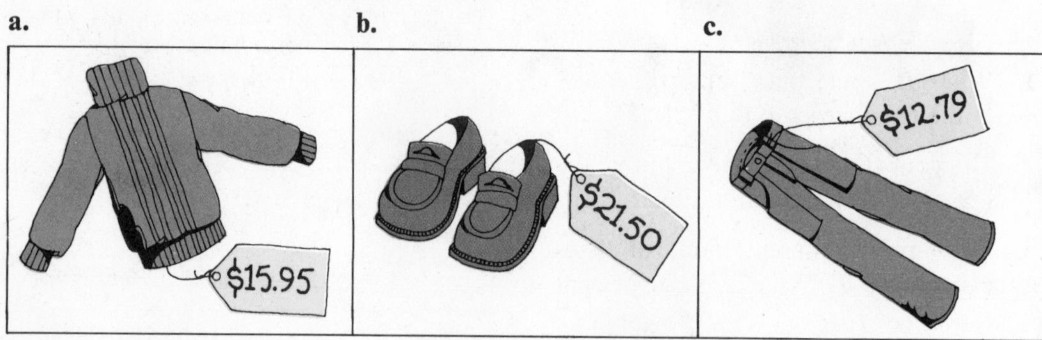

6.

a. How much does the small package cost per ounce?

b. How much does the large package cost per ounce?

c. Which is the better buy?

Which is the better buy?

7. 9.

8. 10.

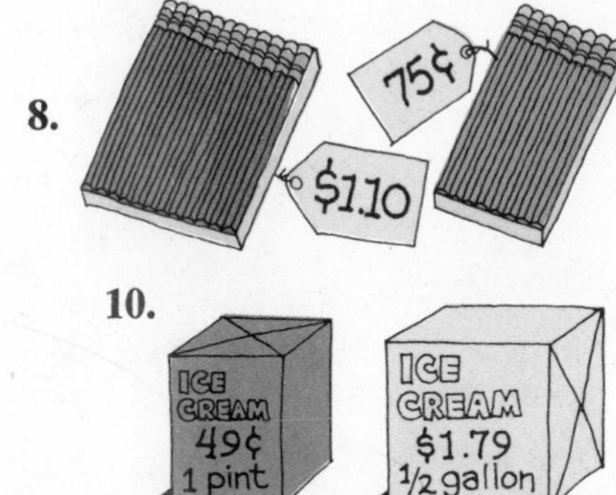

11. Usually a large quantity costs less per unit than a small quantity. Give a reason for sometimes buying the small quantity instead of the large.

12. Ken can buy gasoline directly on his way to work for 56.9¢ per gallon, or he can take another route that is 4 miles longer and buy gas for 4¢ per gallon less. His car averages 16 miles per gallon. If he goes to the cheaper station and buys 16 gallons, how much will he save?

1. Find items in a supermarket that are sold in different sizes. Find the unit cost of each and tell which ones are better buys.
2. Find advertisements for sales. How much could you save on some of the sale items?

CHECKUP
for pages 238–243

1. Mr. Kelly's taxable income was $8531. Use the tax table for single taxpayers on page 240 to compute his income tax.
2. Mary Cooper supports herself and her mother and small son on an income of $4935. What is her income tax? Use the table on page 239.
3. The cost of a winter coat is $59.95. The state sales tax is 5%. How much tax must be paid?

Answers on page 427.

Skill Maintenance, Set 56, page 412

Mental computation with percents

You can do many computations involving percents "in your head." Here are some examples:

Example 1. You can find 10% or 1% of a number by "moving" the decimal point.

1% of 168.3 = 1.683 10% of 168.3 = 16.83

Example 2. You can find some percents of numbers by simple division.

25% of $84 = \frac{84}{4} = 21$ ($\frac{1}{4}$) 50% of $90 = \frac{90}{2} = 45$ ($\frac{1}{2}$)

$33\frac{1}{3}\%$ of $90 = \frac{90}{3} = 30$ ($\frac{1}{3}$) 20% of $65.5 = \frac{65.5}{5} = 13.1$ ($\frac{1}{5}$)

Example 3. Here are some other special cases:

5% of $72 = \frac{1}{2}$ of 10% of $72 = \frac{1}{2}$ of $7.2 = 3.6$

15% of $72 = 10\%$ of $72 + 5\%$ of $72 = 7.2 + 3.6 = 10.8$

EXERCISES

Complete. Do not use paper and pencil.

1. 10% of 58 = ___?___ **2.** 1% of 58 = ___?___ **3.** 10% of 6.23 = ___?___

4. 1% of 6.23 = ___?___ **5.** 20% of 85 = ___?___ **6.** 20% of \$9.20 = ___?___

7. 50% of 4.6 = ___?___ **8.** 50% of \$8.30 = ___?___ **9.** $33\frac{1}{3}\%$ of 123 = ___?___

10. $33\frac{1}{3}\%$ of 66 = ___?___ **11.** $33\frac{1}{3}\%$ of \$4.50 = ___?___ **12.** 25% of .44 = ___?___

13. 25% of \$10.80 = ___?___ **14.** 5% of 88 = ___?___ **15.** 5% of \$2.60 = ___?___

16. When Carol is satisfied with the service in a restaurant, she tips the waiter 15% of the cost of her meal. What would be the tip for each of these amounts?

a. \$6.00 **b.** \$12.40 **c.** \$8.45

KEEPING SKILLS SHARP

Divide. Round quotients to the nearest hundredth.

1. $9\overline{)5.7}$
2. $23\overline{)45}$
3. $4.2\overline{)6.1}$
4. $3.8\overline{)9.22}$
5. $.81\overline{).498}$

Here are three functions, *f*, *g*, and *h*.

$f(n) = 4.2n$ $\qquad g(n) = \frac{n^2}{2}$ $\qquad h(n) = 4(3n - 1)$

Complete each equation.

6. $f(5) = \underline{\ ?\ }$
7. $g(5) = \underline{\ ?\ }$
8. $h(5) = \underline{\ ?\ }$
9. $g(0) = \underline{\ ?\ }$
10. $f(\underline{?}) = 0$
11. $g(\underline{?}) = 0$
12. $h(\underline{?}) = 0$
13. $h(8.1) = \underline{\ ?\ }$

Solve.

14. $5n + 7 = 52$
15. $5n + 7 = 53$
16. $5n + 7 = 56$
17. $2(15 - 2x) = 22$
18. $2(15 - 2x) = 23$
19. $\frac{7a - 3}{5} = 12$

Multiply.

20. 43×20
21. 8.96×47
22. 7.64×24.9

Complete.

23. 12% of 68 = ___?___
24. 50% of 16.2 = ___?___
25. 90% of 9 = ___?___
26. 50% of 12 = ___?___
27. 50% of ___?___ = 12
28. ___?___% of 50 = 12

How many lines of symmetry? Points of symmetry?

29. 

30. 

31. 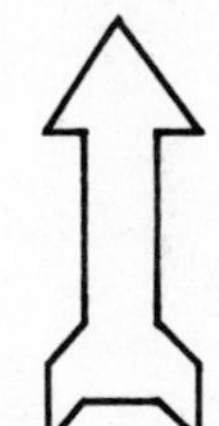

True or false?

32. If a polygon has more than 1 line of symmetry, then it has a point of symmetry.

33. If a polygon has a point of symmetry, then it has more than 1 line of symmetry.

These statements are about the sets that are pictured. Are they true or false?

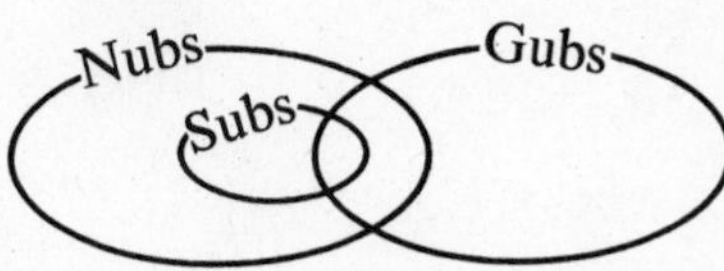

34. All Gubs are Nubs.
35. Some Nubs are Gubs.
36. All Subs are Nubs.
37. No Subs are Gubs.

Skill Maintenance, Set 57, page 412

Borrowing money—simple interest

Almost everyone borrows money at some time. For example:

Individuals borrow money to buy cars.

Companies borrow money to build factories.

Nations borrow money to pay for defense.

When we borrow money we pay for the use of it. The amount we pay for the use of money is called **interest**. The interest paid depends on the **principal** (amount borrowed), the length of time the money is borrowed (**time**), and the **rate** (percent of interest) charged. This example shows how to compute simple interest.

> Suppose that you borrow \$1000 at a rate of 12% per year for two years. The interest for 1 year would be 12% of \$1000.
>
> $$12\% \text{ of } \$1000 = \$120$$
>
> You keep the money for two years, so you pay 2 times as much.
>
> $$\$120 \times 2 = \$240 = \text{interest}$$

This example suggests a formula for computing interest (i) from the principal (p), the rate (r) per interest period, and the time (t).

$$i = prt$$

The time and the interest period of the rate must be in the same unit. In the example the rate was a yearly rate, so the time must be in years.

Here is how the example above is done using the formula.

$$i = \$1000 \times 12\% \times 2 = \$240$$

Here is another example:

Principal = \$2000	$i = prt$
Rate = 11% per year	$i = \$2000 \times 11\% \times \frac{1}{2}$
Time = 6 months	$i = \$110$

EXERCISES

Compute the interest.

1. Principal = \$1000
   Rate = 14% per year
   Time = 1 year

2. Principal = \$1000
   Rate = 14% per year
   Time = 3 years

3. Principal = \$1000
   Rate = 14% per year
   Time = 6 months

4. Principal = \$500
   Rate = 12% per year
   Time = 3 months ($\frac{1}{4}$ year)

5. Principal = \$800
   Rate = 2% per month
   Time = 6 months

6. Principal = \$800
   Rate = 3% per month
   Time = 5 months

7. Principal = \$5000
   Rate = 12.5% per year
   Time = 2 years

8. Principal = \$450
   Rate = 2.5% per month
   Time = 6 months

9. Principal = \$300
   Rate = 3.25% per month
   Time = 8 months

Solve.

10. Chris wanted to borrow \$2500 to buy a car. She could borrow from a bank at 16.12% per year or from a small loan company for 2.5% per month. Which loan would cost less?

Ken borrowed \$500 at 15% per year.

11. How much interest did he owe after 1 month?

12. At the end of the first month Ken paid \$100. Part of the \$100 was for the interest (exercise 11), and the rest was payment on the principal. How much principal did he pay?

13. After that first payment how much principal did he still owe?

14. How much interest did he owe after another month?

EXCURSION

Look at the excursions on pages 237, 239, and 243. Can you find one formula that relates the area of any figure on a geoboard to the number of boundary points and the number of interior points? Use A for area, B for the number of boundary points, and I for the number of interior points.

Supplementary Exercises, Set 52, page 388

Borrowing—installment buying

Mrs. Abbott wants to buy this color TV but she does not have enough money to pay the full price. She could save her money for ten months and then she would have the full $525. But she doesn't want to wait that long. She wants the TV now. Instead of paying cash she can buy on the **installment plan.** She can pay a small **down payment** and take the TV set home with her. Then she will pay regular payments to the dealer until the set is paid for. Notice that the dealer is really lending Mrs. Abbott an amount of money, so he charges her interest on that amount. Here is exactly how Mrs. Abbott paid for the TV set.

Cash Plan	*Installment Plan*
$525	$50 down and $52.25 per month for 10 months

$$\begin{array}{r} \$52.25 \\ \times 10 \\ \hline \$522.50 \end{array} + \$50 = \$572.50$$

$522.50 ↑ monthly payments; $50 ↑ down payment; $572.50 ↑ total installment price

The installment price is $47.50 greater than the cash price. That extra amount is the interest. Mrs. Abbott must decide which of these two plans is better for her:

Cash plan—save $47.50 and use her old TV for the next 10 months.
Installment plan—pay $47.50 extra and have her new TV 10 months earlier.

EXERCISES

How much greater than the cash price is the installment price?

1. Refrigerator: $675 cash or $150 down and $50.31 per month for 1 year.
2. Automobile: $3498 cash or $1900 down and $63.20 per month for 3 years.
3. TV set: $265.88 cash or $60 down and $37.40 per month for 6 months.
4. Automobile: $5275.80 cash or $3300 down, $73.44 per month for 35 months, and a 36th payment of $45.41.

5. Motorcycle: $1650 cash or $400 down and $119.79 per month for 12 months.

6. House: $40,750 cash or $17,000 down and $190 per month for 20 years.

7. Freezer: $475 cash or $100 down and $34.37 per month for 12 months.

8. Hi-fi: $358 cash or $75 down and $33.34 per month for 9 months.

9. Jed Cooper bought a $627 dishwasher on the installment plan. His down payment was $150.
   a. How much of the value of the dishwasher did Jed still owe? This amount is the principal of the installment loan.
   b. The first monthly payment was $43.72. Of that payment $3.98 was interest and the rest was principal. How much was paid on the principal?
   c. After the first payment was made, how much principal was still owed?
   d. Since the principal during the second month was less, the interest was also less. Of the next $43.72 payment, $3.64 was interest. How much was principal?
   e. After the second payment was made, how much principal was still owed?

10. Miss Jasper bought a $3400 car for $1000 down and 30 monthly payments of $120. She was charged an installment interest rate, but by law the dealer had to tell her the equivalent simple interest rate.
   a. What was the total amount of the monthly payments?
   b. What was the principal of the installment loan?
   c. What was the amount of interest?
   d. What was the equivalent simple interest rate?

CHECKUP
for pages 248–249

Compute the interest.

1. Principal: $1000
   Rate: 9% per year
   Time: 6 months
2. Principal: $650
   Rate: 8% per year
   Time: 4 months
3. Principal: $2400
   Rate: 10% per year
   Time: 2 years
4. Principal: $700
   Rate: 2% per month
   Time: 7 months

Answers on page 427.

Skill Maintenance, Set 58, page 413

Checking accounts

You can get many services from a bank. One important service is a checking account. The basic idea of a checking account is simple. You give the bank some of your money to keep safe for you. When you wish to use the money, you write a note to the bank telling it to give the money to you or to someone else. The money you give to the bank is a **deposit** and the notes you use to **withdraw** money are **checks.** Here is an example of a check:

Carl R. Parker
1525 Oak Street   TOLEDO CITY BANK
Toledo, Ohio 43606   Sept. 19 1976

Pay to the
order of Hudson Hardware ———— $ 56 $\frac{34}{100}$

Fifty-six and 34/100 ———————— Dollars

Carl R. Parker
660 883

This check tells the Toledo City Bank that Carl R. Parker wants the bank to take $56.34 from his checking account and pay it to Hudson Hardware. Notice the blanks that Mr. Parker filled in: the date, the person or company to whom the money is to be given, the amount of money (written in two ways), and his signature. The amount is written in two ways as a safety measure, so that it is difficult for a dishonest person to change the amount of the check. His signature is the proof that Mr. Parker really wrote the check. The bank has a copy of his signature and can compare the signature on the check with the one in its files.

The check also acts as a receipt, because the person who receives the money **endorses** the check (signs his name on the back of the check). This is proof that he received the money.

One other safety measure is important. The amounts on the check are written as close to the dollar sign and as close to the left edge of the check as possible. Why do you think this is important?

The following exercises will help you to understand checking accounts.

EXERCISES

Show how you would fill in the blanks on this check for each of these exercises.

Carl R. Parker 1525 Oak Street Toledo, Ohio 43606	TOLEDO CITY BANK __________19__
Pay to the order of ____________________	$______
__________________________	Dollars
	____________ 660 883

1. On October 21, 1976, Mr. Parker took his dog to the Central Animal Clinic for some shots. The shots cost $15.75.
2. On October 21, 1976, Mr. Parker bought a TV set for $695.20 from Nichols Furniture Company.
3. On October 23, 1976, Mr. Parker paid his electric bill by check. The amount was $50.25. The company was Northwest Power Company.
4. Mr. Parker had a total of $1375.17 in his checking account before he wrote the checks in exercises 1–3. How much did he have after writing these checks?
5. Then Mr. Parker deposited $432.28 in his checking account. How much was in his account then?
6. In one week in December Mr. Parker wrote checks for these amounts:

$57.60	$38.29	$105.04
$68.77	$19.20	$83.80

He had $423.17 in his account at the beginning of the week and deposited $88.46 during the week. How much was in his account at the end of the week?

Project

Find out how banks in your area charge for checking accounts. What do they do when someone accidentally has an overdraft (writes a check for a greater amount than is in the account)?

CHECKUP
for pages 250–251

1. A $1300 motorcycle can be purchased for $300 down and $100 per month for a year. How much will it cost in all on the installment plan?
2. A $485 refrigerator can be purchased on the installment plan for $150 down and $61.40 per month for 6 months. How much more does it cost on the installment plan?

Answers on page 427.

Skill Maintenance, Set 59, page 413

Checking accounts

Mr. Parker keeps a record of his checking account. The record looks like this.

Check No.	Date	Pay To	Amount	Deposit	Balance	
					$1375	17
874	Oct. 21	Central Animal Clinic	15.75			
875	Oct. 21	Nichols Furniture Co.	695.20			
876	Oct. 23	Northwest Power Co.	50.25	438.28	1046	26

The balance is the amount in the account. The $1375.17 is the balance from the preceding page of the record book.

EXERCISES

1–26. Compute each balance.

Check No.	Date	Pay To	Amount	Deposit	Balance	
					823	41
1013	Mar. 3	Marshall Hughes	37.50			
1014	Mar. 3	Ogdens' Dept. Store	43.86			
1015	Mar. 5	Cash	50.00	168.20		
1016	Mar. 6	Coopers Feed Store	82.97			
1017	Mar. 10	Northwest Power	53.16			
1018	Mar. 10	Ohio Telephone Co.	38.15			
1019	Mar. 10	Toledo Savings & Loan	283.50	342.10		
1020	Mar. 11	Smiths Service Station	24.16			
1021	Mar. 15	George Carter	10.95			
1022	Mar. 16	Cash	100.00			
1023	Mar. 20	St. Marks Church	20.00	65.00		
1024	Mar. 22	The Ranch Restuarant	24.77			
1025	Mar. 25	H & L Supermarket	35.83			

Check No.	Date	Pay To	Amount	Deposit	Balance	
					593	86
1026	Mar. 27	City Water Co.	17.45			
1027	Mar. 30	Cash	100.00			
1028	Apr. 2	J. L. Smith	148.75			
1029	Apr. 3	C. K. Harte	77.35			
1030	Apr. 3	H & L Supermarket	32.57	168.20		
1031	Apr. 10	Northwest Power	48.12	342.10		
1032	Apr. 10	Ohio Telephone Co.	27.65			
1033	Apr. 10	Toledo Savings & Loan	283.50			
1034	Apr. 12	Smiths' Service St.	12.35			
1035	Apr. 15	H & L Supermarket	45.12			
1036	Apr. 20	Cash	50.00			
1037	Apr. 20	St. Marks Church	20.00			
1038	Apr. 21	Cash	100.00			

27. What do you think it means when a check is made payable to "Cash"?

28. Mr. Parker must pay a service charge on his checking account only if his balance goes below $200 during the month. Did Mr. Parker have to pay a service charge in March? In April?

29. Why do you think the bank does not charge for a checking account when the balance stays high?

Find as many reasons as you can for having a checking account. Find reasons for not having a checking account.

EXCURSION

Study this array. The letters identify the columns. The dots indicate that the array goes on and on.

A	B	C	D	E	F	G
1	2	3	4	5	6	7
8	9	10	11	12	13	14
15	16	17	18	19	20	21
22	23	24	25	26	27	28
29	30	31	32	33	34	35
36	37	38	39	40	41	42
⋮	⋮	⋮	⋮	⋮	⋮	⋮

Pick any number in B and any number in D. Add the two numbers. In what column is the sum? Repeat several times with numbers in B and D. What do you notice? Repeat with numbers from columns C and G.

Skill Maintenance, Set 60, page 413

Investments—lending

After earning money, paying taxes, and spending wisely for what you want and need, you may have some money left to save. You can hide the extra money someplace or you can invest it. We will look at two important ways of investing: (1) lending money and earning interest and (2) buying part ownership in a company and sharing in the profits. This lesson is about lending.

You can lend money to banks, to savings and loan companies, to corporations, and to governments.

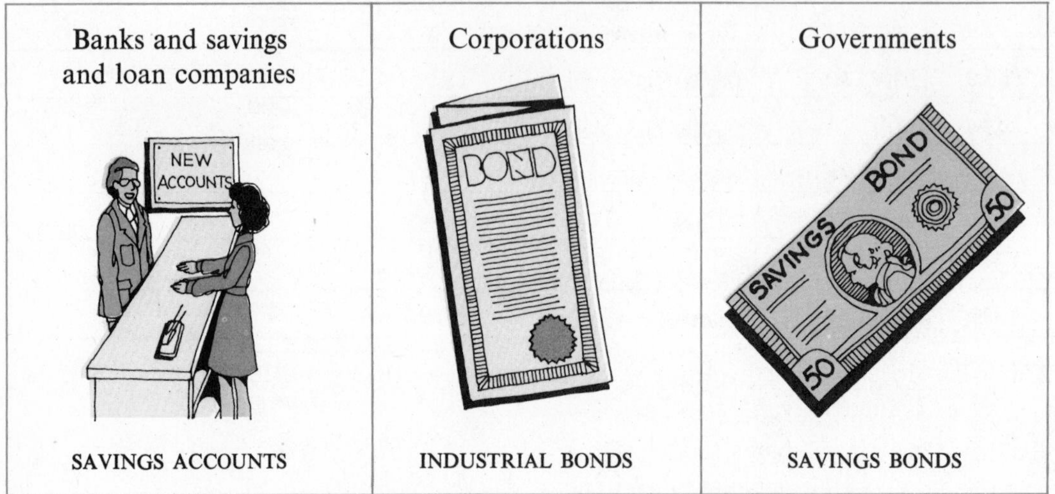

These exercises will help you to understand some facts about lending money.

EXERCISES

1. Jean bought a \$1000 bond from a large company. This means that she lent the company \$1000. The bond pays 9% interest each year.
   - **a.** How much interest does she receive each year?
   - **b.** The company pays the interest quarterly (every 3 months). How much is Jean paid each quarter?
   - **c.** The bond matures in 10 years. This means that the company will repay the loan 10 years after she bought the bond. How much interest will she earn in all?

2. Industrial bonds are originally sold by the company and bought back by the company when they mature. Between those two times the bonds may be bought and sold many times by individuals. The price of a bond may differ from its original **face value**. Jack bought an 8% bond with a face value of $1000. He paid only $950 for it. Of course, the company still paid 8% of $1000 each year.
   a. How much interest did Jack receive in a year?
   b. How much money did Jack have invested?
   c. What percent of *his investment* was the interest?
   d. Suppose that he had paid $1050 for the bond. What percent of *his investment* would the interest be?

3. Karen opened a savings account at a local bank. She deposited $200 in her account. This means that she lent the bank $200. The bank paid at a rate equivalent to 5.5% simple interest. How much interest did she earn in a year?

4. Jill bought a government savings bond for $75. In about 7 years she sold it back to the government for $100. What was the percent of gain over the 7 years? About what was the average percent of gain each year?

5. Jerry bought a 9% bond with a face value of $1000. His income was so large that he had to pay 40% of the interest in income taxes.
   a. What interest did he earn?
   b. How much of that interest was paid in income taxes?
   c. How much of the interest did he get to keep?

6. Joan bought a 5% bond with a face value of $1000. This bond was sold by a city government and was **tax-exempt**. This means that she did not have to pay federal income tax on the interest.
   a. How much interest did she earn?
   b. Who made more money after taxes, Jerry (exercise 5) or Joan?

CHECKUP
for pages 252–255

Give the final balance.

Check No.	Date	Pay to	Amount	Deposit	Balance
					327.14
12	9/6	Smith	58.34		
13	9/6	Cash	24.00		
14	9/10	Harper	77.83		
15	9/11	K&L	95.86	217.44	
16	9/12	Cash	60.00		
17	9/17	Bank	52.14		
18	9/17	Jones	10.75		
19	9/17	K&L	24.16		

Answers on page 427.

Skill Maintenance, Set 61, page 413

Compound interest

If you buy an industrial bond, each quarter the company sends you the interest earned. The principal (value of the bond) remains the same and the interest also remains the same every quarter. However, if you deposit your principal in a savings account at a bank (or savings and loan company), the bank will add the interest to your account each quarter (or more often). This means that your principal gets larger and larger each quarter and therefore the interest earned each quarter gets larger, too. This process of regularly adding the interest to the principal is called **compounding**. Yearly interest is compounded **annually**. If the interest is added each 6 months, we say that the interest is **compounded semi-annually**. If the interest is added each 3 months, we say that the interest is **compounded quarterly**.

The exercises will help you to understand compound interest.

EXERCISES

1. Suppose that Mr. Hodge deposited \$1000 in a savings account that paid interest at the rate of 5% per year.
   a. How much interest did his principal earn in the first quarter of that year?
   b. The interest was then added to the principal. What was the new second-quarter principal?
   c. What was the interest earned on the new principal in the second quarter?
   d. Add the interest to the second-quarter principal to get the third-quarter principal.
   e. What was the third-quarter interest?
   f. What was the fourth-quarter principal?
   g. What was the fourth-quarter interest?
   h. What was the total interest earned during the year?
   i. What percent of the \$1000 principal was the interest?
   j. How much greater was the actual percent earned than the 5% rate used to compute the quarterly interest?

This table shows the total interest accumulated when $1000 is on deposit at 4% and at 5% interest both compounded quarterly.

Total Amount of Interest When $1000 Is on Deposit

Years	4% compounded quarterly	5% compounded quarterly
1	$ 40.60	$ 50.94
2	82.86	104.49
3	126.82	160.75
4	172.58	219.89
5	220.19	282.04
...	...	...
10	488.86	643.62

2. How much interest is earned in the first year at 4%?
3. How much interest is earned in the first 2 years at 4%?
4. How much interest is earned at 4% in the 2nd year? 3rd year? 4th year? 5th year?
5. Why does the amount of interest earned increase from year to year?
6. How much more interest is earned in the first year at 5% than at 4%?
7. How much more interest is earned in the first ten years at 5% than at 4%?
8. Is the answer to exercise 7 ten times the answer to exercise 6?
9. Suppose that you invest $1000 at 5% *simple interest* for 10 years. How much interest would you earn? How much more would you earn at 5% compounded quarterly?

1. Find out the interest rates paid by banks, savings and loan companies, and credit unions where you live.
2. Find out the interest rates *charged* by the same institutions when they *lend* money.

EXCURSION

Look at the excursion on page 255. You found that a number in B added to a number in D gave you a number in F. We write B ⊕ D = F and show this in the table in red.

⊕	A	B	C	D	E	F	G
A							
B				F			
C							C
D							
E							
F							
G							

You also found that C ⊕ G = C. This is shown in blue. Find other facts about the columns on page 255 and complete the table.

Skill Maintenance, Set 62, page 414

Estimating

Remember that you can find 1% or 10% of a number just by moving the decimal point.

1% of 168.3 = 1.683 10% of 168.3 = 16.83

These examples give you some hints about how you can estimate with percents.

Example 1. Estimate.

19% of 75 = ___?___

19% is near 20%. Find 10% of 75 and double it.

10% of 75 = 7.5 7.5 × 2 = 15

Or divide 75 by 5 because 20% = $\frac{1}{5}$.

75 ÷ 5 = 15

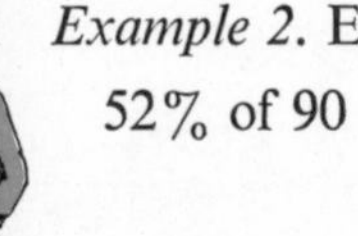

Example 2. Estimate.

52% of 90 = ___?___

52% is near 50%. Find 50% of 90 by dividing by 2.

90 ÷ 2 = 45

EXERCISES

Estimate.

1. 26% of 60 = ___?___ **2.** 48% of 168 = ___?___ **3.** 31% of $1.47 = ___?___

4. 12% of 286.5 = ___?___ **5.** 34% of $6.93 = ___?___ **6.** 53% of $268.40 = ___?___

Example 3.

___?___% of 26 is 12.

12 is 50% of 24

7. ___?___% of 49 = 11 **8.** ___?___% of $250 = $47 **9.** ___?___% of 59 = 19

10. ___?___% of $10.03 = $.99 **11.** ___?___% of 23 = 99 **12.** ___?___% of 611.15 = 148

KEEPING SKILLS SHARP

Find each area and find the perimeter or circumference. Use 3.14 as an approximation for π.

1.

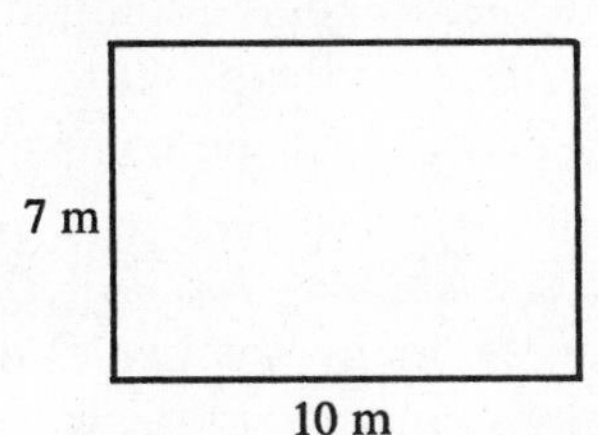

2.

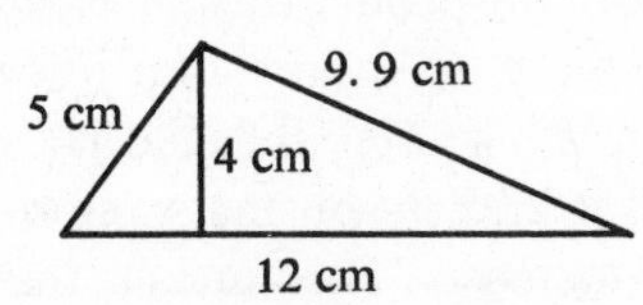

3.

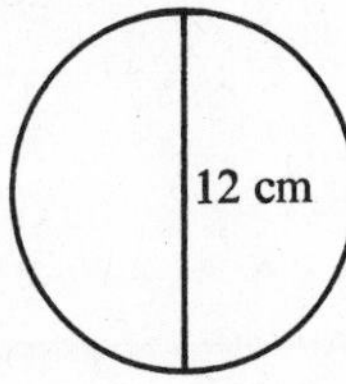

4. This is a drawing of the Coopers' backyard. The Coopers wish to fence in the yard as shown. The fencing they plan to use costs $5.43 per meter. How much will the fence cost?

5. The Coopers also plan to plant grass seed in the yard. The seed they plan to use costs $10.95 for 500 grams. Five hundred grams of seed is enough to plant 200 square meters. How much seed should they buy? How much will it cost?

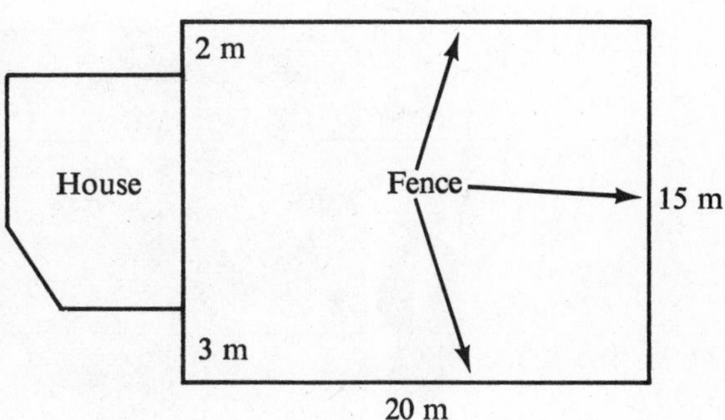

Find each volume. Use 3.14 as an approximation for π.

6.

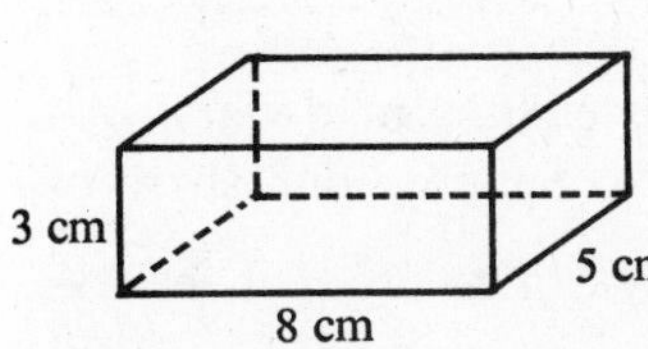

7.

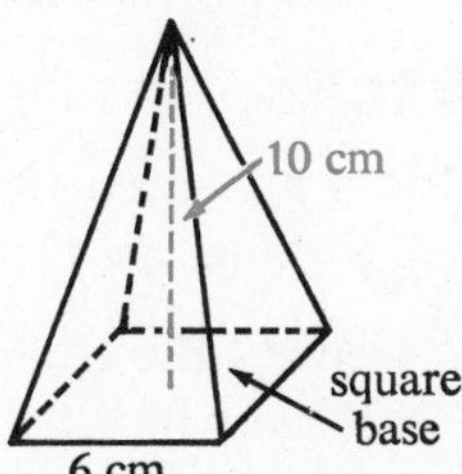

8.

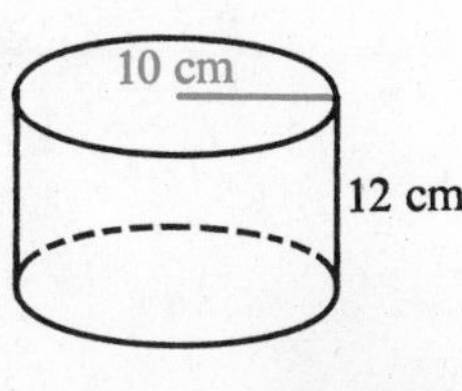

9. The Smiths have a swimming pool. It is 5 m wide, 10 m long, and is an average of 1.2 m deep. How many liters of water does it hold? It costs the Smiths $1.25 per kiloliter to fill the pool. What is the total cost of filling the pool?

10. A pool cover costs about $6.25 per square meter. How much will a cover for the Smiths' pool cost?

Skill Maintenance, Set 63, page 414

Buying stocks

Every person who wants to can own part of almost any major corporation in the world. To become a part owner you buy **shares of stock** in the company. As an owner you can make money in two ways: by sharing in the profits and by sharing in the growth of the company. If the company makes a profit, it may pay some of the profit to the stockholders. The amount paid is called a **dividend.** If the company is successful and its business improves, the value of its stock will probably increase. This means that the stockholder can sell the stock for more than he paid for it. Of course, many companies do not make profits, and the stocks of many companies lose value. Buying stock is always a risk. Some stocks are bigger risks than others.

These exercises will help you to learn some facts about stocks.

EXERCISES

1. Stock prices are given in dollars and eighths of dollars. (An eighth of a dollar is 12.5¢ or \$.125). Suppose one share of stock in General Electronics Company can be brought for $23\frac{3}{8}$ (\$23.375). What will 100 shares cost?

2. In each exercise you are given the price per share of a stock and a number of shares. Tell how much the shares cost.

a. 100 shares at $18\frac{1}{2}$ per share

b. 1000 shares at $3\frac{3}{4}$ per share

c. 50 shares at $47\frac{5}{8}$ per share

d. 200 shares at $83\frac{7}{8}$ per share

e. 25 shares at $10\frac{1}{8}$ per share

f. 43 shares at $112\frac{3}{8}$ per share

3. Ms. Hill bought 100 shares of General Electronics at $21\frac{3}{8}$ per share and sold them a year later at $29\frac{1}{8}$. How much did her stock increase in value? (Not all the gain is profit. She must pay her **stockbroker** a commission both for buying and for selling her stock.)
4. Suppose that Ms. Hill (exercise 3) paid 1% of the buying price and 1% of the selling price as commissions. How much profit did she make?
5. Mrs. Jackman bought 50 shares of International Motor Company stock at $93\frac{1}{4}$ per share. Two years later the same stock was worth only $74\frac{3}{8}$ per share. How much did her shares decrease in value?
6. International Motor Company stock paid an 85¢-per-share dividend each quarter one year. What was the total per-share dividend that year? What would an owner of 50 shares earn from dividends in a year?
7. General Electronics stock was worth about $30 per share and paid a 22¢-per-quarter dividend. About what percent of the value of the stock was the yearly dividend?
8. A company paid 52¢ per share per quarter. Its stock was worth about $35 per share. About what percent of the value was the yearly dividend?

1. Find out what commission rates buyers and sellers pay their stockbrokers.
2. Pretend that you have $10,000 to spend on stocks. Pick stocks to buy and sell for the next month. How much money did you "make" or "lose"?

CHECKUP
for pages 256–259

1. Mrs. Cooper bought an 8% bond with a face value of $1000 for $960. How many dollars in interest would she earn in a year? About what percent interest did she earn on her investment?
2. Mr. Halprin invested $1000 at 5% simple interest for 5 years. How much did he earn? How much would he have earned at 5% compounded quarterly? (Use the table on page 259.)

Answers on page 427.

Skill Maintenance, Set 64, page 414

Mathematics and science

1. Cut from thin carboard an irregular figure like this one:

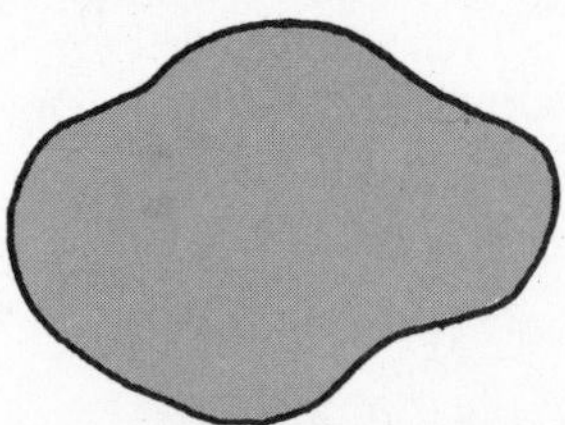

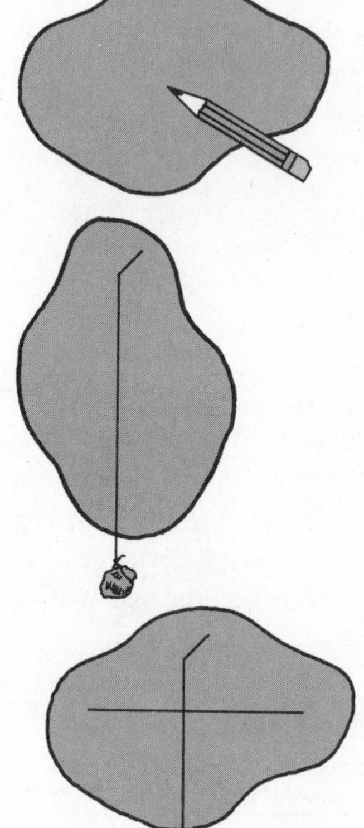

2. Try to balance it on the point of a pencil.
3. Put a pin through the cardboard at any point and let the cardboard hang until it stops moving. Use a weighted string and draw a line straight down from the pin.
4. Repeat with a different point.
5. Try to balance the cardboard again (as in exercise 2) on a pencil point. Try placing the pencil at the point where the two lines cross. The point where the lines cross is called the **center of gravity.** When the center of gravity is directly above or below a point of support, the cardboard will balance.
6. Where do you think the center of gravity is in each of these solid figures?

a.

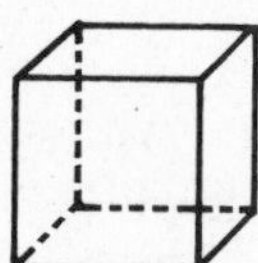

b.

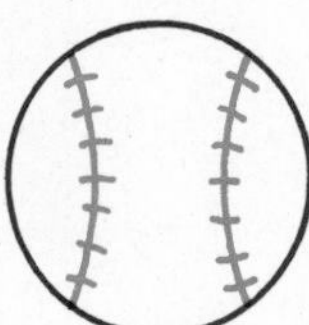

c.

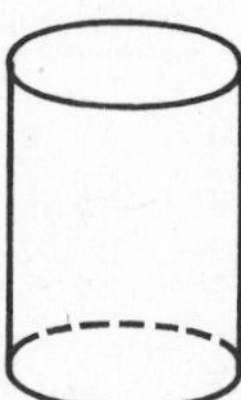

7. The stability of an object is related to its center of gravity. The center of gravity of each block is marked in red and a vertical blue line is drawn through it. How does the intersection of the blue line with the base of a block relate to its stability?

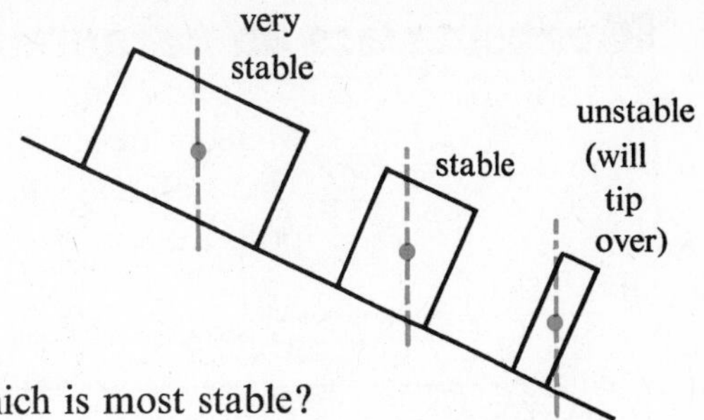

8. This block is shown in three positions. Which is most stable? Which is least stable?

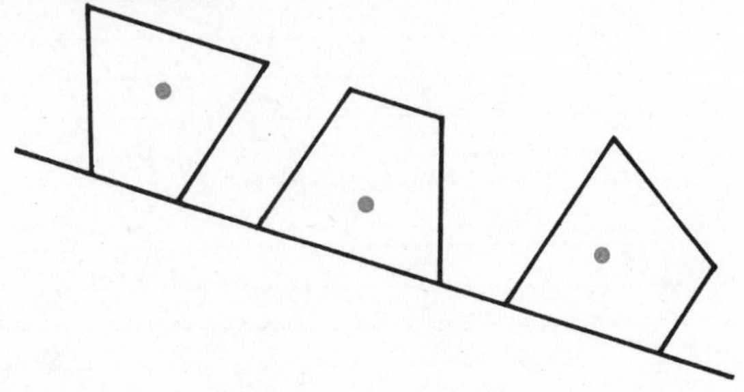

9. Support a pencil in these four ways.

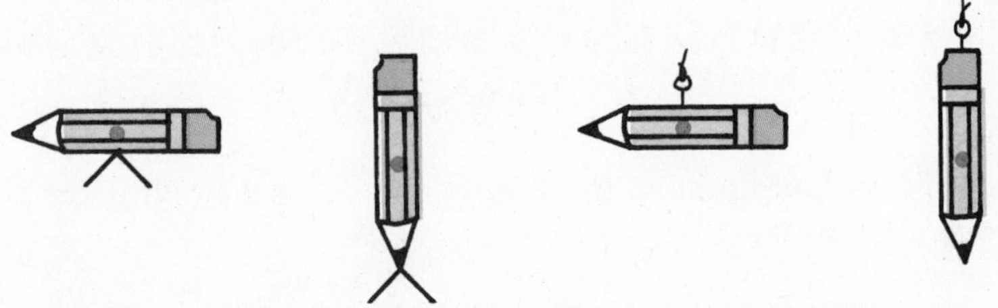

Discuss the relative stability of each position.

CHECKUP
for pages 262–263

In each exercise you are given the price per share of a stock and a number of shares. Tell how much the shares cost.

1. 25 shares at $97\frac{3}{4}$ a share
2. 90 shares at $32\frac{5}{8}$ a share
3. 150 shares at $109\frac{3}{8}$ a share
4. What is the total yearly dividend on 50 shares of stock if the company pays $.75 per share quarterly?
5. What is the total loss on 100 shares of stock that were purchased at $54\frac{1}{2}$ per share and sold at $44\frac{3}{4}$?

Answers on page 427.

Skill Maintenance, Set 65, page 414

Mathematics in careers

Meteorologists study and try to predict weather. They keep many kinds of statistics, including temperature, humidity, rainfall, air pressure, and so on. This graph shows other data that they might keep.

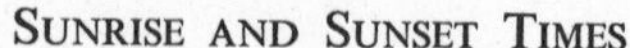

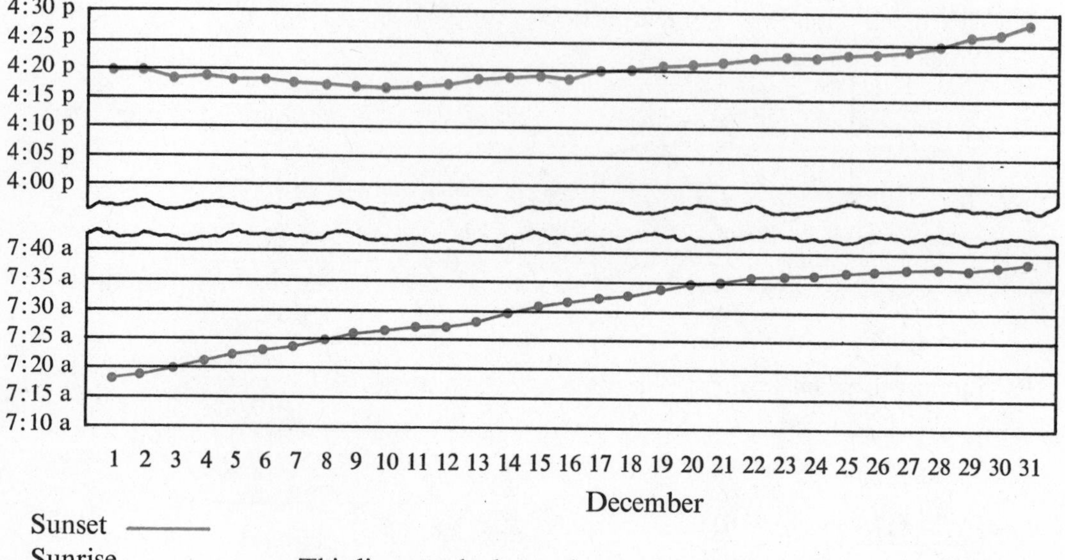

Sunset ———

Sunrise ———

This line graph shows the sunrise and sunset times in December in one place in the United States.

EXERCISES

1. At what times does the sun rise on these dates?
   a. December 1 **b.** December 10 **c.** December 20 **d.** December 30
2. At what times does the sun set on these dates?
   a. December 1 **b.** December 10 **c.** December 20 **d.** December 30
3. On which of these dates does the sun rise latest?
   a. December 1 **b.** December 10 **c.** December 20 **d.** December 30
4. On which of these dates does the sun set earliest?
   a. December 1 **b.** December 10 **c.** December 20 **d.** December 30
5. How many hours and minutes of daylight are there on these dates?
   a. December 1 **b.** December 10 **c.** December 20 **d.** December 30
6. From the graph tell what days are the shortest days of the year.
7. Do the shortest days have the latest sunrises?
8. Do the shortest days have the earliest sunsets?

CHAPTER CHECKUP

Answer each question.

1. Mr. Kapp earns \$6.85 per hour for a 40-hour week with time and a half for overtime. How much does he earn in a 44-hour week? [*page 234*]
2. Miss King earns \$9600 per year plus 7% of all sales above \$150,000. What does she earn in a year if her total sales are \$175,000? [*page 234*]
3. Mrs. Kong's taxable income is \$13,421. This is part of the tax table she uses. What is her income tax? [*page 240*]

If the amount of your taxable income is over—	But not over—	Your tax is	of excess over—
\$10,000	\$12,000	\$2,190 + 32%	\$10,000
\$12,000	\$14,000	\$2,830 + 36%	\$12,000
\$14,000	\$16,000	\$3,550 + 39%	\$14,000

4. In a state the state sales tax is 5%. What would be the sales tax on an item costing \$14.95? [*page 242*]
5. The real estate tax in one city is \$3.12 per one hundred dollars of the value of the house. What is the tax on a house valued at \$17,500? [*page 242*]
6. An item that regularly costs \$25.00 is on sale at 15% off. What is the sale price? [*page 244*]
7. What is the simple interest in each case? [*page 248*]
   a. \$300 at 5% per year for 2 years **b.** \$500 at 8% per year for 3 months
8. Ms. Kendrick bought a \$380 TV set for \$100 down and \$11.95 per week for 26 weeks. How much extra did it cost her to use the installment plan? [*page 250*]
9. Jerry Black had a balance of \$216.12 in his checking account. He then wrote checks for \$85.15, \$26.85, and \$50.00 and he deposited \$89.90. What was his balance then? [*page 252*]
10. Mrs. Pitkin bought 20 shares of stock at $25\frac{1}{4}$ per share, which paid a 10¢ quarterly dividend on each share. How much was her total yearly dividend? She sold the stock at 42 per share. How much profit did she make on the sale? [*page 262*]

MAJOR CHECKUP

Match. [*page 8*]

1. commutative property of addition
2. associative property of addition
3. distributive property
4. multiplying by 0 property
5. adding 0 property

a. $a \times 0 = 0$
b. $a(b + c) = ab + ac$
c. $a + (b + c) = (a + b) + c$
d. $a + 0 = a$
e. $a + b = b + a$

Solve. [*pages 16–19*]

6. $7(a + 9) = 168$ **7.** $7a + 9 = 168$ **8.** $\frac{6 + m}{5} = 32$

9. $6 + \frac{m}{5} = 32$ **10.** $.2g + 3.7 = 5.9$ **11.** $\frac{8a + 3}{.5} = 7$

Round to the nearest .1. [*page 40*]

12. 253.41 **13.** 57.68 **14.** 4.35 **15.** 4.349 **16.** .8499

Round to the nearest 1. [*page 40*]

17. 5.73 **18.** 29.21 **19.** 99.821 **20.** 42.5 **21.** $16\frac{3}{5}$

Compute. [*pages 108, 110, 118, 120*]

22. a. $\frac{1}{2} + \frac{1}{3}$
b. $\frac{1}{2} - \frac{1}{3}$
c. $\frac{1}{2} \times \frac{1}{3}$
d. $\frac{1}{2} \div \frac{1}{3}$

23. a. $\frac{3}{4} + \frac{2}{5}$
b. $\frac{3}{4} - \frac{2}{5}$
c. $\frac{3}{4} \times \frac{2}{5}$
d. $\frac{3}{4} \div \frac{2}{5}$

24. a. $.68 + .25$
b. $.68 - .25$
c. $.68 \times .25$
d. $.68 \div .25$

25. a. $1.2 + .4$
b. $1.2 - .4$
c. $1.2 \times .4$
d. $1.2 \div .4$

Write as percents. [*page 174*]

26. .73 **27.** 1.23 **28.** .08 **29.** $\frac{1}{5}$ **30.** $\frac{3}{4}$ **31.** $\frac{3}{2}$

Complete. [*pages 170, 178, 180*]

32. 50% of 18.4 = ___?___ **33.** 25% of 268.4 = ___?___ **34.** $33\frac{1}{3}$% of 963 = ___?___

35. 160% of 5.8 = ___?___ **36.** ___?___% of 18 = 36 **37.** ___?___% of 36 = 18

Get a federal income tax form from a bank or the Internal Revenue Service. Pretend that you have a certain yearly income and use the short form to compute how much income tax you would pay.

1. Pick some item such as a car, a TV set, or a motorcycle. Visit several dealers to find out how the items can be purchased on the installment plan. Compute how much extra the installment plan would cost. Ask the dealer to tell you the equivalent simple interest rate.

2. Visit a bank to ask about its installment rates. Would you save money by borrowing from a bank to buy the items in part 1?

3. Visit a small-loan company to ask about its interest rates. Would you save money by borrowing from a small-loan company rather than from a bank?

SAVINGS AND LOAN
BUY NOW
SEE US
FOR
MONEY

9 Computing with Rational Numbers

Positive and negative numbers

The numbers that you have worked with so far in this text are sometimes called the "numbers of arithmetic." They are used in counting and in measuring simple quantities. Sometimes we wish to measure quantities that also have direction. When we do, we use positive and negative numbers. For example, we can use $^{+}6$ to represent a 6-dollar **gain** and $^{-}6$ to represent a 6-dollar **loss**. Here are some other examples:

Number	*Quantity*
$^{+}6000$	*6000* meters *above* sea level
$^{-}300$	*300* meters *below* sea level
$^{+}9$	*9* dollars *won*
$^{-}7$	*7* dollars *lost*
$^{+}57$	*57* miles to the *east*
$^{-}30$	*30* miles to the *west*

Any time we work with **directed** quantities we can use positive numbers for quantities with one direction and negative numbers for quantities with the opposite direction.

We can use a line to picture the positive and negative numbers. A point is picked and labeled "0." Then positive numbers show the distance from 0 of points to the right of 0, and negative numbers show the distance from 0 of points to the left of 0. Notice that 0 is neither positive nor negative.
The numbers shown on this number line are **rational numbers.**

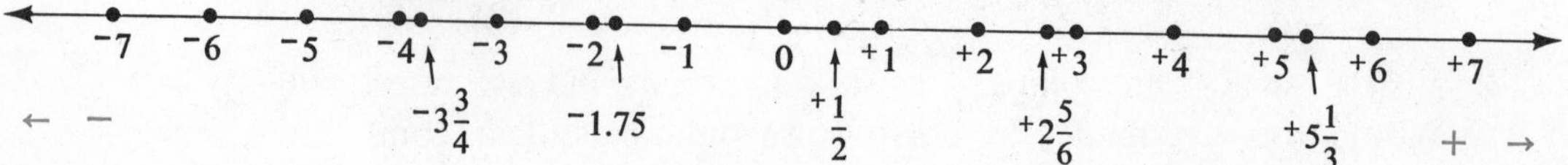

The number line also shows the order of the numbers. A number is less than every number to its right and greater than every number to its left.

$^{+}2 < {}^{+}3$ $\quad$ $^{-}2 > {}^{-}3$ $\quad$ $\frac{^{-}1}{2} < 0$ $\quad$ $\frac{^{+}1}{2} > 0$ $\quad$ $^{-}10 < {}^{+}1$

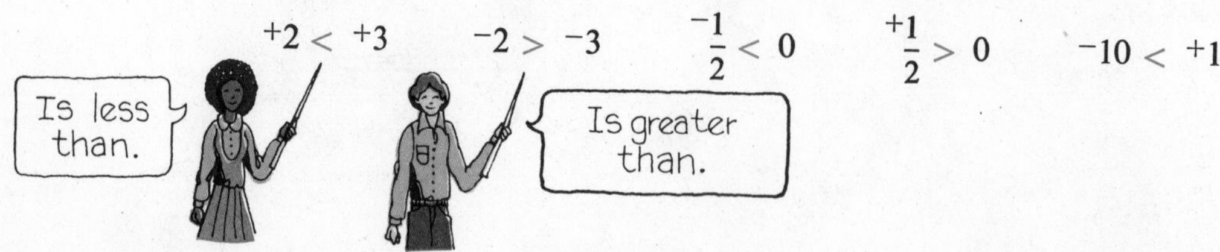

EXERCISES

If $^{+}6$ represents a 6-kilometer trip to the north, what numbers will represent these trips?

1. 9 kilometers to the north
2. 12 kilometers to the south
3. 3.2 kilometers to the south
4. 7.9 kilometers to the north
5. Suppose that you start at a point and take the trips $^{+}9$ and then $^{-}12$. Where do you end in relation to where you started?

If $^{-}4$ represents an elevator trip of 4 floors down, what numbers will represent these trips?

6. 4 floors up
7. 7 floors up
8. 10 floors up
9. 12 floors down
10. Suppose you ride an elevator that starts at the ground floor and takes these trips: $^{+}5$, $^{+}4$, $^{+}2$, $^{-}6$, $^{-}3$, $^{+}5$, $^{+}1$, $^{-}3$. On what floor do you end?

Copy and complete each sentence with the correct sign, < or >.

11. $^{-}8$ ● $^{-}9$
12. $^{+}8$ ● $^{-}9$
13. $^{-}8$ ● $^{+}9$
14. $^{+}8$ ● $^{+}9$
15. $\frac{^{-}1}{2}$ ● $\frac{^{-}1}{3}$
16. $^{+}3\frac{1}{4}$ ● $^{+}3\frac{1}{2}$
17. $^{-}4.3$ ● $^{-}4.03$
18. $^{-}6.09$ ● $^{-}6.1$
19. $\frac{^{-}3}{4}$ ● $^{-}.7$
20. $\frac{^{+}3}{5}$ ● $\frac{^{+}5}{8}$
21. $\frac{^{-}5}{2}$ ● 0
22. 0 ● $\frac{^{+}1}{16}$

Give the end point of each trip on the number line.

$^{-}5$ $^{-}4$ $^{-}3$ $^{-}2$ $^{-}1$ 0 $^{+}1$ $^{+}2$ $^{+}3$ $^{+}4$ $^{+}5$ $^{+}6$

23. Start at 0. Take a trip of $^{+}7$.
24. Start at $^{-}1$. Take a trip of $^{+}7$.
25. Start at $^{-}7$. Take a trip of $^{+}7$.
26. Start at $^{+}4$. Take a trip of $^{-}3$.
27. Start at $^{+}2$. Take a trip of $^{-}3$.
28. Start at $^{-}4$. Take a trip of $^{-}3$.
29. Start at $^{-}5$. Take a trip of $^{+}16$.
30. Start at $^{+}5$. Take a trip of $^{+}16$.
31. Start at $^{-}5$. Take a trip of $^{-}16$.
32. Start at $^{+}5$. Take a trip of $^{-}16$.

EXCURSION

Start with any whole number.

Example. 13

Square the digits and add the squares.

$$1^2 + 3^2 = 10$$

Repeat.

$$1^2 + 0^2 = 1$$

If the squaring pattern ends with 1, the starting number is called a *happy number*. So, 13 is a happy number. There are ten other happy numbers less than 50. Can you find them?

Supplementary Exercises, Set 53, page 389

Adding rational numbers

You can use number-line pictures to find the sum of two rational numbers. Study these examples.

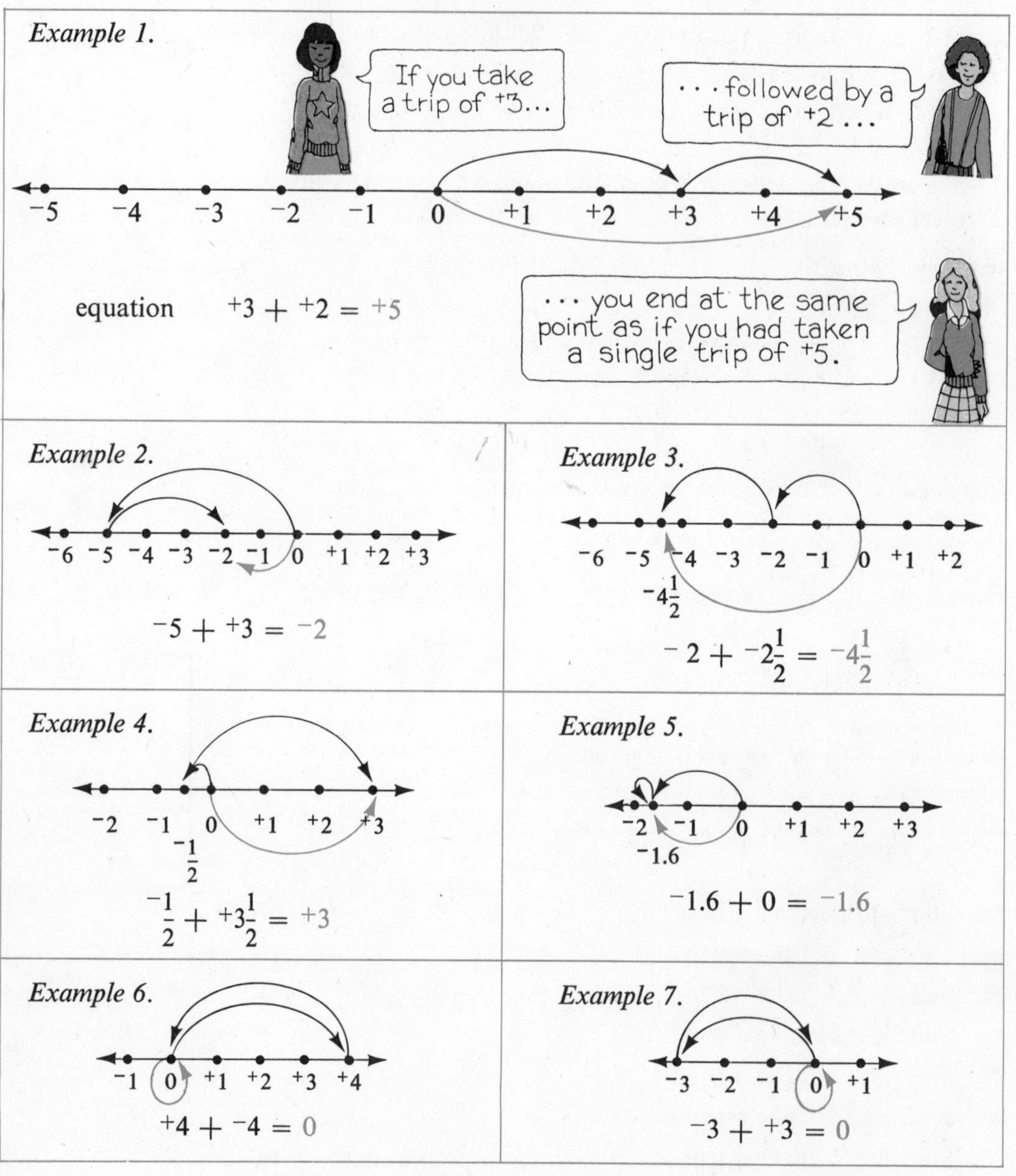

Notice that in the last two examples the sum of the two numbers is 0. We say that the two numbers whose sum is 0 are **opposites**.

$^-4$ is the opposite of $^+4$. $^+3$ is the opposite of $^-3$.

EXERCISES

Give each sum.

1. $^{-}8 + {}^{+}7$ 2. $^{-}8 + {}^{-}7$ 3. $^{+}8 + {}^{-}7$ 4. $^{+}8 + {}^{+}7$

5. $^{-}16 + {}^{-}15$ 6. $^{+}16 + {}^{-}15$ 7. $^{-}16 + {}^{+}15$ 8. $^{+}16 + {}^{+}15$

9. $\frac{^{+}3}{4} + \frac{^{-}1}{2}$ 10. $\frac{^{+}3}{4} + \frac{^{+}1}{2}$ 11. $\frac{^{-}3}{4} + \frac{^{+}1}{2}$ 12. $\frac{^{-}3}{4} + \frac{^{-}1}{2}$

13. $^{-}3.8 + {}^{+}6.9$ 14. $0 + \frac{^{+}5}{8}$ 15. $^{+}8.5 + {}^{-}3.4$ 16. $\frac{^{-}7}{4} + 0$

17. $\frac{^{-}3}{8} + \frac{^{+}3}{8}$ 18. $\frac{^{+}3}{2} + \frac{^{-}3}{2}$ 19. $^{-}2.4 + {}^{+}2.4$ 20. $\frac{^{+}15}{24} + \frac{^{-}15}{24}$

Who am I?

21. I am the opposite of $^{-}8$.

22. I am the opposite of $\frac{^{+}1}{2}$.

23. I am my own opposite.

24. I am the opposite of $^{+}2.3$.

Copy and complete these addition boxes.

25.

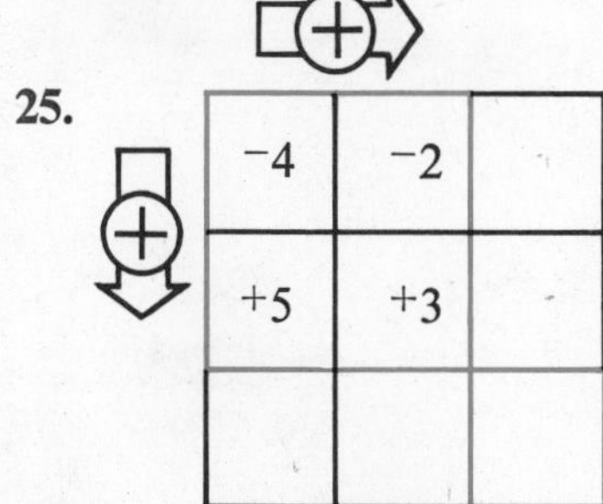

26.

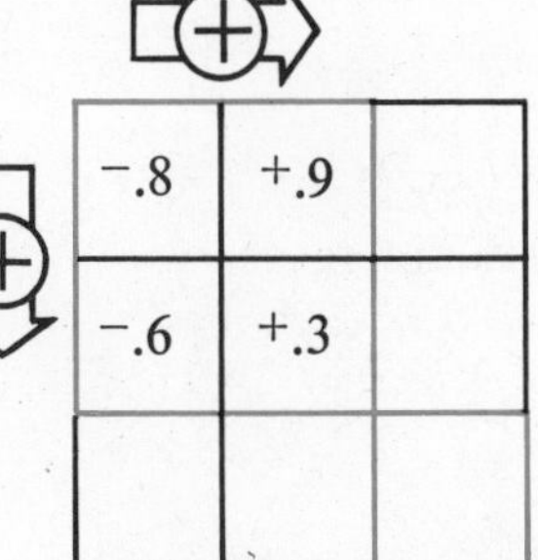

27.

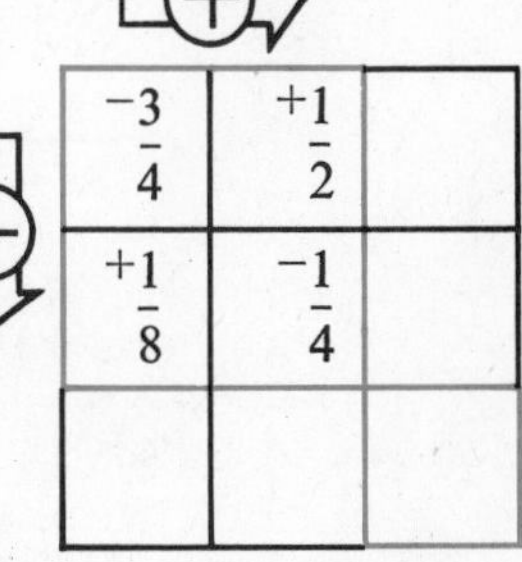

Solve each equation.

28. $y + {}^{-}7 = {}^{-}9$ 29. $y + {}^{-}7 = {}^{-}7$

30. $^{-}12 + y = {}^{+}12$ 31. $^{-}3 + y = {}^{+}17$

32. $y + {}^{+}8 = 0$ 33. $^{+}16 + y = {}^{-}8$

34. $^{+}1.9 + y = {}^{+}2$ 35. $\frac{^{-}3}{8} + y = \frac{^{-}1}{2}$

36. $\frac{^{+}3}{8} + y = \frac{^{+}3}{8}$ 37. $\frac{^{-}1}{2} + y = 0$

38. $\frac{^{+}1}{4} + y = \frac{^{+}3}{4}$ 39. $\frac{^{-}1}{2} + y = \frac{^{+}1}{4}$

EXCURSION

A drawer contains ten pairs of black socks and ten pairs of white socks.

Suppose that you were blindfolded. How many socks would you have to take from the drawer to be sure that you got a matching pair?

Supplementary Exercises, Set 54, page 389

Subtracting rational numbers

Recall that subtraction is finding a missing addend. So, to find the difference of two rational numbers you can find a missing addend.

Example 1.

$^{+}8 - {}^{+}6 = y$

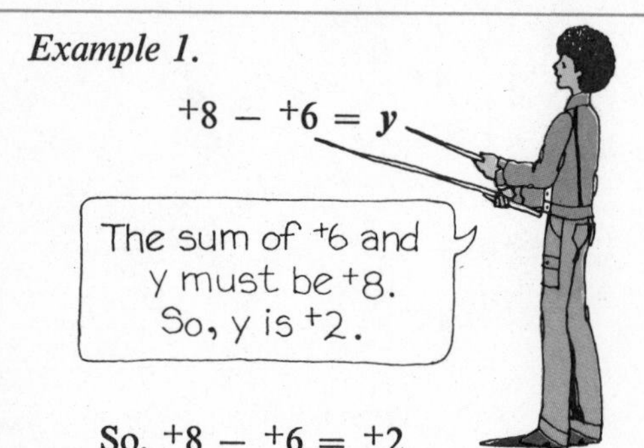

So, $^{+}8 - {}^{+}6 = {}^{+}2$

Example 2.

$^{-}6 + y = {}^{+}8$

$^{+}8 - {}^{-}6 = y$

So, $^{+}8 - {}^{-}6 = {}^{+}14$

Example 3.

$^{+}6 + y = {}^{-}8$

$^{-}8 - {}^{+}6 = y$

So, $^{-}8 - {}^{+}6 = {}^{-}14$

Example 4.

$^{-}6 + y = {}^{-}8$

$^{-}8 - {}^{-}6 = y$

So, $^{-}8 - {}^{-}6 = {}^{-}2$

EXERCISES

Give each difference.

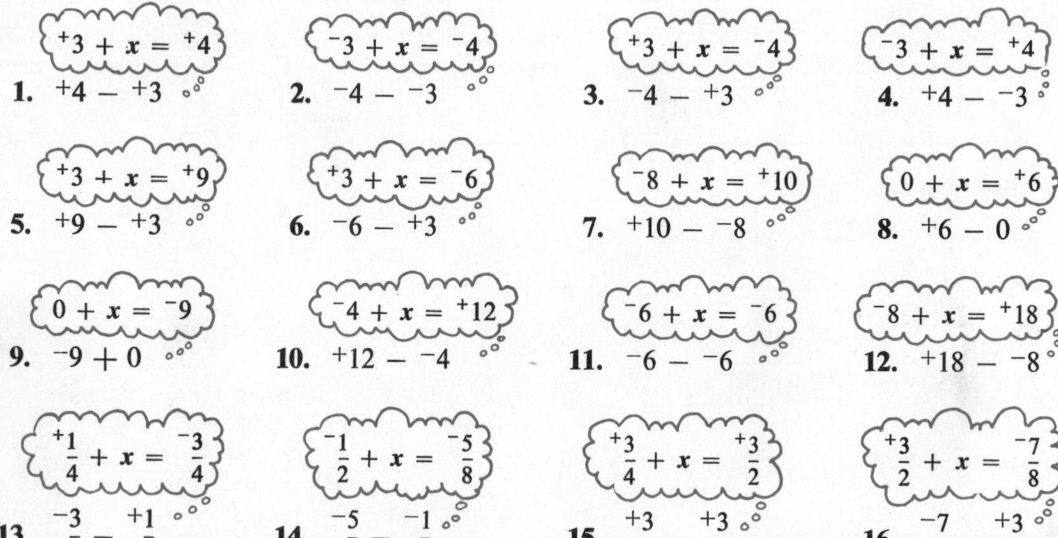

1. $^{+}4 - {}^{+}3$ ($^{+}3 + x = {}^{+}4$)
2. $^{-}4 - {}^{-}3$ ($^{-}3 + x = {}^{-}4$)
3. $^{-}4 - {}^{+}3$ ($^{+}3 + x = {}^{-}4$)
4. $^{+}4 - {}^{-}3$ ($^{-}3 + x = {}^{+}4$)
5. $^{+}9 - {}^{+}3$ ($^{+}3 + x = {}^{+}9$)
6. $^{-}6 - {}^{+}3$ ($^{+}3 + x = {}^{-}6$)
7. $^{+}10 - {}^{-}8$ ($^{-}8 + x = {}^{+}10$)
8. $^{+}6 - 0$ ($0 + x = {}^{+}6$)
9. $^{-}9 + 0$ ($0 + x = {}^{-}9$)
10. $^{+}12 - {}^{-}4$ ($^{-}4 + x = {}^{+}12$)
11. $^{-}6 - {}^{-}6$ ($^{-}6 + x = {}^{-}6$)
12. $^{+}18 - {}^{-}8$ ($^{-}8 + x = {}^{+}18$)
13. $\frac{^{-}3}{4} - \frac{^{+}1}{4}$ ($\frac{^{+}1}{4} + x = \frac{^{-}3}{4}$)
14. $\frac{^{-}5}{8} - \frac{^{-}1}{2}$ ($\frac{^{-}1}{2} + x = \frac{^{-}5}{8}$)
15. $\frac{^{+}3}{2} - \frac{^{+}3}{4}$ ($\frac{^{+}3}{4} + x = \frac{^{+}3}{2}$)
16. $\frac{^{-}7}{8} - \frac{^{+}3}{2}$ ($\frac{^{+}3}{2} + x = \frac{^{-}7}{8}$)

Solve each equation.

17. ($^{-}4 + x = {}^{+}6$)
 a. $^{+}6 - {}^{-}4 = x$
 b. $^{+}6 + {}^{+}4 = x$

18. ($^{+}3 + x = {}^{+}9$)
 a. $^{+}9 - {}^{+}3 = x$
 b. $^{+}9 + {}^{-}3 = x$

19. ($^{-}2 + x = {}^{-}8$)
 a. $^{-}8 - {}^{-}2 = x$
 b. $^{-}8 + {}^{+}2 = x$

20. ($^{+}6 + x = {}^{-}3$)
 a. $^{-}3 - {}^{+}6 = x$
 b. $^{-}3 + {}^{-}6 = x$

21. ($^{+}.1 + x = {}^{-}.3$)
 a. $^{-}.3 - {}^{+}.1 = x$
 b. $^{-}.3 + {}^{-}.1 = x$

22. a. $\frac{^{+}3}{5} - \frac{^{+}1}{5} = x$
 b. $\frac{^{+}3}{5} + \frac{^{-}1}{5} = x$

True or false?

23. In exercise 17, you found that subtracting $^{-}4$ was the same as adding $^{+}4$.
24. In exercise 18, you found that subtracting $^{+}3$ was the same as adding $^{-}3$.
25. In exercise 19, you found that subtracting $^{-}2$ was the same as adding the opposite of $^{-}2$.
26. In exercise 20, you found that subtracting $^{+}6$ was the same as adding the opposite of $^{+}6$.
27. Subtracting a rational number is the same as adding the opposite of the rational number.

To subtract a rational number, add its opposite.

Give each difference.

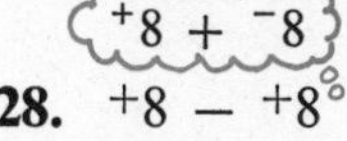

28. $^{+}8 - {}^{+}8$ ($^{+}8 + {}^{-}8$)
29. $^{-}9 - {}^{-}3$ ($^{-}9 + {}^{+}3$)
30. $^{+}6 - {}^{-}8$ ($^{+}6 + {}^{+}8$)
31. $^{-}4 - {}^{-}5$
32. $0 - {}^{+}6$
33. $^{+}12 - {}^{-}6$
34. $^{-}5 - {}^{+}12$
35. $^{+}11 - {}^{-}5$
36. $^{-}15 - {}^{+}9$
37. $^{-}.5 - {}^{+}.7$
38. $^{+}1.3 - {}^{+}2.5$
39. $^{-}3.6 - {}^{-}8.4$
40. $\frac{^{+}3}{5} - \frac{^{-}1}{5}$
41. $\frac{^{-}4}{3} - \frac{^{+}1}{6}$
42. $\frac{^{+}5}{9} - \frac{^{+}2}{3}$
43. $0 - \frac{^{-}3}{4}$
44. $^{-}5.6 - {}^{-}4.7$
45. $^{+}6.3 - {}^{+}2.8$

CHECKUP
for pages 272–273

Give each sum.

1. $0 + {}^{-}4$
2. $^{+}.6 + {}^{+}.3$
3. $^{-}.8 + {}^{-}.2$
4. $\frac{^{+}1}{2} + 0$
5. $\frac{^{+}1}{2} + \frac{^{-}1}{2}$
6. $^{-}8 + 0$
7. $\frac{^{+}5}{8} + \frac{^{-}1}{4}$
8. $\frac{^{-}5}{8} + \frac{^{+}1}{4}$
9. $\frac{^{-}3}{4} + \frac{^{+}3}{4}$
10. $\frac{^{+}5}{9} + \frac{^{-}1}{3}$
11. $\frac{^{-}3}{4} + \frac{^{+}3}{8}$
12. $^{+}1\frac{3}{4} + {}^{-}2\frac{1}{4}$

Answers on page 427.

Supplementary Exercises, Set 55, page 389

Multiplying rational numbers

Imagine a slow train moving along the "track" shown below, which has signs 1 mile apart.

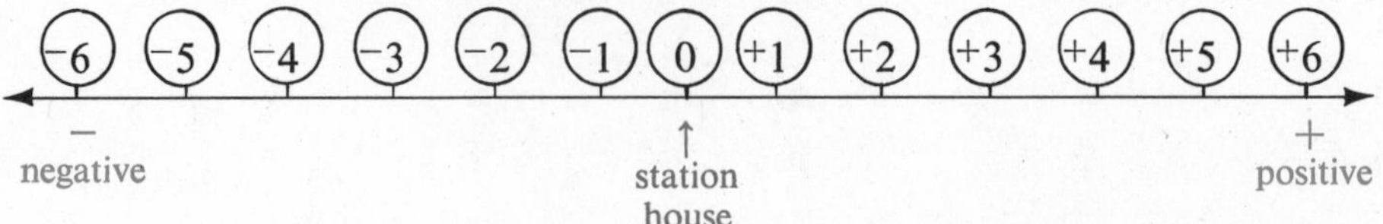

Let's agree that when a train travels 3 miles an hour in the positive direction, its rate is $^+3$. When a train travels 5 miles an hour in the negative direction, let's agree that its rate is $^-5$. Let's also agree that a time of $^+2$ means 2 hours **after** the train passes the station and that a time of $^-4$ means 4 hours **before** the train passes the station.

The situation described above can help you multiply rational numbers.

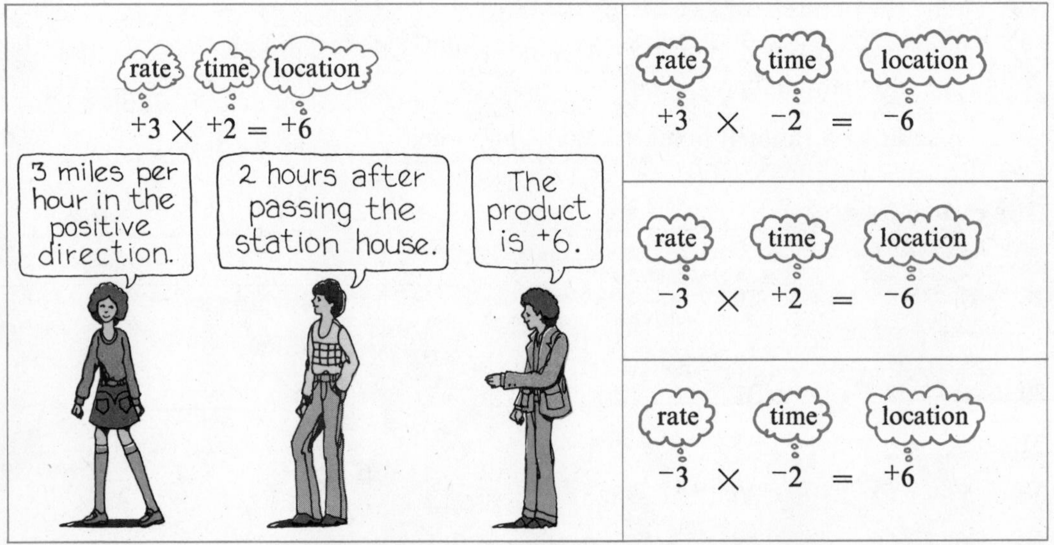

EXERCISES

Give each product.

1. $^+4 \times {}^+2$ **2.** $^-4 \times {}^-2$ **3.** $^+4 \times {}^-2$ **4.** $^-4 \times {}^+2$

5. $^+9 \times {}^+6$ **6.** $^-9 \times {}^-6$ **7.** $^+9 \times {}^-6$ **8.** $^-9 \times {}^+6$

9. $^-13 \times 0$ **10.** $0 \times {}^+28$ **11.** 0×0 **12.** $^+6 \times {}^-16$

13. $^+5 \times {}^-4$ **14.** $^-8 \times {}^-9$ **15.** $^-11 \times {}^+12$ **16.** $^+15 \times {}^-9$

True or false?

17. The product of a positive number and a negative number is a negative number.

18. The product of two positive numbers is a positive number.

19. The product of two negative numbers is a negative number.

20. The product of any rational number and 0 is 0.

Give each product.

21. $\frac{^-1}{4} \times \frac{^+1}{2}$ **22.** $\frac{^+1}{4} \times \frac{^-1}{2}$ **23.** $\frac{^+1}{4} \times \frac{^+1}{2}$ **24.** $\frac{^-1}{4} \times \frac{^-1}{2}$

25. $^-.3 \times {}^-.5$ **26.** $^+.6 \times {}^-1.2$ **27.** $^-3.8 \times 0$ **28.** $^+.11 \times {}^+8.6$

29. $\frac{^-3}{8} \times \frac{^-8}{3}$ **30.** $\frac{^-5}{6} \times \frac{^+3}{5}$ **31.** $^-2\frac{3}{8} \times {}^+1\frac{1}{4}$ **32.** $^+3\frac{2}{5} \times {}^-2\frac{3}{4}$

Substitute and simplify.

a	*r*	*t*	*x*	*f*
0	$^-3$	$^+5$	$^-8$	$^+2$

33. ar **34.** rx **35.** tf **36.** rxf

37. $a(t + f)$ **38.** $r(t + x)$ **39.** $rt + rx$ **40.** $f(t + x)$

41. $r - f$ **42.** $f - r$ **43.** $r(at - f)$ **44.** $a(rt - xf)$

Solve each equation.

45. $^-6y = {}^+48$ **46.** $^+8y = {}^+56$

47. $^-7y = {}^-49$ **48.** $^-9y = 0$

49. $^+8y = {}^+64$ **50.** $^+5y = {}^-45$

51. $^-3y = {}^-33$ **52.** $^+4y = {}^+88$

53. $\frac{^-3}{8}y = {}^+1$ **54.** $\frac{^+2}{5}y = {}^+1$

55. $\frac{^-6}{5}y = {}^-1$ **56.** $\frac{^-3}{5}y = {}^-1$

57. $^+.34y = {}^+1$ **58.** $^-6.4y = {}^+1$

59. $^+2\frac{1}{4}y = {}^-1\frac{1}{2}$ **60.** $^-3\frac{3}{4}y = {}^+3\frac{1}{2}$

CHECKUP

for pages 274–275

Give each difference.

1. $^-3 - {}^+4$ **2.** $^+4 - {}^-3$

3. $^+6 - {}^-8$ **4.** $^-8 - {}^+6$

5. $^-3 - 0$ **6.** $^-12 - {}^-6$

7. $^+18 - {}^+3$ **8.** $^+5.3 - {}^-.4$

9. $\frac{^-3}{8} - \frac{^+1}{2}$ **10.** $\frac{^+5}{6} - \frac{^-2}{3}$

11. $\frac{^+5}{9} - \frac{^+3}{5}$ **12.** $^-2\frac{1}{2} - {}^+3\frac{1}{4}$

Answers on page 428.

Supplementary Exercises, Set 56, page 389

Dividing rational numbers

Remember that division is finding a missing factor. So, to find the quotient of two rational numbers you can find a missing factor. Study the following examples.

Two rational numbers are **reciprocals** if their product is $^{+}1$.

Since $\frac{^{+}2}{3} \times \frac{^{+}3}{2} = {}^{+}1$, $\frac{^{+}2}{3}$ and $\frac{^{+}3}{2}$ are reciprocals.

Since $^{-}8 \times \frac{^{-}1}{8} = {}^{+}1$, $^{-}8$ and $\frac{^{-}1}{8}$ are reciprocals.

Is the reciprocal of a negative number positive or negative?
Is the reciprocal of a positive number positive or negative?
What rational number does not have a reciprocal?

EXERCISES

Give each quotient.

1. $^{-}32 \div {}^{-}8$ ($^{-}8y = {}^{-}32$)
2. $^{-}32 \div {}^{+}8$ ($^{+}8y = {}^{-}32$)
3. $^{+}32 \div {}^{-}8$ ($^{-}8y = {}^{+}32$)
4. $^{+}32 \div {}^{+}8$ ($^{+}8y = {}^{+}32$)
5. $^{+}45 \div {}^{+}9$ ($^{+}9y = {}^{+}45$)
6. $^{-}45 \div {}^{+}9$ ($^{+}9y = {}^{-}45$)
7. $^{+}45 \div {}^{-}9$ ($^{-}9y = {}^{+}45$)
8. $^{-}45 \div {}^{-}9$ ($^{-}9y = {}^{-}45$)
9. $^{-}72 \div {}^{+}8$ ($^{+}8y = {}^{-}72$)
10. $^{+}56 \div {}^{+}7$ ($^{+}7y = {}^{+}56$)
11. $^{-}63 \div {}^{-}9$ ($^{-}9y = {}^{-}63$)
12. $^{+}72 \div {}^{-}8$ ($^{-}8y = {}^{+}72$)
13. $^{+}63 \div {}^{+}9$ ($^{+}9y = {}^{+}63$)
14. $0 \div {}^{-}6$ ($^{-}6y = 0$)
15. $^{-}84 \div {}^{-}12$ ($^{-}12y = {}^{-}84$)
16. $^{+}96 \div {}^{-}8$ ($^{-}8y = {}^{+}96$)

Positive, negative, or 0?

17. The quotient of two positive numbers is a ___?___ number.
18. The quotient of two negative numbers is a ___?___ number.
19. If you divide 0 by any rational number, the quotient is ___?___.
20. If you divide a positive number by a negative number, the quotient is ___?___.
21. If you divide a negative number by a positive number, the quotient is ___?___.

Solve each equation.

22. a. $^-8 \div {^+2} = x$
    b. $^-8 \times \frac{^+1}{2} = x$
23. a. $^-24 \div {^-6} = x$
    b. $^-24 \times \frac{^-1}{6} = x$
24. a. $^+48 \div {^-6} = x$
    b. $^+48 \times \frac{^-1}{6} = x$
25. a. $^+54 \div {^+6} = x$
    b. $^+54 \times \frac{^+1}{6} = x$
26. a. $^-81 \div {^-9} = x$
    b. $^-81 \times \frac{^-1}{9} = x$
27. a. $^+72 \div {^-9} = x$
    b. $^+72 \times \frac{^-1}{9} = x$

> Dividing by a rational number is the same as multiplying by its reciprocal. [Study your answers to exercises 22–27.]

Give each quotient.

28. $^-15 \div {^+3}$
29. $^+28 \div {^-7}$
30. $^-60 \div {^-12}$
31. $^+65 \div {^+13}$
32. $\frac{^-2}{3} \div \frac{^-1}{3}$
33. $\frac{^+2}{4} \div \frac{^-1}{4}$
34. $\frac{^+5}{9} \div \frac{^-1}{9}$
35. $\frac{^+6}{11} \div \frac{^+2}{11}$
36. $\frac{^-3}{8} \div \frac{^+1}{4}$
37. $\frac{^+1}{2} \div \frac{^-1}{3}$

Remember that a fraction bar indicates division.

38. $\dfrac{\frac{^+3}{4}}{\frac{^+1}{8}}$
39. $\dfrac{\frac{^-3}{4}}{\frac{^-3}{5}}$
40. $\dfrac{^-.6}{^+.4}$
41. $\dfrac{^+.5}{^-.25}$
42. $\dfrac{^+4.5}{^-1.5}$
43. $\dfrac{^-4.2}{^-.2}$
44. $\dfrac{^-2\frac{3}{4}}{^+1\frac{2}{3}}$
45. $\dfrac{^+5\frac{7}{8}}{^+2\frac{3}{4}}$

EXCURSION

Find the pattern. Then draw the missing figure.

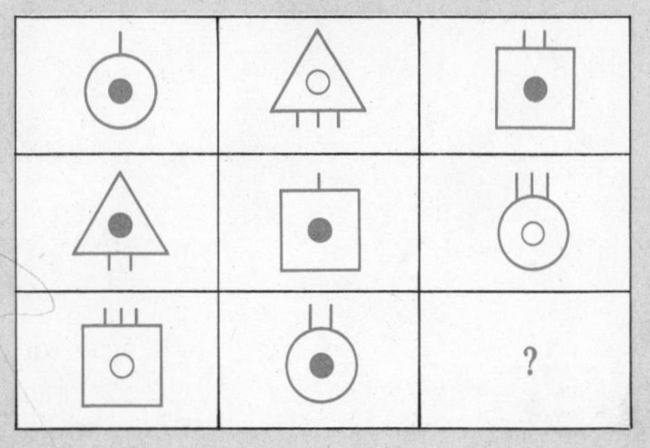

Supplementary Exercises, Set 57, page 390

KEEPING SKILLS SHARP

Multiply.

1. $\begin{array}{r} 3.8 \\ \times 5 \\ \hline \end{array}$ **2.** $\begin{array}{r} 5.64 \\ \times .6 \\ \hline \end{array}$ **3.** $\begin{array}{r} 34.8 \\ \times .16 \\ \hline \end{array}$ **4.** $\begin{array}{r} 2.93 \\ \times 2.5 \\ \hline \end{array}$ **5.** $\begin{array}{r} 46.3 \\ \times 18.2 \\ \hline \end{array}$ **6.** $\begin{array}{r} 5.94 \\ \times 106 \\ \hline \end{array}$

Divide. Round quotients to the nearest .01.

7. $3\overline{)9.68}$ **8.** $.5\overline{).348}$ **9.** $.8\overline{)3.956}$ **10.** $.18\overline{).95367}$ **11.** $.58\overline{)2.3469}$ **12.** $19.6\overline{).0582}$

Change to a decimal.

13. $\frac{3}{5}$ **14.** $\frac{3}{4}$ **15.** $\frac{5}{8}$ **16.** $\frac{8}{5}$ **17.** $\frac{2}{3}$ **18.** $\frac{5}{9}$

Give each sum in lowest terms.

19. $\frac{3}{5} + \frac{1}{5}$ **20.** $\frac{3}{2} + \frac{3}{4}$ **21.** $\frac{5}{8} + \frac{1}{3}$ **22.** $\frac{3}{4} + \frac{2}{5}$

Give each difference in lowest terms.

23. $\frac{5}{8} - \frac{1}{8}$ **24.** $\frac{1}{2} - \frac{3}{8}$ **25.** $\frac{5}{6} - \frac{3}{4}$ **26.** $\frac{11}{8} - \frac{0}{5}$

Give each product in lowest terms.

27. $\frac{5}{9} \times \frac{3}{4}$ **28.** $\frac{5}{8} \times \frac{4}{5}$ **29.** $\frac{5}{6} \times \frac{6}{5}$ **30.** $\frac{3}{8} \times \frac{2}{2}$

Give each quotient in lowest terms.

31. $\frac{5}{6} \div \frac{3}{2}$ **32.** $\frac{7}{8} \div \frac{1}{4}$ **33.** $\frac{5}{3} \div \frac{3}{5}$ **34.** $\frac{9}{2} \div \frac{3}{4}$

Solve each proportion.

35. $\frac{2}{3} = \frac{x}{10}$ **36.** $\frac{7}{4} = \frac{8}{y}$ **37.** $\frac{5}{r} = \frac{16}{9}$ **38.** $\frac{s}{15} = \frac{32}{15}$

Change to a percent.

39. $\frac{3}{5}$ **40.** $\frac{1}{5}$ **41.** $\frac{7}{10}$ **42.** $\frac{1}{3}$ **43.** $\frac{6}{5}$ **44.** $\frac{5}{6}$

Change to a fraction in lowest terms.

45. 25% **46.** 65% **47.** 108% **48.** $66\frac{2}{3}\%$ **49.** 9.5% **50.** 62.5%

Mathematics and science

Earlier you learned that the density of a substance is the ratio of its weight to its volume. The **specific gravity** of a substance compares its density to the density of water.

Density of substance

$$\frac{196 \text{ lb}}{2 \text{ ft}^3} = \frac{98 \text{ lb}}{1 \text{ ft}^3}$$

Density of water

$$\frac{124.8 \text{ lb}}{2 \text{ ft}^3} = \frac{62.4 \text{ lb}}{1 \text{ ft}^3}$$

196 2′ lb 1′ 1′

Substance

Specific gravity of substance

$$\frac{\text{Density of substance}}{\text{Density of water}} = \frac{\frac{98 \text{ lb}}{1 \text{ ft}^3}}{\frac{62.4 \text{ lb}}{1 \text{ ft}^3}} = \frac{98 \cancel{\text{lb}}}{1 \cancel{\text{ft}^3}} \times \frac{1 \cancel{\text{ft}^3}}{62.4 \cancel{\text{lb}}} \approx 1.6$$

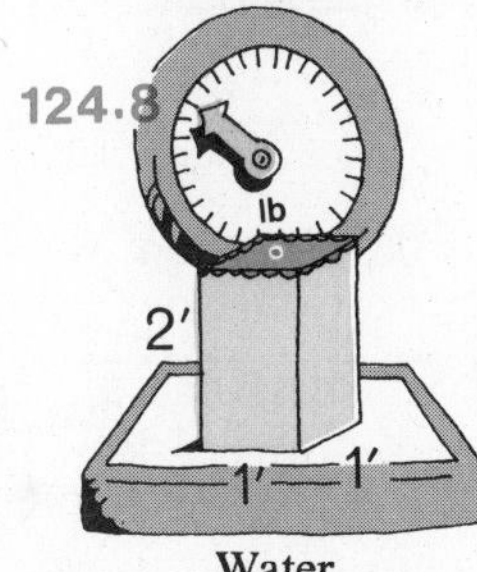

Water

Notice that in computing the specific gravity of the substance the units canceled out. So, to find the specific gravity of a substance, you can just divide its weight by the weight of an equal volume of water.

Now let's find the specific gravity of the glass block shown on this scale.

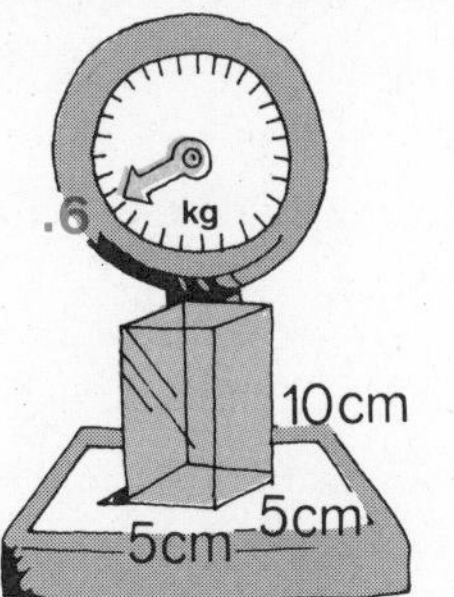

Solution.

The volume is 250 cm³. Now we must find the weight of an equal volume of water. Since 1000 cm³ (1 liter) of water weighs 1 kilogram (remember that 1 cm³ of water weighs 1 gram), 250 cm³ weighs .25 kilogram. So the specific gravity of the glass block is

$$\frac{.6 \cancel{\text{kg}}}{.25 \cancel{\text{kg}}} = 2.4$$

EXERCISES

Compute the specific gravity of each block to the nearest .1.

1.

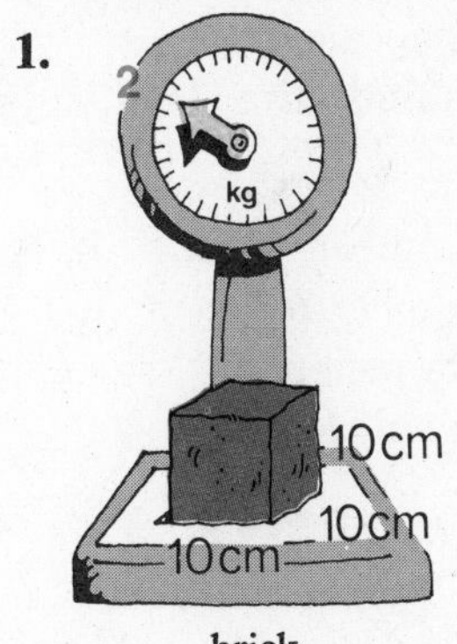

brick

2.

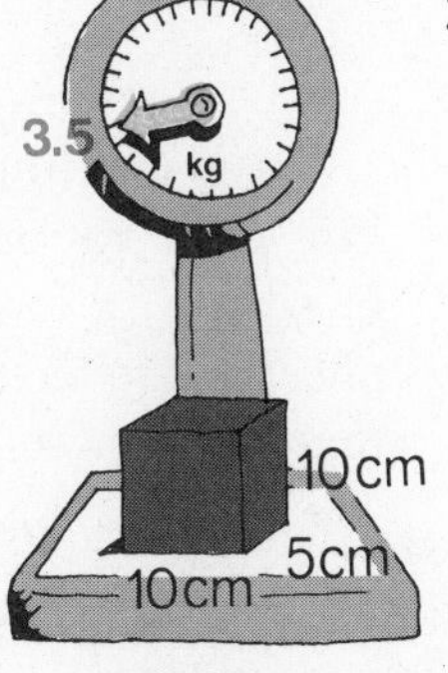

cast iron

3.

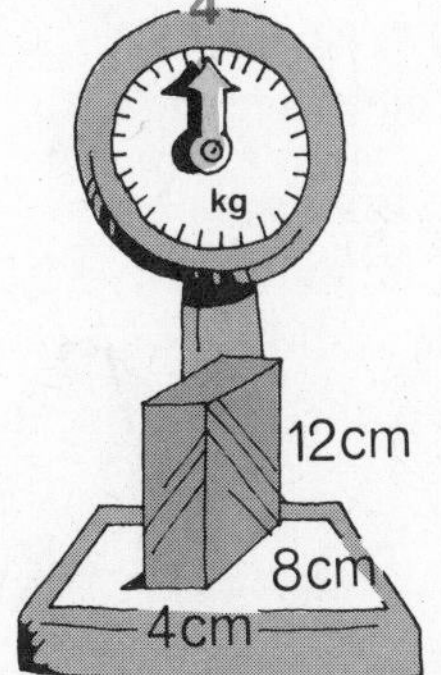

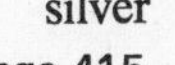
silver

4.

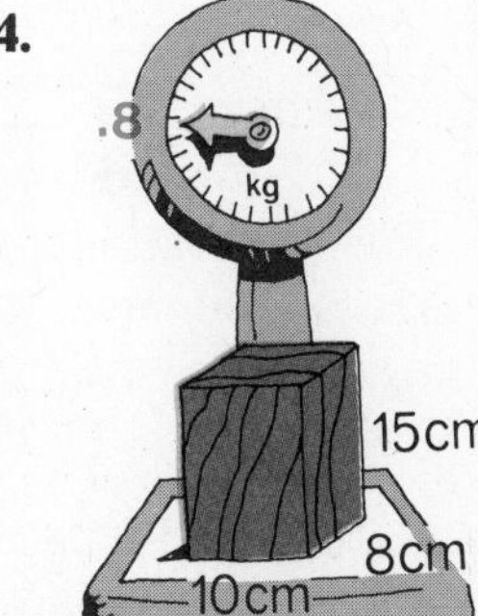

oak

Skill Maintenance, Set 66, page 415

Properties of rational numbers

You know that the numbers in the set

$\{\ldots\ ^{-}5, ^{-}4, ^{-}3, ^{-}2, ^{-}1, 0, ^{+}1, ^{+}2, ^{+}3, ^{+}4, \ldots\}$

are called **integers.**

Rational numbers are those numbers that can be expressed as the quotient of two integers: $\frac{a}{b}$ $(b \neq 0)$.

Are all integers rational numbers? Are all rational numbers integers?

***a, b,* and *c* are any rational numbers. Tell what goes in the blank in each example.**

Properties of Rational Numbers

Addition	Multiplication
Closure Property $a + b$ is a rational number. $\frac{^{-}1}{2} + \frac{^{+}3}{4} = \underline{?} \leftarrow$ a rational number	Closure Property $a \cdot b$ is a rational number. $\frac{^{-}3}{5} \cdot \frac{^{+}2}{3} = \underline{?} \leftarrow$ a rational number
Commutative Property $a + b = b + a$ $\frac{^{-}5}{8} + {^{+}3} = {^{+}3} + \underline{?}$	Commutative Property $a \cdot b = b \cdot a$ $\frac{^{+}5}{8} \cdot \frac{^{-}3}{5} = \underline{?} \cdot \frac{^{+}5}{8}$
Associative Property $(a + b) + c = a + (b + c)$ $\left(\frac{^{-}2}{3} + {^{+}5}\right) + \frac{^{+}1}{2} = \frac{^{-}2}{3} + \left(\underline{?} + \frac{^{+}1}{2}\right)$	Associative Property $(a \cdot b) \cdot c = a \cdot (b \cdot c)$ $\left(\frac{^{-}3}{4} \cdot \underline{?}\right) \cdot \frac{^{-}4}{5} = \frac{^{-}3}{4} \cdot \left(\frac{^{+}2}{5} \cdot \frac{^{-}4}{5}\right)$
Identity Property $a + 0 = a$ $\underline{?} + 0 = \frac{^{-}3}{4}$ 0 is called the **additive identity.**	Identity Property $a \cdot {^{+}1} = a$ $\underline{?} \cdot {^{+}1} = {^{+}7}$ ⁺1 is called the **multiplicative identity.**
Additive Inverse For each rational number ***a***, there is a rational number ***b*** (its additive inverse, or opposite) such that the sum of ***a*** and ***b*** is 0. $a + b = 0$ $\frac{^{-}3}{8} + \underline{?} = 0$	Multiplicative Inverse For each rational number ***a*** $(a \neq 0)$, there is a rational number ***b*** (its multiplicative inverse, or reciprocal) such that the product of ***a*** and ***b*** is ⁺1. $a \cdot b = {^{+}1}$ $\frac{^{+}5}{6} \cdot \underline{?} = {^{+}1}$

Distributive Property

$a \cdot (b + c) = a \cdot b + a \cdot c$

$^-3 \cdot \left(\frac{^-1}{2} + \frac{^+3}{4}\right) = {^-3} \cdot \underline{?} + {^-3} \cdot \frac{^+3}{4}$

EXERCISES

Tell which property is described.

1. If you add two rational numbers, the sum is a rational number.
2. When adding three rational numbers you can change the grouping of the addends without changing the sum.
3. The product of $^+1$ and any rational number is that rational number.
4. If you multiply two rational numbers, the product is a rational number.
5. The sum of 0 and any rational number is that rational number.

First complete the equation. Then tell what property the completed equation illustrates.

6. $\frac{^+3}{4} + \underline{?} = \frac{^+3}{4}$

7. $^-5 + \frac{^+1}{2} = \frac{^+1}{2} + \underline{?}$

8. $^+5 \times \left(\frac{^-3}{8} + \frac{^+1}{4}\right) = (^+5 \times \underline{?}) + \left(^+5 \times \frac{^+1}{4}\right)$

9. $\left(\frac{^+1}{2} + \frac{^-3}{8}\right) + \underline{?} = \frac{^+1}{2} + \left(\frac{^-3}{8} + \frac{^+1}{5}\right)$

10. $\left(\frac{^-3}{4} \times \frac{^+5}{3}\right) \times {^-6} = \frac{^-3}{4} \times (\underline{?} \times {^-6})$

11. $\frac{^-3}{8} \times \underline{?} = {^+1}$

12. $\frac{^-5}{2} \times \underline{?} = \frac{^-5}{2}$

13. $\left(\frac{^-5}{2} + \frac{^-4}{5}\right) + \underline{?} = \frac{^-5}{2} + \left(\frac{^-4}{5} + \frac{^+3}{8}\right)$

14. $\left(\frac{^-2}{5} \times \underline{?}\right) \times \frac{^-1}{4} = \frac{^-2}{5} \times \left(\frac{^-5}{8} \times \frac{^-1}{4}\right)$

15. $\frac{^+5}{2} \times \underline{?} = {^+1}$

16. $\frac{^+7}{4} + {^+2\frac{1}{2}} = \underline{?} + \frac{^+7}{4}$

CHECKUP
for pages 276–279

Give each product or quotient.

1. $^+8 \times {^-3}$
2. $\frac{^+1}{3} \times \frac{^+1}{2}$
3. $\frac{^-6}{5} \times \frac{^-5}{6}$
4. $\frac{^+7}{8} \times \frac{^-4}{5}$
5. $^+2\frac{1}{2} \times \frac{^+2}{5}$
6. $\frac{^-5}{3} \times \frac{^-5}{8}$
7. $\frac{^-3}{5} \div \frac{^-1}{5}$
8. $^-3 \div \frac{^+3}{2}$
9. $\frac{^+6}{5} \div \frac{^+1}{3}$
10. $^+.45 \div {^-.5}$
11. $^-5 \div \frac{^+2}{3}$
12. $^-.8 \div {^-.02}$

Answers on page 428.

Skill Maintenance, Set 67, page 415

Solving equations

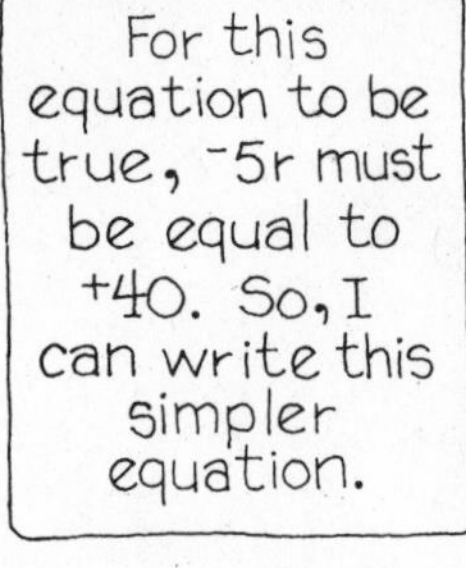

$$^{-}5r + {}^{-}8 = {}^{+}32$$
$$^{-}5r = {}^{+}40$$
$$r = {}^{-}8$$

Here is another way to solve the same equation.

$$^{-}5r + {}^{-}8 = {}^{+}32$$
$$^{-}5r + {}^{-}8 + {}^{+}8 = {}^{+}32 + {}^{+}8 \quad \text{[add } {}^{+}8\text{]}$$
$$^{-}5r = {}^{+}40 \quad \text{[simplify]}$$
$$\frac{^{-}1}{5} \times {}^{-}5r = \frac{^{-}1}{5} \times {}^{+}40 \quad \left[\text{multiply by } \frac{^{-}1}{5}\right]$$
$$r = {}^{-}8 \quad \text{[simplify]}$$

Notice that to solve the equation we first added the same number to both sides of the equation and then multiplied both sides of the equation by the same number. We used both of the following properties of equations:

> Adding the same number to both sides of an equation gives an **equivalent equation**, that is, an equation having the same solution.

> Multiplying both sides of an equation by the same number (not 0) gives an equivalent equation.

Study this example.

Example.

$$^{+}6y + {}^{-}8 = {}^{+}15$$
$$^{+}6y + {}^{-}8 + {}^{+}8 = {}^{+}15 + {}^{+}8 \quad \text{[add } {}^{+}8\text{]}$$
$$^{+}6y = {}^{+}23 \quad \text{[simplify]}$$
$$\frac{^{+}1}{6} \times {}^{+}6y = \frac{^{+}1}{6} \times {}^{+}23 \quad \left[\text{multiply by } \frac{^{+}1}{6}\right]$$
$$y = \frac{^{+}23}{6} \quad \text{[simplify]}$$

To check, substitute the solution $\frac{^{+}23}{6}$ for y in the original equation.

$$^{+}6 \cdot \frac{^{+}23}{6} + {}^{-}8 \stackrel{?}{=} {}^{+}15$$
$$^{+}23 + {}^{-}8 \stackrel{?}{=} {}^{+}15$$
$$^{+}15 = {}^{+}15$$

It checks!

EXERCISES

Copy and complete.

1. $^-9x + \frac{^+3}{4} = {}^+1$

$\underline{\quad ? \quad} = \underline{\quad ? \quad}$ [add $\frac{^-3}{4}$]

$^-9x = \frac{^+1}{4}$ [simplify]

$\underline{\quad ? \quad} = \underline{\quad ? \quad}$ [multiply by $\frac{^-1}{9}$]

$x = \underline{\quad ? \quad}$ [simplify]

Check:

$^-9(\underline{\ ?\ }) + \frac{^+3}{4} \stackrel{?}{=} {}^+1$

$\underline{\quad ? \quad} \stackrel{?}{=} {}^+1$

Solve each equation.

2. $^-5x + {}^-3 = \frac{^-3}{2}$

3. $\frac{^+2}{3}x + {}^+2 = 0$

4. $\frac{^-3}{4}x + {}^-5 = \frac{^-3}{8}$

5. $^-6 + \frac{^-3}{4}x = {}^-4$

6. $\frac{^+1}{4}x + \frac{^+2}{5} = \frac{^+2}{5}$

7. $^-3x + {}^+8 = {}^-3$

8. $\frac{^+5}{6} + \frac{^+5}{3}x = \frac{^-2}{3}$

9. $\frac{^+2}{3}x + \frac{^-5}{9} = \frac{^+1}{2}$

10. $\frac{^+5}{2} + \frac{^-5}{3}x = \frac{^+2}{5}$

11. $\frac{^-5}{9} + {}^+3x = \frac{^+5}{4}$

12. $\frac{^+4}{5} + \frac{^-1}{4}x = \frac{^-3}{4}$

13. $\frac{^-1}{5}x + \frac{^+3}{2} = 0$

Equation: $\frac{^-3}{4}x - \frac{^-1}{2} = {}^+1$

Solution:

$$\frac{^-3}{4}x - \frac{^-1}{2} = {}^+1$$

$$\frac{^-3}{4}x + \frac{^+1}{2} = {}^+1$$

$$\frac{^-3}{4}x + \frac{^+1}{2} + \frac{^-1}{2} = {}^+1 + \frac{^-1}{2}$$

$$\frac{^-3}{4}x = \frac{^+1}{2}$$

$$\frac{^-4}{3} \cdot \frac{^-3}{4}x = \frac{^-4}{3} \cdot \frac{^+1}{2}$$

$$x = \frac{^-4}{6} = \frac{^-2}{3}$$

Solve each equation.

14. $^+3x - {}^-3 = 0$

15. $^-4x - {}^+6 = {}^+4$

16. $\frac{^-2}{3}x - {}^-5 = \frac{^-5}{6}$

17. $\frac{^+3}{4}x - \frac{^-1}{2} = \frac{^+1}{2}$

18. $\frac{^+9}{2}x - \frac{^+2}{3} = \frac{^-3}{4}$

19. $\frac{^-5}{4}x - \frac{^-5}{8} = \frac{^+3}{8}$

20. $\frac{^-3}{2}x - \frac{^+3}{5} = \frac{^-3}{5}$

21. $\frac{^+7}{8}x - \frac{^+11}{8} = \frac{^-1}{4}$

Supplementary Exercises, Set 58, page 390

Solving inequalities

$$x + {}^{+}2 < {}^{+}5$$
$$x < {}^{+}3$$

Notice that we can solve the inequality by adding $^{-}2$ to both sides.

$$x + {}^{+}2 < {}^{+}5$$
$$x + {}^{+}2 + {}^{-}2 < {}^{+}5 + {}^{-}2 \quad \text{[add } {}^{-}2\text{]}$$
$$x < {}^{+}3 \quad \text{[simplify]}$$

Adding the same number to both sides of an inequality gives an equivalent inequality.

$$\frac{^{+}1}{3}w > {}^{+}1$$
$$w > {}^{+}3$$

Any number greater than +3 is a solution.

We could have solved the inequality by multiplying both sides by $^{+}3$.

$$\frac{^{+}1}{3}w > {}^{+}1$$
$$^{+}3 \times \frac{^{+}1}{3}w > {}^{+}3 \times {}^{+}1 \quad \text{[multiply by } {}^{+}3\text{]}$$
$$w > {}^{+}3 \quad \text{[simplify]}$$

Multiplying both sides of an equality by a **positive** number gives an equivalent inequality.

$$^{-}2y > {}^{+}4$$
$$y < {}^{-}2$$

If we multiply by a negative number the sign is reversed.

Any number less than 2 is a solution.

$$^{-}2y > {}^{+}4$$
$$\frac{^{-}1}{2} \times {}^{-}2y < \frac{^{-}1}{2} \times {}^{+}4 \quad \left[\text{multiply by } \frac{^{-}1}{2}\right]$$
$$y < {}^{-}2 \quad \text{[simplify]}$$

Multiplying both sides of an inequality by a **negative** number gives an equivalent inequality with the inequality sign reversed.

Example.

$$^{+}3y + \frac{^{-}1}{2} > {}^{+}1$$
$$^{+}3y + \frac{^{-}1}{2} + \frac{^{+}1}{2} > {}^{+}1 + \frac{^{+}1}{2} \quad \left[\text{add } \frac{^{+}1}{2}\right]$$
$$^{+}3y > \frac{^{+}3}{2} \quad \text{[simplify]}$$
$$\frac{^{+}1}{3} \times {}^{+}3y > \frac{^{+}1}{3} \times \frac{^{+}3}{2} \quad \left[\text{multiply by } \frac{^{+}1}{3}\right]$$
$$y > \frac{^{+}1}{2} \quad \text{[simplify]}$$

Is $\frac{^{+}1}{2}$ a solution? Is any number greater than $\frac{^{+}1}{2}$ a solution?

EXERCISES

Copy and complete.

1. $^{-}6y + \frac{^{+}3}{4} > \frac{^{+}1}{2}$

$\underline{\quad ? \quad} > \underline{\quad ? \quad}$ $\left[\text{add } \frac{^{-}3}{4}\right]$

$^{-}6y > \frac{^{-}1}{4}$ [simplify]

$\underline{\quad ? \quad} < \underline{\quad ? \quad}$ $\left[\text{multiply by } \frac{^{-}1}{6}\right]$

$y < \underline{\quad ? \quad}$ [simplify]

2. $\frac{^{+}1}{3}y + \frac{^{-}1}{5} > \frac{^{+}1}{3}$

$\underline{\quad ? \quad} > \underline{\quad ? \quad}$ $\left[\text{add } \frac{^{+}1}{5}\right]$

$\frac{^{+}1}{3}y > \underline{\quad ? \quad}$ [simplify]

$\underline{\quad ? \quad} > \underline{\quad ? \quad}$ [multiply by $^{+}3$]

$y > \underline{\quad ? \quad}$ [simplify]

Solve each inequality.

3. $\frac{^{+}5}{9}w + \frac{^{-}1}{3} < {^{+}1}$

4. $\frac{^{-}5}{2}w + \frac{^{+}1}{2} > 0$

5. $^{+}5 + \frac{^{-}1}{4}w > \frac{^{-}1}{4}$

6. $^{-}3 + \frac{^{-}3}{5}w < \frac{^{+}3}{5}$

7. $^{+}9w + \frac{^{-}1}{2} > \frac{^{-}3}{4}$

8. $\frac{^{-}2}{3} + \frac{^{-}3}{8}w < {^{-}4}$

9. $\frac{^{+}7}{4}w + \frac{^{+}9}{2} > \frac{^{-}1}{2}$

10. $\frac{^{-}3}{8} + \frac{^{+}1}{2}w < {^{-}7}$

11. $^{-}6w + \frac{^{+}3}{4} < \frac{^{-}5}{2}$

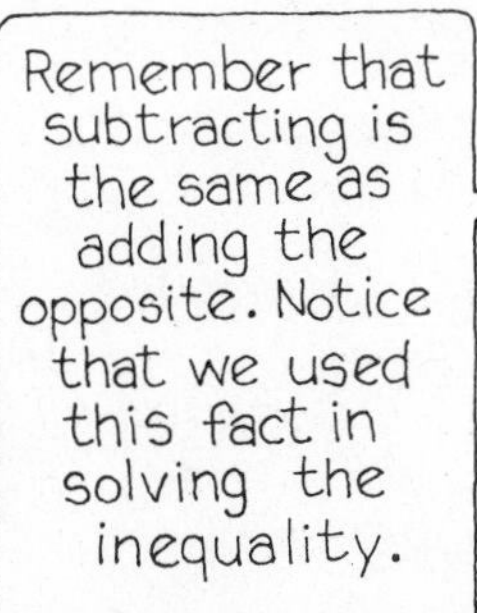

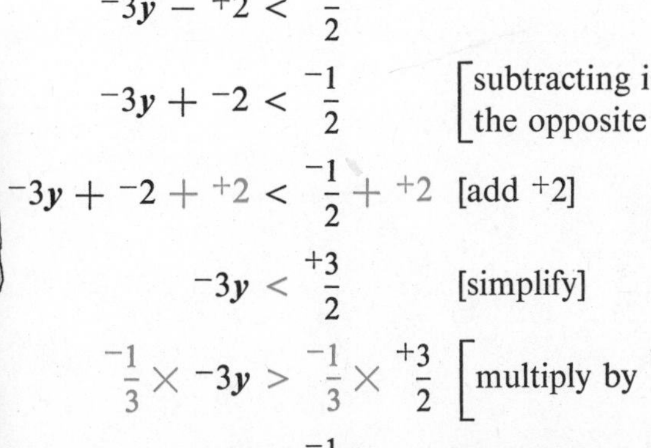

$^{-}3y - {^{+}2} < \frac{^{-}1}{2}$

$^{-}3y + {^{-}2} < \frac{^{-}1}{2}$ [subtracting is adding the opposite]

$^{-}3y + {^{-}2} + {^{+}2} < \frac{^{-}1}{2} + {^{+}2}$ [add $^{+}2$]

$^{-}3y < \frac{^{+}3}{2}$ [simplify]

$\frac{^{-}1}{3} \times {^{-}3y} > \frac{^{-}1}{3} \times \frac{^{+}3}{2}$ $\left[\text{multiply by } \frac{^{-}1}{3}\right]$

$y > \frac{^{-}1}{2}$ [simplify]

Solve each inequality.

12. $^{-}2z - \frac{^{-}1}{4} > {^{-}1}$

13. $\frac{^{+}3}{4}z + {^{+}3} > \frac{^{-}1}{2}$

14. $^{+}6z - \frac{^{+}5}{2} < 0$

15. $^{+}3z - \frac{^{-}5}{8} < {^{-}2}$

16. $\frac{^{-}2}{3}z + {^{-}4} > {^{+}3}$

17. $\frac{^{-}3}{8}z - \frac{^{-}1}{2} < \frac{^{-}5}{4}$

EXCURSION

Arrange the numbers 1, 2, 3, 4, and 5 in the circles so that no two consecutive numbers are connected by a line.

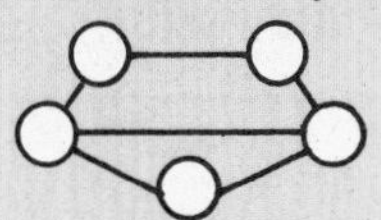

Supplementary Exercises, Set 59, page 390

Graphing solution sets

Study these examples.

$${}^{-}5y + {}^{-}3 = {}^{+}7$$
$${}^{-}5y + {}^{-}3 + {}^{+}3 = {}^{+}7 + {}^{+}3$$
$${}^{-}5y = {}^{+}10$$
$$\frac{{}^{-}1}{5} \times {}^{-}5y = \frac{{}^{-}1}{5} \times {}^{+}10$$
$$y = {}^{-}2$$

Solution set: $\{{}^{-}2\}$

Graph of solution set:

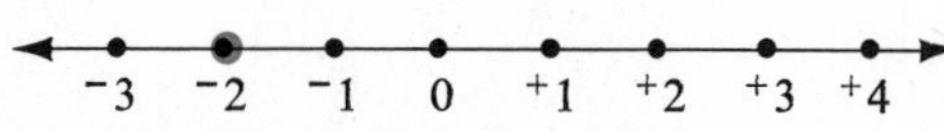

$${}^{+}2y - {}^{+}3 = {}^{-}2$$
$${}^{+}2y + {}^{-}3 = {}^{-}2$$
$${}^{+}2y + {}^{-}3 + {}^{+}3 = {}^{-}2 + {}^{+}3$$
$${}^{+}2y = {}^{+}1$$
$$\frac{{}^{+}1}{2} \times {}^{+}2y = \frac{{}^{+}1}{2} \times {}^{+}1$$
$$y = \frac{{}^{+}1}{2}$$

Solution set: $\left\{\frac{{}^{+}1}{2}\right\}$

Graph of solution set:

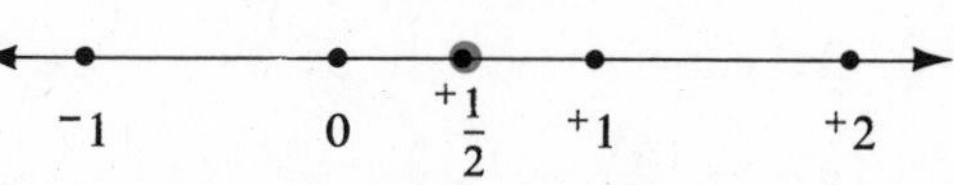

$$\frac{{}^{+}3}{4} + \frac{{}^{-}1}{3}y \geq \frac{{}^{-}1}{6}$$
$$\frac{{}^{-}3}{4} + \frac{{}^{+}3}{4} + \frac{{}^{-}1}{3}y \geq \frac{{}^{-}3}{4} + \frac{{}^{-}1}{6}$$
$$\frac{{}^{-}1}{3}y \geq \frac{{}^{-}11}{12}$$
$${}^{-}3 \times \frac{{}^{-}1}{3}y \leq {}^{-}3 \times \frac{{}^{-}11}{12}$$
$$y \leq \frac{{}^{+}11}{4}$$

Solution set:

$\left\{\text{all numbers less than or equal to } \frac{{}^{+}11}{4}\right\}$

The dot tells
you that $^{+}11/4$
belongs to the
solution set.

Graph of solution set:

$^{-}2$ $^{-}1$ 0 $^{+}1$ $^{+}2$ $\frac{{}^{+}11}{4}$ $^{+}3$

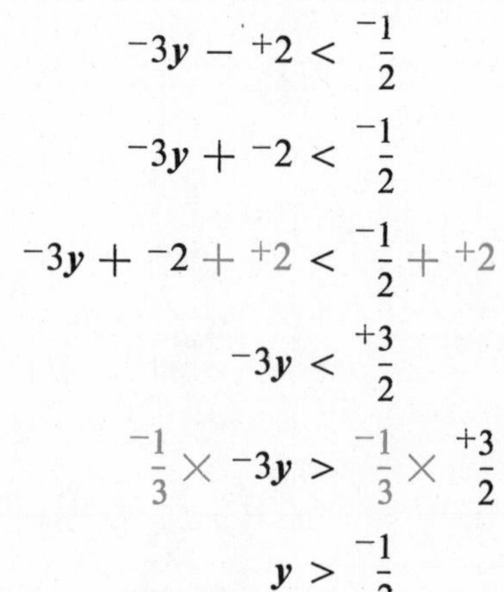

$${}^{-}3y - {}^{+}2 < \frac{{}^{-}1}{2}$$
$${}^{-}3y + {}^{-}2 < \frac{{}^{-}1}{2}$$
$${}^{-}3y + {}^{-}2 + {}^{+}2 < \frac{{}^{-}1}{2} + {}^{+}2$$
$${}^{-}3y < \frac{{}^{+}3}{2}$$
$$\frac{{}^{-}1}{3} \times {}^{-}3y > \frac{{}^{-}1}{3} \times \frac{{}^{+}3}{2}$$
$$y > \frac{{}^{-}1}{2}$$

Solution set:

$\left\{\text{all numbers greater than } \frac{{}^{-}1}{2}\right\}$

Graph of solution set:

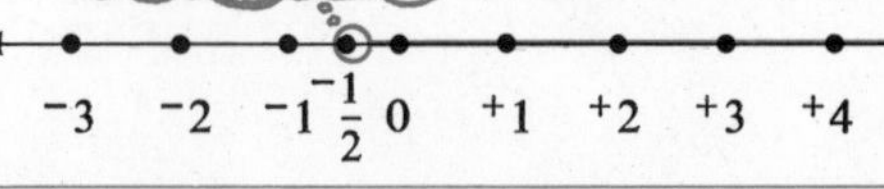

EXERCISES

Match each equation or inequality with the graph of its solution set.

1. $x = {}^{+}1$
2. $x \leq {}^{-}1$
3. $x < {}^{+}1$
4. $x > {}^{-}1$
5. $x \leq {}^{+}1$
6. $x = {}^{-}1$
7. $x \geq {}^{+}1$
8. $x < {}^{-}1$
9. $x > {}^{+}1$
10. $x \geq {}^{-}1$

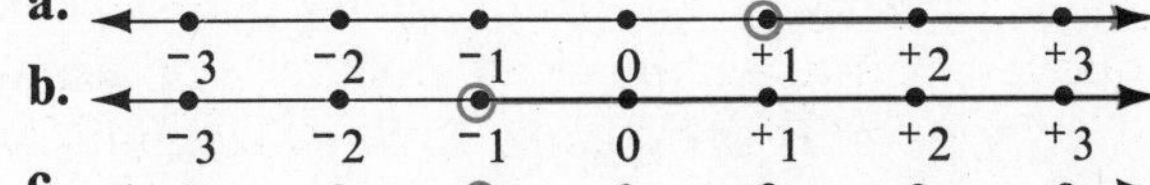

a. b. c. d. e. f. g. h. i. j.

$^{-}3 \quad ^{-}2 \quad ^{-}1 \quad 0 \quad ^{+}1 \quad ^{+}2 \quad ^{+}3$

Write an inequality for the graph.

11. 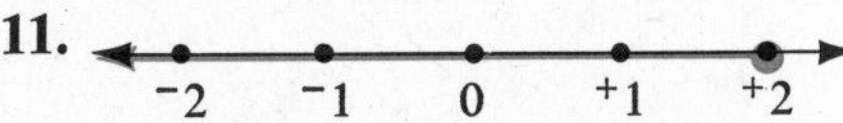

12. 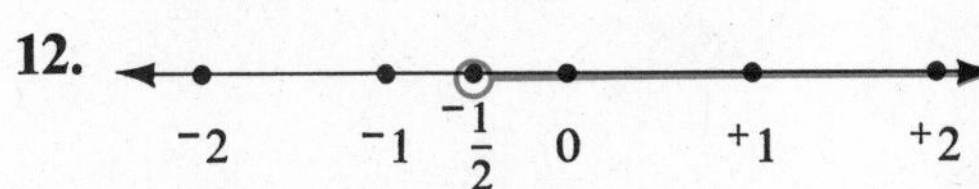

Solve and graph the solution set.

13. ${}^{+}3y + {}^{-}2 = {}^{+}10$
14. ${}^{-}5y + {}^{-}8 > 0$
15. ${}^{+}5y - {}^{-}4 = {}^{-}8$
16. ${}^{-}6 + \frac{{}^{+}1}{2}y \geq \frac{{}^{+}3}{4}$
17. ${}^{+}6 + {}^{-}4y \leq 0$
18. $\frac{{}^{-}2}{3}y - {}^{-}3 \leq {}^{+}6$
19. $\frac{{}^{+}4}{3}y - \frac{{}^{-}3}{8} > \frac{{}^{+}1}{2}$
20. $\frac{{}^{-}1}{3}y - \frac{{}^{+}3}{4} = {}^{-}2$
21. $\frac{{}^{-}2}{3}x - {}^{-}3 \geq {}^{-}3$

EXCURSION

If the number printed is 127, what was A?

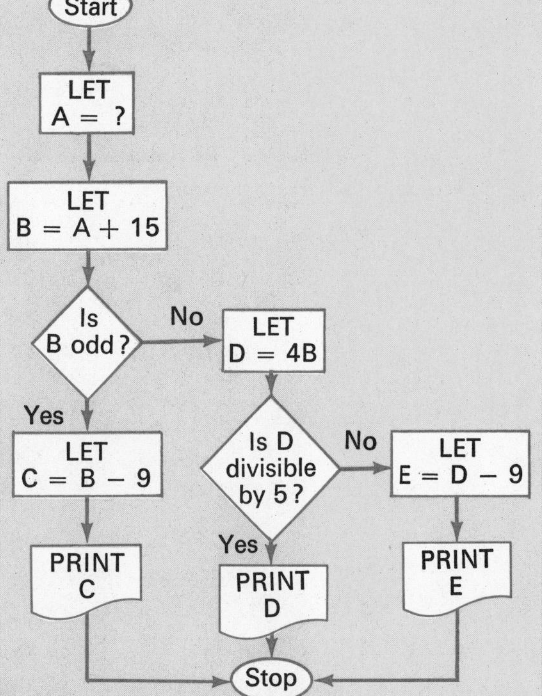

Supplementary Exercises, Set 60, page 390

Mathematics in careers

Some salespeople are paid a salary plus a percentage of their sales above a certain number of dollars. For example, an automobile agency pays its salespeople $100 a week plus 4% of all sales from $4800 to $8400 and 5% of all sales over $8400.

EXERCISES

Below is a sales report for each salesperson of the agency. Compute the weekly salary of each. Round computations to the nearest cent.

Johnson's Automobile Agency

Weekly Sales Report

Salesperson: Krantz

Week April 6 to April 12

	Sales
Monday	$2486.00
Tuesday	$3246.60
Wednesday	(no sales)
Thursday	(day off)
Friday	$3581.00
Saturday	(no sales)

Johnson's Automobile Agency

Weekly Sales Report

Salesperson: Adams

Week April 6 to April 12

	Sales
Monday	(day off)
Tuesday	(no sales)
Wednesday	$3582.70
Thursday	(no sales)
Friday	$4116.25
Saturday	$5361.80

Johnson's Automobile Agency

Weekly Sales Report

Salesperson: Davis

Week April 6 to April 12

	Sales
Monday	$1860.00
Tuesday	(day off)
Wednesday	$3140.00
Thursday	(no sales)
Friday	(no sales)
Saturday	(no sales)

Johnson's Automobile Agency

Weekly Sales Report

Salesperson: Garcia

Week April 6 to April 12

	Sales
Monday	$960.00
Tuesday	$2463.50
Wednesday	(day off)
Thursday	(no sales)
Friday	$1348.60
Saturday	$3987.00

CHAPTER CHECKUP

Give each sum. [*page 272*]

1. $^-3 + {}^+8$ 2. $^+5 + {}^+7$ 3. $^-9 + {}^-15$ 4. $^+8 + {}^-9$

5. $\frac{^-2}{3} + \frac{^+1}{2}$ 6. $\frac{^+3}{8} + \frac{^+3}{4}$ 7. $^-.6 + {}^-2.1$ 8. $\frac{^+5}{3} + \frac{^-3}{2}$

Give each difference. [*page 274*]

9. $^-3 - {}^+4$ 10. $^+5 - {}^-6$ 11. $^+8 - {}^+9$ 12. $^-11 - {}^+6$

13. $\frac{^-1}{3} - \frac{^+2}{3}$ 14. $\frac{^-5}{8} - \frac{^-3}{4}$ 15. $^+1.2 - {}^-.4$ 16. $^-.08 - {}^+.57$

Give each product. [*page 276*]

17. $^-5 \times {}^+8$ 18. $^+11 \times {}^-7$ 19. $^+20 \times {}^+9$ 20. $^-16 \times {}^-5$

21. $\frac{^-3}{8} \times \frac{^+5}{3}$ 22. $^-.6 \times {}^-.3$ 23. $^+2.4 \times {}^-3.6$ 24. $\frac{^+5}{7} \times \frac{^+7}{5}$

Give each quotient. [*page 278*]

25. $^-18 \div {}^+2$ 26. $^-63 \div {}^-9$ 27. $^+54 \div {}^-6$ 28. $^+126 \div {}^-3$

29. $\frac{^-3}{5} \div \frac{^+3}{4}$ 30. $\frac{^-6}{5} \div \frac{^-18}{5}$ 31. $\frac{^+4}{5} \div \frac{^+2}{9}$ 32. $0 \div \frac{^-3}{8}$

Complete. [*pages 275, 279, 282*]

33. Subtracting a rational number is the same as adding its ___?___.
34. Dividing by a rational number is the same as multiplying by its ___?___.
35. The sum of two rational numbers is a ___?___ number.
36. $\frac{^-3}{7} + \frac{^+5}{8} = \frac{^+5}{8} + \frac{^-3}{7}$ is an example of the ___?___ property of addition.
37. $\left(\frac{^+2}{3} \times \frac{^-3}{8}\right) \times \frac{^+5}{9} = \frac{^+2}{3} \times \left(\frac{^-3}{8} \times \frac{^+5}{9}\right)$ is an example of the ___?___ property of multiplication.
38. ___?___ is called the multiplicative identity.
39. For each rational number there exists a rational number such that the ___?___ is 0.

Solve and graph the solution set. [*pages 284–289*]

40. $^+6y - {}^-2 = {}^+7$ 41. $\frac{^-3}{5} + {}^+2y = {}^-11$ 42. $^-5y + {}^-3 < {}^+4$

43. $\frac{^-1}{3}y - \frac{^+1}{5} > \frac{^-2}{5}$ 44. $\frac{^-2}{5}y + \frac{^-3}{4} \le \frac{^+3}{8}$ 45. $\frac{^+7}{9} + \frac{^-5}{4}y \ge \frac{^-1}{3}$

MAJOR CHECKUP

Simplify. [*page 6*]

1. 2^5 **2.** 5^2 **3.** 10^5 **4.** 6^3 **5.** 8^4 **6.** 1^{10}

Follow the flow chart. [*pages 46, 48*]

7.

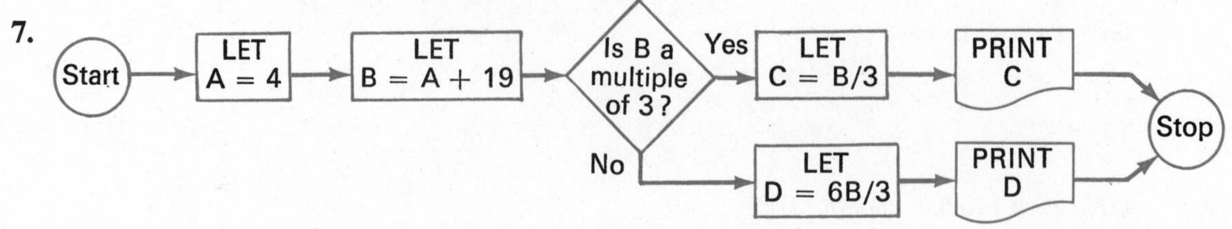

8. Repeat exercise 7 but let A = 11 instead of 4.

<, =, or >? [*page 102*]

9. $.5 \bullet \frac{1}{5}$ **10.** $\frac{1}{4} \bullet .3$ **11.** $.625 \bullet \frac{5}{8}$ **12.** $4.5 \bullet \frac{9}{2}$

Give each quotient in lowest terms. [*page 126*]

13. $\dfrac{\frac{2}{3}}{\frac{3}{4}}$ **14.** $\dfrac{\frac{3}{4}}{\frac{2}{3}}$ **15.** $\dfrac{\frac{5}{8}}{\frac{5}{3}}$ **16.** $\dfrac{\frac{7}{4}}{\frac{13}{9}}$ **17.** $\dfrac{\frac{8}{6}}{\frac{4}{3}}$ **18.** $\dfrac{\frac{0}{9}}{\frac{6}{5}}$

The dashed line is a line of symmetry. Complete. [*pages 142, 146*]

19. $\overline{AF} \cong$ __?__ **20.** $\overline{AB} \cong$ __?__

21. $\overline{EF} \cong$ __?__ **22.** $\angle D \cong$ __?__

23. $\angle A \cong$ __?__ **24.** $\angle ABE \cong$ __?__

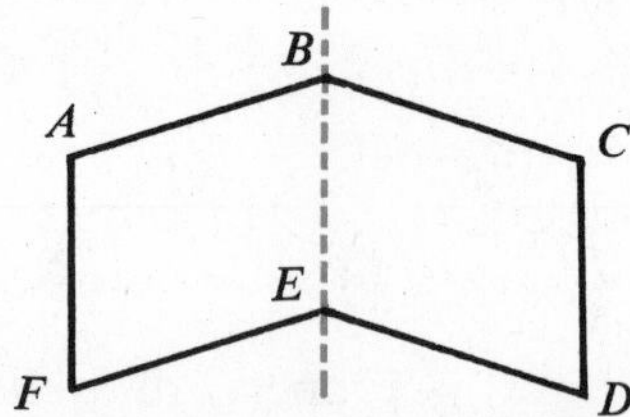

Solve. [*pages 166, 168*]

25. Mr. Jackson drove 356 km in 5 hours. At that rate, how long would it take him to drive 520 km?

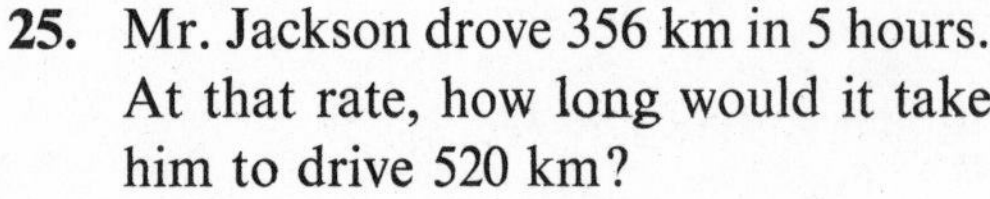

26. A cycle club rode 38 km during the first $1\frac{3}{4}$ hours of an 82-km bike trip. If they continued at the same rate, how much more time did they need to finish the trip?

Solve each equation. [*pages 178, 180*]

27. 10% of \$60 = \$*x* **28.** 8% of \$43 = \$*x* **29.** $12\frac{1}{2}$% of \$144 = \$*x*

Project

The year's high for a share of Bank of Virginia stock → was $\$27\frac{1}{4}$, or \$27.25.

The year's low for a share of this stock was \$8.75.

DAILY STOCK QUOTATIONS

Year				Day			Net
High	Low	Stocks	Div.	High	Low	Close	Chg.
$25\frac{1}{2}$	$12\frac{1}{8}$	BalGE	1.96	$13\frac{7}{8}$	$13\frac{5}{8}$	$13\frac{3}{4}$	....
$24\frac{3}{4}$	$11\frac{3}{8}$	BanCal	1.34	$11\frac{1}{2}$	$11\frac{3}{8}$	$11\frac{3}{8}$	$-\frac{1}{8}$
$36\frac{7}{8}$	$21\frac{1}{2}$	Bandag Inc		$25\frac{1}{2}$	25	$25\frac{1}{2}$	$+\frac{3}{4}$
$5\frac{3}{4}$	$2\frac{5}{8}$	Bangr Punt		$2\frac{3}{4}$	$2\frac{1}{2}$	$2\frac{3}{4}$	....
$36\frac{1}{2}$	22	Bkof NY	2.20	$24\frac{1}{2}$	24	$24\frac{1}{2}$	$+\frac{1}{4}$
$27\frac{1}{4}$	$8\frac{3}{4}$	Bk of Va	.88	$9\frac{1}{8}$	9	$9\frac{1}{8}$	$+\frac{3}{8}$
$57\frac{1}{4}$	$29\frac{1}{2}$	BankTr	3	31	$30\frac{5}{8}$	$30\frac{7}{8}$	$+\frac{1}{8}$
34	$17\frac{3}{4}$	BarbOil	.80e	19	19	19	$-\frac{1}{4}$
$24\frac{1}{4}$	$9\frac{5}{8}$	BardCR	.20	10	$9\frac{5}{8}$	$9\frac{5}{8}$	$-\frac{1}{4}$
$22\frac{3}{4}$	$2\frac{1}{4}$	BarnM	2.79e	$4\frac{1}{2}$	$4\frac{1}{8}$	$4\frac{1}{2}$	$+\frac{3}{8}$
$10\frac{1}{4}$	$6\frac{3}{8}$	BasicInc	.40	$6\frac{1}{2}$	$6\frac{1}{4}$	$6\frac{1}{2}$	$-\frac{1}{8}$
30	$24\frac{3}{4}$	Basic	pf 2.50	$24\frac{3}{4}$	$24\frac{3}{4}$	$24\frac{3}{4}$	....
$15\frac{1}{4}$	$10\frac{3}{4}$	BatesMf	.20	$12\frac{1}{4}$	$12\frac{1}{8}$	$12\frac{1}{8}$	$-\frac{1}{4}$
$19\frac{1}{2}$	$14\frac{3}{4}$	Bate Mf pf	1	$15\frac{7}{8}$	$15\frac{3}{4}$	$15\frac{3}{4}$	....
$22\frac{1}{4}$	$4\frac{5}{8}$	BathInd	.40	$6\frac{3}{8}$	6	$6\frac{1}{8}$	$-\frac{3}{8}$
45	$17\frac{3}{4}$	BauschL	.60	$26\frac{1}{4}$	$25\frac{1}{4}$	$25\frac{3}{8}$	$-\frac{5}{8}$
$48\frac{5}{8}$	$24\frac{1}{8}$	BaxtLab	.17	26	$24\frac{3}{4}$	25	$-\frac{3}{4}$
6	$4\frac{1}{2}$	BaykCig	.32	$4\frac{5}{8}$	$4\frac{1}{2}$	$4\frac{1}{2}$	....
$28\frac{7}{8}$	10	Bearing	.32	$11\frac{1}{8}$	11	$11\frac{1}{8}$	$+\frac{1}{8}$
$23\frac{3}{8}$	$12\frac{3}{4}$	BeatFds	.72	$12\frac{7}{8}$	$12\frac{1}{8}$	$12\frac{5}{8}$	$-\frac{1}{4}$
40	16	Beckmn	.50	$19\frac{1}{8}$	18	$18\frac{1}{2}$	$-\frac{5}{8}$
40	$20\frac{3}{8}$	BectDick	.40	$21\frac{3}{4}$	$21\frac{1}{8}$	$21\frac{5}{8}$	$+\frac{1}{8}$
$9\frac{7}{8}$	$6\frac{5}{8}$	BeecAir	.60	$7\frac{1}{8}$	$6\frac{3}{4}$	$6\frac{3}{4}$	$-\frac{1}{4}$
$21\frac{3}{4}$	$16\frac{1}{4}$	Beker	.28	$17\frac{7}{8}$	17	$17\frac{3}{4}$	$+\frac{1}{4}$
$18\frac{1}{2}$	$9\frac{1}{2}$	BelcoP	.77t	11	$10\frac{3}{4}$	11	$+\frac{1}{8}$

What was the day's high for a share of Bank of Virginia? The day's low? At what price was the stock selling when the market closed?

The day's net change (the difference between yesterday's closing price and today's closing price) was $+\frac{3}{8}$. That means that the price of each share of stock gained, or went up, $\frac{3}{8}$ of a dollar, or $37\frac{1}{2}$¢. Notice that some stocks had a negative net change. That means the price of the stock lost, or went down, that day.

Select eight stocks that are listed on the New York Stock Exchange. Pretend that you own 100 shares of each of the eight stocks. For one week, compute the total dollar net change of your 800 shares.

Example.

Bausch and Lomb, Inc. lost $\frac{5}{8}$ of a dollar, or $62\frac{1}{2}$¢ a share. So, if you owned 100 shares of Bausch and Lomb you would have a loss of \$62.50 for that day.

10 Probability and Statistics

A basic counting principle

EVENT

Spinning this spinner

If you spin this spinner, there are 3 possible outcomes. Since the "chance" of getting each outcome is the same, we say that the outcomes are **equally likely**.

EVENT

Tossing this coin

There are 2 equally likely outcomes, "heads" and "tails."

Now think about combining the events, that is, first spinning the spinner and then flipping the coin. We can use a **tree diagram** to show the outcomes.

EVENT

Spinning the spinner and then flipping the coin.

TREE DIAGRAM OF OUTCOMES

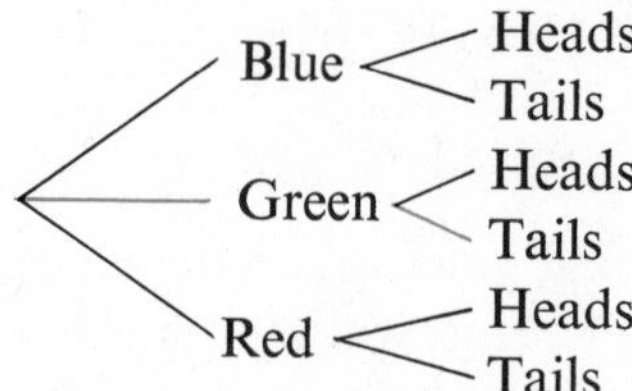

Notice that each "branch" of the tree diagram shows a possible outcome. For example, the red branch shows the outcome "spinning green" **and then** "flipping tails." How many outcomes are there for spinning the spinner? For flipping the coin? For spinning the spinner and then flipping the coin?

A Basic Counting Principle

> If a first event has m outcomes and if a second event has n outcomes, then the first event followed by the second event has $m \times n$ outcomes.

EXERCISES

First tell how many outcomes there are for the event. Then tell whether the outcomes are equally likely.

1. Tossing the cube

(The faces are numbered 1 through 6. The outcome is the number on the top face.)

2. Spinning the spinner

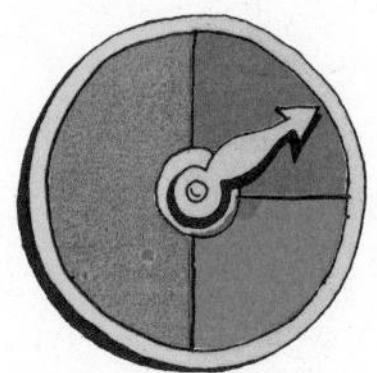

3. Without looking, picking a marble from the bag

Draw a tree diagram that shows all possible outcomes. Then decide whether or not all the outcomes are equally likely.

4. EVENT

Picking a card and then tossing the cube

5. EVENT

Picking a card and then flipping the coin

6. How many outcomes are there for the event flipping a coin and then tossing a cube? Are the outcomes equally likely?
7. Sarah has 3 sweaters and 4 pair of slacks. How many different sweater-slacks outfits does she have?
8. There are 4 highways from City A to City B. There are 5 highways from City B to City C. How many different highway routes are there from City A to City C that go through City B?
9. How many license plates can be made using 5 digits? (Assume that 0 can be the first digit.)

10. In how many ways can 6 people be seated in 6 chairs?

When you toss a paper cup, there are these possible outcomes:

Toss a paper cup at least 50 times and record each outcome. Do you think that the outcomes are equally likely?

EXCURSION

How can 6 toothpicks be arranged to make 4 equilateral triangles?

Supplementary Exercises, Set 61, page 391

Probability

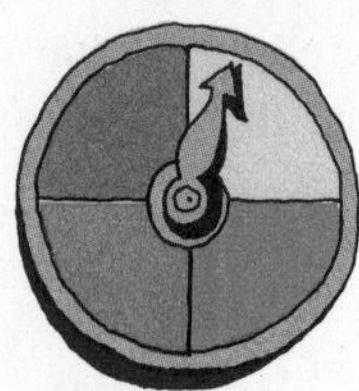

When you spin the spinner, there are 4 equally likely outcomes. The **probability** of each outcome is $\frac{1}{4}$.

$P(\text{red}) = \frac{1}{4}$ ← Number of "red" outcomes / Total number of outcomes

Here are some other probabilities:

$P(\text{blue}) = \frac{1}{4}$ $P(\text{green}) = \frac{1}{4}$ $P(\text{not red}) = \frac{3}{4}$ $P(\text{red } \mathbf{or} \text{ green}) = \frac{2}{4} = \frac{1}{2}$

The probability of an impossible outcome is 0. $P(\text{brown}) = \frac{0}{4} = 0$.

> If an event has m equally likely outcomes, then the probability of one of the outcomes is $\frac{1}{m}$.

Notice the words *equally likely* in the sentence above. Let's consider an event where the outcomes are not equally likely.

EVENT

Picking a marble from the bag

$P(\text{red}) = \frac{2}{8} = \frac{1}{4}$

$P(\text{not green}) = \frac{5}{8}$

$P(\text{green}) = \frac{3}{8}$

$P(\text{not red}) = \frac{6}{8} = \frac{3}{4}$

$P(\text{blue}) = \frac{1}{8}$

$P(\text{black}) = \frac{0}{8} = 0$

$P(\text{orange}) = \frac{1}{8}$

$P(\text{not black}) = \frac{8}{8} = 1$

Notice that the probability of the last outcome is 1. If an outcome is *certain* to occur, then the probability of that outcome is 1.

EXERCISES

Give each probability.

EVENT

Picking a marble from the bag

1. $P(\text{blue})$
2. $P(\text{not blue})$
3. $P(\text{not green})$
4. $P(\text{red})$
5. $P(\text{yellow})$
6. $P(\text{not yellow})$

EVENT

Tossing a cube

7. $P(1)$

8. $P(6)$

9. $P(\text{odd number})$

10. $P(\text{factor of } 6)$

11. $P(\text{number greater than } 6)$

12. $P(4$ **or** $6)$

EVENT

Picking a card from a deck of cards of the first 50 counting numbers

13. $P(\text{even number})$

14. $P(\text{number greater than } 40)$

15. $P(\text{multiple of } 5)$

16. $P(\text{number less than } 36)$

17. $P(\text{one-digit number})$

18. $P(\text{square number})$

Complete.

19. If the probability of an outcome is $\frac{5}{8}$, then the outcome is ___?___ (more/less) likely to happen than not to happen.

20. If the probability of an outcome is $\frac{1}{4}$, then the outcome is ___?___ (more/less) likely to happen than not to happen.

Solve.

21. If a coin is tossed, what is the probability that it will land heads up?

22. If a letter is picked from the word MATHEMATICS, what is the probability that it's a vowel?

23. Suppose that 12 red marbles and 18 white marbles are placed in a bag and thoroughly mixed. If one marble is picked, what is the probability that it is red? That it is white?

24. If you toss a cube twice, what is the probability of getting the sum 9?

Toss two pennies 50 times. Keep a record of the number of times that each outcome occurs: 1. Both heads. 2. Both tails. 3. One head and one tail.
Are the outcomes equally likely?

EXCURSION

How many cubes?
Clue 1. There are more than 50.
Clue 2. There are fewer than 100.
Clue 3. All the cubes can be used to make a larger cube.

Supplementary Exercises, Set 62, page 392

Odds

Imagine placing the marbles in the bag, thoroughly mixing them up, and then picking a marble.

$$P(\text{red}) = \frac{2}{6} = \frac{1}{3}$$

$$P(\text{not red}) = \frac{4}{6} = \frac{2}{3}$$

The **odds** in favor of picking a red marble are:

$$\frac{P(\text{red})}{P(\text{not red})} = \frac{\frac{1}{3}}{\frac{2}{3}} = \frac{1}{2}$$

Read as "1 to 2."

> The *odds* of an outcome occurring are the ratio of the probability that the outcome will occur to the probability that the outcome will not occur.

The odds *against* picking a red marble are:

$$\frac{P(\text{not red})}{P(\text{red})} = \frac{\frac{2}{3}}{\frac{1}{3}} = \frac{2}{1}$$

Notice that if the odds in favor of an outcome are $\frac{a}{b}$, then the odds against the outcome are $\frac{b}{a}$.

Here is another example:
Imagine thoroughly shuffling these cards and then picking one card.

$$P(\text{multiple of 3}) = \frac{2}{8}$$

$$P(\text{not a multiple of 3}) = \frac{6}{8}$$

$$\frac{\frac{2}{8}}{\frac{6}{8}} = \frac{2}{6} = \frac{1}{3}$$

So, the odds in favor of a multiple of 3 are $\frac{1}{3}$.

The odds against a multiple of 3 are $\frac{3}{1}$.

You can also think of the odds in favor of an outcome as the ratio of the number of ways the outcome can occur to the number of ways that the outcome cannot occur.

EXERCISES

Complete.

EVENT

Picking one marble

1. $P(\text{red}) = ?$
2. $P(\text{not red}) = ?$
3. Odds in favor of picking red = ?
4. $P(\text{blue}) = ?$
5. $P(\text{not blue}) = ?$
6. Odds in favor of picking blue = ?
7. Odds against picking blue = ?

EVENT

Tossing the cube

8. $P(5) = ?$
9. $P(\text{not } 5) = ?$
10. $P(2 \text{ or } 3) = ?$
11. Odds in favor of 5 = ?
12. Odds against 5 = ?
13. Odds in favor of an even number = ?
14. Odds against an even number = ?

EVENT

Picking one card

15. $P(\text{green}) = ?$
16. $P(\text{triangle}) = ?$
17. Odds in favor of a square = ?
18. Odds in favor of a circle = ?
19. Odds against red = ?

20. Ten balls, numbered 1 through 10, are placed in an urn and thoroughly mixed. If one ball is drawn, what are the odds in favor of its being a multiple of 4?

21. A full deck of playing cards (52) is thoroughly shuffled and 1 card is picked. What are the odds in favor of its being *either* a jack, a queen, or a king?

22. Some black marbles and some red marbles are in a bag. The odds in favor of picking a black marble are $\frac{2}{3}$. What is the probability of picking a black marble? A red marble?

EXCURSION

3-digit number* →	735
Reverse digits →	−537
Difference →	198
Reverse digits →	+891
Sum →	1089

* hundreds digit > ones digit

Start with a similar 3-digit number of your own. Did you get a final sum of 1089? Try some others.

Supplementary Exercises, Set 63, page 392

Sample space

When flipping a coin there are two possible outcomes:

Heads Tails

The set S of all possible outcomes of an event is called the **sample space** of the event.

So, the sample space for the event of flipping a coin is:

$S = \{H, T\}$, where H stands for *heads* and T stands for *tails.*

To find the probability of an outcome, it is often very helpful to list the sample space. Consider flipping a coin twice. What is the probability of getting two heads? Let's first list the sample space:

$S = \{HH, HT, TH, TT\}$

There are 4 possible outcomes, one of which is HH. So, $P(HH) = \frac{1}{4}$.

Now consider the event of flipping a coin three times. What is the probability of getting heads once and tails twice (in any order)?

The sample space is shown by this tree diagram:

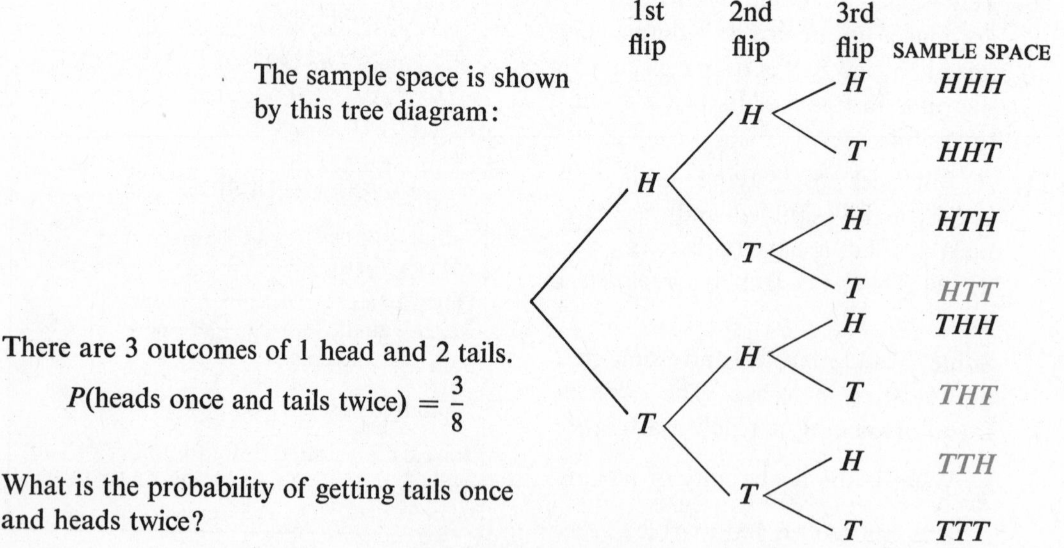

There are 3 outcomes of 1 head and 2 tails.

$P(\text{heads once and tails twice}) = \frac{3}{8}$

What is the probability of getting tails once and heads twice?

EXERCISES

1. Think about tossing these cubes:

The outcome shown can be represented by the number pair (1, 4).

   a. Copy and complete this table.

Number on red cube (columns); Number on blue cube (rows)

	1	2	3	4	5	6
1				(1, 4)		
2						
3						
4						
5						
6						

   b. How many outcomes are in the sample space?

2. Think about tossing the two cubes shown in exercise 1. Complete the following probabilities.
   a. $P(\text{doubles}) = ?$
   b. $P(\text{not doubles}) = ?$
   c. $P(\text{sum of } 2) = ?$
   d. $P(\text{sum of } 12) = ?$
   e. $P(\text{sum of } 7) = ?$
   f. $P(\text{not sum of } 7) = ?$

3. Consider a family with 3 children.
   a. List the sample space. Use *BGG* to represent a boy as the oldest child, a girl as the "middle" child, and a girl as the youngest child.
   b. Assume that the probability of the birth of a boy is the same as the probability of the birth of a girl. What is the probability that there are 2 boys and 1 girl in the family?
   c. What is the probability that the children are *not* all boys or all girls?

4. These five marbles are placed in a bag:

Then two marbles are picked, one after the other.
   a. Make a tree diagram of the sample space.
   b. What is the probability that a red marble will be picked?
   c. What are the odds against picking the green marble?

CHECKUP
for page 296

True or false?

1. If the probability of picking a green marble is $\frac{2}{3}$, then the probability of not picking a green marble is $\frac{1}{3}$.
2. If $P(\text{black}) = 0$, then $P(\text{not black}) = 1$.

Answers on page 428.

Supplementary Exercises, Set 64, page 392

Probability—independent and dependent events

Now let's consider a first event followed by a second event.

FIRST EVENT

Picking a marble

SECOND EVENT

Flipping a coin

Here is a sample space of the outcomes:

	Heads	Tails
Red	(R, H)	(R, T)
Blue	(B, H)	(B, T)
Yellow	(Y, H)	(Y, T)
Green	(G, H)	(G, T)

In the first event, $P(R) = \frac{1}{4}$.

In the second event, $P(H) = \frac{1}{2}$.

From the sample space, $P(R, H) = \frac{1}{8}$.

This is an example of the following important probability principle:

> If the probability of an outcome of a first event is $\frac{1}{m}$ and the probability of an outcome of a second event is $\frac{1}{n}$, then the probability of the first outcome followed by the second outcome is $\frac{1}{m} \times \frac{1}{n}$, or $\frac{1}{mn}$.

The two events described above are **independent** events, since the outcome of the first event does not affect the outcome of the second event.

Now let's consider two **dependent** events, that is, two events such that the outcome of the first event affects the outcome of the second event.

FIRST EVENT: Picking a card 

SECOND EVENT: Without replacing the first card, picking a second card

Since the first card was not replaced there are only 4 cards left in the deck.

What is the probability of picking a 3 first and then a 2?

$P(3 \text{ and then } 2) = \frac{1}{5} \times \frac{1}{4} = \frac{1}{20}$

EXERCISES

Complete.

FIRST EVENT	SECOND EVENT
Picking a marble	Tossing a cube

1. $P(R$ and then $5) = ?$
2. $P($not R and then $4) = ?$
3. $P(B$ and then not $2) = ?$
4. $P($not G and then not odd$) = ?$

FIRST EVENT	SECOND EVENT
Spinning this spinner	Spinning this spinner

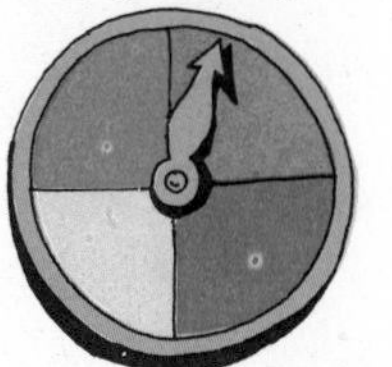

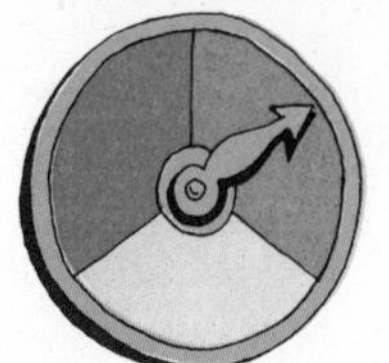

5. $P(G$ and then $G) = ?$
6. $P(B$ and then $B) = ?$
7. $P($not Y and then $R) = ?$
8. $P(Y$ and then not $R) = ?$

FIRST EVENT: Picking a card

SECOND EVENT: Without replacing the first card, picking a second card

9. $P($A and then F$) = ?$
10. $P($not A and then F$) = ?$
11. $P($vowel and then C$) = ?$
12. $P($consonant and then vowel$) = ?$
13. From a full deck of 52 playing cards, imagine drawing a first card, replacing it, and then drawing a second card. What is the probability that both cards are hearts? What is the probability that both cards are hearts if the first card is not replaced before the second card is drawn?

1. Construct a spinner like this.

2. Divide the circular region into 3 different-sized parts.
3. Spin the spinner 100 times and record each outcome.
4. Use your findings to estimate what fraction of the circle is each color.

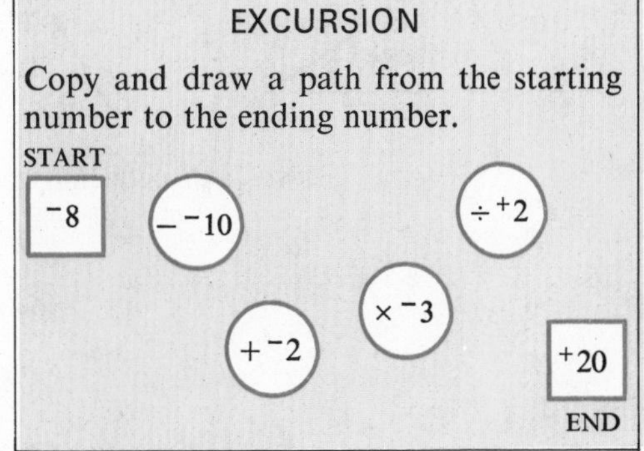

EXCURSION

Copy and draw a path from the starting number to the ending number.

Supplementary Exercises, Set 65, page 393

KEEPING SKILLS SHARP

Give each sum.

1. $3\frac{1}{4} + 2\frac{1}{4}$ **2.** $5\frac{1}{3} + 2\frac{2}{3}$ **3.** $8\frac{1}{8} + 7\frac{3}{4}$ **4.** $19\frac{5}{6} + 14\frac{2}{3}$ **5.** $27\frac{5}{8} + 16\frac{3}{4}$ **6.** $19\frac{7}{10} + 5\frac{4}{5}$

Give each difference.

7. $5\frac{1}{2} - 2\frac{1}{4}$ **8.** $9\frac{5}{8} - 3\frac{1}{2}$ **9.** $16\frac{1}{4} - 12\frac{1}{2}$ **10.** $25 - 13\frac{5}{8}$ **11.** $39\frac{5}{9} - 24\frac{2}{3}$ **12.** $20\frac{1}{8} - 16\frac{3}{5}$

Give each product.

13. $3 \times 2\frac{1}{4}$ **14.** $2\frac{1}{2} \times 3\frac{1}{3}$ **15.** $4\frac{2}{5} \times 3\frac{3}{4}$ **16.** $5\frac{1}{3} \times 8\frac{2}{3}$

Give each quotient.

17. $3 \div 2\frac{1}{2}$ **18.** $5\frac{1}{3} \div 6\frac{1}{3}$ **19.** $7\frac{2}{3} \div 4\frac{3}{4}$ **20.** $8\frac{1}{4} \div 6\frac{3}{4}$

Complete.

21. 15 m = ___?___ dm **22.** 15 m = ___?___ cm **23.** 421 mm = ___?___ cm

24. 21.5 km = ___?___ hm **25.** 16.1 dl = ___?___ *l* **26.** 16.1 dl = ___?___ cl

27. 23.1 cg = ___?___ mg **28.** 532 mm = ___?___ m **29.** 5.2 hg = ___?___ g

30. 3.2 kl = ___?___ *l* **31.** .093 m = ___?___ mm **32.** 3.52 g = ___?___ cg

Give each area. Use 3.14 as an approximation for π.

33.

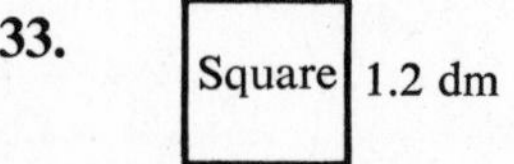

34.

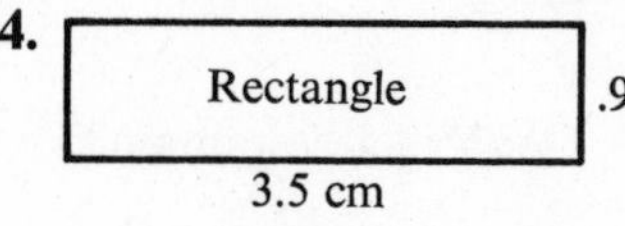

35.

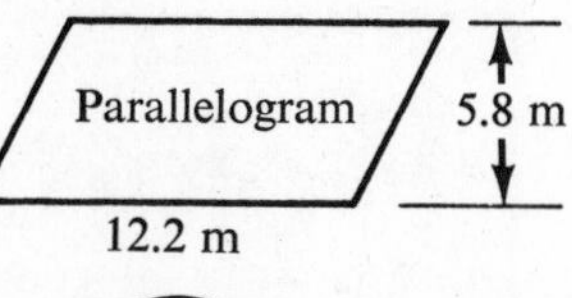

36.

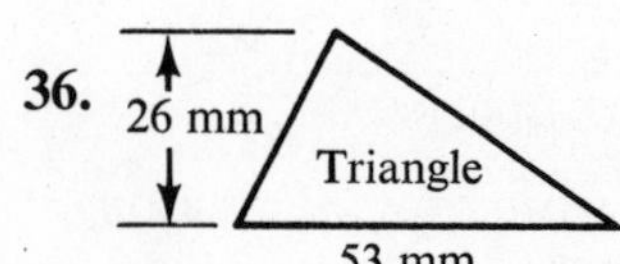

37.

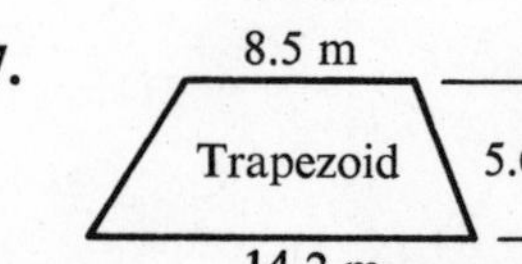

38.

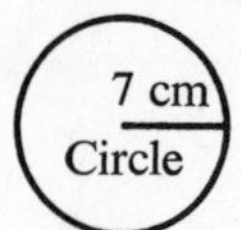

Solve each equation or inequality.

39. ${}^{+}3y + {}^{-}9 = {}^{+}7$ **40.** ${}^{-}2y + {}^{+}3 = {}^{-}5$ **41.** ${}^{+}6y + {}^{-}3 < 0$

42. ${}^{-}4y + {}^{+}5 > {}^{-}2$ **43.** ${}^{+}6y + \frac{{}^{-}3}{4} > \frac{{}^{-}5}{8}$ **44.** ${}^{-}4y - \frac{{}^{+}1}{2} = \frac{{}^{-}1}{4}$

45. ${}^{-}2 + {}^{+}4y < \frac{{}^{-}3}{2}$ **46.** ${}^{-}2y - \frac{{}^{-}4}{5} < {}^{-}3$ **47.** ${}^{-}8y - \frac{{}^{-}3}{4} > \frac{{}^{-}3}{4}$

Mathematics and science

Temperature can be measured in both degrees Celsius and degrees Fahrenheit. On the Celsius scale, water freezes at 0° and boils at 100°. On the Fahrenheit scale, water freezes at 32° and boils at 212°.

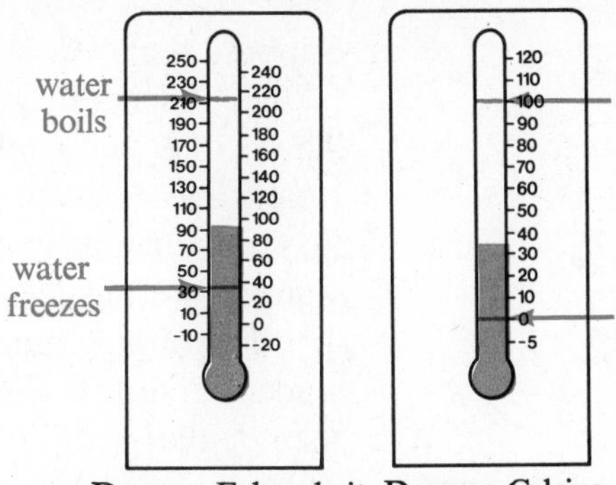

Sometimes it is necessary to convert from one temperature unit to another. Study these conversion formulas.

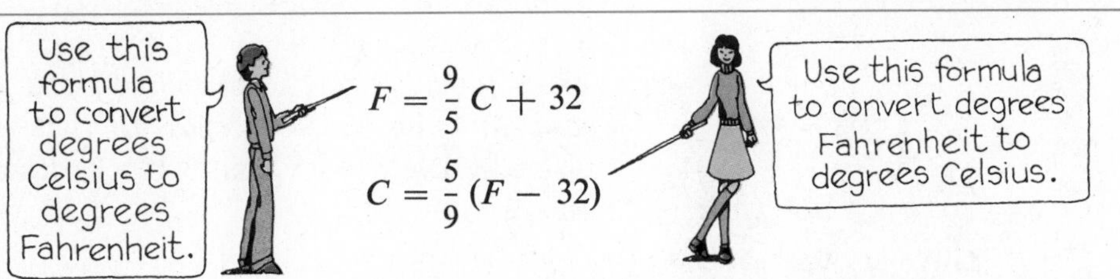

$$F = \frac{9}{5}C + 32$$

$$C = \frac{5}{9}(F - 32)$$

Examples.

Convert 20° C to degrees Fahrenheit.

$$F = \frac{9}{5}C + 32$$

$$F = \frac{9}{\cancel{5}_1} \cdot \cancel{20}^4 + 32$$

$$F = 36 + 32 = 68$$

So, 20° C = 68° F

Convert 50° F to degrees Celsius.

$$C = \frac{5}{9}(F - 32)$$

$$C = \frac{5}{9}(50 - 32)$$

$$C = \frac{5}{\cancel{9}_1}(\cancel{18}^2) = 10$$

So, 50° F = 10° C

EXERCISES

Convert to degrees Fahrenheit.

1. 50° C **2.** 18° C **3.** 0° C **4.** −12° C

Convert to degrees Celsius.

5. 68° F **6.** 150° F **7.** 20° F **8.** 0° F

9. The melting point of gold is 958° C. What is its melting point in degrees Fahrenheit?

10. The melting point of silver is 1761° F. What is its melting point in degrees Celsius?

Skill Maintenance, Set 68, page 416

Sampling to estimate probabilities

Suppose that you have the assignment of finding out what percent of the students in your school live less than 3 blocks from school. To do this, you could ask each student in school. But that takes a lot of time. Instead, you could take a **sample** of the student population and then estimate, or infer, from your sample the percent of students who live less than 3 blocks from school.

The sample must be representative of the **population** (the entire student body). It should be **unbiased** and large enough to represent the population.

Example.

A BIASED SAMPLE

The sample is likely to be biased because students who ride bicycles to school probably live farther than 3 blocks from school.

AN UNBIASED SAMPLE

Here is the tally taken by a student:

Distance from Home to School	
Less than 3 blocks	Not less than 3 blocks
𝍸 𝍸 𝍸 𝍸 𝍸 ||	𝍸 𝍸 𝍸 𝍸 𝍸 𝍸 𝍸 𝍸 𝍸 𝍸 𝍸 𝍸 𝍸 ||

From the sample we can predict what percent of students live less than 3 blocks from school.

(Number that live less than 3 blocks from school) (Number in sample)

$$\frac{27}{94} = \frac{x}{100}$$

$$94x = 2700$$

$$x \approx 28.7$$

So, 28.7% of the students in the sample live less than 3 blocks from school. Therefore, we estimate that 28.7% of the whole population lives within 3 blocks of school.

EXERCISES

There are only these 3 kinds of cards in a deck of 100 cards.

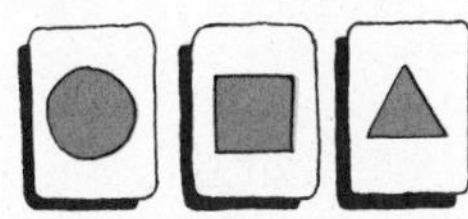

1. The cards were thoroughly shuffled and the following sample of 5 cards was taken.

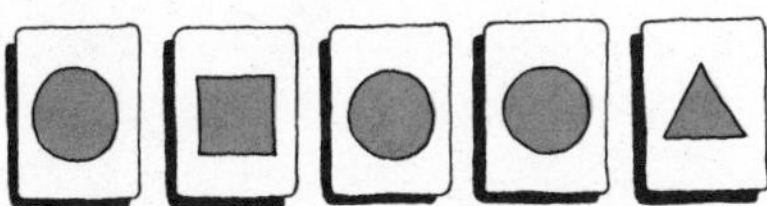

   a. Is it possible that there is only one triangle card in the deck? Is it very likely?
   b. Which shape would you predict that there are fewest of?
   c. Is it possible that there are 90 square cards in the deck? Is it very likely?

2. Then 15 more cards were added to the sample.

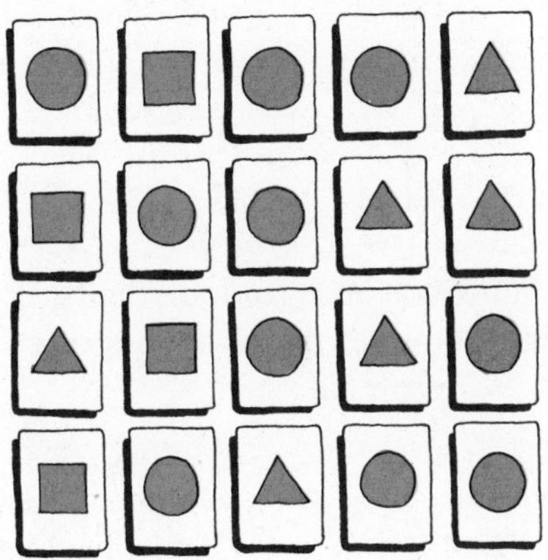

   a. Which shape would you predict that there are the most of?
   b. Would you predict that there are more square cards or triangle cards?
   c. Which sample (exercise 1 or 2) would allow you to make the more accurate prediction about the number of each kind of card in the deck? Why?
   d. Predict the number of each kind of card.

1. Take a sample to predict the percent of students in your school who have eaten candy bars within the last 24 hours.

2. Take a sample to predict the number of students in your school who sleep less than 9 hours a night. [You will need to know the total number of students.]

EXCURSION

A false equation is shown below. The numerals are made of toothpicks. Make the equation true by moving only one toothpick.

XX − II = X

Skill Maintenance, Set 69, page 416

Random digits

Suppose that this spinner is a fair spinner; that is, that the probability of its stopping on any one of the ten digits is $\frac{1}{10}$. Then you could generate **random digits** by spinning the spinner and recording in order the digits on which the spinner stops. Since a fair spinner is difficult to construct, we will use the following random digits, which have been generated by another device.

250 Random Digits*

49487	52802	28667	62058	87822	14704	18519	17889	45869	14454
29480	91539	46317	84803	86056	62812	33584	70391	77749	64906
25252	97738	23901	11106	86864	55808	22557	23214	15021	54268
02431	42193	96960	19620	29188	05863	92900	06836	13433	21709
69414	89353	70724	67893	23218	72452	03095	68333	13751	37260

There are tables that contain 1,000,000 random digits. Random digits may be used to **simulate** (imitate) the outcomes of events by assigning digits to outcomes. For example:

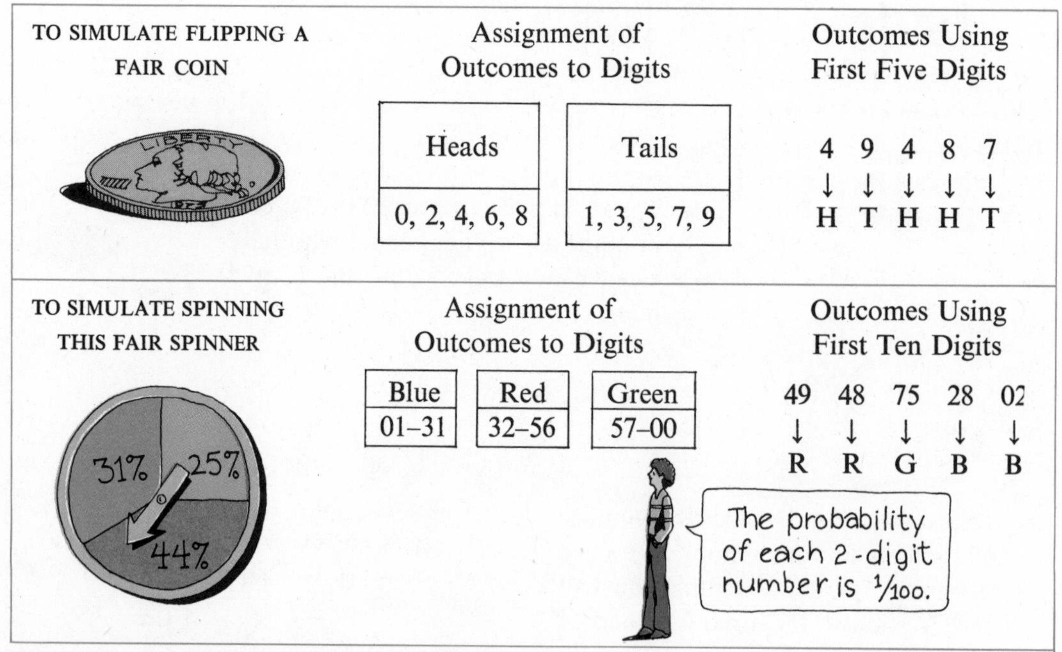

* Reprinted by permission of the Rand Corporation.

EXERCISES

Tell how you would assign random digits to simulate the outcomes of the following events.

1. Spinning this spinner

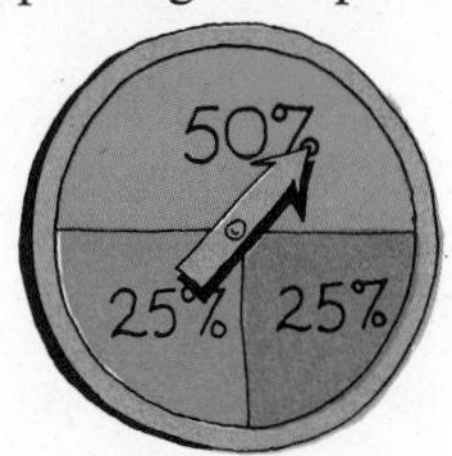

List the first 20 outcomes.

2. After shuffling, picking a card, replacing it

List the first 30 outcomes. (*Hint:* Let 0 or 1 be A, 2 or 3 be B, and so on.)

3. Tossing a cube

List the first 30 outcomes. (*Hint:* You may ignore four digits in the table.)

4. Seven hundred twenty students attend Taft Junior High School. The principal wants to randomly select 60 students. How might the principal use the table of random digits on the preceding page to select the 60 students?

Hint: Number the students from 1 through 720. Work with blocks of three digits.

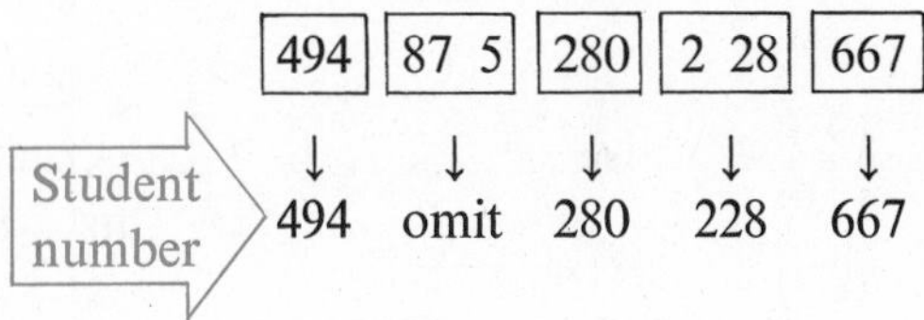

1. Generate your own table of random digits by first tossing a cube and then flipping a coin.

Outcome	$(1, H)$	$(2, H)$	$(3, H)$	$(4, H)$	$(5, H)$	~~$(6, H)$~~
Digit Assigned	1	2	3	4	5	
Outcome	$(1, T)$	$(2, T)$	$(3, T)$	$(4, T)$	$(5, T)$	~~$(6, T)$~~
Digit Assigned	6	7	8	9	0	

Notice that you ignore the outcomes $(6, H)$ and $(6, T)$.

2. Use your random digits to randomly select two ten-member teams from your classmates.

CHECKUP
for page 296

Imagine thoroughly shuffling the cards and then picking a card.

Give each probability.

1. *P*(red triangle)
2. *P*(blue circle)
3. *P*(red square)
4. *P*(blue square)
5. *P*(not a square)
6. *P*(blue circle **or** red triangle)

Answers on page 428.

Skill Maintenance, Set 70, page 416

Presenting data—graphs

Statistics is a branch of mathematics that involves collecting data, analyzing them, and then making inferences (drawing probable conclusions) from the data.

Graphs provide a visual organization of the data. The data listed in the table below are represented on three different kinds of graphs: a bar graph, a pictograph, and a broken-line graph.

Population Density of the United States	
Year	Population per square mile
1880	16.9
1890	21.2
1900	25.6
1910	31.0
1920	35.5
1930	41.2
1940	44.2
1950	50.7
1960	50.6
1970	57.5

BAR GRAPH
POPULATION DENSITY OF THE UNITED STATES

Population per square mile
60 55 50 45 40 35 30 25 20 15 10 5
1880 1890 1900 1910 1920 1930 1940 1950 1960 1970
Year

PICTOGRAPH
POPULATION DENSITY OF THE UNITED STATES
Each 🯅 represents 5 persons.

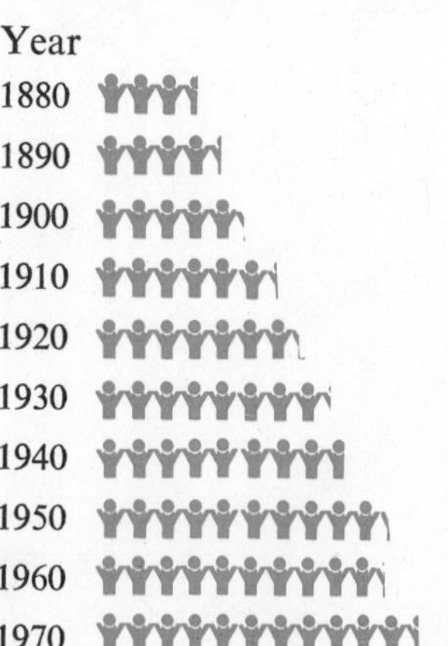

BROKEN-LINE GRAPH
POPULATION DENSITY OF THE UNITED STATES

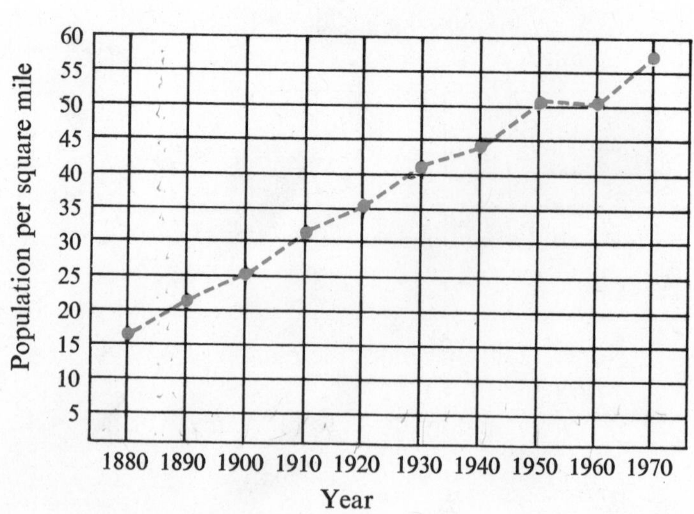

EXERCISES

Study the four ways in which the population density was presented.

1. Which is the most accurate?
2. Which is probably the least accurate?
3. Which do you think is least attractive?
4. Which do you think is the most attractive?
5. Could the bar graph have been made so that the population density could be read to the nearest tenth of a person? How?

6. Look at the broken-line graph. Is it possible that the population density in 1965 was 60 persons per square mile? Why or why not? Does the broken-line graph really tell you anything about the population density of any years except those that are listed?
7. Construct a bar graph, a broken-line graph, and a pictograph for the data given in the table below.

Automobile Sales

Year	1950	1955	1960	1965	1970
Number of passenger cars sold	6,666,000	7,920,000	6,675,000	9,306,000	6,547,000

From a magazine or a newspaper, cut out a graph. Construct a different kind of graph that shows the same information.

Find out your school's daily attendance for each day of the past two full weeks. Show the daily attendance on two different kinds of graphs.

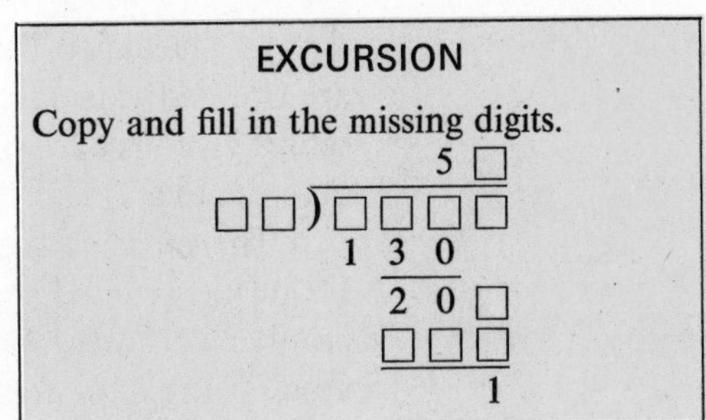

Skill Maintenance, Set 71, page 416

Mean, median, and mode

The list below shows how the members of a mathematics class scored on a test. To analyze data, it is often helpful to arrange them in order. Here the test scores have been listed from lowest to highest.

Name	*Test Score*	*Ordered Scores*
Adams, A.	84	58
Allen, J.	86	63
Borwick, A.	58	65
Burner, G.	94	68
Callon, A.	63	70
Cooke, C.	82	74
Davis, F.	87	75
Drivers, R.	65	76
Fallon, C.	84	78
Howards, F.	76	79
Jackson, H.	96	81
Johnson, N.	75	82
Laventi, B.	68	84
Logan, D.	89	84
Marshall, G.	79	84
Needam, R.	98	85
Osley, J.	70	86
Parker, N.	84	87
Rogers, D.	81	89
Sweetman, W.	74	90
Trotter, L.	85	94
Tulman, M.	78	96
Wallace, K.	90	98

When the data are ordered, we can tell at a glance the least score and the greatest score. Such scores tell how far the grades are spread out. This "spread" is generally called the *range*. The range is from 58 to 98, or 40.

The **mean**, or average, is the sum of all the numbers divided by the number of numbers.

$$\text{number of scores} \rightarrow 23\overline{)1846.00}^{\;80.26} \leftarrow \text{sum of scores}$$

Rounded to the nearest tenth, the mean is 80.3.

The **median** is the middle number. Notice that when the numbers are ordered it is easy to determine the median. The median for the scores given is 82. To find the median of an even number of numbers, take the average of the two middle numbers.

The **mode** is the number (or numbers) that occur most often. From the ordered scores above we see that 84 occurred the greatest number of times. So, the mode is 84. Is it easier to determine the mode if the data are ordered?

EXERCISES

Mean, median, or mode?

1. Half the numbers in the set are less than the __?__ and half are greater.
2. The __?__ is always a number in the set.
3. The median and __?__ may not be numbers in the set.
4. Some sets of numbers do not have a __?__ .
5. Jerry's monthly savings for one year were \$6.25, \$5.35, \$4.25, \$6.50, \$6.25, \$8.10, \$4.75, \$5.50, \$5.75, \$6.75, \$4.00, and \$6.25. Give the range and the mean.

6. Find seven whole numbers that have a range of 17 to 25, a median of 22, a mode of 23, and a mean of 21.
7. Find the range, the mean, the median, and the mode(s) of the data in the table below.

Professional Golfers—Leading Money Winners
1950–1970

Year	*Player*	*Amount*	*Year*	*Player*	*Amount*
1950	Snead	\$36,000	1961	Player	\$65,000
1951	Mangrum	\$26,000	1962	Palmer	\$81,000
1952	Boros	\$37,000	1963	Palmer	\$128,000
1953	Worsham	\$34,000	1964	Nicklaus	\$113,000
1954	Toski	\$66,000	1965	Nicklaus	\$141,000
1955	Boros	\$65,000	1966	Casper	\$122,000
1956	Kroll	\$73,000	1967	Nicklaus	\$189,000
1957	Mayer	\$66,000	1968	Casper	\$205,000
1958	Palmer	\$42,000	1969	Beard	\$175,000
1959	Wall	\$53,000	1970	Trevino	\$157,000
1960	Palmer	\$75,000			

Take a survey of 30 schoolmates to find the mean, or average, family size.

EXCURSION

The labels fell off and were put back so that each box is labeled incorrectly.

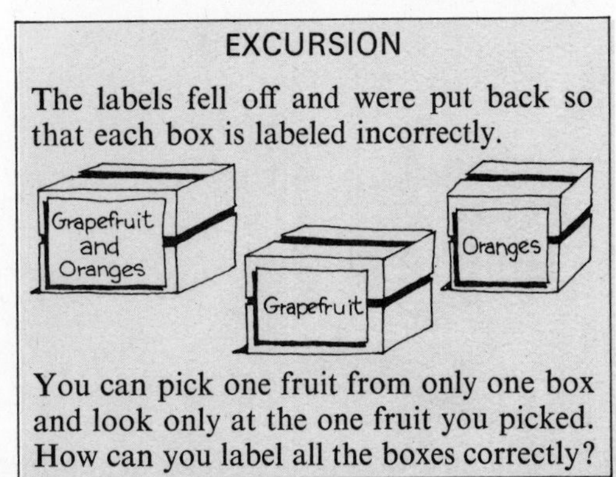

You can pick one fruit from only one box and look only at the one fruit you picked. How can you label all the boxes correctly?

Supplementary Exercises, Set 66, page 393

Frequency distribution

To determine the mean word-length of the headline story in a newspaper, we first took a sample and recorded our findings in the table below.

The table is called a **frequency distribution.** It tells the frequency of each word-length in our sample. What word-length is the mode? Now let's think about finding the mean word-length. To find the number of letters in our sample we first multiply each word-length by its frequency, then add all the products. To find the mean word-length we divide that sum by the number of words (sum of frequencies) in our sample.

Word-length (Number of letters)	Frequency		Total number of letters
1	||	2	2
2	卌 卌 ||	12	24
3	卌 卌 ||||	14	42
4	卌 卌	10	40
5	|||	3	15
6	卌 卌 |	11	66
7	卌	5	35
8	卌 ||||	9	72
9	卌 |||	8	72
10	|	1	10
11	||	2	22

If I add these numbers, I get the total number of words.

If I add these numbers, I get the total number of letters.

Compute the mean word-length to the nearest tenth. A **histogram** is a special kind of bar graph that is used to show a frequency distribution. Here is an example.

Test Scores of a Mathematics Class	
Score	**Frequency**
41–50	|
51–60	||||
61–70	卌 ||
71–80	卌 卌 |
81–90	卌 |
91–100	|||

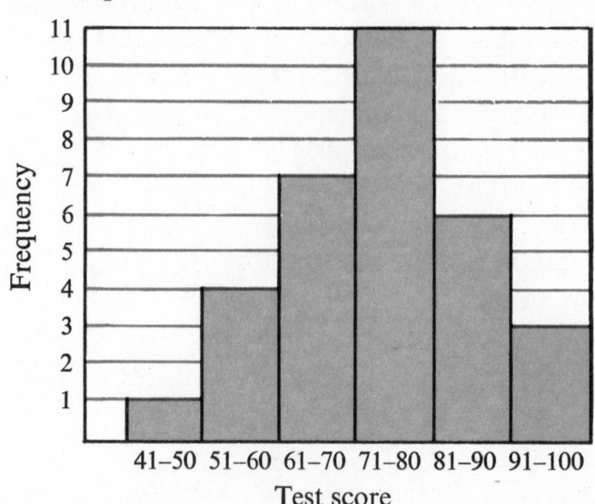

Notice that in a histogram the intervals (41–50, 51–60, 61–70, etc.) are all equal.

EXERCISES

Study the given frequency distribution to answer the following questions.

Fifth Hour Physical Education	
Time for 50-meter dash in seconds	Frequency
7	ǁ
8	ǁǁ
9	~~||||~~ ~~||||~~
10	~~||||~~ ǁ
11	~~||||~~
12				
13		

1. How many students ran an 8-second 50-meter dash?
2. How many took over 10 seconds to run the dash?
3. How many ran the dash in 9 seconds or less?
4. How many ran the 50-meter dash?
5. Which time is the mode?
6. What is the range of times?
7. What is the mean time?
8. What is the median time?

1. Use the method given on the preceding page to determine the mean word-length of a story found in a school library book.
2. Get a piece of string that is from 10 to 15 inches long. Have at least 20 schoolmates estimate its length. Keep a frequency distribution of their estimates in a table as shown. (*Note:* In this case the interval 14 to 16 includes 14 inches but not 16 inches.)
3. Show your findings on a histogram.

Estimated Length (in inches)	Frequency
18–20	
16–18	
14–16	
12–14	
10–12	
8–10	
6–8	

CHECKUP
for page 312

Give the range, the mean, the median, and the mode.

1. 1, 2, 3, 4, 5
2. 2, 4, 4, 5, 8
3. 3, 7, 8, 9, 15, 22
4. 12, 12, 12, 12, 12, 12, 12
5. 5, 8, 3, 7, 5
6. 11, 3, 14, 8, 6, 10
7. 16, 17, 18, 19, 20
8. 20, 16, 42, 58

Answers on page 428.

Skill Maintenance, Set 72, page 417

Mathematics in careers

A professional football team employs a person to keep the "statistics" on the team and on the individual players.

One statistic computed is the average number of yards gained each time an offensive back carries the ball (rushing average).

EXERCISES

Compute the lifetime rushing average for these offensive backs. Round averages to the nearest tenth of a yard.

	Player	Number of Carries	Total Yardage
1.	Jim Brown	2,359	12,312
2.	Joe Perry	1,929	9,723
3.	Jim Taylor	1,941	8,597
4.	John Johnson	1,571	6,803

Jim Brown: Perhaps the greatest running back of all time. Had a total rushing yardage of nearly 7 miles (8 yards under, to be exact).

John Unitas: Perhaps the greatest quarterback of all time. Had a total passing yardage of just under 22 miles.

Another statistic computed is the percent of pass completions of a quarterback. Compute the pass-completion percent for each of the following quarterbacks. Round to the nearest tenth of a percent.

	Player	Number of passes attempted	Number completed
5.	John Unitas	4,953	2,708
6.	Y. A. Tittle	4,395	2,427
7.	Bobby Layne	3,700	1,814
8.	Bart Starr	3,149	1,808

CHAPTER CHECKUP

Complete. [*pages 296, 298*]

EVENT

Picking a marble from the bag

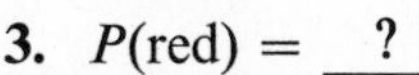

1. P(green) = ___?___
2. P(blue) = ___?___
3. P(red) = ___?___
4. P(not green) = ___?___
5. P(red **or** blue) = ___?___
6. P(yellow) = ___?___
7. Odds in favor of red = ___?___
8. Odds against blue = ___?___

Complete. [*page 302*]

FIRST EVENT	SECOND EVENT
Picking a card	Flipping the coin

9. P(square and then heads) = ___?___
10. P(circle and then tails) = ___?___
11. P(not a triangle and then heads) = ___?___

Give the range, the mean, the median, and the mode. [*page 312*]

12. 5, 6, 7, 8, 9
13. 13, 8, 11, 13, 17, 19
14. 10.3, 8.4, 9.6, 8.4, 7.5, 11.4, 8.2

Use the frequency distribution table to answer the following questions. [*page 314*]

15. During which hour was the traffic the "lightest"?
16. During which hour was the traffic the "heaviest"?
17. How many vehicles used Highway 19 between 9:00 A.M. and 10:00 A.M.?
18. How many more vehicles used the highway from 5:00 P.M. to 6:00 P.M. than from 4:00 P.M. to 5:00 P.M.?
19. How many vehicles used Highway 19 during the entire 12-hour period?
20. Construct a histogram of the frequency distribution.

Traffic Survey
Traffic on Highway 19 at Bridge Road

Time	Frequency
A.M. 6:00 to 7:00	𝍸 ||
7:00 to 8:00	𝍸 𝍸 𝍸 𝍸 𝍸 𝍸 ||
8:00 to 9:00	𝍸 𝍸 𝍸 𝍸 𝍸 𝍸
9:00 to 10:00	𝍸 𝍸 𝍸
10:00 to 11:00	𝍸 𝍸 ||
11:00 to 12:00	𝍸 𝍸
P.M. 12:00 to 1:00	𝍸 𝍸 𝍸 𝍸 ||
1:00 to 2:00	𝍸 𝍸 |||
2:00 to 3:00	𝍸 |||
3:00 to 4:00	𝍸 𝍸 𝍸 |
4:00 to 5:00	𝍸 𝍸 𝍸 𝍸
5:00 to 6:00	𝍸 𝍸 𝍸 𝍸 𝍸 𝍸 ||||

MAJOR CHECKUP

True or false? [*pages 10, 12*]

$A = \{0, 2, 4, 6, 8\}$ $B = \{0, 1, 2, 3, 4\}$

1. 0 is an element of A.
2. 3 is an element of B.
3. $A \subseteq B$
4. $A \cup B = \{0, 1, 2, 3, 4, 6, 8\}$
5. $A \cap B = \{0, 2, 4\}$
6. $B \subseteq A$

Give each quotient to the nearest .01. [*pages 82–87, 90*]

7. $3\overline{).85}$ **8.** $19\overline{)16.35}$ **9.** $3.5\overline{)97.84}$ **10.** $.89\overline{)2.653}$ **11.** $15.3\overline{)39.562}$

Give each sum or difference in lowest terms. [*pages 100, 108, 110*]

12. $\frac{5}{8} + \frac{2}{3}$ **13.** $\frac{3}{2} + \frac{3}{4}$ **14.** $\frac{2}{3} - \frac{5}{9}$ **15.** $\frac{5}{3} - \frac{3}{5}$

Give each product or quotient in lowest terms. [*pages 118, 120, 129*]

16. $\frac{5}{9} \times \frac{3}{5}$ **17.** $\frac{7}{2} \times \frac{8}{9}$ **18.** $\frac{6}{5} \div \frac{3}{2}$ **19.** $\frac{4}{7} \div \frac{6}{7}$

Solve each proportion. [*pages 164–165*]

20. $\frac{5}{9} = \frac{x}{18}$ **21.** $\frac{3}{x} = \frac{7}{5}$ **22.** $\frac{13}{19} = \frac{18}{x}$ **23.** $\frac{2.3}{4.2} = \frac{x}{16}$ **24.** $\frac{x}{23} = \frac{.9}{8}$

Find each volume. Use 3.14 for π. [*pages 214, 220*]

25.
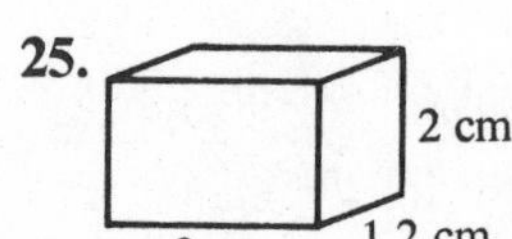

26.
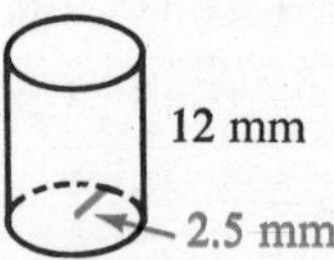

27.
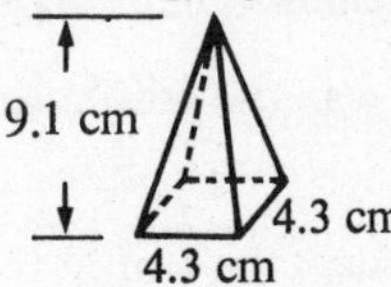

28.
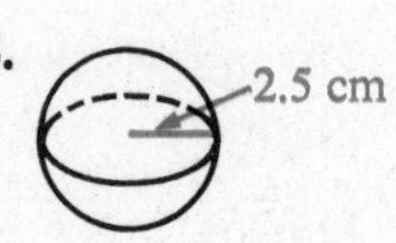

Give each sum or difference. [*pages 272, 274*]

29. $^{+}16 + {}^{-}5$ **30.** $^{-}8 + {}^{-}19$ **31.** $\frac{^{+}3}{4} + \frac{^{+}3}{2}$ **32.** $^{-}2.6 + {}^{+}3.5$

33. $^{+}19 - {}^{+}6$ **34.** $^{-}23 - {}^{+}11$ **35.** $\frac{^{-}5}{8} - \frac{^{-}3}{4}$ **36.** $^{+}.83 - {}^{-}.39$

Give each product or quotient. [*pages 276, 278*]

37. $^{+}8 \times {}^{-}11$ **38.** $^{+}15 \times {}^{+}10$ **39.** $\frac{^{-}3}{8} \times \frac{^{+}4}{7}$ **40.** $^{+}7.3 \times {}^{+}4.6$

41. $^{-}18 \div {}^{+}2$ **42.** $^{+}24 \div {}^{+}6$ **43.** $\frac{^{-}5}{8} \div \frac{^{-}1}{4}$ **44.** $^{+}6.9 \div {}^{-}.23$

1. Take a survey of at least 20 schoolmates to see how they travel to school. In a frequency table record what you found.

How do you travel to school?	
Walk	
Bicycle	
Bus	
Family car	
Other	

2. On a circle graph show what you found.

Example. Suppose that $\frac{5}{12}$ of the students in your sample walk to school. You would solve the following proportion to find out how many degrees to make the "walking" angle.

$$\frac{5}{12} = \frac{x}{360}$$

$$12x = 1800$$

$$x = 150$$

So, the central angle for "walking" will be a 150° angle.

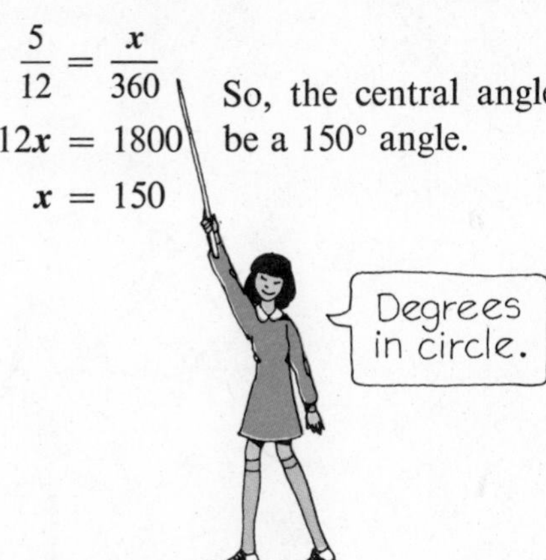

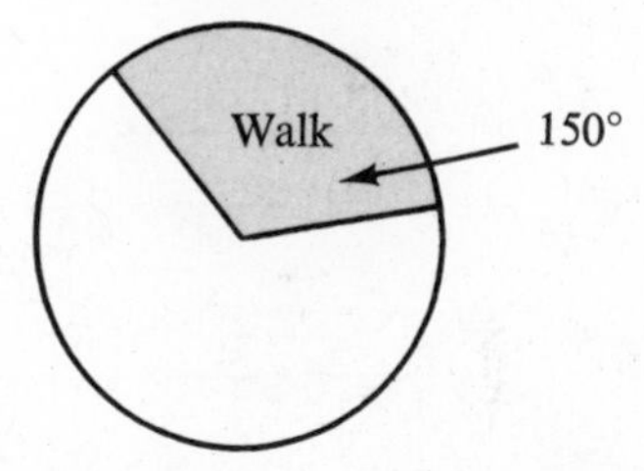

Project 2

1. Determine the pulse rate of at least 20 schoolmates.
2. Record your findings in a frequency table.
3. Determine the range, the median, the mode, and the mean.

PULSE RATE	
Beats per minute	Frequency
58	
59	
60	
61	

11 Real Numbers and the Coordinate Plane

Rational numbers

In an earlier chapter you worked with the integers, that is, the numbers in this set: $\{\ldots, ^-5, ^-4, ^-3, ^-2, ^-1, 0, ^+1, ^+2, ^+3, \ldots\}$. From now on we will not write the raised plus sign ($^+$) to indicate a positive number. For example, $^+3$ will simply be written 3.

Remember that a rational number is a number that can be expressed as the quotient of two integers. Every rational number can be expressed as either a terminating decimal or a repeating decimal. A rational number in fraction form can be changed to a decimal by dividing the numerator by the denominator.

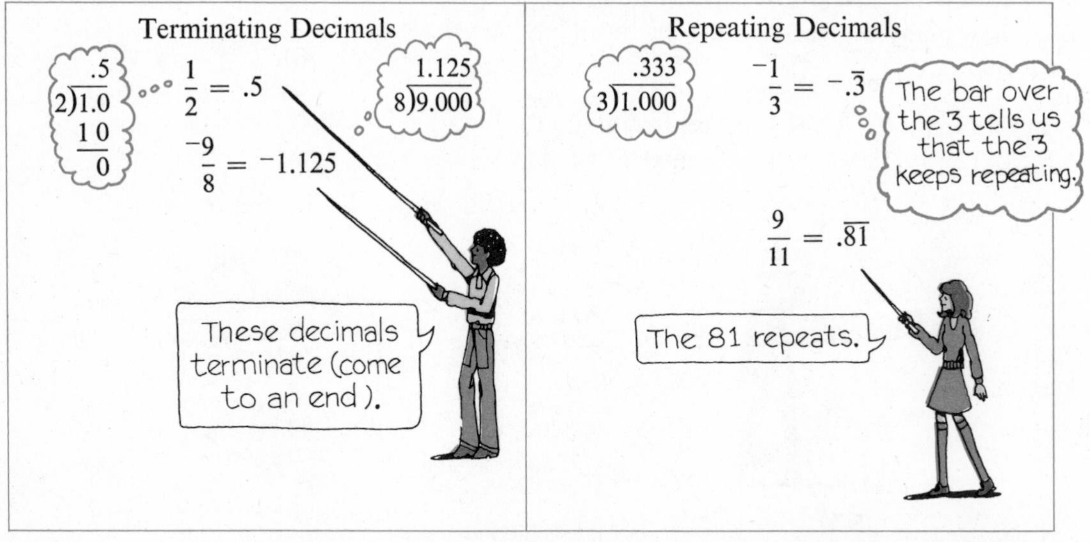

The set of rational numbers is **dense;** that is, between any two rational numbers there is another rational number. Of course, you can always find a rational number that is between two others by finding their average.

Example. $\frac{1}{2}$ and $\frac{5}{6}$

$$\frac{\frac{1}{2}+\frac{5}{6}}{2} = \frac{\frac{3}{6}+\frac{5}{6}}{2} = \frac{8}{6}\times\frac{1}{2} = \frac{8}{12} = \frac{2}{3}$$

So, $\frac{2}{3}$ is between $\frac{1}{2}$ and $\frac{5}{6}$.

EXERCISES

Express as decimals. Use a bar in each repeating decimal to show which digits repeat.

1. $\frac{1}{4}$ **2.** $\frac{1}{5}$ **3.** $\frac{-3}{8}$ **4.** $\frac{-2}{3}$ **5.** $\frac{5}{2}$ **6.** $\frac{2}{5}$

7. $\frac{7}{8}$ **8.** $\frac{1}{16}$ **9.** $\frac{-5}{12}$ **10.** $\frac{-11}{4}$ **11.** $\frac{5}{7}$ **12.** $\frac{-4}{13}$

Complete.

13. If $\frac{-1}{8} = {}^{-}.125$, then $\frac{-2}{8} =$ __?__.

14. If $\frac{1}{5} = .2$, then $\frac{3}{5} =$ __?__.

15. If $\frac{1}{4} = .25$, then $\frac{3}{4} =$ __?__.

16. If $\frac{1}{3} = .\overline{3}$, then $\frac{2}{3} =$ __?__.

Give a rational number that is between the two rational numbers.

17. $\frac{-5}{7}, \frac{-6}{7}$ **18.** $\frac{15}{33}, \frac{16}{33}$ **19.** .256, .257 **20.** .38, .3801

Each exercise gives a rational number in terminating decimal form. Change to a fraction in lowest terms.

$.6 = \frac{6}{10} = \frac{3}{5}$

21. .6 **22.** ⁻.25 **23.** .45 **24.** ⁻.625 **25.** 1.125 **26.** ⁻3.5

Express as a fraction. If you don't remember how, study page 104.

27. $.\overline{8}$ **28.** $.\overline{12}$ **29.** $.\overline{123}$

Hint: Multiply by 100.

Find six rational numbers that are between $\frac{1}{3}$ and $\frac{1}{4}$.

EXCURSION

Gina and John raise cats and birds. They counted all the heads and got 10. They counted all the feet and got 34. How many birds and how many cats did they have?

Supplementary Exercises, Set 67, page 393

Irrational numbers

You know that if ***n*** is a rational number, then ***n*** can be expressed as a terminating decimal or a repeating decimal.

Terminating Decimal	Repeating Decimal
$\frac{3}{4} = .75$	$\frac{^-5}{6} = {^-}.8\overline{3}$

It is also true that:
If ***n*** cannot be expressed as a terminating decimal or repeating decimal, then ***n*** is not a rational number.

Here is a decimal that neither terminates nor repeats:

.1 2 3 4 5 6 7 8 9 10 11 12 13 . . .

The decimal represents an **irrational number**, that is, a number that can be expressed as a nonterminating, nonrepeating decimal.

The graph of the irrational number above is the red point on this number line:

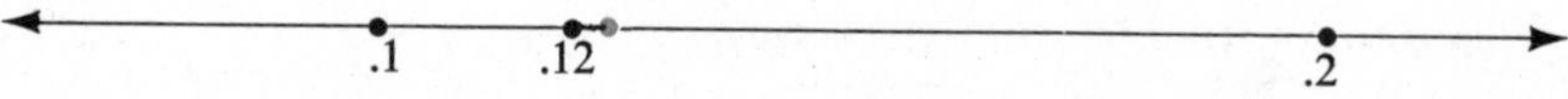

Notice how the following rational numbers (terminating decimals) get closer and closer to the irrational number above:

.1, .12, .123, .1234, .12345

Earlier you saw that between any two rational numbers there is another rational. Do you think that there is also an irrational number between any two rational numbers? For example, is there an irrational number between 3.08 and 3.09? Actually, there are infinitely many.

Here are two.

3.08 1 2 3 4 5 6 7 8 9 10 11 . . .
3.08 112 113 114 115 116 117 . . .

Notice that both are less than 3.09.

EXERCISES

Rational number or irrational number?

1. $\frac{^-11}{37}$ **2.** $.1\overline{6}$ **3.** 5.7468

4. $^-.4142434445\ldots$ **5.** 3.25262728 **6.** $2.363363336\ldots$

Match each number with its point on the number line.

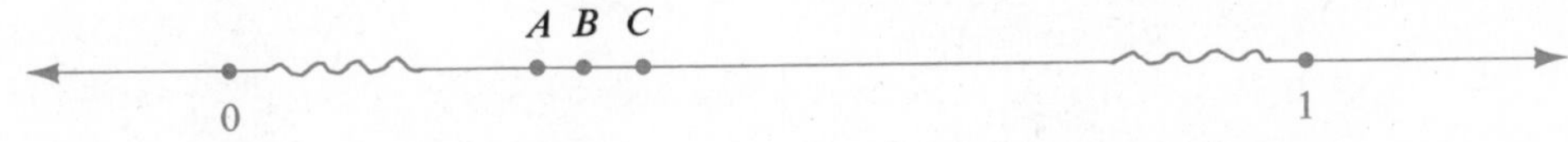

7. $\frac{1}{3}$ **8.** .32 **9.** $.3212113114115\ldots$

<, >, or = ?

10. 5.36 ● 5.369 **11.** $^-5.368$ ● $^-5.369$ **12.** 82.409 ● 82.49

13. $\frac{4}{3}$ ● $1.\overline{3}$ **14.** $\frac{^-5}{6}$ ● $^-.83$ **15.** $\frac{23}{4}$ ● 5.75

16. .358 ● $.357123456789101112\ldots$ **17.** $.712131415\ldots$ ● $.7112113114\ldots$

Give both a rational number and an irrational number that are between the two given numbers.

18. .25, .26 **19.** .3, .31 **20.** 5.08, 5.09 **21.** 8.207, 8.27

Earlier you worked with the irrational number π. (Remember that π is the ratio of the circumference of a circle to its diameter.) Unlike some irrational numbers, the decimal representation of π does not have a pattern.

$$\pi = 3.1415926\ldots$$

Computers have now computed π to over 100,000 decimal places. See if you can find an expression for π that has more decimal places than the one given above.

CHECKUP
for pages 320–321

Express as decimals.

1. $\frac{^-4}{5}$ **2.** $\frac{^-3}{4}$

3. $\frac{4}{3}$ **4.** $\frac{^-15}{6}$

5. $\frac{7}{4}$ **6.** $\frac{^-5}{7}$

7. $\frac{14}{9}$ **8.** $\frac{29}{5}$

9. $\frac{13}{8}$ **10.** $\frac{^-2}{11}$

Answers on page 428.

Supplementary Exercises, Set 68, page 393

Real numbers

Let's review the different sets of numbers that you have worked with in your study of mathematics.

The set of whole numbers: {0, 1, 2, 3, 4, . . .}

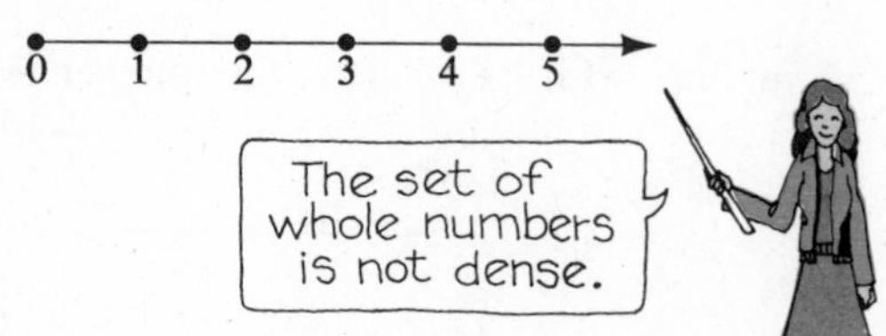

The set of integers: {. . . $^-4$, $^-3$, $^-2$, $^-1$, 0, 1, 2, 3, 4, . . .}

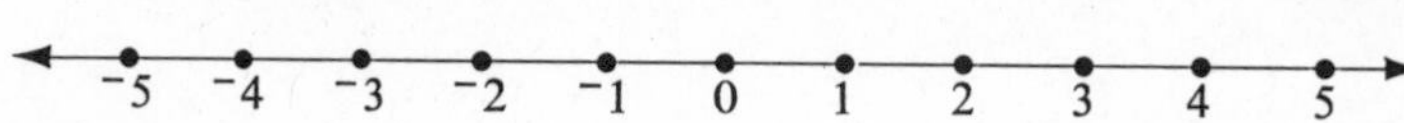

The set of rational numbers

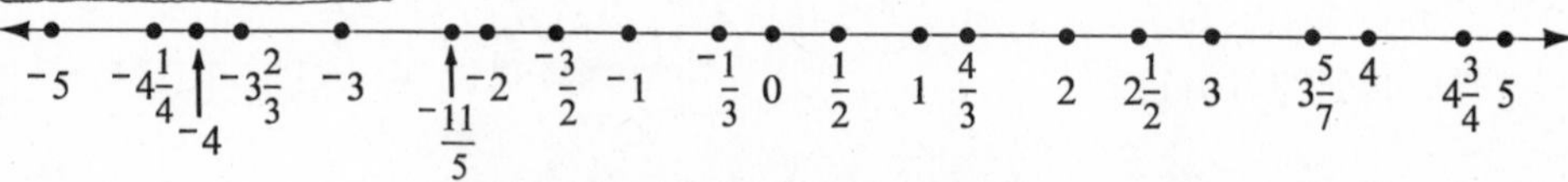

The set of rational numbers, together with the set of irrational numbers, makes up a new set of numbers, the set of **real numbers.**

The set of real numbers

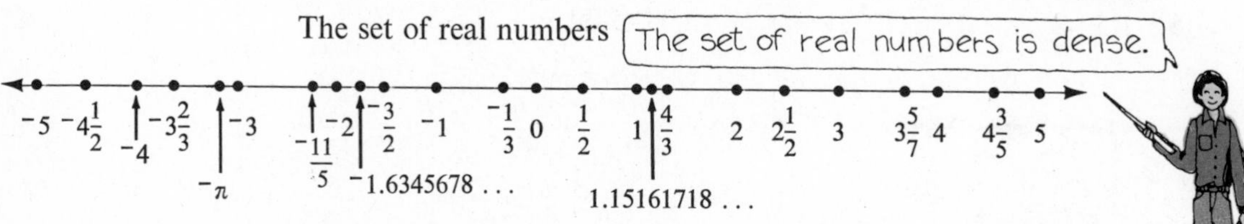

Of course, only a few real numbers are shown on the number line above. Actually, each point on the number line has associated with it a real number, and each real number has associated with it a point on the number line.

Here are the basic properties of real numbers.

Addition Properties	Multiplication Properties
Commutative Property of Addition For all substitutions, $a + b = b + a$.	Commutative Property of Multiplication For all substitutions, $a \cdot b = b \cdot a$.
Associative Property of Addition For all substitutions, $(a + b) + c = a + (b + c)$.	Associative Property of Multiplication For all substitutions, $(a \cdot b)c = a(b \cdot c)$.

Identity Property of Addition	Identity Property of Multiplication
There exists a real number 0 such that for all substitutions, $$a + 0 = a$$ [0 is called the *additive identity*.]	There exists a real number 1 such that for all substitutions, $$a \cdot 1 = a$$ [1 is called the *multiplicative identity*.]
Additive Inverse Property For each real number a there exists a real number, the opposite of a, such that their sum is the additive identity, 0. $$a + \text{opposite of } a = 0$$ [a and its opposite are called *additive inverses*.]	**Multiplicative Inverse Property** For each nonzero real number a there exists a real number $\frac{1}{a}$ such that their product is the multiplicative identity, 1. $$a \cdot \frac{1}{a} = 1 \quad [a \neq 0]$$ [a and $\frac{1}{a}$ are called *reciprocals* or *multiplicative inverses*.]
Distributive Property of Multiplication over Addition For all substitutions, $a \cdot (b + c) = (a \cdot b) + (a \cdot c)$.	

EXERCISES

True or false?

1. The set of whole numbers is a subset of the set of integers.
2. All integers are rational numbers.
3. All rational numbers are integers.
4. Some real numbers are integers.
5. All irrational numbers are real numbers.
6. Every real number is either positive or negative.
7. Every real number is either a rational number or an irrational number.
8. Every real number has a corresponding point on the number line.

Give an example of each of the following properties.

9. associative property of multiplication
10. identity property of addition
11. commutative property of multiplication
12. additive inverse property
13. distributive property of multiplication over addition
14. commutative property of addition
15. identity property of multiplication
16. associative property of addition
17. multiplicative inverse property

Supplementary Exercises, Set 69, page 394

Divide the class into two teams, Team A and Team B.

A player from each team writes a real number on the chalkboard.

A player from Team A may earn two points by giving both a rational and an irrational number that are between the two given numbers.

He then erases the two "original" numbers.

A player from Team B may earn two points by giving a rational and an irrational number that are between the numbers written by the player from Team A.

Play continues for 15 or 20 minutes. The team having the greater number of points at the end of the time period wins!

KEEPING SKILLS SHARP

Substitute and simplify.

a	b	x	y
3	2	4	6

1. $(a + b) \cdot y$ **2.** $\frac{b}{a} + \frac{x}{y}$ **3.** a^b **4.** b^a **5.** $\frac{ab + y}{x}$

Divide. Round each quotient to the nearest .01.

6. $29\overline{)38.56}$ **7.** $5.2\overline{)84.367}$ **8.** $.37\overline{)297.48}$ **9.** $29.5\overline{)360.15}$ **10.** $.106\overline{)4.9732}$

Solve each proportion.

11. $\frac{a}{11} = \frac{7}{4}$ **12.** $\frac{9}{15} = \frac{3}{x}$ **13.** $\frac{1.6}{2.1} = \frac{y}{10}$ **14.** $\frac{2\frac{1}{2}}{k} = \frac{8}{3}$

The dashed line is a line of symmetry.

15. What is the flip image of point A?
16. What is the flip image of point E?
17. What is the flip image of $\overline{AB}$?
18. What is the flip image of $\angle C$?

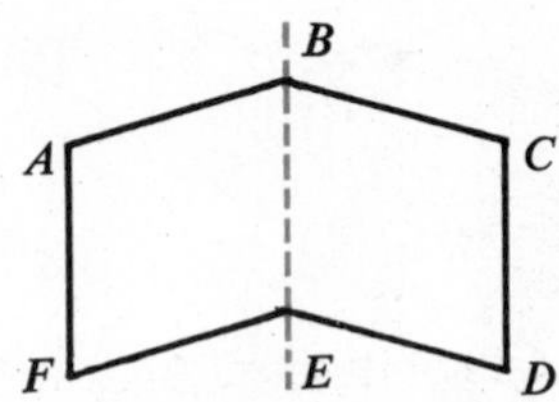

Give each sum or difference.

19. $5\frac{1}{2} + 8\frac{1}{3}$

20. $13\frac{3}{5} + 4\frac{9}{10}$

21. $18\frac{3}{4} + 19\frac{2}{3}$

22. $15\frac{3}{5} - 9\frac{1}{4}$

23. $19 - 11\frac{5}{6}$

24. $23\frac{1}{6} - 15\frac{5}{9}$

Complete.

25. 3.6 m = __?__ dm **26.** 82.3 m = __?__ cm **27.** 528 mm = __?__ dm
28. 9 km = __?__ m **29.** 5.96 dm = __?__ cm **30.** 5293 m = __?__ km

Imagine thoroughly mixing the marbles and then, without looking, picking a marble. Complete the following probabilities.

31. P(blue) = __?__ **32.** P(red) = __?__
33. P(green) = __?__ **34.** P(not red) = __?__
35. P(yellow) = __?__ **36.** P(blue or red) = __?__

Skill Maintenance, Set 73, page 417

Graphing solution sets

Earlier you learned that to solve an open sentence (an equation or inequality) you find all numbers that make the open sentence true. The set of all numbers that make an open sentence true is called the **solution set**. (In this lesson the solution set will consist of all the *real numbers* that make the open sentence true.)

Remember that if you add the same number to both sides of an equation you get an equivalent equation, that is, an equation having the same solution set.

If you multiply both sides of an equation by the same nonzero number you get an equivalent equation.

Example 1.

$$2x + 1 = 7$$
$$2x + 1 + {}^{-}1 = 7 + {}^{-}1 \quad \text{[add } {}^{-}1 \text{ to both sides]}$$
$$2x = 6 \quad \text{[simplify]}$$
$$\frac{1}{2} \times 2x = \frac{1}{2} \times 6 \quad \left[\text{multiply both sides by } \frac{1}{2}\right]$$
$$x = 3 \quad \text{[simplify]}$$

Solution set: {3}

Graph of solution set:

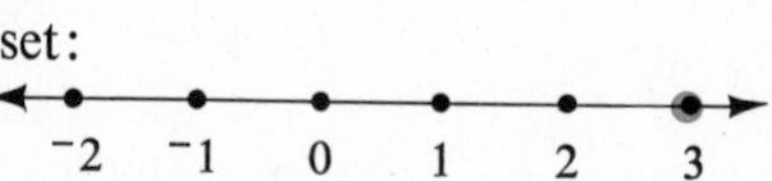

Example 2.

$$4x + {}^{-}3 = {}^{-}6$$
$$4x + {}^{-}3 + 3 = {}^{-}6 + 3$$
$$4x = {}^{-}3$$
$$\frac{1}{4} \times 4x = \frac{1}{4} \times {}^{-}3$$
$$x = \frac{{}^{-}3}{4}$$

Solution set: $\left\{\frac{{}^{-}3}{4}\right\}$

Graph:

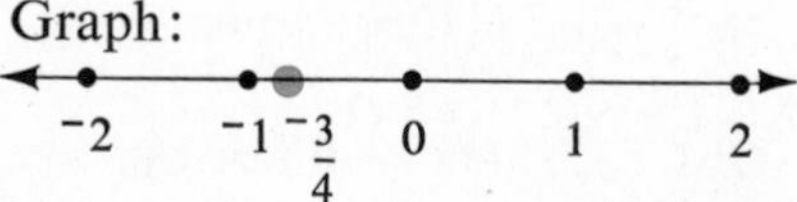

If you add the same number to both sides of an inequality you get an equivalent inequality.

If you multiply both sides of an inequality by a positive number you get an equivalent inequality.

If you multiply both sides of an inequality by a negative number you get an equivalent inequality with the inequality sign reversed.

Study these examples.

Example 1.

$$3x + {}^{-}6 \leq 8$$
$$3x + {}^{-}6 + 6 \leq 8 + 6$$
$$3x \leq 14$$
$$\frac{1}{3} \times 3x \leq \frac{1}{3} \times 14$$
$$x \leq \frac{14}{3}$$

The solid dot tells us that 14/3 is in the solution set.

Graph of solution set:

⁻3 ⁻2 ⁻1 0 1 2 3 4 $\frac{14}{3}$ 5

Solution set: $\left\{\text{all numbers less than or equal to } \frac{14}{3}\right\}$

Example 2.

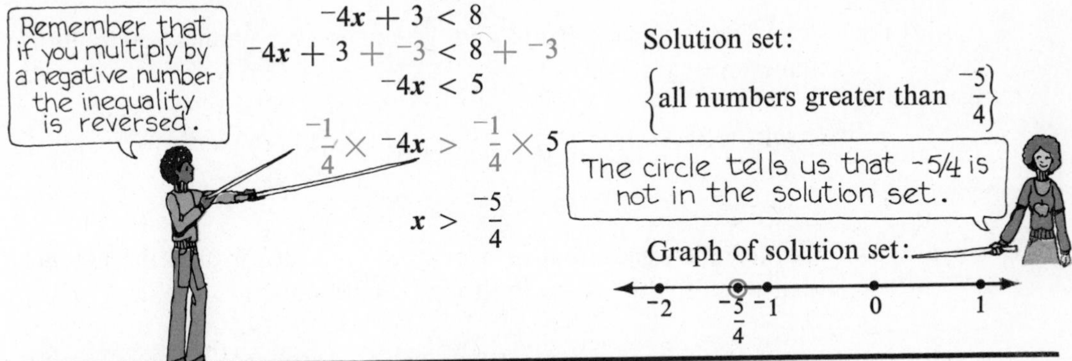

$$^-4x + 3 < 8$$
$$^-4x + 3 + {}^-3 < 8 + {}^-3$$
$$^-4x < 5$$
$$\frac{^-1}{4} \times {}^-4x > \frac{^-1}{4} \times 5$$
$$x > \frac{^-5}{4}$$

Solution set:

$\left\{\text{all numbers greater than } \frac{^-5}{4}\right\}$

Graph of solution set:

$^-2 \quad \frac{^-5}{4} \quad {}^-1 \quad 0 \quad 1$

EXERCISES

Match each open sentence with the graph of its solution set.

1. $x > {}^-2$
2. $x = {}^-2$
3. $x < {}^-2$
4. $x \leq {}^-2$
5. $x \geq {}^-2$

a. $^-3 \quad {}^-2 \quad {}^-1 \quad 0 \quad 1$

b. $^-3 \quad {}^-2 \quad {}^-1 \quad 0 \quad 1$

c. $^-3 \quad {}^-2 \quad {}^-1 \quad 0 \quad 1$

d. $^-3 \quad {}^-2 \quad {}^-1 \quad 0 \quad 1$

e. $^-3 \quad {}^-2 \quad {}^-1 \quad 0 \quad 1$

Solve each open sentence and graph each solution set.

6. $3x + 6 = 11$
7. $5x + {}^-6 = 4$
8. $8x + {}^-6 = 0$
9. $^-4x + 3 = {}^-1$
10. $^-6x + {}^-3 = 5$
11. $^-2x + 8 = {}^-2$
12. $2x + 3 < 5$
13. $3x + 2 > 0$
14. $5x + {}^-6 \leq 4$
15. $6x + {}^-5 \geq 3$
16. $^-4x + 6 < 2$
17. $^-2x + {}^-5 \geq {}^-15$
18. $\frac{3x + {}^-6}{2} \geq {}^-6$
19. $4(5x - 6) \leq {}^-2$
20. $\frac{^-2x - 3}{^-8} > 6$

Project

How many open sentences can you find that have the solution {all numbers less than or equal to $^-4$}?

EXCURSION

How many marbles are in the box?

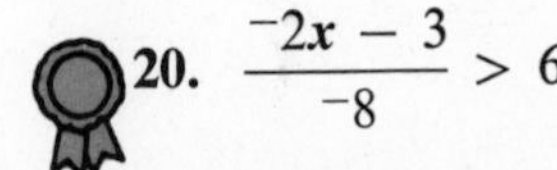

Clues:

1. There are more than 50 and fewer than 100.
2. If you divide the number of marbles by 8, you get a remainder of 5.
3. If you divide by 9, you get a remainder of 4.

Supplementary Exercises, Set 70, page 394

Square root

You learned earlier that to find the square of a number you multiply the number by itself.

$4^2 = 16$ (4 | 16, 4)

To find the **square root** of a number you have to find the number that when multiplied by itself gives that number.

$x^2 = 49$ (x | 49, x)

7 is the square root of 49. We write $7 = \sqrt{49}$.
Notice that when you work with real numbers there are actually two square roots of 49, 7 and $^-7$. Let's agree that the symbol $\sqrt{49}$ represents the positive square root of 49.
Here are some other examples:

$$\sqrt{25} = 5 \qquad \sqrt{1} = 1 \qquad \sqrt{1.69} = 1.3 \qquad \sqrt{\frac{4}{9}} = \frac{2}{3}$$

Notice that in these examples the square roots are rational numbers. However, some square roots are irrational numbers and cannot be represented as terminating or repeating decimals. Here is an example.

$\sqrt{19}$ (? | 19, ?)

The following method, called the **divide-and-average** method, can be used to find a decimal equivalent or a decimal approximation for square roots. Here the method is used to find the decimal approximation of $\sqrt{19}$ to the nearest hundredth.

Step 1. Estimate $\sqrt{19}$.

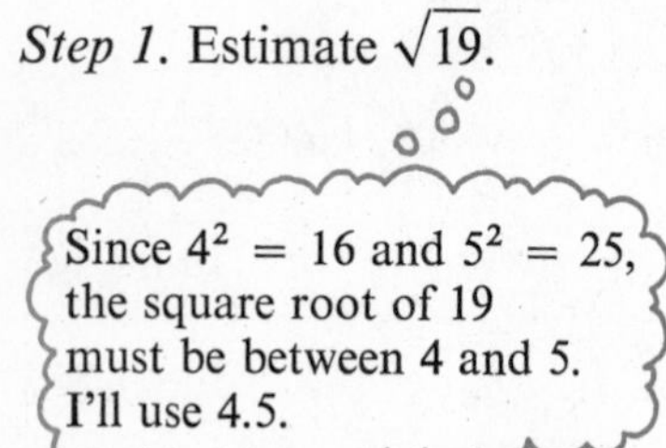

Step 2. Divide 19 by estimate.

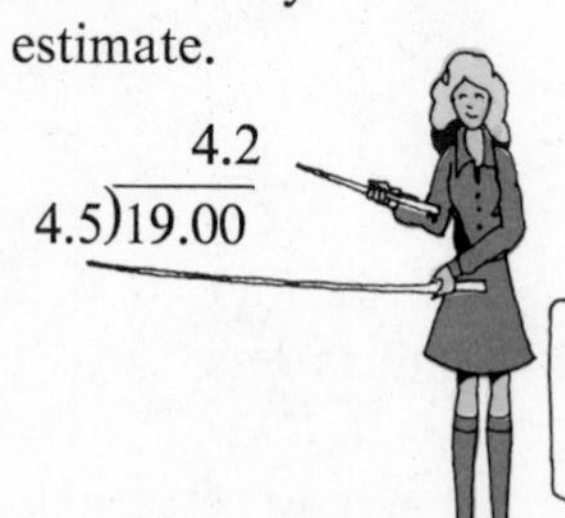

Step 3. Average the divisor and quotient.

$$\frac{4.5 + 4.2}{2} = 4.35$$

If 4.5 were the square root of 19 then these numbers would be the same.

Step 4. Use the average as a better estimate. Divide 19 by 4.35.

$$\text{Average} \rightarrow 4.35\overline{)19.00\,000}\quad 4.367$$

Rounding 4.367 in step 4 to 4.37, we now know that the square root of 19 is between 4.35 and 4.37. So, $\sqrt{19}$ is approximately 4.36. If a closer approximation than 4.36 is needed, the process can be continued.

Here is a flow chart that tells you how to use the divide-and-average method to find the square root of a number, n, to the hundredths place.

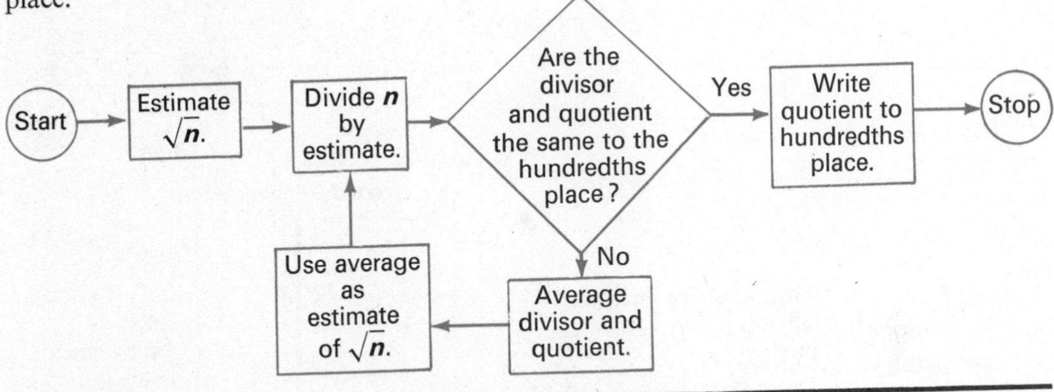

EXERCISES

Simplify.

1. $\sqrt{64}$ **2.** $\sqrt{100}$ **3.** $\sqrt{81}$ **4.** $\sqrt{36}$ **5.** $\sqrt{144}$ **6.** $\sqrt{400}$

7. $\sqrt{\frac{1}{4}}$ **8.** $\sqrt{\frac{9}{16}}$ **9.** $\sqrt{\frac{25}{49}}$ **10.** $\sqrt{.01}$ **11.** $\sqrt{.16}$ **12.** $\sqrt{.0025}$

Fill in each blank with the "closest" integer.

13. __?__ $< \sqrt{8} <$ __?__ **14.** __?__ $< \sqrt{11} <$ __?__ **15.** __?__ $< \sqrt{35} <$ __?__

16. __?__ $< \sqrt{20} <$ __?__ **17.** __?__ $< \sqrt{90} <$ __?__ **18.** __?__ $< \sqrt{105} <$ __?__

19. __?__ $< \sqrt{150} <$ __?__

20. __?__ $< \sqrt{1000} <$ __?__

Use the divide-and-average method to approximate the following square roots to the hundredths place.

21. $\sqrt{32}$ **22.** $\sqrt{60}$ **23.** $\sqrt{43}$

24. $\sqrt{96}$ **25.** $\sqrt{110}$ **26.** $\sqrt{250}$

27. $\sqrt{9.6}$ **28.** $\sqrt{18.4}$ **29.** $\sqrt{42.3}$

EXCURSION

Make a small dot any place on a piece of unlined paper.

Now on another piece of unlined paper make a dot in the *same* place. You may use a ruler, protractor, or compass. You cannot place one paper on top of the other except to check your work.

How many different ways can you find to do this?

Supplementary Exercises, Set 71, page 394

The coordinate plane

Earlier in this chapter you learned that each point on a number line has associated with it a real number (its **coordinate**) and that each real number has associated with it a point on the number line (its **graph**).

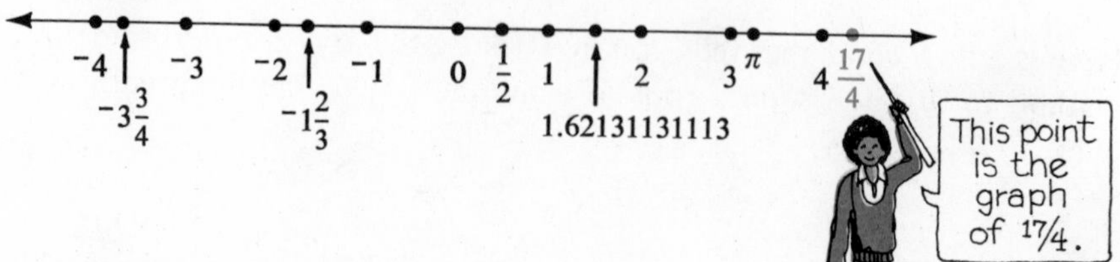

Ordered pairs of real numbers are graphed on a **coordinate plane.** Notice that a coordinate plane has a horizontal axis, which is the **first component axis**, and a vertical axis, which is the **second component axis.** The point where the two axes intersect is called the **origin.**

Here is how to graph the ordered pair (−4, 3).

Since −4 is the first component of the ordered pair, start at the origin and move along the first component axis to −4. Then move parallel to the second component axis to the second component, 3. So point *A* has coordinates (−4, 3).

Do you see that the coordinates of point *B* are (4, 3)? What are the coordinates of point *C*? Of point *D*?

Each point in a coordinate plane has associated with it an ordered pair of real numbers. Each ordered pair of real numbers has associated with it a point in the coordinate plane.

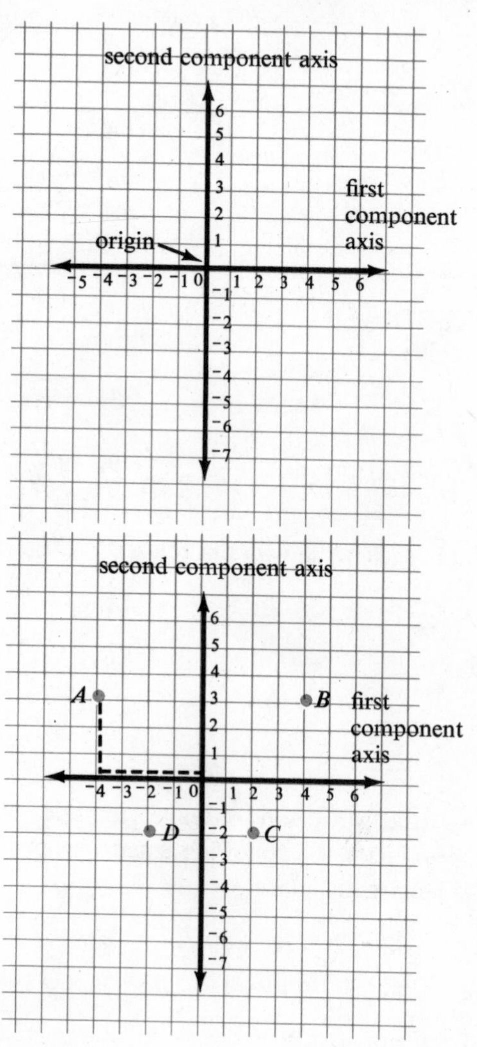

EXERCISES

Give the coordinates of:

1. point A
2. point B
3. point C
4. point D
5. point E
6. point F
7. point G
8. point H
9. point I
10. point J
11. point K
12. point L

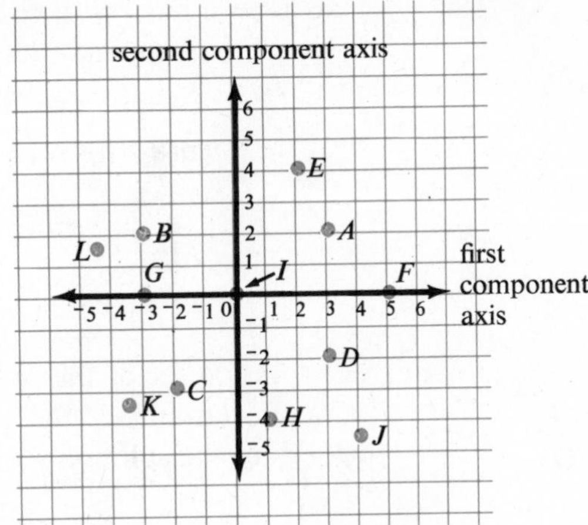

Draw the first and second component axes on a piece of graph paper. Use integers to label points on each axis as shown above. Graph the following ordered pairs. Label each with its coordinates.

13. $(3, ^-6)$ 14. $(4, ^-2)$ 15. $(^-3, ^-1)$ 16. $(2, ^-4)$ 17. $(^-3, 5)$
18. $(^-2, ^-2)$ 19. $(^-3, 0)$ 20. $(3, 4)$ 21. $(0, 0)$ 22. $(4, 4)$
23. $\left(\frac{1}{2}, 4\right)$ 24. $\left(4, \frac{1}{2}\right)$ 25. $\left(\frac{1}{2}, \frac{5}{2}\right)$ 26. $\left(^-5, ^-4\frac{1}{2}\right)$ 27. $\left(3\frac{1}{2}, ^-2\right)$

28. Here are some ordered pairs in which the second component is twice the first.

    $(^-2, ^-4), (^-1, ^-2), \left(\frac{^-1}{2}, ^-1\right)$
    $(0, 0), (1, 2)$

    a. List 5 more ordered pairs such that the second component is two times the first.
    b. Graph all ten ordered pairs.
    c. Do the points "line up"?

29. a. List 10 ordered pairs such that the second component is the square of the first component.
    b. Graph the ordered pairs.
    c. Do the points "line up"?

CHECKUP
for pages 330–331

Use the divide-and-average method to estimate each square root to the nearest tenth.

1. $\sqrt{37}$ 2. $\sqrt{53}$
3. $\sqrt{69}$ 4. $\sqrt{22}$
5. $\sqrt{44}$ 6. $\sqrt{88}$
7. $\sqrt{60.5}$ 8. $\sqrt{108.6}$

Answers on page 428.

Supplementary Exercises, Set 72, page 394

Equations with two placeholders

Thus far we have worked with equations that have only one placeholder. For example:

$$x + {}^{-}6 = 5 \qquad\qquad {}^{-}3x + 6 = {}^{-}12$$

Now we'll work with some equations that have two placeholders.

The solution set of the equation above consists of a set of ordered pairs. For example, the ordered pair (1, 4) is one solution and belongs to the solution set.

$2x + y = 6$ (with 1 thought for x and 4 thought for y) (1, 4) is a solution.

Mathematicians have agreed that the first component of the ordered pair is the replacement for x and the second component of the ordered pair is the replacement for y.

Notice that (4,1) is not a solution.

$2x + y = 6$ (with 4 thought for x and 1 thought for y)

To find a solution, you can first choose a replacement for x and then solve to find the replacement for y.

Example.

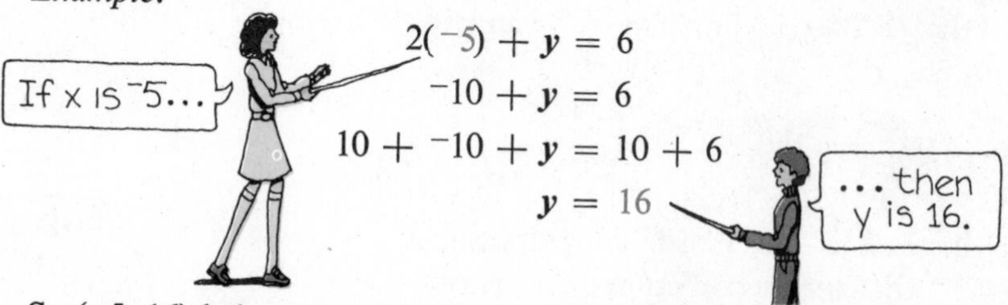

$$2({}^{-}5) + y = 6$$
$${}^{-}10 + y = 6$$
$$10 + {}^{-}10 + y = 10 + 6$$
$$y = 16$$

So (⁻5, 16) belongs to the solution set. Actually, the solution set has infinitely many such ordered pairs. Here a table of values is used to list some of the ordered pairs in the solution set.

$2x + y = 6$

x	y
1	4
⁻5	16
0	6

Is each ordered pair shown in the table of values in the solution set of $2x + y = 6$?

(*Hint:* Do you get a true sentence when you make both replacements?)

EXERCISES

Copy and complete each table of values.

1. $2x + 3y = 6$

	x	y
a.	3	
b.	2	
c.	1	
d.	0	
e.	$^{-}1$	
f.	$^{-}2$	

$$2(3) + 3y = 6$$
$$6 + 3y = 6$$
$$3y = 0$$
$$y = 0$$

2. $x + y = 0$

	x	y
a.	5	
b.	3	
c.	$^{-}4$	
d.	0	
e.		6
f.	$^{-}2$	

3. $x + 2y = {}^{-}12$

	x	y
a.	$^{-}4$	
b.	$^{-}8$	
c.	0	
d.	3	
e.	5	
f.	2	

4. $^{-}2x + y = {}^{-}6$

	x	y
a.	$^{-}3$	
b.	$^{-}2$	
c.	$^{-}1$	
d.	0	
e.	1	
f.	2	

5. $4x + {}^{-}2y = 8$

	x	y
a.	1	
b.	$^{-}2$	
c.	2	
d.	0	
e.	$\frac{^{-}1}{2}$	
f.	$\frac{1}{4}$	

6. $^{-}3x + y = 0$

	x	y
a.	$^{-}2$	
b.	$^{-}1$	
c.	0	
d.	1	
e.	$1\frac{1}{2}$	
f.	$^{-}2\frac{1}{3}$	

7. $6x + {}^{-}3y = {}^{-}12$

	x	y
a.	$^{-}1$	
b.	$\frac{1}{2}$	
c.	$\frac{^{-}2}{3}$	
d.	0	
e.	$\frac{^{-}1}{2}$	
f.	$\frac{5}{6}$	

True or false?

8. (3, $^{-}3$) is in the solution set of $x + y = 6$.

9. The equation $3x + y = 12$ has infinitely many solutions.

See how many different equations you can find that have the ordered pair (4, 3) as a solution.

EXCURSION

A *googol* is one of the largest numbers that have been named. It can be written as 10^{100}, or as 1 followed by 100 zeros. A still larger number is called a *googolplex*. It can be expressed as 1 followed by a googol of zeros. Tell how to write a googolplex as a power of 10.

Supplementary Exercises, Set 73, page 395

Graphing solution sets in the coordinate plane

The equation $x + y = 2$ has infinitely many ordered pairs in its solution set. The table of values below shows only a few solutions.

$x + y = 2$

x	y
−2	4
−1	3
0	2
1	1
2	0
3	−1

Of course, it is impossible to graph all the ordered pairs in the solution set. However, we can graph the ordered pairs given in the table of values and see if they show some kind of pattern.

To graph the solution set we label the first component axis as the x-axis and the second component axis as the y-axis. We then plot the ordered pairs given above. Do you see that the "red points" suggest that the ordered pairs of the solution set lie on a straight line?

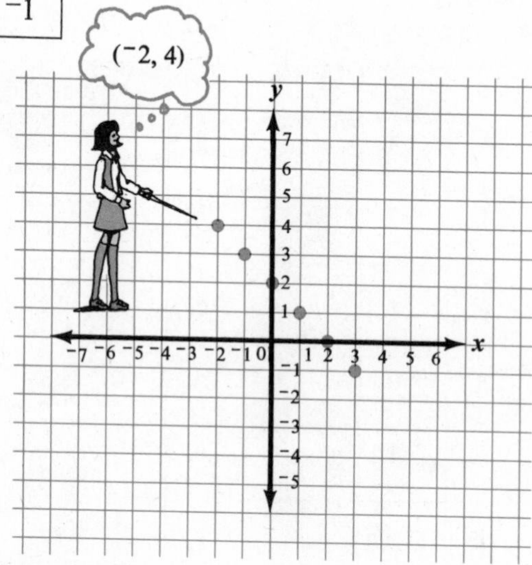

From the observation above we graph the solution set of $x + y = 2$ by drawing a line through the "red points."

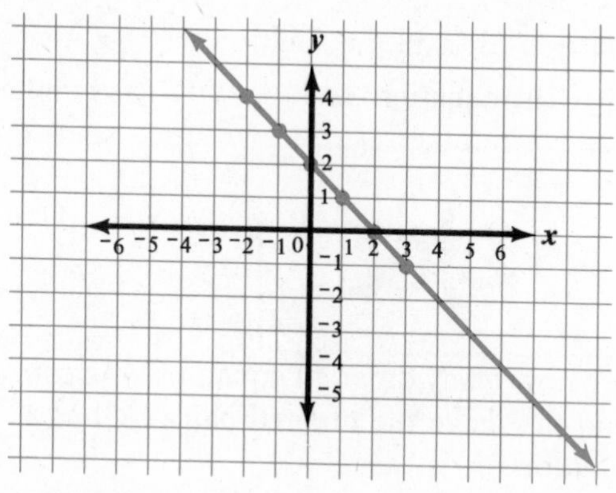

EXERCISES

First complete the table of values. Then graph the solution set.

1. $x + 3y = 6$

x	y
$^-3$	
0	
3	
6	
9	

2. $3x + y = 6$

x	y
$^-2$	
$^-1$	
0	
1	
2	

3. $2x + {}^-3y = 0$

x	y
$^-3$	
$^-2$	
$^-.5$	
0	
.5	

Graph the solution set.

4. $3x + y = 0$

5. $x + {}^-4y = 0$

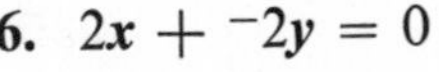

6. $2x + {}^-2y = 0$

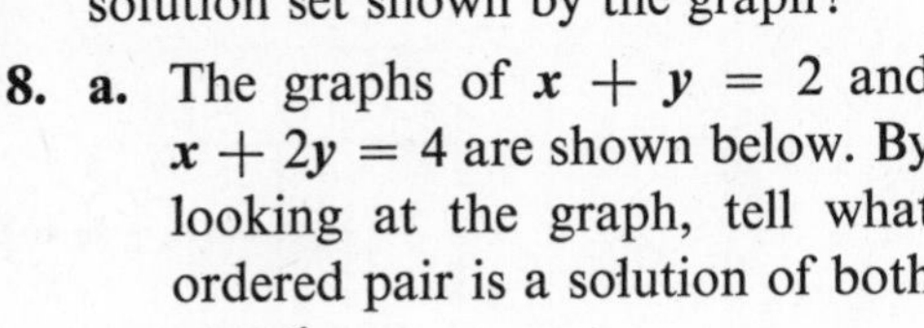

7. Can you find an equation that has the solution set shown by the graph?

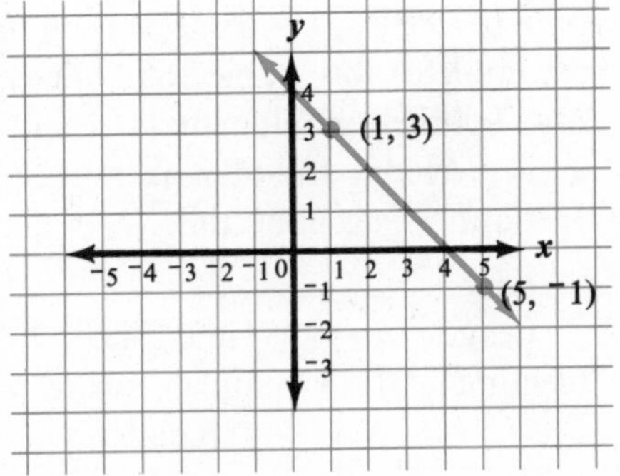

8. a. The graphs of $x + y = 2$ and $x + 2y = 4$ are shown below. By looking at the graph, tell what ordered pair is a solution of both equations.

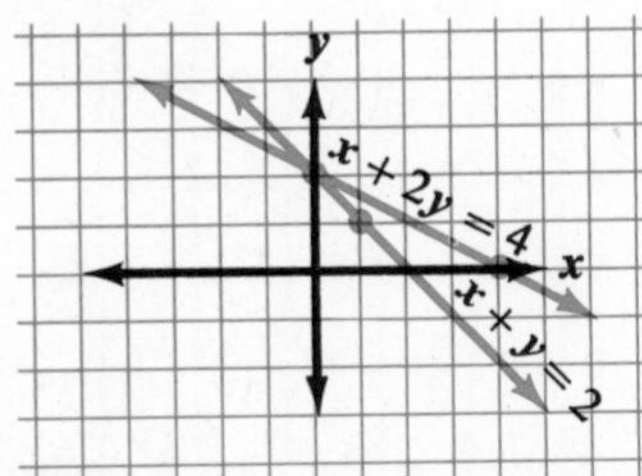

b. What ordered pair is a solution of both $x + y = 1$ and $2x + 3y = 0$? (*Hint:* Graph each solution set.)

Graph the solution set of $xy = 1$. Is the graph a straight line?

CHECKUP
for pages 330–331

Use the divide-and-average method to estimate each square root to the nearest tenth.

1. $\sqrt{19}$
2. $\sqrt{28}$
3. $\sqrt{39}$
4. $\sqrt{50}$
5. $\sqrt{59}$
6. $\sqrt{65}$
7. $\sqrt{72}$
8. $\sqrt{108}$
9. $\sqrt{200}$

Answers on page 428.

Supplementary Exercises, Set 74, page 395

Mathematics and science

From a fixed point, a simple pendulum swings back and forth through an arc.

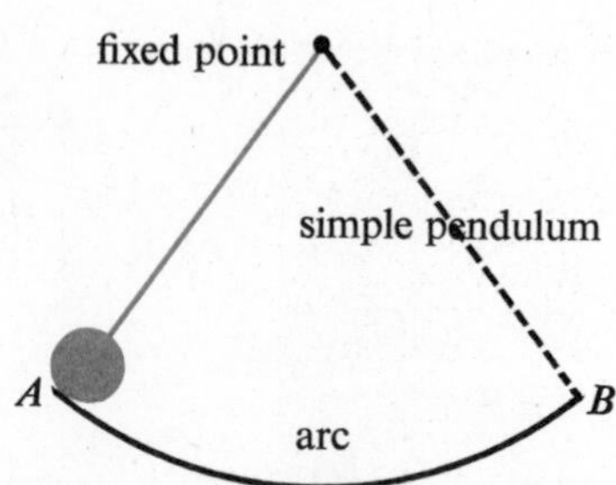

Scientists have learned that the time needed for the pendulum to swing from A to B and then back to A (one complete swing) depends only on the length of the pendulum.

1. Make a simple pendulum by tying a weight to a string. Use your pendulum to complete this table of values. (*Hint:* Let the pendulum make several complete swings and take an average to get a more accurate time.)

Length (centimeters)	Time for a complete swing (seconds)

You may wish to extend the table.

2. Make a graph of your data.

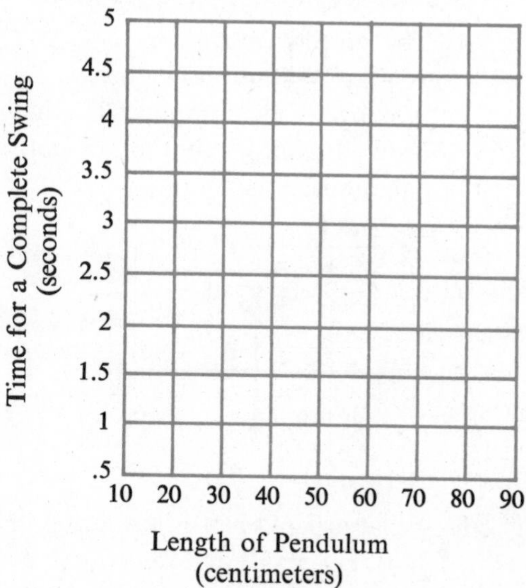

3. The formula for computing the time in seconds of a complete swing of a simple pendulum is $T = 2\pi\sqrt{\frac{L}{980}}$, where L is the length of the pendulum in centimeters. Compute the time for a complete swing for the following pendulum lengths. Use 3.14 as an approximation for π.

a. 980 cm **b.** 3920 cm **c.** 245 cm 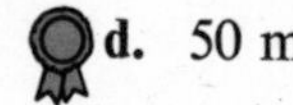 **d.** 50 m

CHAPTER CHECKUP

True or false? [*pages 320–325*]

1. A rational number is a number that can be expressed as the quotient of two integers.
2. Every rational number can be written as a terminating decimal.
3. Between any two rational numbers there is another rational number.
4. An irrational number is a number that can be expressed by a nonterminating, repeating decimal.
5. The set of all rational numbers, together with the set of all irrational numbers, makes up the set of real numbers.
6. All integers are both rational numbers and real numbers.
7. Some irrational numbers are also rational numbers.
8. Each point on a number line corresponds to exactly one real number, and each real number corresponds to exactly one point on a number line.

Match each open sentence with the graph of its solution set. [*pages 328–329*]

9. $y \leq 4$ 10. $y \geq 4$

11. $y > 4$ 12. $y < 4$

a. (number line from $^-1$ to 5)

b. 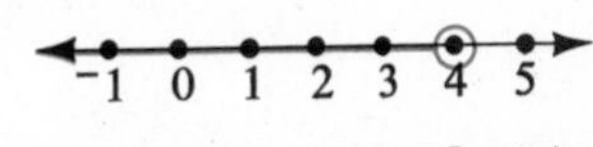

c. 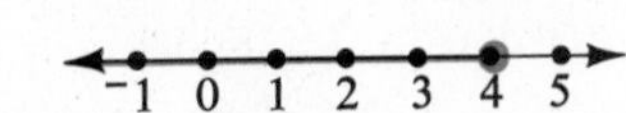

d. (number line from $^-1$ to 5)

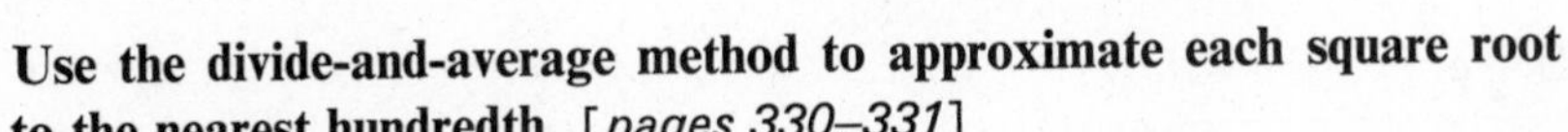

Use the divide-and-average method to approximate each square root to the nearest hundredth. [*pages 330–331*]

13. $\sqrt{56}$ 14. $\sqrt{32}$ 15. $\sqrt{75}$ 16. $\sqrt{130}$ 17. $\sqrt{196}$

Give the coordinates of: [*page 332*]

18. point A 19. point B 20. point C
21. point D 22. point E 23. point F
24. point G 25. point H 26. point I

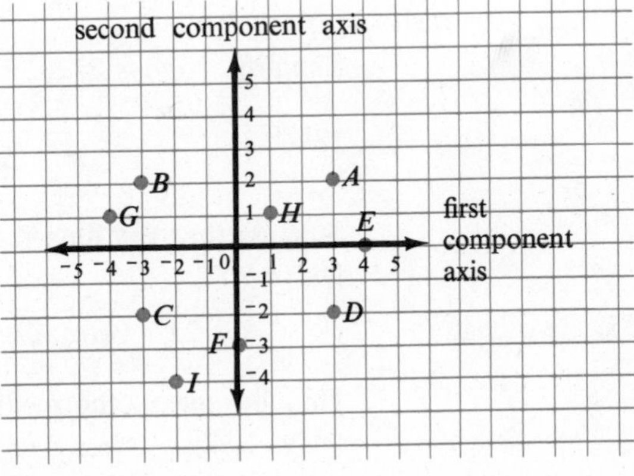

27. a. Copy and complete this table of values. [*page 334*]

$$^-2x + 4y = 8$$

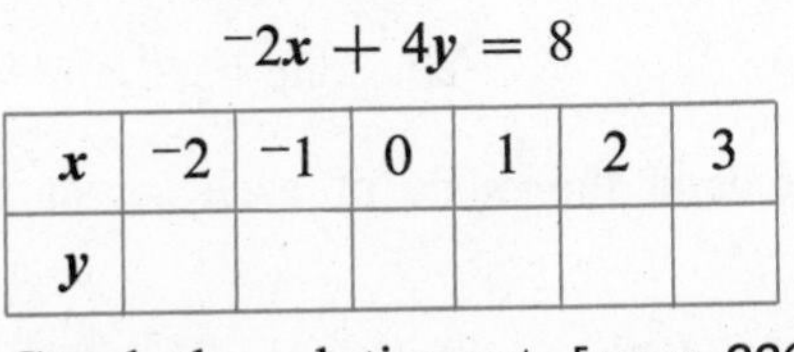

x	$^-2$	$^-1$	0	1	2	3
y						

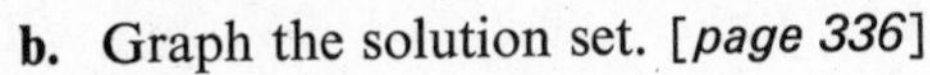

b. Graph the solution set. [*page 336*]

MAJOR CHECKUP

$f: x \rightarrow x^2 - 5$ $\quad g: x \rightarrow 3x + 6$ $\quad h: x \rightarrow \frac{2x - 1}{2}$

Complete. [*pages 24–27*]

1. $f(3) = \underline{\ ?\ }$
2. $g(4) = \underline{\ ?\ }$
3. $h(9) = \underline{\ ?\ }$
4. $f(9) = \underline{\ ?\ }$
5. $g\left(\frac{2}{3}\right) = \underline{\ ?\ }$
6. $h\left(\frac{5}{2}\right) = \underline{\ ?\ }$

Give each sum or difference in lowest terms. [*pages 100, 108–111*]

7. $\frac{3}{5} + \frac{1}{2}$
8. $\frac{3}{4} + \frac{2}{3}$
9. $2 - \frac{5}{8}$
10. $\frac{5}{6} - \frac{3}{4}$

Give each product or quotient in lowest terms. [*pages 118–121, 124*]

11. $\frac{3}{8} \times \frac{8}{3}$
12. $\frac{5}{6} \times \frac{3}{10}$
13. $\frac{5}{4} \div \frac{3}{2}$
14. $\frac{7}{5} \div \frac{21}{10}$

Copy and complete the following table. [*pages 200–203*]

15.

Unit used for measurement	Measurement	Greatest possible error	Relative error
inch	9 inches		
$\frac{1}{2}$ inch	$6\frac{1}{2}$ inches		

Solve. [*page 248*]

16. A merchant borrowed \$9000 from a bank at 12% simple interest for a period of 1 year. How much did he owe the bank at the end of one year?

Simplify. [*pages 272–279*]

17. $^-3 + \frac{^-2}{5}$
18. $\frac{5}{6} \times \frac{^-2}{5}$
19. $\frac{3}{8} - \frac{^-5}{4}$
20. $^-6 \div \frac{^-2}{3}$

Suppose that you flipped two coins. What is the probability of getting: [*page 302*]

21. two heads?
22. two tails?
23. one head and one tail?

Find the mean, the median, and the mode of each set of numbers. [*page 312*]

24. 5, 8, 3, 5, 7
25. 2, 9, 11, 8, 3, 7
26. 5, 5, 9, 13, 8

1. Find out the cost of lunch in your school.

2. Complete this table of values.

Number of lunches	Cost
0	$0
1	
2	
3	
4	

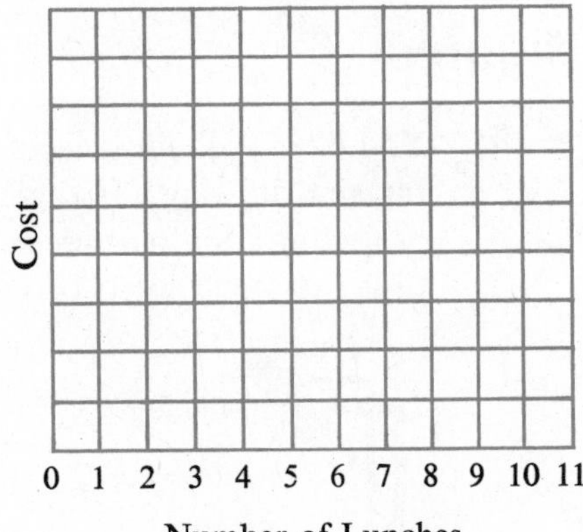

3. Use your completed table of values to make a lunches-to-cost graph like the one shown. (*Hint:* Your graph should not be a line, since you are probably not allowed to buy, for example, $\frac{1}{2}$ of a lunch.)
4. Do the points on your graph "line up"?

Remember that distance equals rate multiplied by time

$$d = rt$$

or that $\frac{d}{t} = r$.

1. Complete this table of values for a 60-mile trip. Find the rates for times (in hours) of 3, 4, . . ., 9, 10.

Time (in hours)	Rate (in mph)
1	60
2	30
3	

2. Use your completed table of values to make a time-rate graph for a 60-mile trip.
3. Do the points on your graph "line up"?
4. Draw a curve through the points.
5. From your graph estimate the rate you would need to travel to complete the 60-mile trip in 1.5 hours. In 2.5 hours.

12 Geometry – Similarity

Similar figures

You have probably seen an overhead projector used in your school. Imagine drawing a triangle on a transparent sheet of plastic and then projecting it onto a screen.

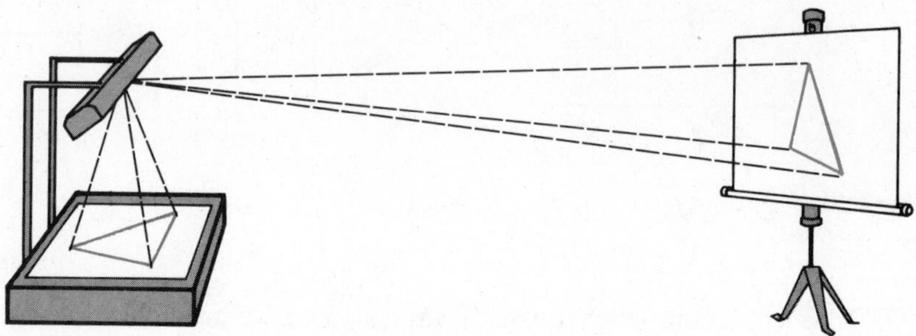

The figure on the screen is an **image** of the figure on the plastic sheet. The figures are the **same shape**, but they are not necessarily the same size. Two figures that are the same shape are called **similar figures**.

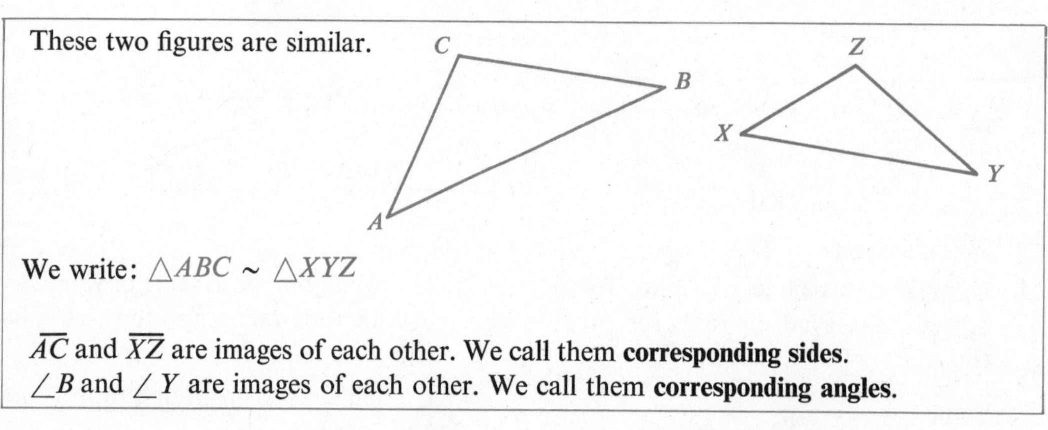

These two figures are similar.

We write: $\triangle ABC \sim \triangle XYZ$

$\overline{AC}$ and $\overline{XZ}$ are images of each other. We call them **corresponding sides**.
$\angle B$ and $\angle Y$ are images of each other. We call them **corresponding angles**.

These two figures are not similar.

These two figures are similar. They are also congruent.

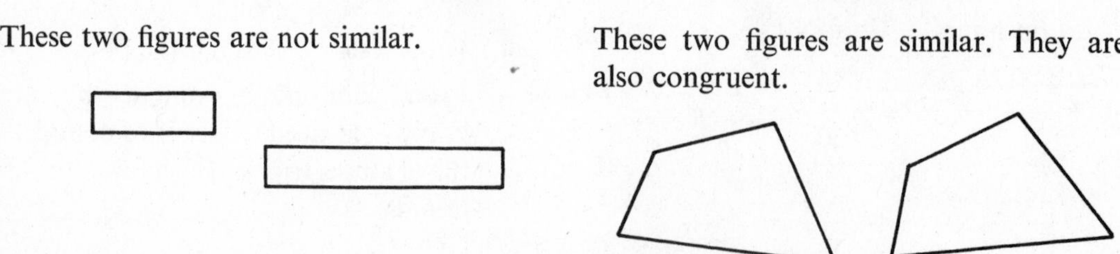

EXERCISES

Are the two figures similar?

1\. 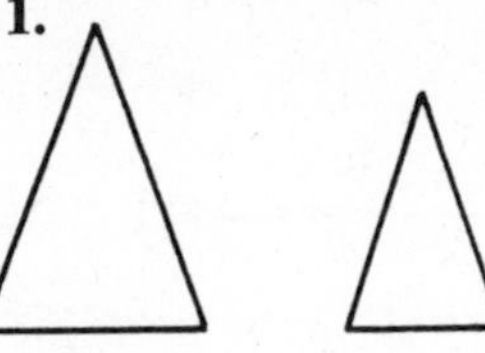

2\. 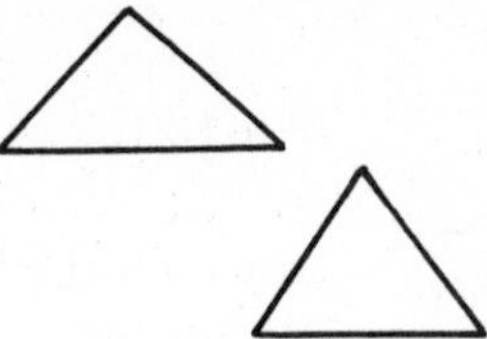

3\. 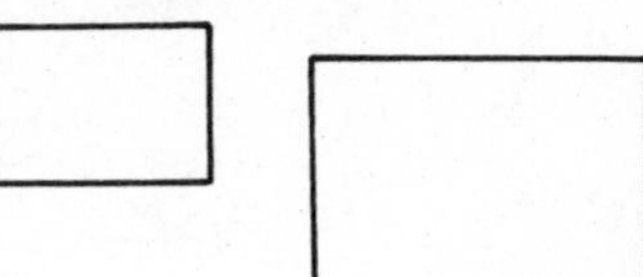

4\. 5. 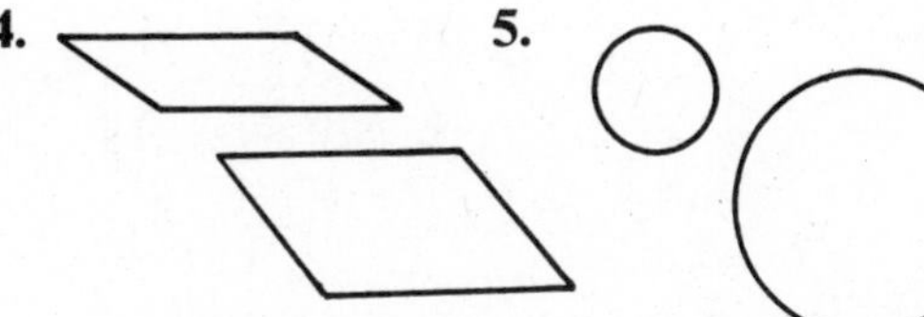

6\. 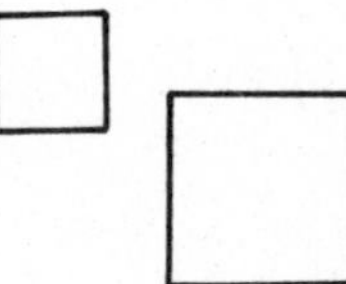

The two figures below are similar. Complete each sentence.

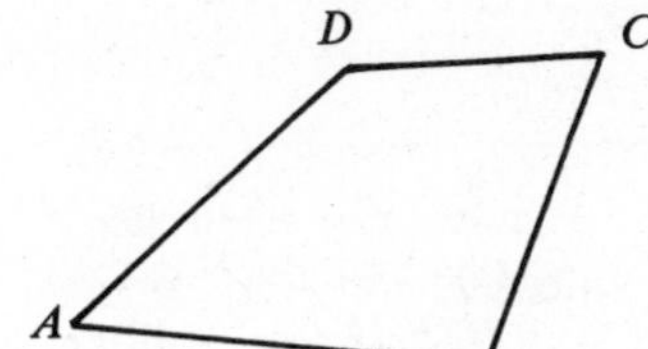

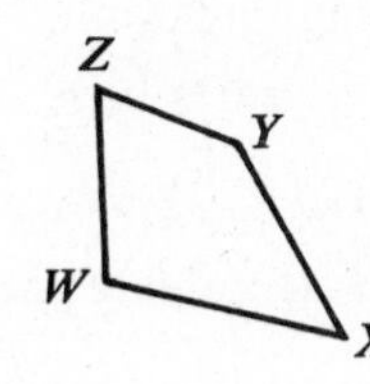

7. __?__ is the image of $\overline{BC}$.
8. $\overline{ZY}$ and __?__ are corresponding sides.
9. __?__ is the image of $\angle W$.
10. $\angle X$ and __?__ are corresponding angles.

These two triangles are similar. Answer each question.

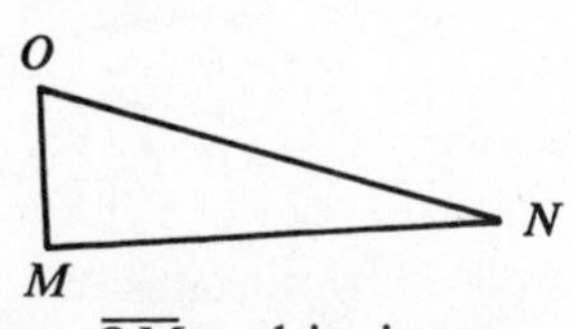

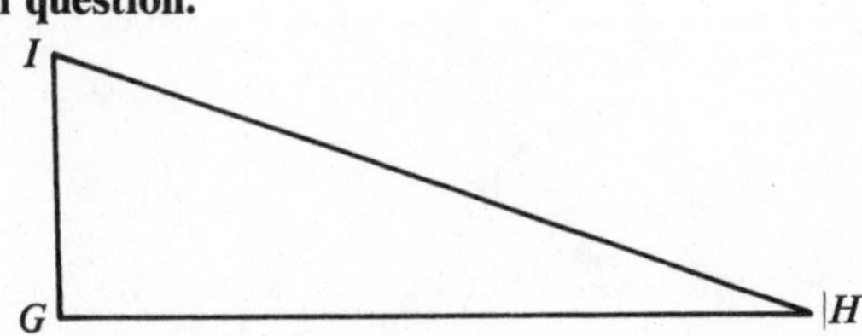

11. Measure $\overline{OM}$ and its image.
12. What is the ratio of the length of $\overline{OM}$ to the length of its image?
13. Repeat with $\overline{MN}$ and its image.
14. Repeat with $\overline{ON}$ and its image.
15. What can you say about the ratios of corresponding sides of similar triangles?
16. Measure $\angle M$ and its image.
17. Repeat with $\angle N$ and its image.
18. Repeat with $\angle O$ and its image.
19. What can you say about corresponding angles of similar triangles?

Skill Maintenance, Set 74, page 417

Properties of similar triangles

These two triangles are similar.

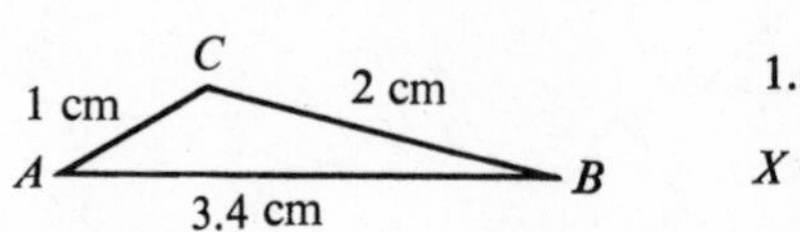

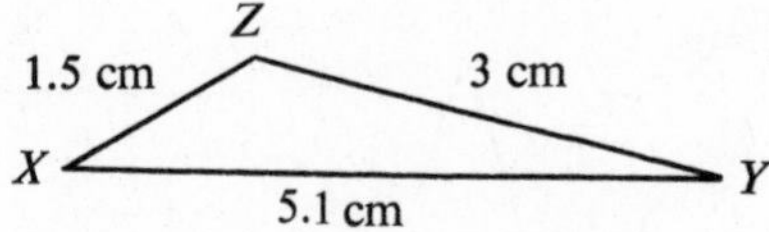

Notice the ratios of the lengths of corresponding sides.

Read as "measure of segment BC."

$$\frac{m(\overline{BC})}{m(\overline{YZ})} = \frac{2}{3} \qquad \frac{m(\overline{AB})}{m(\overline{XY})} = \frac{3.4}{5.1} = \frac{2}{3} \qquad \frac{m(\overline{AC})}{m(\overline{XZ})} = \frac{1}{1.5} = \frac{2}{3}$$

Measure the pairs of corresponding angles. You will find that

$$\angle A \cong \angle X \qquad \angle B \cong \angle Y \qquad \angle C \cong \angle Z$$

In similar figures:

corresponding angles are congruent;
corresponding sides have equal ratios.

Because corresponding sides have equal ratios, we can often use proportions to compute the lengths of some sides.

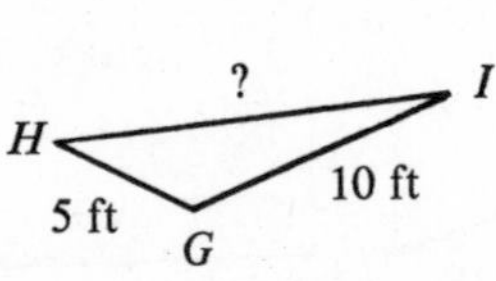

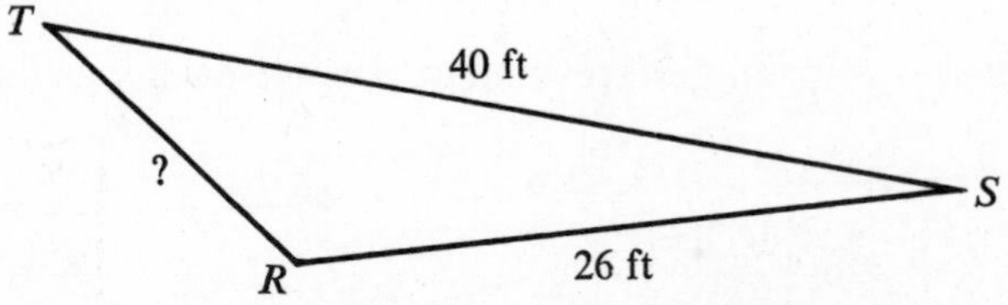

We can find $m(\overline{TR})$ because we know the lengths of two corresponding sides and the length of the image of $\overline{TR}$.

$$\frac{m(\overline{GI})}{m(\overline{RS})} = \frac{m(\overline{HG})}{m(\overline{TR})}$$

$$\frac{10}{26} = \frac{5}{x}$$

$$10x = 130$$

$$x = 13$$

$$m(\overline{TR}) = 13 \text{ ft}$$

We can find $m(\overline{HI})$ because we know the lengths of two corresponding sides and the length of the image of $\overline{HI}$.

$$\frac{m(\overline{GI})}{m(\overline{RS})} = \frac{m(\overline{HI})}{m(\overline{TS})}$$

$$\frac{10}{26} = \frac{x}{40}$$

$$26x = 400$$

$$x = 15\frac{5}{13}$$

$$m(\overline{HI}) = 15\frac{5}{13} \text{ ft}$$

We could have written the proportion: $\frac{m(\overline{GI})}{m(\overline{HI})} = \frac{m(\overline{RS})}{m(\overline{TS})}$

EXERCISES

These two triangles are similar.

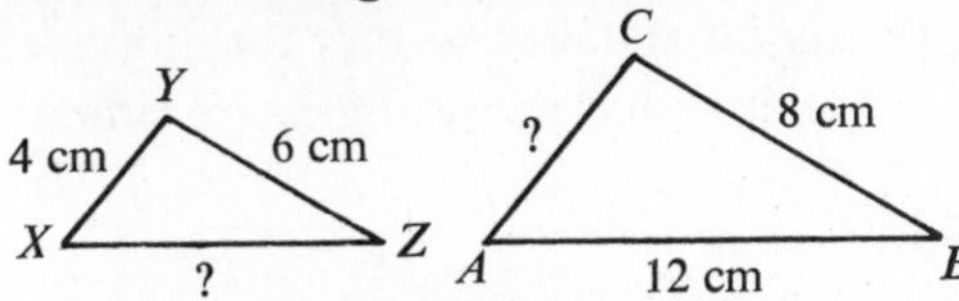

1. Find a pair of corresponding sides with both lengths given.
2. What side corresponds to $\overline{XZ}$?
3. Write a proportion using the lengths of the four sides from exercises 1 and 2.
4. How long is $\overline{XZ}$?
5. How long is $\overline{AC}$, to the nearest .1 cm?
6. If $\angle A$ is a 50° angle, what other angle is a 50° angle?
7. If $\angle Z$ is a 30° angle, what other angle is a 30° angle?

The two figures in each exercise are similar. Find the missing lengths. Round answers to the nearest tenth unit. In some cases there may not be enough information to find the length.

8.

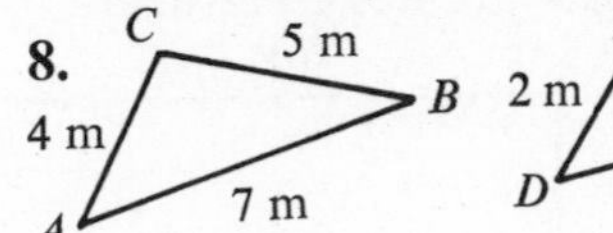

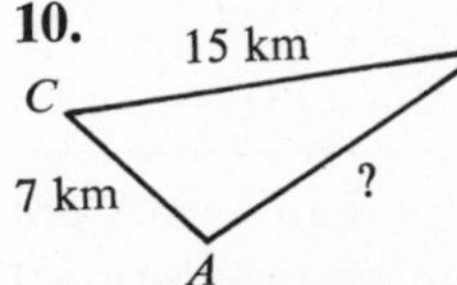

9.

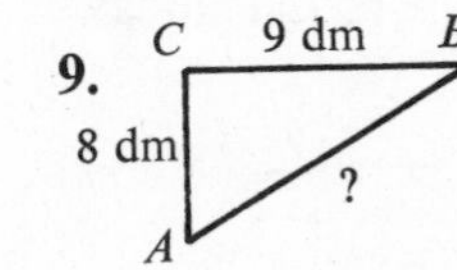

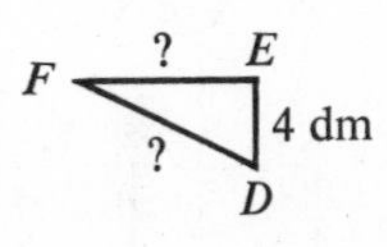

10.

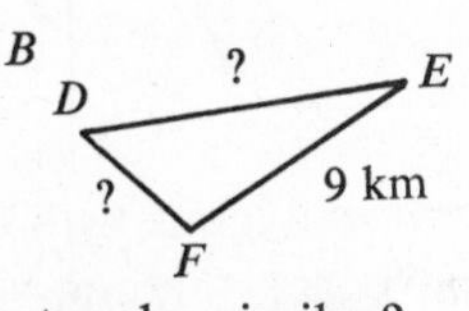

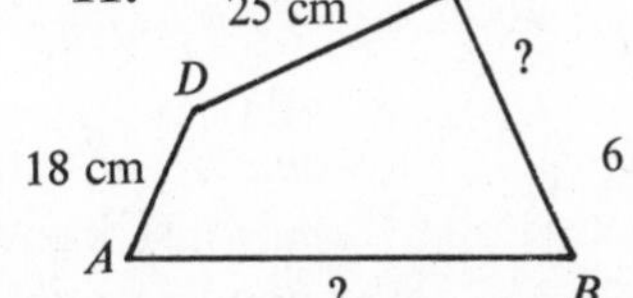

11.

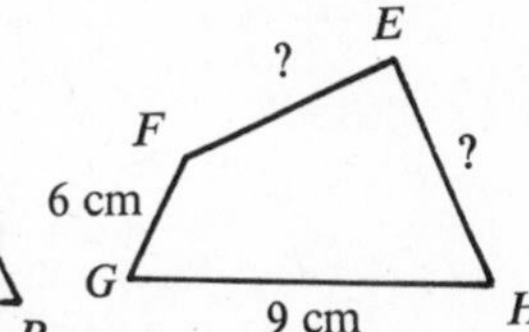

12. Are these two rectangles similar?

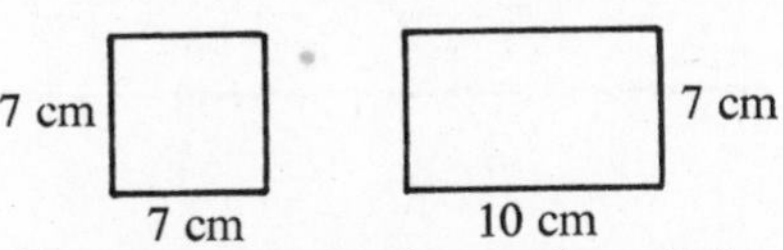

13. Can you match the angles of the first rectangle with the angles of the second so that the two angles of each pair are congruent?
14. Can you match the sides of the first rectangle to the sides of the second so that all the pairs are proportional?
15. Repeat exercises 12–14 with these two parallelograms.

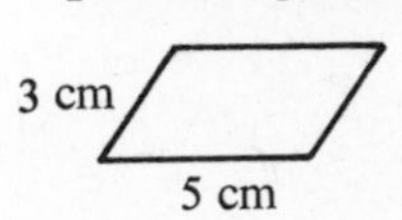

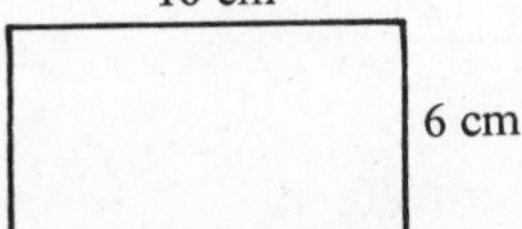

EXCURSION

Cut a circular piece of cardboard about 5 centimeters in diameter.

Hold the circular cardboard parallel to a wall and use a flashlight to make a shadow of the circle on the wall.

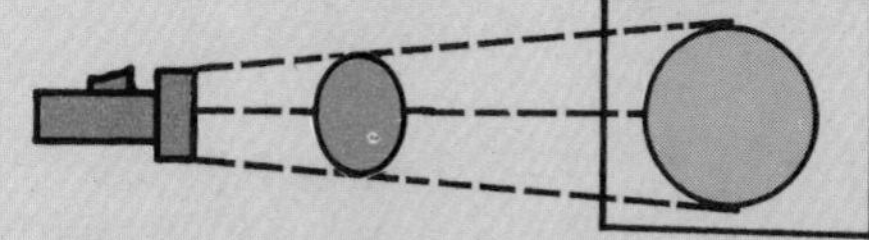

Move the cardboard nearer to and then farther from the wall. Tilt the cardboard.

Write a report with pictures to show what changes occur in the shadow.

Supplementary Exercises, Set 75, page 395

Similar polygons

If you know that two *triangles* can be matched so that the angles of the pair are congruent, then you know that the triangles are similar.

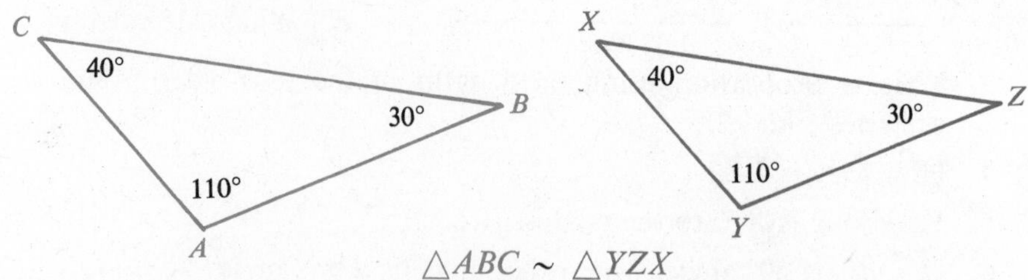

$\triangle ABC \sim \triangle YZX$

Exercises 12–15 on page 345 show you that this is *not* true for 4-sided figures.

These two figures have matching pairs of congruent angles, but they are not similar. The pairs of sides are not proportional.

These two figures have matching pairs of proportional sides, but they are not similar. The angles are not congruent.

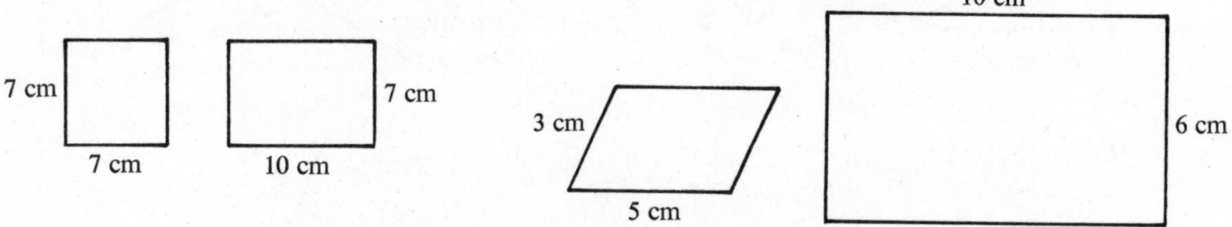

In order to know that two polygons with more than 3 sides are similar, you must know that corresponding sides are proportional *and* corresponding angles are congruent.

EXERCISES

Are the figures similar?

1. **2.** **3.**

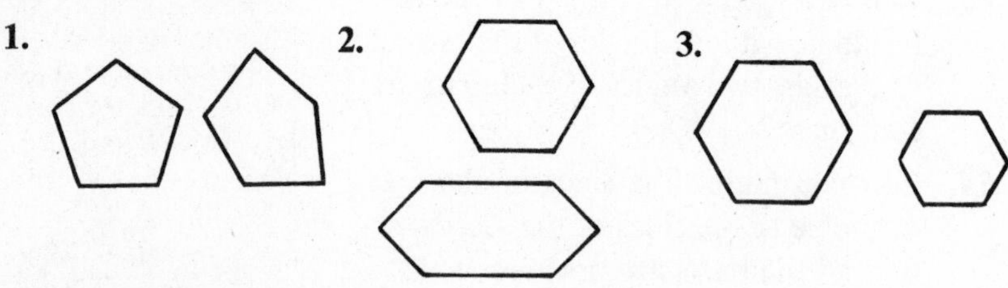

True or false?

4. All squares are similar.
5. All rectangles are similar.
6. All parallelograms are similar.

7. All equilateral triangles are similar.
8. All right triangles are similar.
9. All pentagons are similar.

10. All circles are similar.

The figures are similar. Find the missing lengths to the nearest .1 unit.

11.

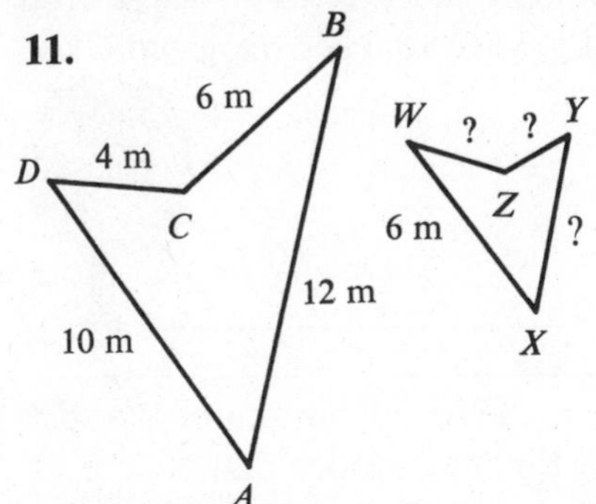

12.

Remember that the sum of the angle measures of a triangle is 180°. In these exercises you are given two of the angles. Find the third.

13. 90°, 30°
14. 90°, 45°
15. 60°, 60°
16. 50°, 38°
17. 110°, 35°
18. 145°, 27°
19. 27° 18′, 59° 17′
20. 93° 16′ 16″, 46° 19′ 41″
21. $\triangle ABC$ has a 50° angle and a 70° angle. $\triangle XYZ$ also has a 50° angle and a 70° angle. Are the triangles similar?
22. Suppose that two *right* triangles have 45° angles too. Are they similar?
23. Suppose that two *right* triangles also have 30° angles. Are they similar?

These two squares are similar.

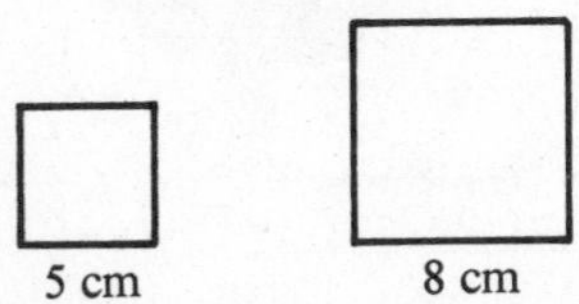

24. What is the ratio of corresponding sides?
25. What is the ratio of the perimeters?
26. What is the ratio of the areas?

EXCURSION

Repeat the Excursion on page 345, using a square instead of a circle.

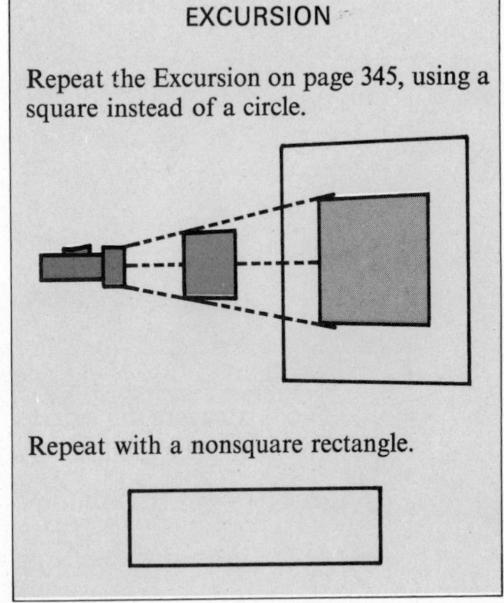

Repeat with a nonsquare rectangle.

Skill Maintenance, Set 75, page 417

Indirect measurement

Similar triangles can be used to find lengths that would be difficult to measure directly. For example, suppose that you wish to know the height of a tree. You could, perhaps, climb to the top with a tape measure, but that might not be wise. Here is a better way.

Get a meter stick. Find a spot where you can sight from the ground and line up the top of the stick and the top of the tree as shown in the picture. Be sure that the stick touches the ground and is vertical.

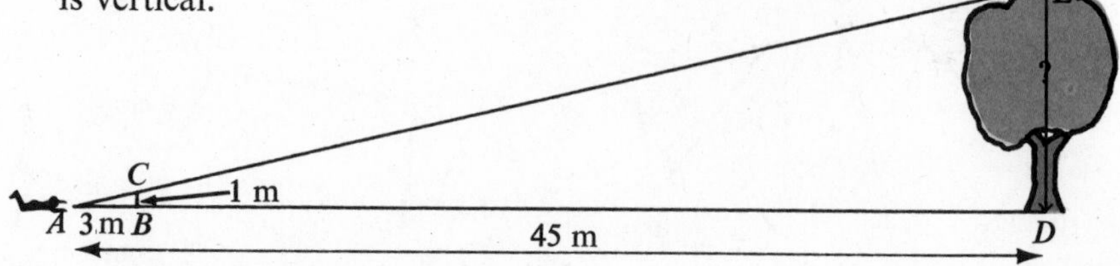

Measure the distances from your eye to the bottom of the stick and from your eye to the bottom of the tree. Notice that

$$\triangle ABC \sim \triangle ADE.$$

Therefore, $$\frac{m(\overline{AB})}{m(\overline{AD})} = \frac{m(\overline{BC})}{m(\overline{DE})}$$

$$\frac{3}{45} = \frac{1}{x}$$

$$3x = 45$$

$x = 15$ The tree is 15 meters tall.

Another way to do the problem is to work with the shadows.

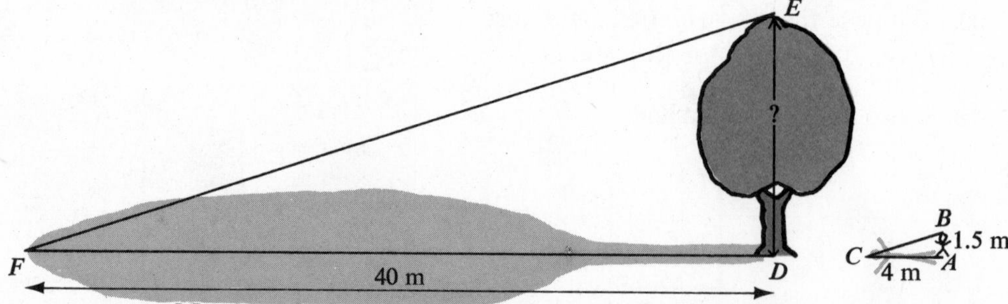

Measure the length of the tree's shadow, your height, and the length of your shadow. Notice that $\triangle ABC \sim \triangle DEF$.

$$\frac{m(\overline{AB})}{m(\overline{DE})} = \frac{m(\overline{AC})}{m(\overline{DF})}$$

$$\frac{1.5}{x} = \frac{4}{40}$$

$$4x = 60$$

$x = 15$ The tree is 15 meters tall.

EXERCISES

1. A building casts a 450-foot shadow while a 6-foot man casts a 9-foot shadow. How tall is the building?

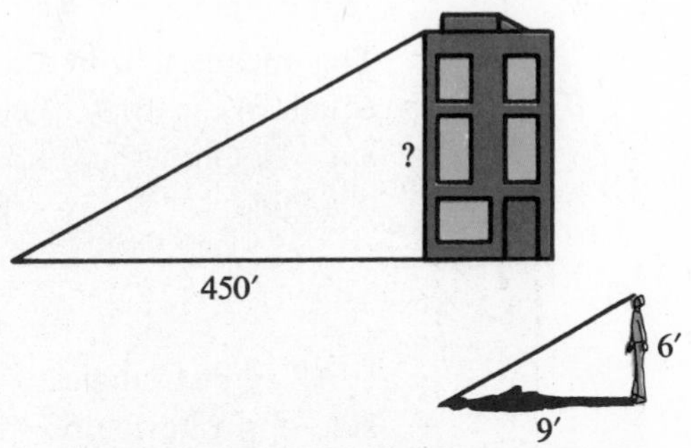

2. How tall is this flagpole?

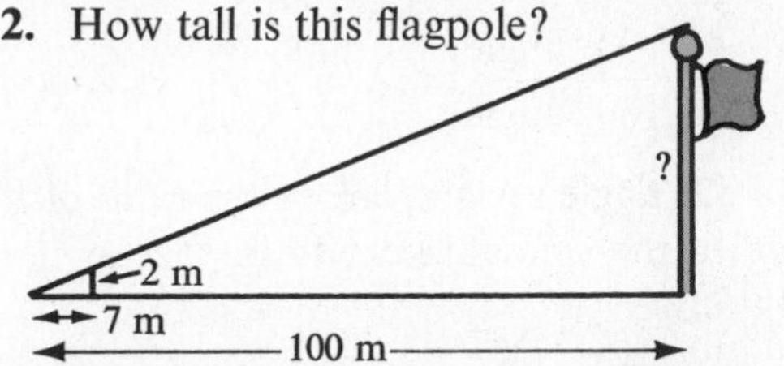

3. How tall is this tree?

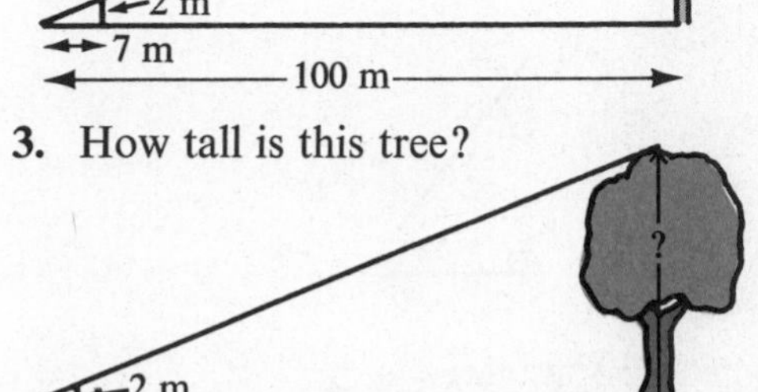

The ratio of two lengths is given. Find the missing length.

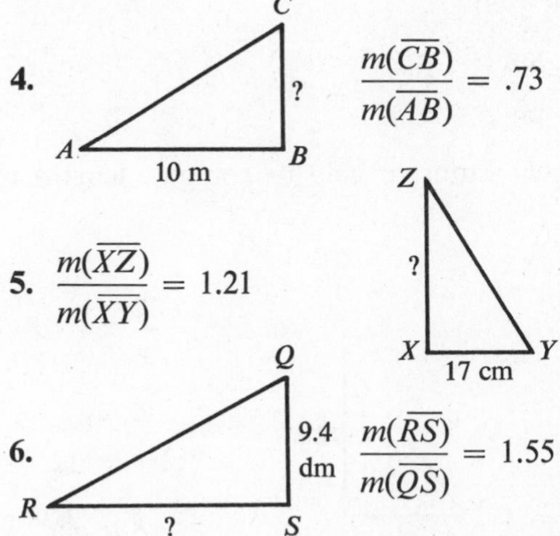

4. $\frac{m(\overline{CB})}{m(\overline{AB})} = .73$

5. $\frac{m(\overline{XZ})}{m(\overline{XY})} = 1.21$

6. $\frac{m(\overline{RS})}{m(\overline{QS})} = 1.55$

CHECKUP
for pages 342–347

Are the two figures similar?

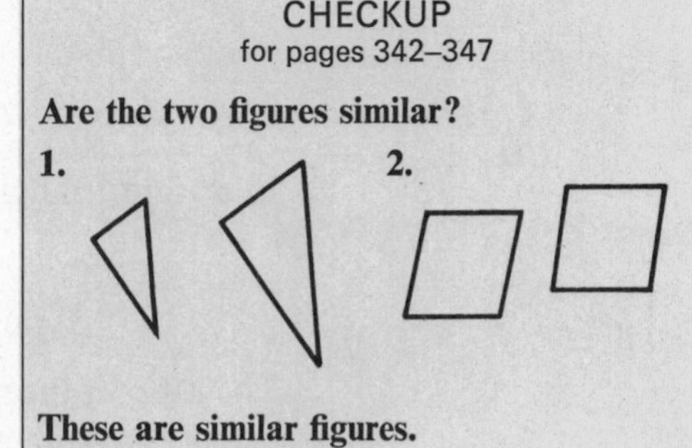

These are similar figures.

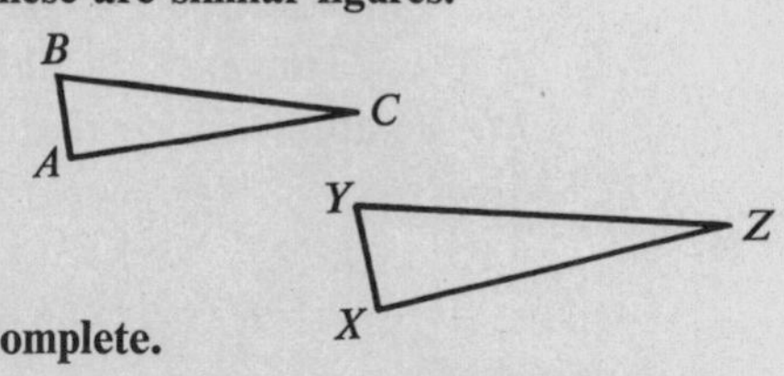

Complete.

3. $\overline{BC}$ and _?_ are corresponding parts.
4. $\angle X$ and _?_ are corresponding parts.
5. These are similar figures. Find the length of $\overline{AB}$.

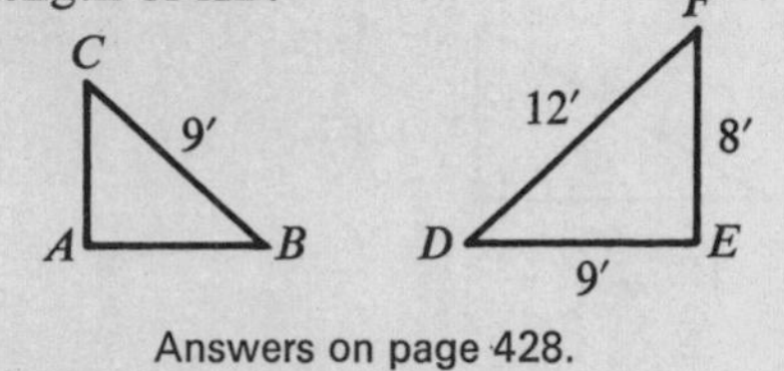

Answers on page 428.

Skill Maintenance, Set 76, page 418

Tangent ratios

All right triangles with a 30° angle are similar. (What is the measure of the other acute angle in each triangle?)

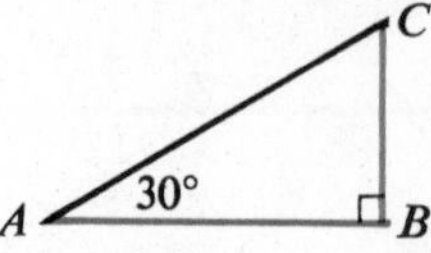

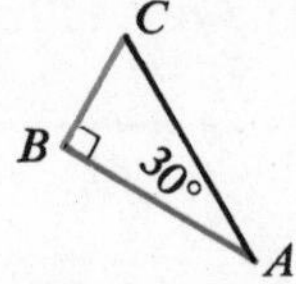

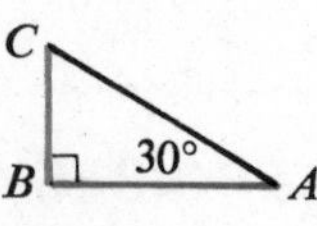

This means that in all these triangles the ratios $m(\overline{CB}) : m(\overline{AB})$ are equal. We call $\overline{BC}$ (shown in red) the **side opposite** the 30° angle, and $\overline{AB}$ (shown in blue) the **side adjacent** to the 30° angle. In a right triangle

$$\frac{\text{side opposite (30° angle)}}{\text{side adjacent (30° angle)}} \approx .58$$

All right triangles with a 52° angle are similar, so the ratio of the side opposite the 52° angle to the side adjacent to the 52° angle is the same in all these triangles.

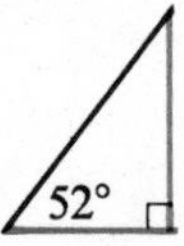

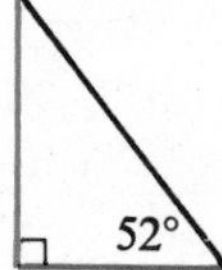

In a right triangle:

$$\frac{\text{side opposite (52° angle)}}{\text{side adjacent (52° angle)}} \approx 1.28$$

The ratio of the side opposite an acute angle to the side adjacent to the acute angle in a right triangle is called the **tangent** of the angle. "Tangent" is abbreviated "tan." We can shorten the statements about ratios that are given above:

$$\tan 30° \approx .58$$

$$\tan 52° \approx 1.28$$

We can use the tangent ratios to help us compute lengths of sides of right triangles.

Examples.

(1)

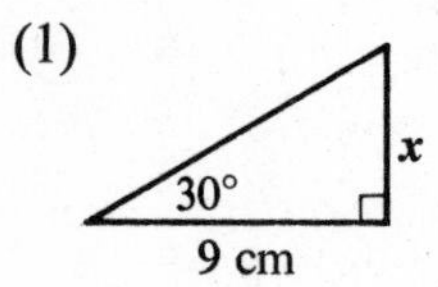

$\tan 30° = \frac{x}{9} \approx .58$

$x \approx 5.22$ cm

(2)

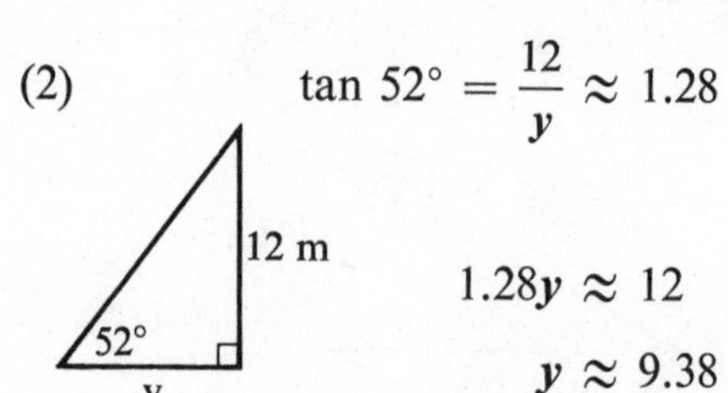

$\tan 52° = \frac{12}{y} \approx 1.28$

$1.28y \approx 12$

$y \approx 9.38$ m

EXERCISES

Name the side opposite the given angle and the side adjacent to the given angle.

1.

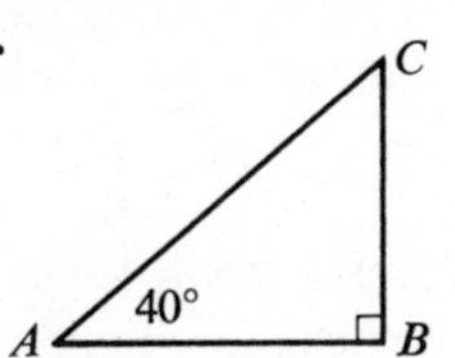

2.

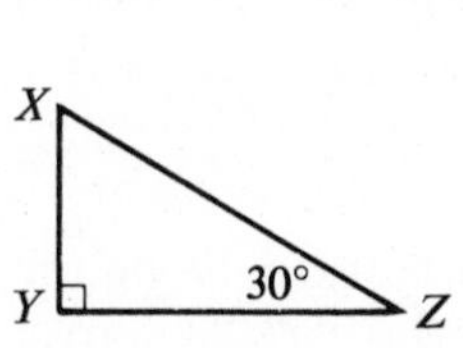

3.

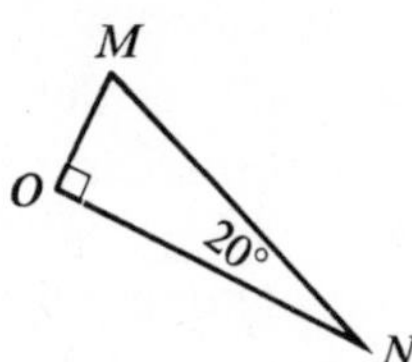

Find the missing lengths. Use the table of tangent ratios given at the right.

Some tangent ratios

tan 10° ≈	.18
tan 20° ≈	.36
tan 30° ≈	.58
tan 40° ≈	.84
tan 50° ≈	1.19
tan 60° ≈	1.73
tan 70° ≈	2.75
tan 80° ≈	5.67

4.

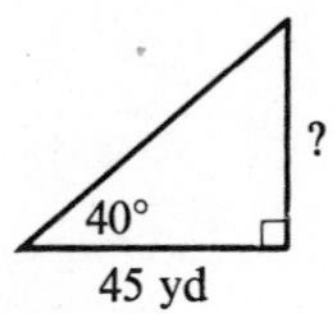

5.

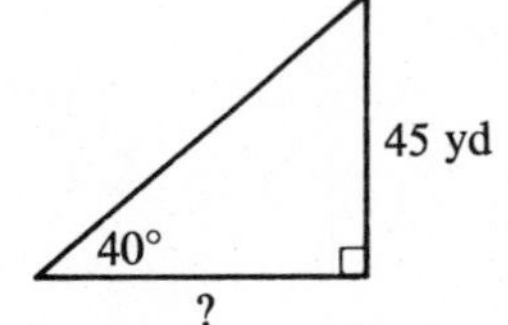

6.

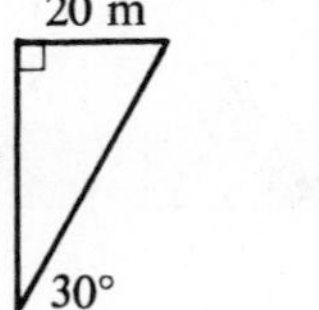

7.

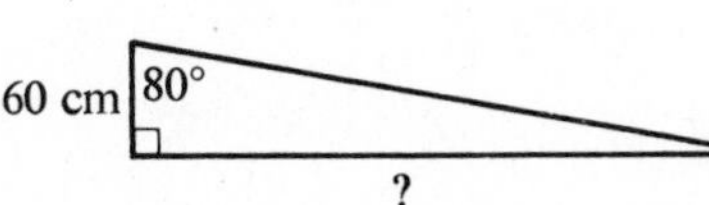

8.

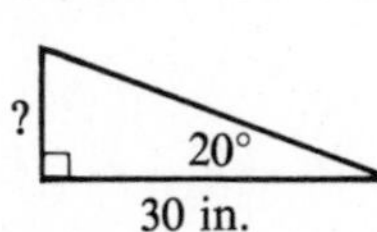

9.

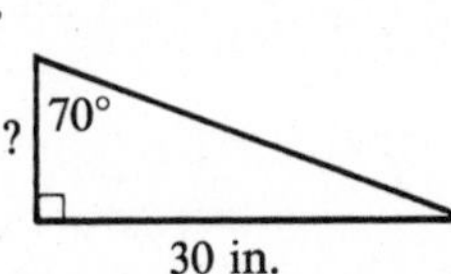

10.

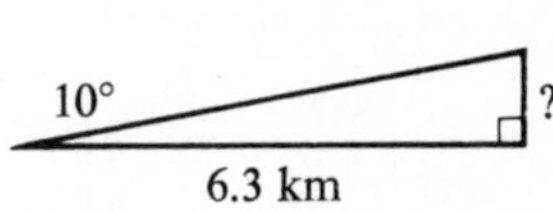

11.

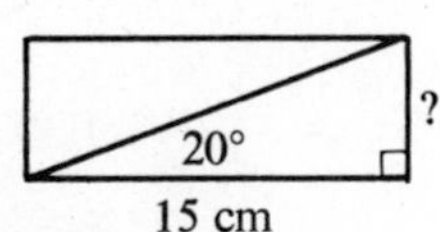

12.

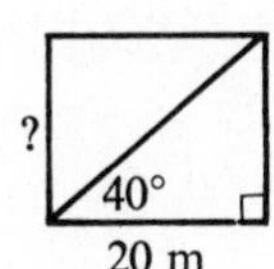

13.

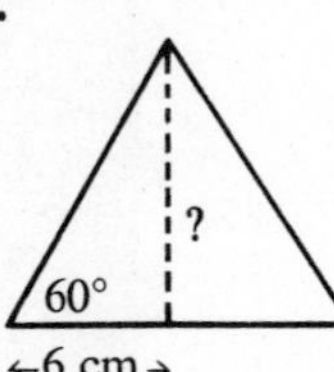

14.

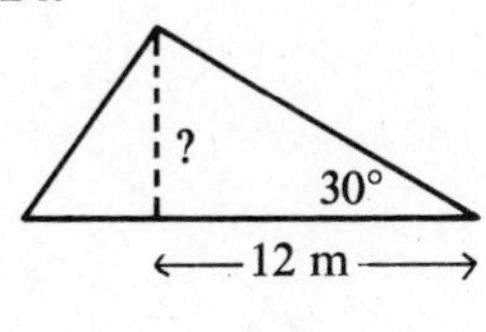

15. Look at the table of tangent ratios. Guess the solution of this equation:

$$\tan x^\circ = 1$$

Can you prove that your answer is correct?

EXCURSION

Repeat the Excursion on page 345, using a cubical block instead of a flat piece of cardboard.

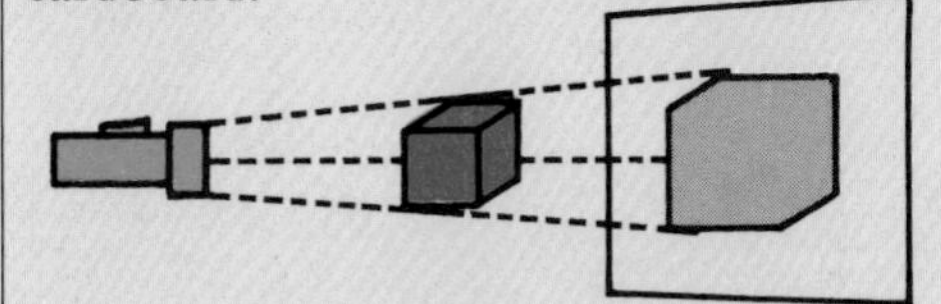

Can you make a square shadow?
Can you make another kind of rectangle?
Can you make triangles?

Supplementary Exercises, Set 76, page 396

Using tangent ratios

On page 348 you learned to use similar triangles to help find lengths that would be difficult to measure directly. That was an example of an **indirect measurement**. The tangent ratios can also be used in indirect measurement. Study these examples.

Example 1. An airplane is flying directly over a small town. A man who is 10 kilometers away can look directly at the airplane by sighting 30° above horizontal. How high is the airplane?

$$\frac{x}{10} = \tan 30^\circ$$

$$\frac{x}{10} \approx .58$$

$$x \approx 5.8$$

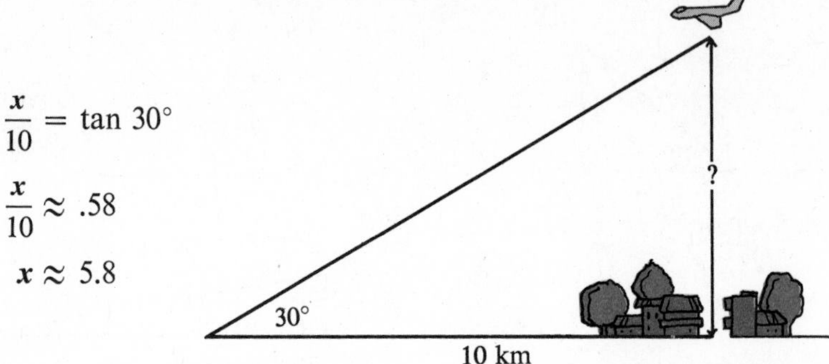

The plane is about 5.8 kilometers above the ground.

Example 2. How far away from an 800-foot building would you have to stand in order to see the top by sighting 40° above horizontal?

$$\frac{800}{x} = \tan 40^\circ$$

$$\frac{800}{x} \approx .84$$

$$800 \approx .84x$$

$$952.4 \approx x$$

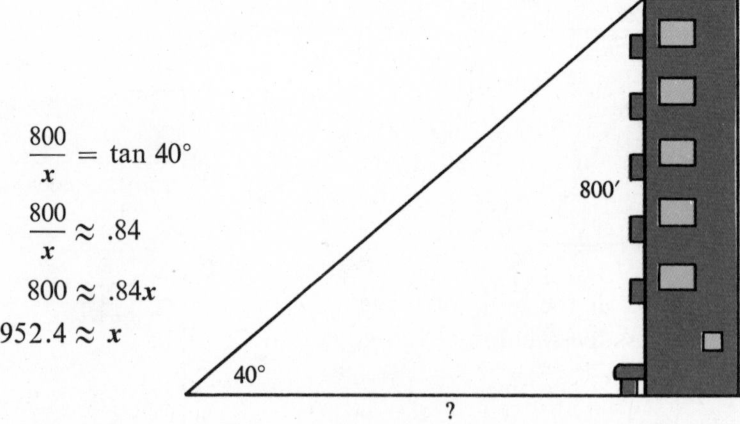

You would have to stand about 952 feet away.

EXERCISES

1. How tall is this tree?

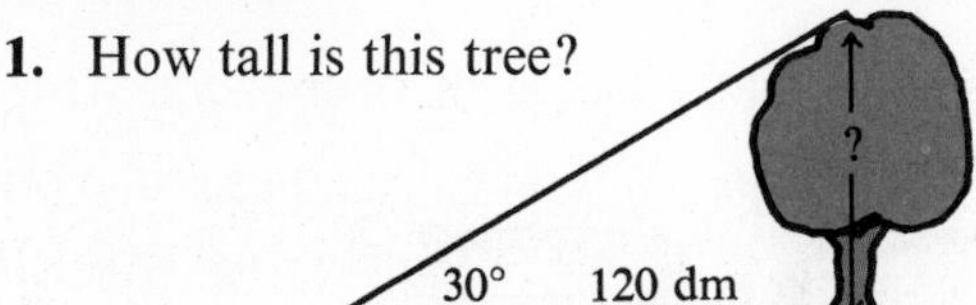

2. How tall is a fire tower, if someone standing 600 feet away can look directly at the top by sighting 20° above horizontal?

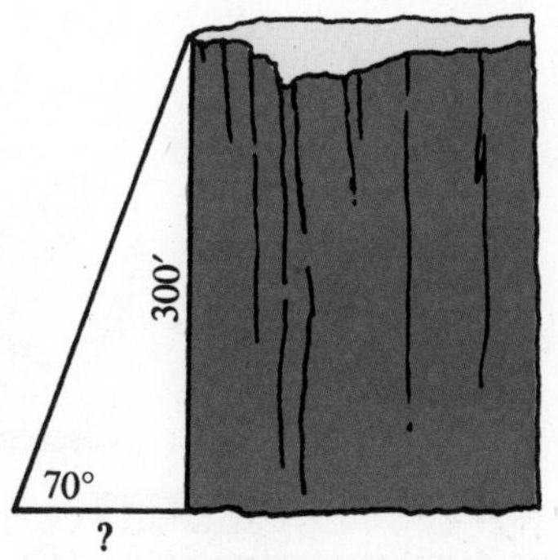

3. How far away from a 300-foot cliff would you have to stand in order to look directly at the top by sighting 70° above horizontal?

4. A cloud is directly above Jill's house. Jill, who is standing 500 meters away, can look directly at the cloud by sighting 70° above horizontal. How high above the ground is the cloud?

5. Jim's eyes are 6 feet above the ground. He is standing 40 feet from the base of a flagpole. He can look directly at the top of the pole by turning his eyes up 60° from horizontal. How tall is the flagpole?

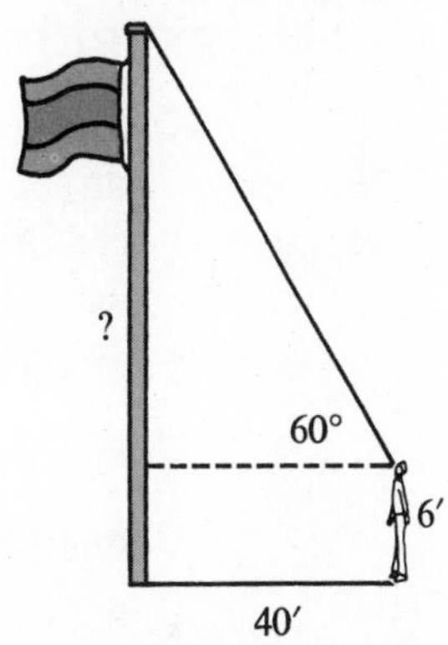

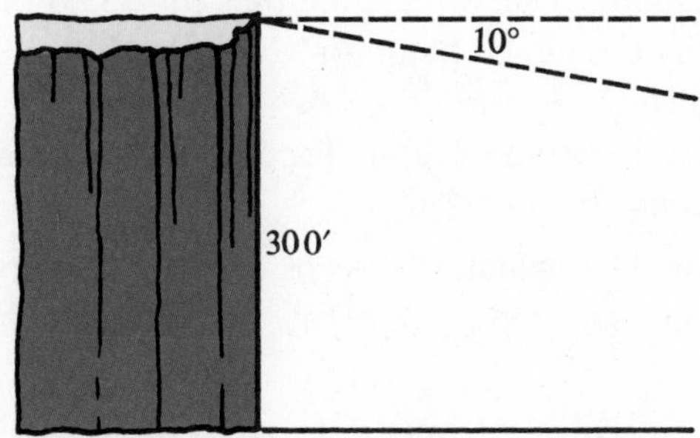

6. From the top of a 300-foot cliff Kay could see her house by turning her eyes down 10° from horizontal. How far was her house from the base of the cliff?

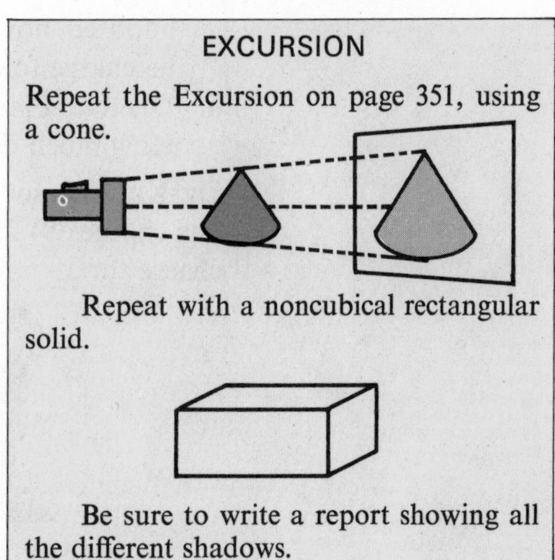

EXCURSION

Repeat the Excursion on page 351, using a cone.

Repeat with a noncubical rectangular solid.

Be sure to write a report showing all the different shadows.

Skill Maintenance, Set 77, page 418

Mathematics in careers

Veterinarians often use simple mathematics in their work. These exercises will give some examples.

EXERCISES

1. The amount of medicine used with dogs sometimes depends on the weight of the dog. The dosage for one medicine is 1 cubic centimeter per 10 kilograms of weight. How much of the medicine would be used for a 45-kilogram dog?
2. One kind of tablet can easily be broken into quarters. The dosage is $\frac{1}{4}$ tablet per 8 kilograms of dog, rounded to the nearest quarter tablet. What is the dosage for a 50-kilogram dog?
3. **a.** Dr. Kornblume buys his drugs wholesale and marks them up 50% when he sells them. If he buys some pills for $3.00 per hundred, how much does he sell them for? How much would he charge for 10 pills?

   b. Dr. Kornblume sells one kind of tablet for $15 per hundred. How much did he pay for them?
4. Dr. Katt has some kennels in which she keeps dogs for owners. She charges $4.25 per day to keep a dog. How much would she charge for 13 days?

5. Dr. Katt weighs a dog by holding the dog in her arms and weighing both herself and the dog. Together she and one dog weigh 85 kilograms. Dr. Katt weighs 67 kilograms. How much does the dog weigh?

KEEPING SKILLS SHARP

1. Follow this flow chart.

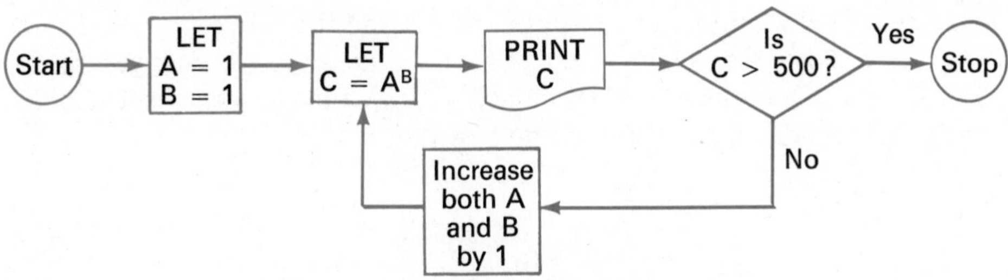

Solve.

2. $12a + 15 = 72$ **3.** $16 - 2c = {}^{-}8$ **4.** $\frac{4x + 3}{9} = 7$

Graph the solution sets on the number line.

5. ${}^{+}3x > {}^{+}15$ **6.** ${}^{+}3x > {}^{-}15$ **7.** $a + {}^{-}3 \leq {}^{-}7$

8. Give the mean, median, and mode of these scores.

Score	Number of students
50	|||
55	~~||||~~
60	||
65	~~||||~~ ||
70	~~||||~~
75	||||
80	|
85	||

Imagine that these marbles are put into a box and one is drawn without looking. Complete each sentence.

9. P (black) = ? **10.** P (red) = ?

11. P (blue) = ? **12.** P (not black) = ?

Now draw two marbles.

13. P (black or red) = ?

Here are three functions.

$$f(x) = 5x - 2 \qquad g(x) = \frac{x^2}{2} \qquad h(x) = 2(x - 4)$$

Complete.

14. $f(0) =$? **15.** $g(0) =$? **16.** $h(0) =$? **17.** $f(12) =$?

18. $g(12) =$? **19.** $h(12) =$? **20.** $f($? $) = 148$ **21.** $h($? $) = 148$

Skill Maintenance, Set 78, page 418

Right triangles

Right triangles have some very interesting properties. You studied one of them when you learned about tangent ratios. You will learn about another property in this lesson and the next one.

The sides of right triangles have special names. The longest side—the one opposite the right angle—is called the **hypotenuse**. The other two sides are called the **legs**.

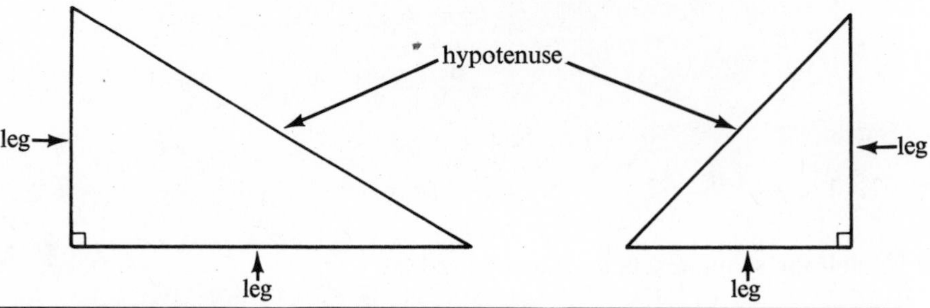

EXERCISES

Which side is the hypotenuse?

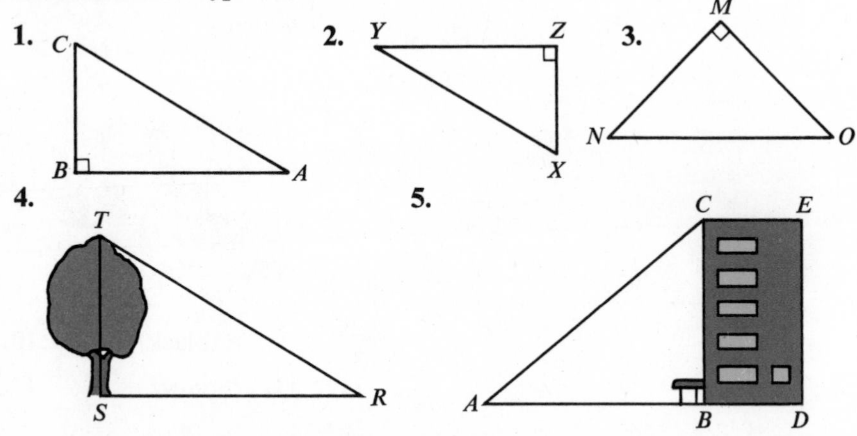

6. **a.** Square the length of the hypotenuse.
   b. Square the lengths of the legs.

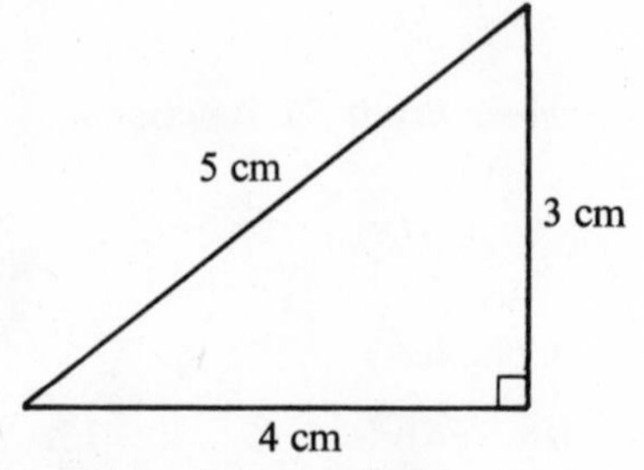

   c. Add the two squares from part b. What did you find?

7. Study this tile pattern. Parts of it have been colored to help you see a special pattern.
   a. Which side is the hypotenuse of right triangle ABC?
   b. Look at the squares on the legs and the square on the hypotenuse. How are the three squares related?

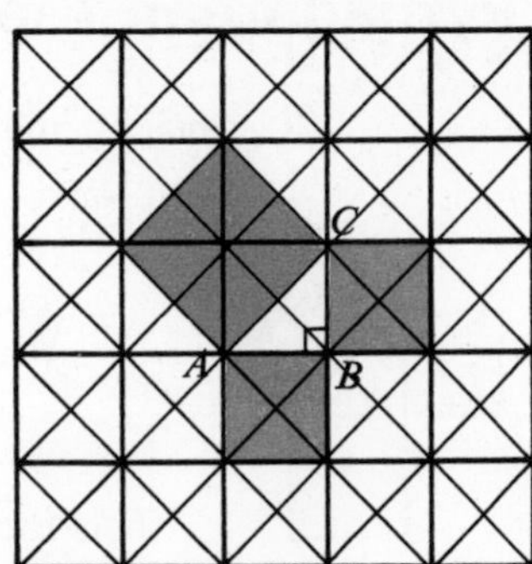

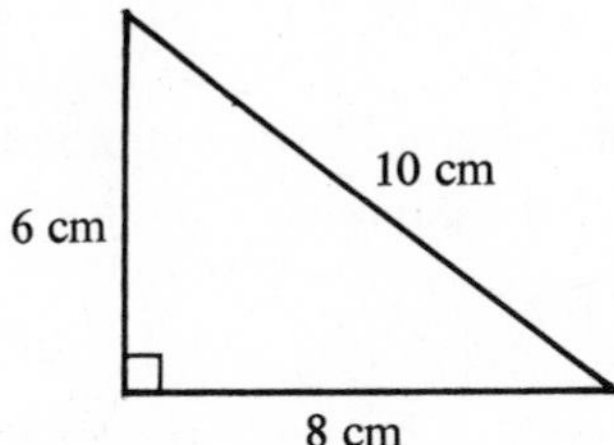

8. a. Square the length of the hypotenuse.
   b. Square the lengths of the legs.
   c. Add the squares of the two legs. What do you notice?

9. Repeat exercise 8 with this right triangle.

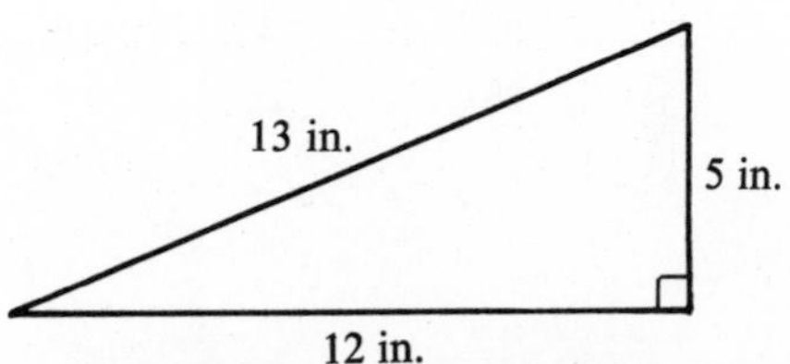

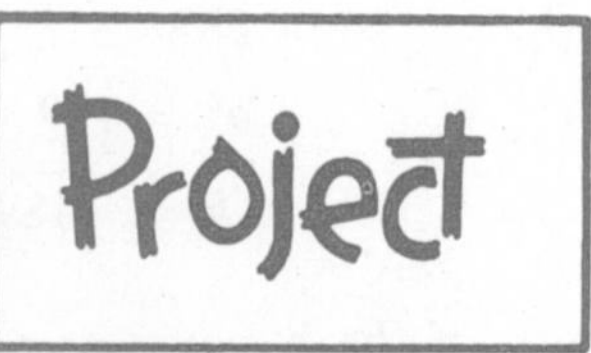

1. Use a protractor and carefully draw a right triangle.
2. Measure the sides to the nearest .1 millimeter.
3. Square the lengths of the hypotenuse.
4. Square the lengths of the legs.
5. Add the squares of the legs.
6. How does the sum compare to the square of the hypotenuse?
7. Draw another right triangle and repeat steps 2–6.

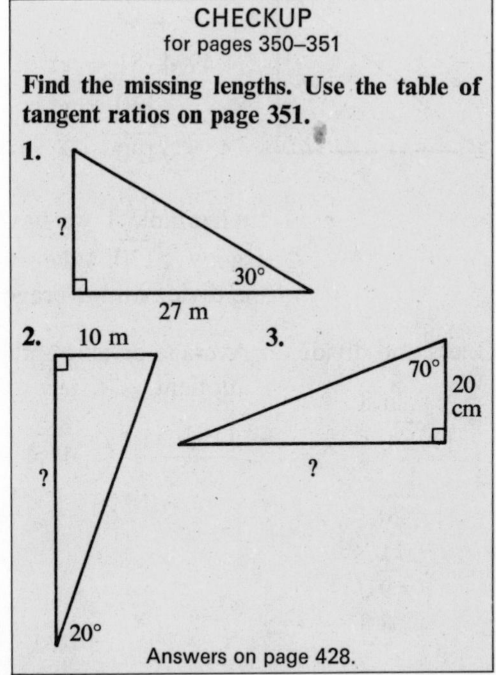
CHECKUP
for pages 350–351

Find the missing lengths. Use the table of tangent ratios on page 351.

Answers on page 428.

Skill Maintenance, Set 79, page 418

The Pythagorean theorem

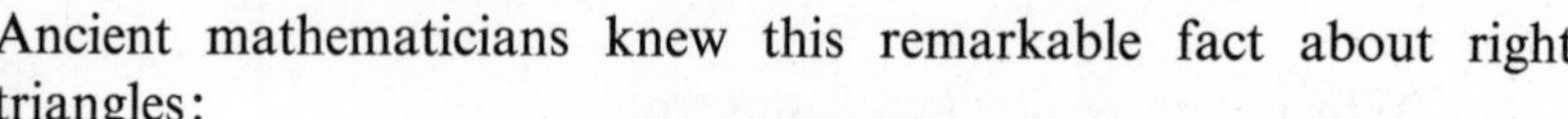

Ancient mathematicians knew this remarkable fact about right triangles:

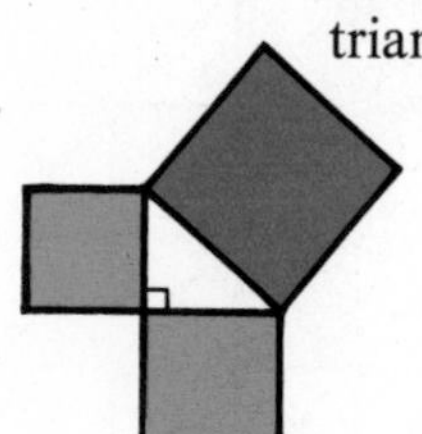

> The square drawn on the hypotenuse is equal in area to the sum of the areas of the squares drawn on the legs.

This fact is called the Pythagorean theorem. It is often stated in algebraic terms rather than in geometric terms.

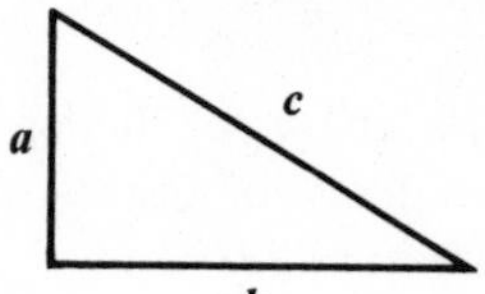

> In a right triangle the square of the hypotenuse is equal to the sum of the squares of the legs:
>
> $$a^2 + b^2 = c^2$$

We can use the Pythagorean theorem to compute the length of any side of a right triangle from the known lengths of the other two sides.

Example 1.

(Right triangle with legs 7 and 9, hypotenuse ?)

$$a^2 + b^2 = c^2$$
$$7^2 + 9^2 = c^2$$
$$49 + 81 = c^2$$
$$130 = c^2$$
$$\sqrt{130} = c$$

Example 2.

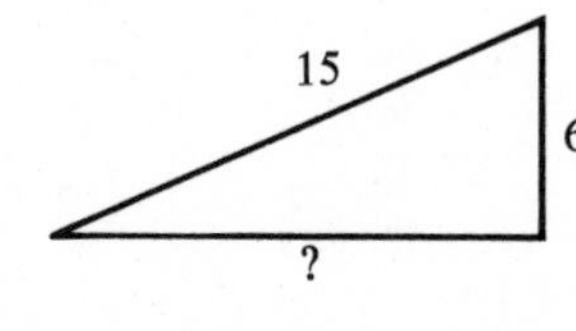

$$a^2 + b^2 = c^2$$
$$6^2 + b^2 = 15^2$$
$$36 + b^2 = 225$$
$$b^2 = 189$$
$$b = \sqrt{189}$$

In Example 1 we have found that the length of the hypotenuse is exactly $\sqrt{130}$. When we need a decimal approximation, we can use the divide-and-average method.

Guess and divide.

```
     11.8
 11)130
    11
     20
     11
      90
      88
       2
```

Average divisor and quotient.

$$\frac{11 + 11.8}{2} = 11.4$$

Divide.

```
          1 1.40
 11.4)130.0 0
      114
       16 0
       11 4
        4 6 0
        4 5 6
           40
```

The answer to the nearest tenth is 11.4.

EXERCISES

Find the missing lengths.

1.
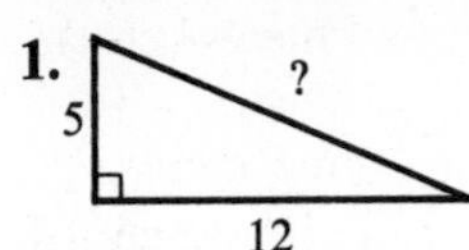

2.
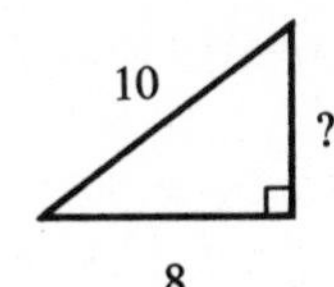

3.
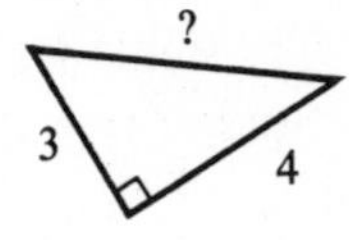

4. 1 ? 1

5.
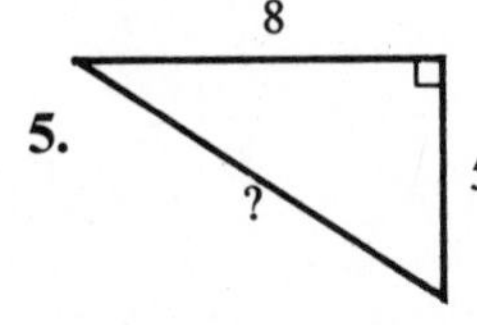

6.
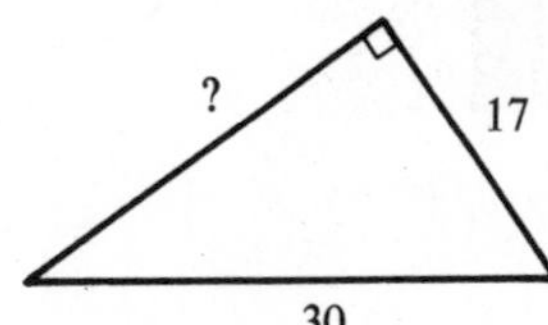

Find the decimal approximation to the nearest tenth.

7. $\sqrt{41}$ **8.** $\sqrt{150}$ **9.** $\sqrt{196}$ **10.** $\sqrt{477}$ **11.** $\sqrt{2025}$

Find the missing lengths. Give decimal values correct to the nearest tenth.

12.
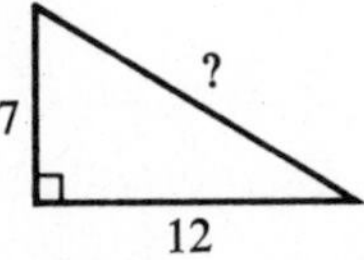

13.
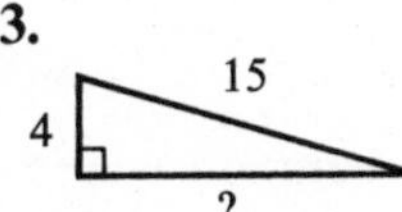

14.
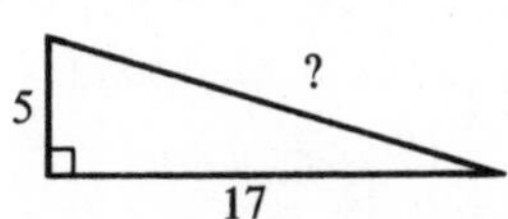

15.
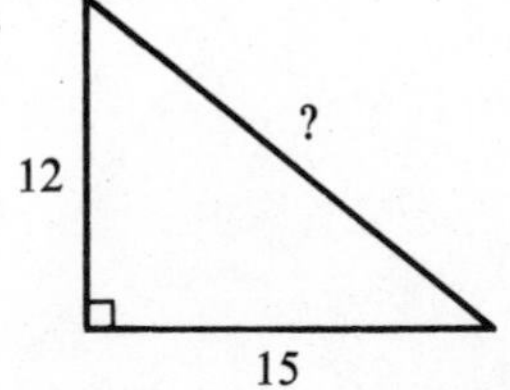

16.
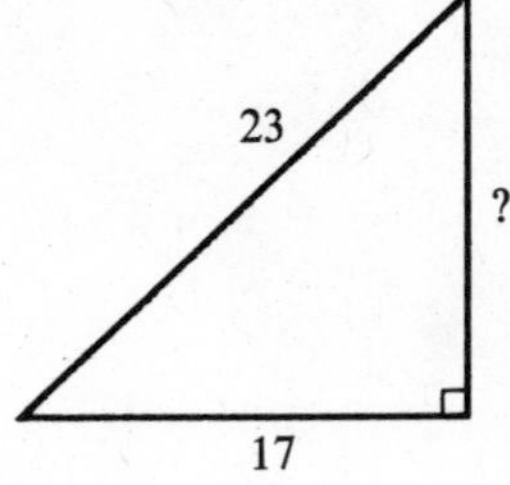

EXCURSION

A scale drawing uses the idea of similar figures.

Make a scale drawing of the floor plan of your "dream house." Use a scale of 1 cm : 1 ft. That is, a 1-centimeter length on your drawing will represent a 1-foot length in your house.

Supplementary Exercises, Set 77, page 396

Using the Pythagorean theorem

The Pythagorean theorem can also be used for indirect measurement. Study these examples.

Example 1. How high on a wall will a 30-foot ladder reach if it is placed 8 feet from the base of the wall?

$$a^2 + b^2 = c^2$$
$$8^2 + b^2 = 30^2$$
$$64 + b^2 = 900$$
$$b^2 = 836$$
$$b = \sqrt{836}$$
$$b \approx 28.9$$

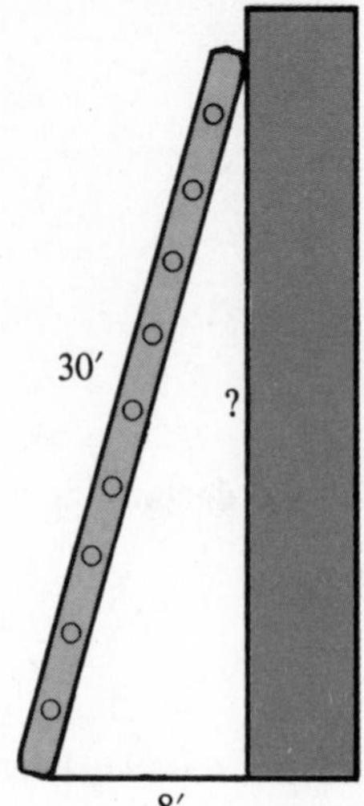

The ladder would reach about 28.9 feet up on the wall.

Example 2. A baseball diamond is a 90-foot square. How long a throw is it from home plate to second base?

$$a^2 + b^2 = c^2$$
$$90^2 + 90^2 = c^2$$
$$8100 + 8100 = c^2$$
$$16200 = c^2$$
$$\sqrt{16200} = c$$
$$127.3 \approx c$$

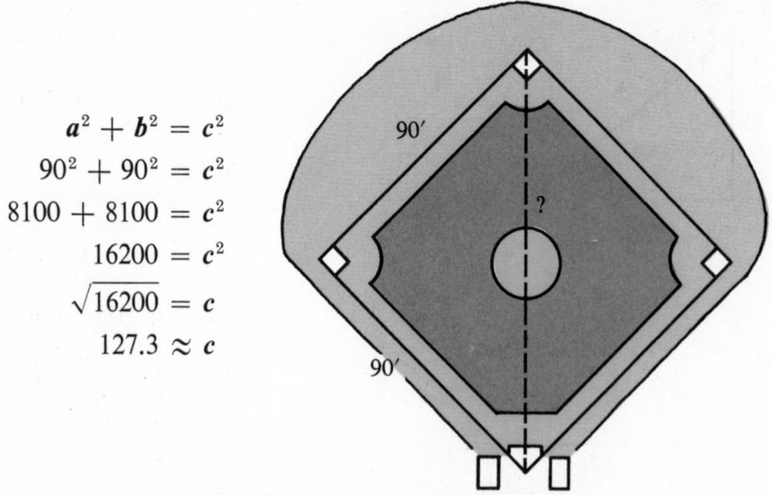

The distance from home plate to second base is about 127.3 feet.

EXERCISES

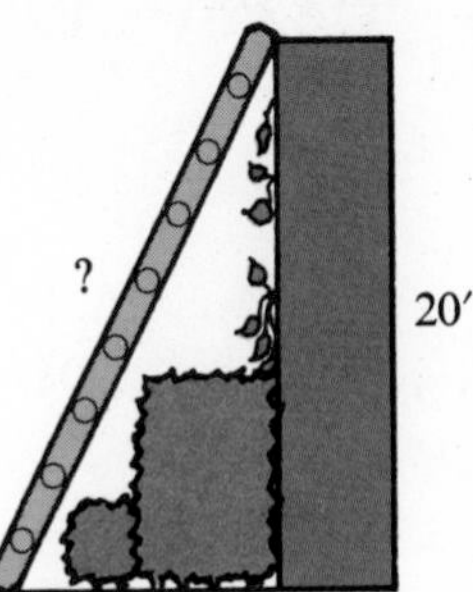

1. A wall is 20 feet high. There are bushes at the base of the wall, so a ladder must be placed 10 feet from the base of the wall. What is the length of the shortest ladder that will reach the top of the wall?

2. Suppose a bug is at one corner of a 1-foot-square tile. If it crawls straight to the opposite corner, how far does it go?

3. B, 1 mi, 2 mi, A — Pam jogs from A to B around the outside of the field while her younger brother, Ted, jogs straight from A to B. How much farther does Pam jog than Ted?

4. A 15-meter cable is fastened at the top of a pole and at a point on the ground 5 meters from the base of the pole. About how tall is the pole?

5. A plane passes over a ground point at a height of 8 kilometers. An observer on the ground is 15 kilometers from that ground point. How far is the plane from the observer?

6. What is the height of this equilateral triangle?

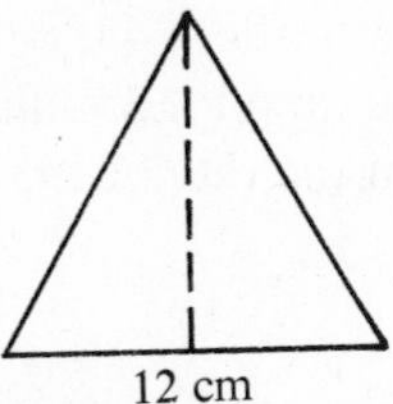

7. Check your answer to exercise 6 by using the tangent. (Each angle of the triangle is a 60° angle.)

8. What is the area of the triangle in exercise 6?

CHECKUP
for pages 356–359

1. Which side is the hypotenuse? Which sides are the legs?

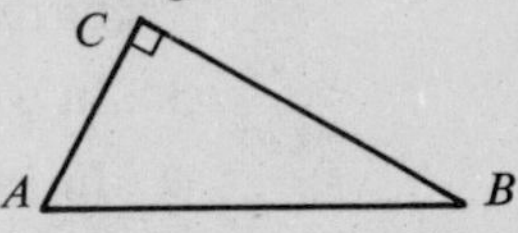

2. Find the missing length. Give an exact answer.

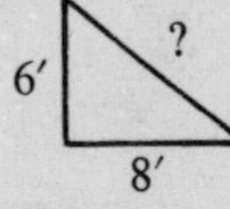

3. Find the missing length. Give an approximation correct to the nearest tenth.

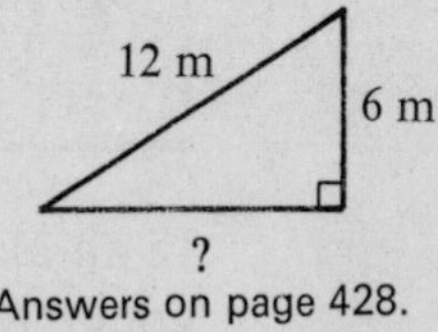

Answers on page 428.

Supplementary Exercises, Set 78, page 396

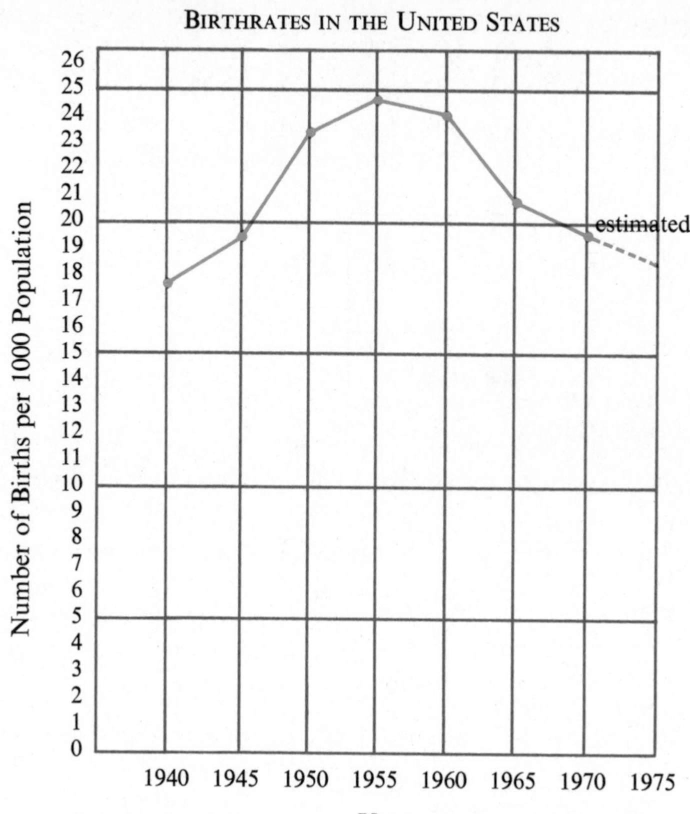

1. How many births per 1000 population were there in 1945?
2. In what year was the birthrate the greatest? What was that birthrate?
3. In what year was the rate lowest? What was that rate?
4. In 1950 the total population was about 151 million. About how many babies were born?

5. The total number of births in 1955 was about 4.0 million, and in 1960 the total number of births was about 4.3 million. Explain how the rate in 1960 was lower than the rate in 1955.

In an almanac look up similar information on death rates. Make a graph. Make up questions about your graph.

CHAPTER CHECKUP

Are the two figures similar? [*page 342*]

1.

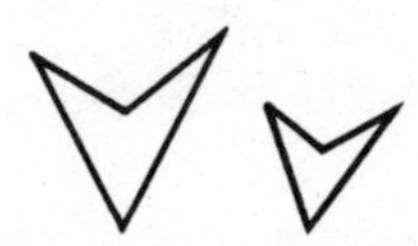

2.

3.

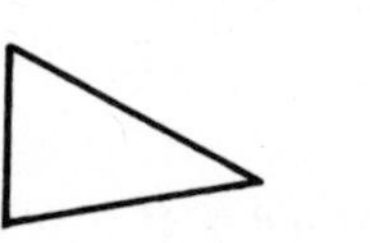

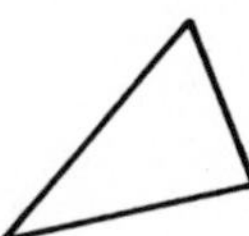

These two figures are similar.
Complete each sentence. [*page 344*]

4. $\angle A \cong$ ___?___

5. $\angle B \cong$ ___?___

6. $\dfrac{m(\overline{AB})}{m(\overline{MN})} = \dfrac{m(\overline{AC})}{?}$

7. $\dfrac{m(\overline{BC})}{m(\overline{AB})} = \dfrac{m(\overline{MO})}{?}$

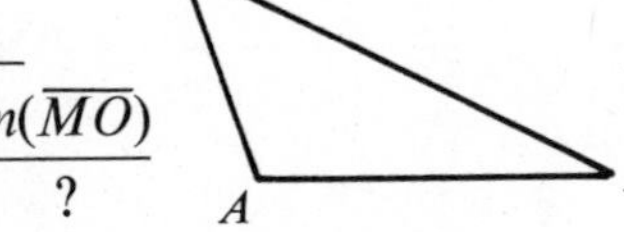

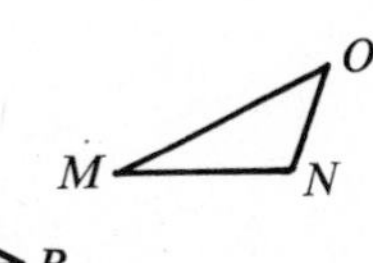

Find the missing lengths. There is not enough information to find some lengths. [*page 344*]

8.

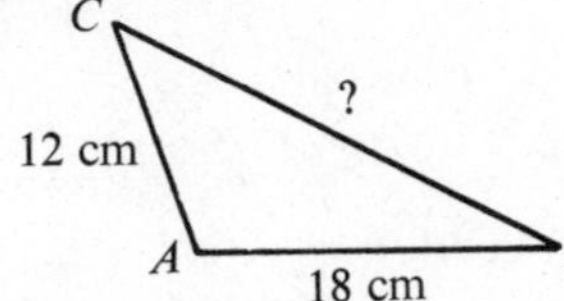

D
23 cm
?
E
F 9 cm

9.

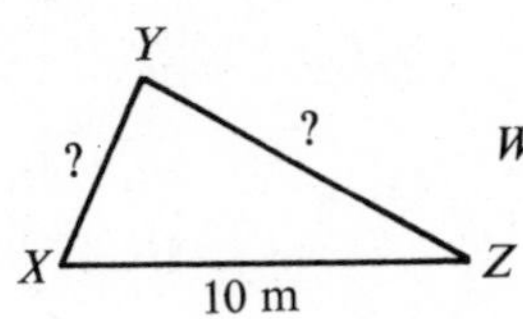

U
5 m
3 m
W
V
?

Use the table of tangents and find the missing lengths. (*Hint:* One exercise cannot be done.) [*pages 350, 352*]

10.

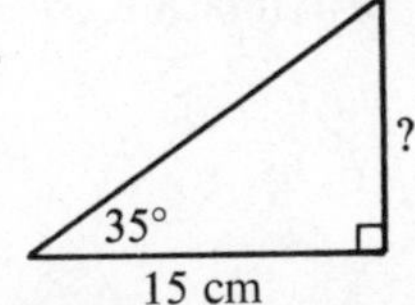

11.

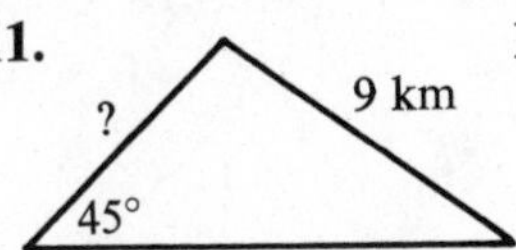

12.

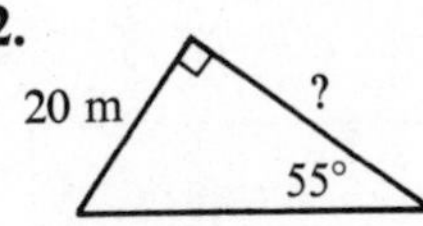

tan 35° ≈ .70
tan 45° = 1
tan 55° ≈ 1.43

Use the Pythagorean theorem and find the missing length. Give approximations correct to the nearest tenth unit. [*pages 356, 358*]

13.

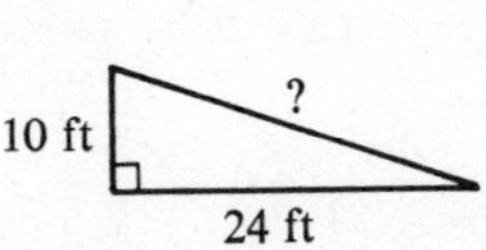

14.

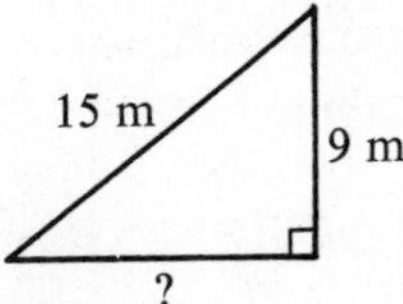

15. What is the length of the cable?

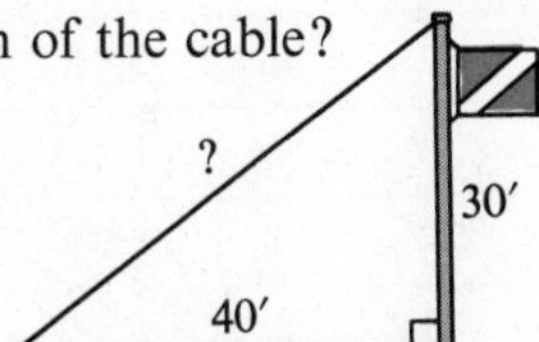

MAJOR CHECKUP

Solve. [*pages 16–19*]

1. $9a = 135$
2. $g + 6.8 = 15.3$
3. $87.4 - x = 53.1$
4. $\frac{a}{12} = 6$
5. $\frac{12}{a} = 6$
6. $3(2m + 5) = 117$

Compute. If rounding is necessary, round to the nearest tenth.
[*pages 79, 91, 109–110, 118, 120*]

7. a. $76 + 58$
   b. $76 - 58$
   c. 76×58
   d. $76 \div 58$
8. a. $2.43 + .98$
   b. $2.43 - .98$
   c. $2.43 \times .98$
   d. $2.43 \div .98$
9. a. $\frac{3}{4} + \frac{1}{2}$
   b. $\frac{3}{4} - \frac{1}{2}$
   c. $\frac{3}{4} \times \frac{1}{2}$
   d. $\frac{3}{4} \div \frac{1}{2}$
10. a. $2\frac{2}{5} + 1\frac{4}{5}$
    b. $2\frac{2}{5} - 1\frac{4}{5}$
    c. $2\frac{2}{5} \times 1\frac{4}{5}$
    d. $2\frac{2}{5} \div 1\frac{4}{5}$

Solve. [*pages 178–185*]

11. 10% of 96 = ___?___
12. 60% of 80 = ___?___
13. 120% of 75 = ___?___
14. 16% of \$50 = ___?___
15. 7.5% of 36 = ___?___
16. 43% of \$8.20 = ___?___
17. ___?___% of 20 = 10
18. ___?___% of 10 = 20
19. ___?___% of 81 = 27
20. 20% of ___?___ = 7
21. 50% of ___?___ = 20
22. 18% of ___?___ = 6.3

Find each perimeter and area. Use 3.14 as an approximation for π.
[*pages 206–211*]

23.
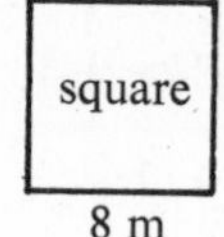

24.
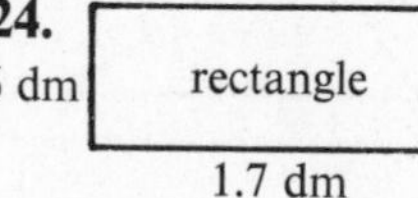

25.
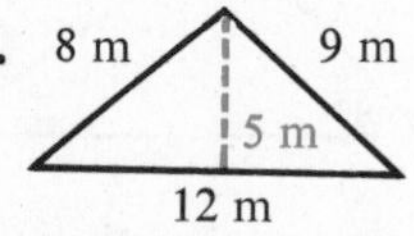

26.
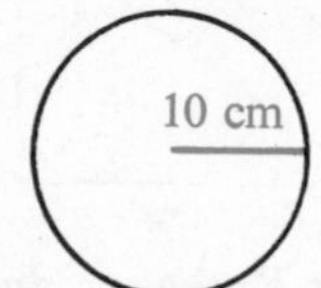

Solve. [*pages 250–251*]

27. Kasper bought a motorcycle marked \$1595 for \$300 down and \$47.08 per month for 3 years. How much extra did he pay on the installment plan?

Match the inequality with its graph. [*pages 286–289*]

28. $m \neq 3$
29. $5y \geq 15$
30. $x - 2 < 1$
31. $g + 4 \leq 7$

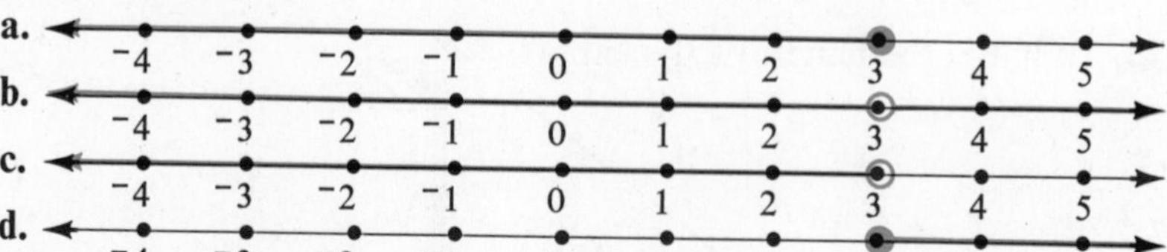

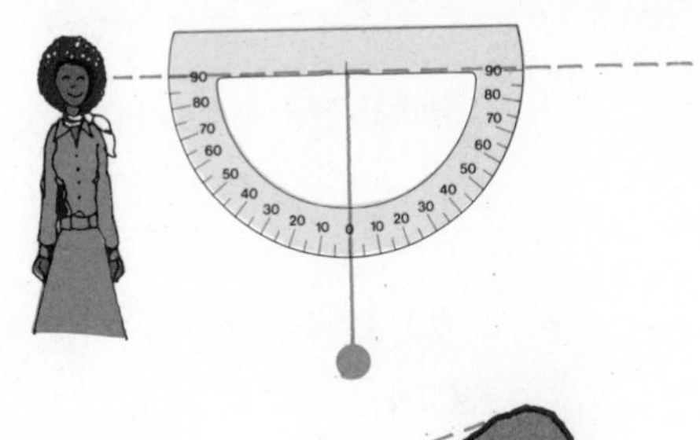

1. Get or make a large protractor and make an instrument for measuring angles above and below horizontal.

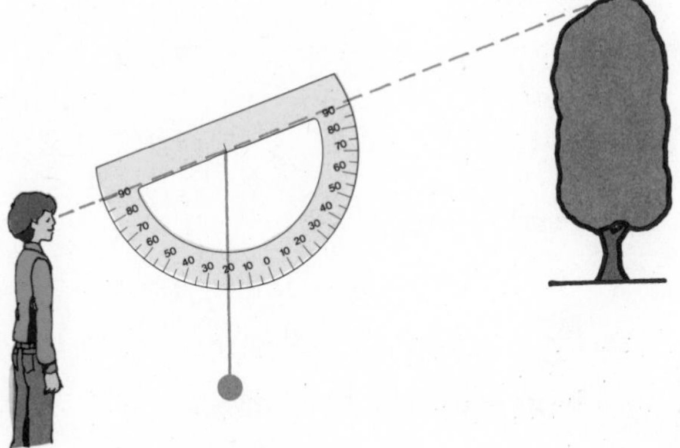

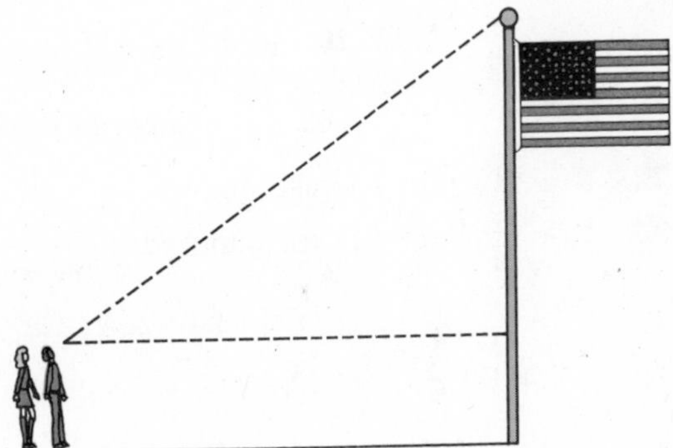

2. Use your instrument and a table of tangents to measure the heights of trees, flagpoles, buildings, and so on. (You can find tables of tangents in many high school mathematics textbooks.)

Project 2

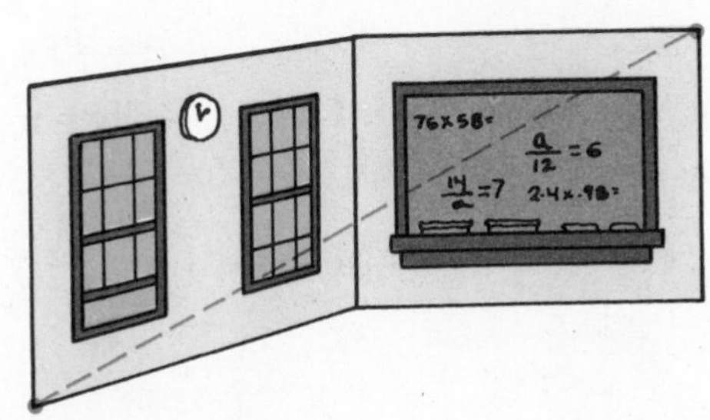

Use the Pythagorean theorem and find the distance from one corner of your room to the opposite corner.

FINAL TEST

Name______________________

Substitute and simplify. [*Chapter 1*]

a	b	c	B
3	5	2	6

1. $18 - B - b$ **2.** $12 \div (B \div c)$ **3.** ab **4.** $\frac{B}{a}$ **5.** B^a **6.** $a(B + c)$

Solve.

7. $x + 12 = 53$ **8.** $a - 16 = 48$ **9.** $51 - b = 14$ **10.** $\frac{g}{6} = 12$

11. $3a + 16 = 52$ **12.** $5(a - 4) = 75$ **13.** $\frac{m + 7}{8} = 96$ **14.** $\frac{3c + 2}{2} = 19$

Complete. [*Chapter 1*]

15. If $f(n) = 7n - 5$, then $f(8) =$ ___?___

16. If $g(m) = 5m^2$, then $g($___?___$) = 180$

Write in decimal form. [*Chapter 2*]

17. three tenths **18.** seven hundredths **19.** twelve hundredths

20. four and eight tenths **21.** fifty-four thousandths

Use this number in exercises 22–25: 573.549. [*Chapter 2*]

22. Round to the nearest ten. **23.** Round to the nearest one.

24. Round to the nearest hundredth. **25.** Round to the nearest tenth.

Add or subtract. [*Chapter 2*]

26. $5.7 + 3.8$ **27.** $2.09 + .86$ **28.** $4.75 - 2.77$ **29.** $30.04 - .98$

Write a flow chart that tells how to solve this problem. [*Chapter 2*]

30. At a party each of the 12 children had 5 cookies and each of the 3 adults had 2 cookies. How many cookies were eaten?

Solve. [*Chapter 2*]

31. Mrs. Kelly bought 15.9 gallons of gas for $8.25 and 1 quart of oil for $1.05. How much change did she get from a $10 bill?

Multiply. [*Chapter 3*]

32. 4.6×7 **33.** 5.2×16 **34.** $3.14 \times .8$ **35.** $.56 \times 2.4$ **36.** $.06 \times .03$

Divide. Round quotients to the nearest hundredth. [*Chapter 3*]

37. $6\overline{)3.24}$ 38. $25\overline{)62.4}$ 39. $.3\overline{)11.1}$ 40. $.04\overline{)2.7}$ 41. $3.8\overline{)75.2}$

Solve. [*Chapter 3*]

42. If 1 liter of gasoline costs 13.8¢, what will 23.6 liters cost?

43. If 1 pound of fish costs $.89, how much can you buy for $5.00?

Write as decimals. [*Chapter 4*]

44. $\frac{3}{4}$ 45. $\frac{3}{5}$ 46. $\frac{3}{8}$ 47. $\frac{1}{3}$ 48. $\frac{2}{11}$

Write as fractions. [*Chapter 4*]

49. .7 50. .07 51. .27 52. 3.8 53. .014

Compute. [*Chapter 4*]

54. a. $\frac{2}{3} + \frac{1}{2}$
    b. $\frac{2}{3} - \frac{1}{2}$
    c. $\frac{2}{3} \times \frac{1}{2}$
    d. $\frac{2}{3} \div \frac{1}{2}$

55. a. $4\frac{2}{5} + 2\frac{1}{5}$
    b. $4\frac{2}{5} - 2\frac{1}{5}$
    c. $4\frac{2}{5} \times 2\frac{1}{5}$
    d. $4\frac{2}{5} \div 2\frac{1}{5}$

56. a. $8\frac{3}{7} + 6\frac{5}{7}$
    b. $8\frac{3}{7} - 6\frac{5}{7}$
    c. $8\frac{3}{7} \times 6\frac{5}{7}$
    d. $8\frac{3}{7} \div 6\frac{5}{7}$

Which figures are congruent to the black figure? [*Chapter 5*]

57. a.  b.  c.  d. 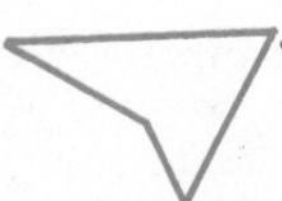

If the figure is flipped about the line of symmetry, what is the image of $\overline{AB}$? [*Chapter 5*]

58. 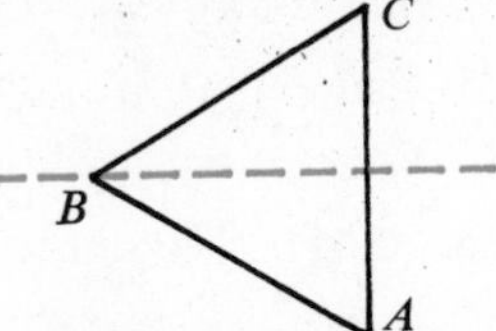

If the figure is turned a half-turn about the point of symmetry, what is the image of $\angle A$? [*Chapter 5*]

59. 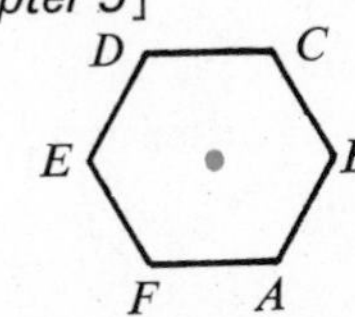

Each figure is half covered. The red line is a line of symmetry and the red point is a point of symmetry. Sketch each figure. [*Chapter 5*]

60. 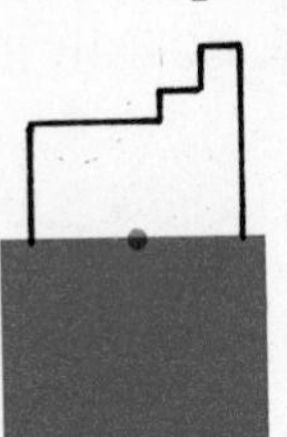

61. 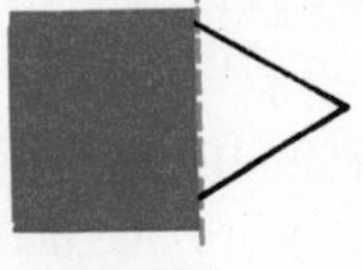

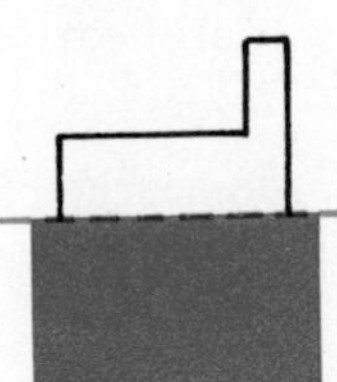

Write as percents. [*Chapter 6*]

62. $\frac{1}{2}$ 63. $\frac{3}{4}$ 64. $\frac{5}{4}$ 65. $\frac{1}{3}$ 66. $\frac{1}{10}$

Write as fractions. [*Chapter 6*]

67. 25% 68. 200% 69. 1% 70. $66\frac{2}{3}$% 71. 80%

Complete. [*Chapter 6*]

72. 10% of 83 = ___?___
73. 15% of 96 = ___?___
74. 150% of 26 = ___?___
75. ___?___% of 6 = 24
76. ___?___% of 24 = 6
77. 10% of ___?___ = 3.4

Give the perimeter and area. Use 3.14 as an approximation for π. [*Chapter 7*]

78. 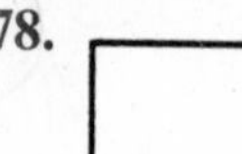

79. 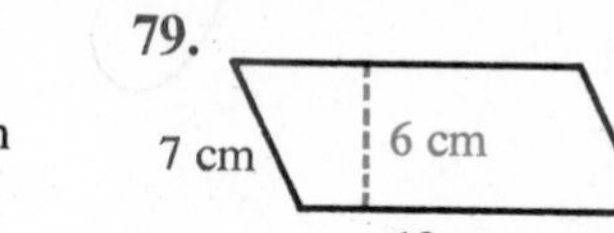

80. 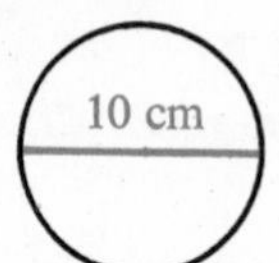

Give the surface area and volume. Use 3.14 as an approximation for π. [*Chapter 7*]

81. 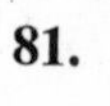

82. 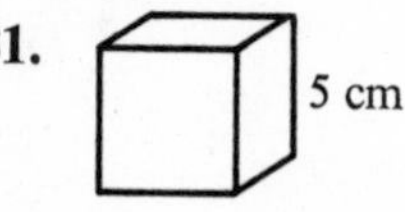 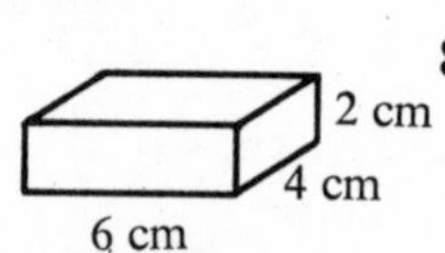

83. 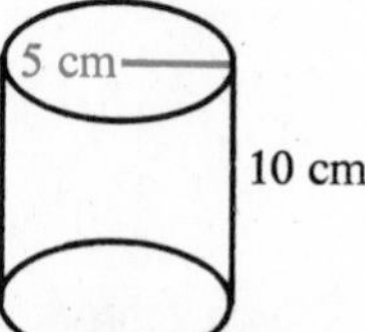

Complete. [*Chapter 7*]

84. ___?___ mm = 1 cm
85. ___?___ cm = 1 dm
86. ___?___ dm = 1 m
87. ___?___ cm = 1 m
88. ___?___ cg = 1 g
89. ___?___ cl = 1 *l*
90. ___?___ mm = 1 m
91. ___?___ m = 1 dm
92. ___?___ m = 1 hm
93. ___?___ m = 1 km
94. ___?___ g = 1 kg
95. 34 cm = ___?___ m
96. 57 g = ___?___ mg
97. 6.4 *l* = ___?___ cl
98. 1.2 kg = ___?___ g

99. What is the greatest possible error of measurement, if the unit used is the centimeter?

100. What is the percent of error in a measurement of 50 cm to the nearest cm?

Solve. [*Chapter 8*]

101. Carol earned $4.50 per hour. How much did she earn in $35\frac{1}{2}$ hours?

102. Jan earned $800 per month plus 4% of her sales above $20,000. One month her sales were $22,000. What were her earnings?

103. Karl bought a suit for \$79.95. He paid 4% sales tax. How much was the sales tax?

104. Karen wants a coat that cost \$55.00. Next month the coat will be on sale for 20% off. How much will she save by waiting?

105. June can buy a car that costs \$3495 cash or \$900 down and \$87.50 per month for 3 years. How much will she save by paying cash?

106. Jim invested \$1000 at 5% per year simple interest for 2 years. How much interest did he earn?

107. Jules invested \$1000 at 5% per year compounded quarterly for 2 years. Did he earn more interest or less interest than Jim?

Which is the better buy? [*Chapter 8*]

108.

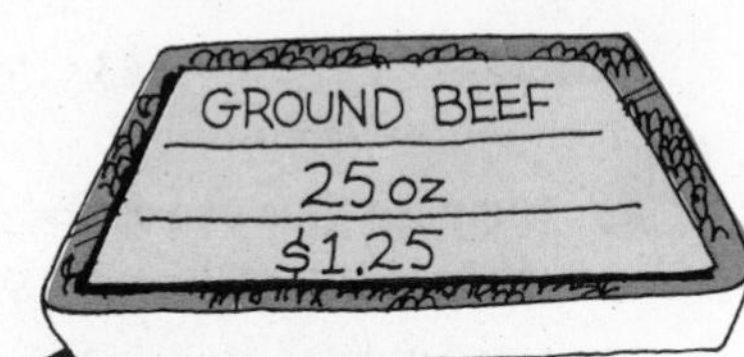

109. Jody bought 50 shares of stock for $38\frac{3}{4}$ per share. Later she sold them for $47\frac{1}{4}$. How much profit did she make?

Complete. [*Chapter 9*]

110. If $^{+}9$ represents a gain of 9 pounds, then $^{-}3$ represents ___?___.

111. If $^{-}4$ represents a 4-mile-to-the-south trip, then $^{+}7$ represents ___?___.

Add. [*Chapter 9*]

112. $^{+}6 + ^{+}4$ **113.** $^{+}6 + ^{-}4$ **114.** $^{-}6 + ^{+}4$ **115.** $^{-}6 + ^{-}4$

Subtract. [*Chapter 9*]

116. $^{+}10 - ^{+}3$ **117.** $^{+}3 - ^{+}10$ **118.** $^{-}6 - ^{+}4$ **119.** $^{-}6 - ^{-}8$

Give the opposite of each number. [*Chapter 9*]

120. $^{+}8$ **121.** $^{-}9$ **122.** 0 **123.** $\frac{^{-}1}{2}$ **124.** $\frac{^{+}3}{4}$

Multiply. [*Chapter 9*]

125. $^{+}6 \times ^{+}4$ **126.** $^{+}7 \times ^{-}3$ **127.** $^{-}8 \times ^{+}4$ **128.** $^{-}6 \times ^{-}7$

Divide. [*Chapter 9*]

129. $\frac{^{+}8}{^{+}4}$ **130.** $\frac{^{+}12}{^{-}3}$ **131.** $\frac{^{-}27}{^{+}9}$ **132.** $\frac{^{-}45}{^{-}5}$

Solve. [*Chapter 9*]

133. $x + {}^{+}7 = {}^{-}3$ **134.** $y - {}^{-}3 = {}^{-}3$ **135.** ${}^{+}2g = {}^{-}18$

Match. [*Chapter 9*]

136. $a + {}^{-}2 < {}^{-}1$ **a.** ${}^{-}3$ ${}^{-}2$ ${}^{-}1$ 0 ${}^{+}1$ ${}^{+}2$ ${}^{+}3$

137. ${}^{+}6a \neq {}^{+}6$ **b.** ${}^{-}3$ ${}^{-}2$ ${}^{-}1$ 0 ${}^{+}1$ ${}^{+}2$ ${}^{+}3$

138. $g - {}^{-}2 \geq {}^{+}3$ **c.** ${}^{-}3$ ${}^{-}2$ ${}^{-}1$ 0 ${}^{+}1$ ${}^{+}2$ ${}^{+}3$

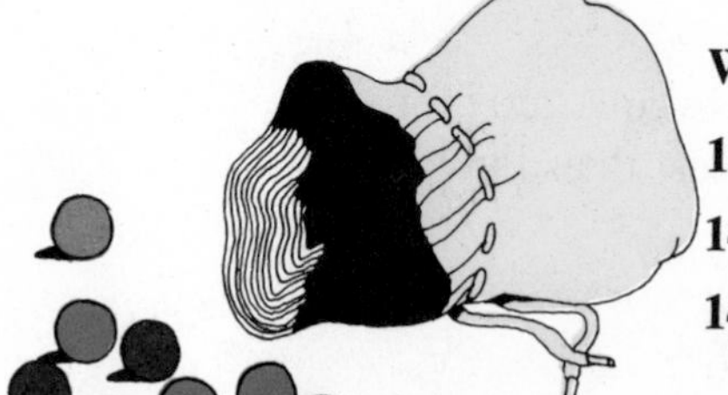

What is each probability in lowest terms? [*Chapter 10*]

139. P(red) **140.** P(blue)

141. P(black) **142.** P(not red)

143. P(red or black or blue) **144.** P(green)

Suppose that you first spin the spinner and then toss the coin. Give each probability. [*Chapter 10*]

145. P(red and head)

146. P(blue and tail)

Complete. [*Chapter 10*]

Draw 1 card. Do not replace. Draw a second card.

147. P(1 and then 4) = ___?___

148. What is the mean of these scores?

149. What is the mode?

150. What is the median?

46, 50, 45, 38, 47, 46, 43, 46, 41, 43, 40

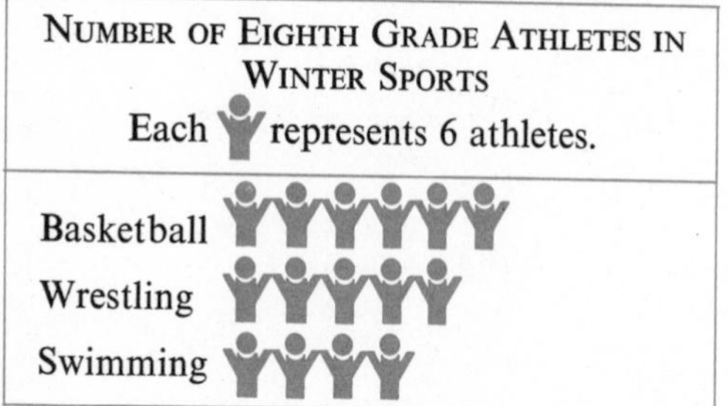

151. How many basketball players?

152. How many wrestlers?

153. What fraction of the athletes were swimmers?

Write as terminating or repeating decimals. [*Chapter 11*]

154. $\frac{1}{8}$ **155.** $\frac{1}{7}$ **156.** $\frac{1}{3}$ **157.** $\frac{5}{9}$ **158.** $\frac{5}{11}$ **159.** $\frac{4}{21}$

Match. [*Chapter 11*]

160.	Commutative property of multiplication	**a.**	$a(b + c) = ab + ac$
161.	Associative property of multiplication	**b.**	$a \cdot 1 = a$
162.	Identity property of multiplication	**c.**	$ab = ba$
163.	Inverse property of multiplication	**d.**	$a\left(\frac{1}{a}\right) = {}^{+}1,\ a \neq 0$
164.	Distributive property	**e.**	$a(bc) = (ab)c$
165.	Identity property of addition	**f.**	$a + 0 = a$

Match. [*Chapter 11*]

166. $a \leq {}^{-}2$ **a.** $^{-}4$ $^{-}3$ $^{-}2$ $^{-}1$ 0 1 2 3 4

167. $b \geq {}^{-}2$ **b.** $^{-}4$ $^{-}3$ $^{-}2$ $^{-}1$ 0 1 2 3 4

168. $c \neq {}^{-}2$ **c.** $^{-}4$ $^{-}3$ $^{-}2$ $^{-}1$ 0 1 2 3 4

169. $d < {}^{-}2$ **d.** $^{-}4$ $^{-}3$ $^{-}2$ $^{-}1$ 0 1 2 3 4

Give decimal approximations correct to the nearest tenth. [*Chapter 11*]

170. $\sqrt{18}$ **171.** $\sqrt{53}$ **172.** $\sqrt{187}$

Match points with their coordinates. [*Chapter 11*]

173. (2, 4)

174. (0, 0)

175. ($^{-}4$, $^{-}2$)

176. ($^{-}2$, 5)

177. (0, 2)

178. (1, 1)

179. (4, $^{-}2$)

180. (2, $^{-}4$)

181. ($^{-}3$, 2)

182. ($^{-}2$, $^{-}3$)

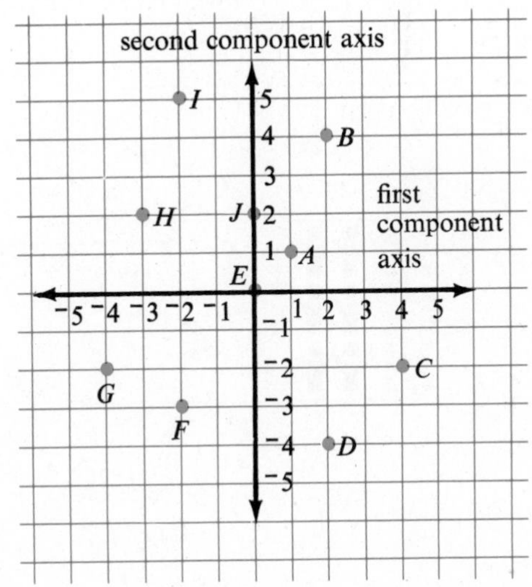

The pairs of figures are similar. Answer the questions. [*Chapter 12*]

183. What is the image of $\overline{AB}$?

184. What is the image of $\angle X$?

185. $m(\overline{XY}) = \underline{\ \ ?\ \ }$

186. $m(\overline{XZ}) = \underline{\ \ ?\ \ }$

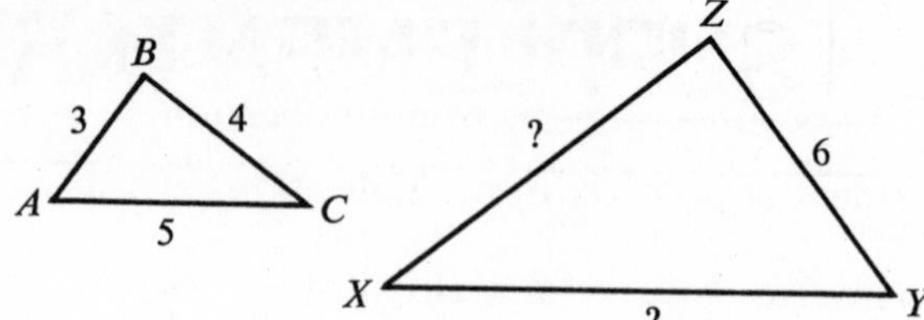

187. Find the missing lengths. Some may be impossible to find.

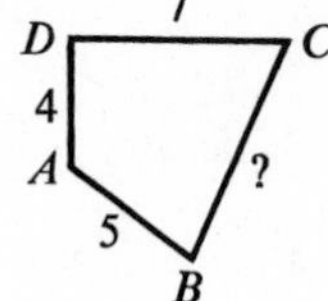

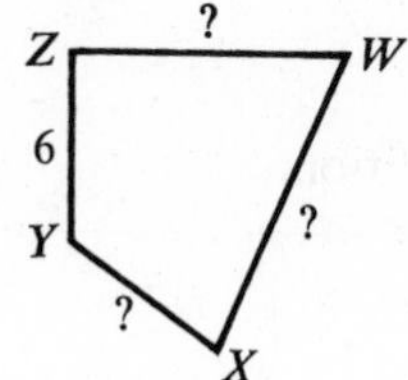

Angle *B* is a right angle. Answer the questions. [*Chapter 12*]

188. In triangle *ABC*, which side is the hypotenuse?

189. Find the exact length of $\overline{AC}$. Give an approximation of the length of $\overline{AC}$ correct to the nearest tenth.

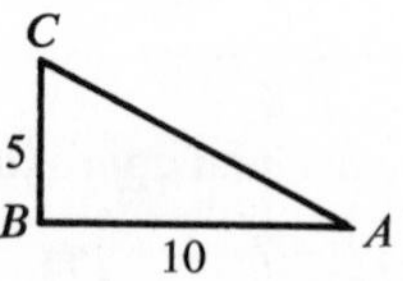

Use the tangent table to find the length of $\overline{XY}$. [*Chapter 12*]

190.

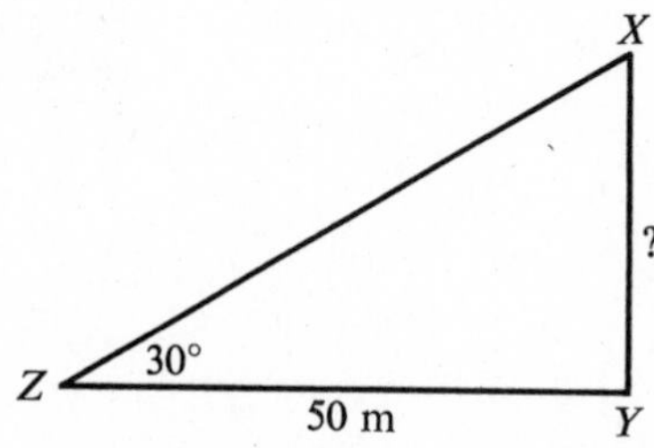

tan 30° ≈	.58
tan 40° ≈	.84
tan 50° ≈	1.19

SUPPLEMENTARY EXERCISES

pages 374-396

The Supplementary Exercises, which are correlated with pages in the textbook, provide additional practice in the skills developed on those pages.

SKILL MAINTENANCE

pages 397-418

The Skill Maintenance exercises are designed to maintain proficiency in skills that were developed earlier. So, rather than relating to the content of the pages they are correlated with, they relate to the content of earlier pages.

Supplementary exercises

Set 1 (after page 3) **Simplify.**

1. $6 + 3 \times 7$
2. $12 \div 2 \times 3$
3. $5 \times 3 + 6 \times 2$
4. $16 \div 4 \div 2$
5. $(3 + 2) \times 6$
6. $12 \div (2 \times 3)$
7. $4 + 3 \times 2 + 5$
8. $(3 + 2) \times (4 + 5)$
9. $6 \times (4 + 1)$
10. $5 + 2 \times 5 \times 3$
11. $[3 + 4 - (6 - 1) + 2] \times 5$
12. $15 \div 5 \div 3 \times 2 \times 4 \times 2$
13. $18 \div (6 \div 3) + 4 \times 2 - 7$

Set 2 (after page 7) **Substitute and simplify.**

a	b	B	c	d	x
1	3	5	4	0	2

1. bc
2. Bx
3. dB
4. $B(b + c)$
5. $8b$
6. $10c$
7. $8(B + x)$
8. ab
9. $c(B - x)$
10. c^2
11. B^2
12. b^2
13. x^3
14. B^b
15. d^2
16. d^8
17. d^{53}
18. a^2
19. a^3
20. a^{58}
21. $(b + B)^2$
22. c^x
23. B^x
24. x^c

Set 3 (after page 15)
Use the prime factorization method to find the LCM and GCF.

1. 9, 21
2. 14, 20
3. 6, 24
4. 36, 54
5. 12, 18, 24
6. 15, 72
7. 4, 20, 32
8. 16, 10, 64
9. 11, 25, 55

Set 4 (after page 17) **Is the first number a solution of the equation?**

1. 6, $3a + 5 = 23$
2. 7, $9x + 8 = 70$
3. 7, $10g - 8 = 71$
4. 9, $4(2y + 3) = 84$
5. 10, $\frac{9m}{2} = 45$
6. 54, $\frac{g}{9} = 6$
7. 30, $\frac{n}{3} \times 4 = 40$
8. 21, $\frac{h + 3}{3} = 6$
9. 7, $(x + 4)6 = 60$
10. 15, $(r - 7)2 = 16$
11. 21, $\frac{3(y - 10)}{3} = y$
12. 7, $3a + 2 = 4a - 5$
13. 8, $4(m - 2) = 3m$
14. 12, $\frac{2g}{4} = 6$
15. 9, $\frac{4c}{6} = 7$
16. 15, $\frac{2y}{3} - 4 = 6$

Set 5 (after page 19) **Solve.**

1. $3x + 6 = 27$
2. $\frac{4}{4}x = 9$
3. $\frac{18 - 2x}{3} = 4$
4. $\frac{24}{2}x = 6$
5. $2(3x + 1) = 32$
6. $7x - 2 = 19$
7. $2(7 - x) = 12$
8. $\frac{28 - 8x}{7} = 4$
9. $2(x + 5) = 18$
10. $\frac{7x - 3}{5} = 5$
11. $5x + 9 = 24$
12. $\frac{3}{4}x = 9$
13. $9x - 4 = 32$
14. $\frac{18}{3}x = 6$
15. $14 - 9x = 14$
16. $\frac{7}{2}x = 14$
17. $\frac{14 - 5x}{3} = 3$
18. $\frac{21 - 6x}{9} = 1$
19. $6(x - 5) = 36$
20. $\frac{8}{2}x = 0$

Set 6 (after page 25) **Complete.**

1. $h: n \rightarrow 8n - 5$
   a. (1, _?_)
   b. (2, _?_)
   c. (3, _?_)
   d. (4, _?_)
   e. (5, _?_)
   f. (_?_, 75)
2. $g: k \rightarrow 4k + 3$
   a. (_?_, 7)
   b. (_?_, 3)
   c. (_?_, 19)
   d. (5, _?_)
   e. (9, _?_)
   f. (7, _?_)
3. $f: t \rightarrow 3(t + 1)$
   a. (0, _?_)
   b. (4, _?_)
   c. (8, _?_)
   d. (2, _?_)
   e. (_?_, 12)
   f. (_?_, 18)

Set 7 (after page 27) **Complete.**

1. $f: t \rightarrow 2t + 6$
   a. $f(1) =$ _?_
   b. $f(3) =$ _?_
   c. $f(0) =$ _?_
   d. $f(8) =$ _?_
   e. $f($_?_$) = 20$
   f. $f($_?_$) = 24$
2. $g: t \rightarrow 8t - 3$
   a. $g(8) =$ _?_
   b. $g(4) =$ _?_
   c. $g(3) =$ _?_
   d. $g($_?_$) = 37$
   e. $g($_?_$) = 45$
   f. $g($_?_$) = 53$
3. $h: t \rightarrow t^2 + 3$
   a. $h(8) =$ _?_
   b. $h(6) =$ _?_
   c. $h(7) =$ _?_
   d. $h($_?_$) = 3$
   e. $h($_?_$) = 19$
   f. $h($_?_$) = 12$

Set 8 (after page 39) **Complete.**

1 year = .1 decade

1 year = .01 century

1. 2 years = _?_ decade
2. 2 years = _?_ century
3. 7 years = _?_ century
4. 7 years = _?_ decade
5. 10 years = _?_ decade
6. 10 years = _?_ century
7. 12 years = _?_ decades
8. 12 years = _?_ century
9. 97 years = _?_ decades
10. 93 years = _?_ century
11. 100 years = _?_ decades
12. 100 years = _?_ century
13. 127 years = _?_ decades
14. 127 years = _?_ centuries
15. _?_ years = .6 decade
16. _?_ years = .06 century
17. _?_ years = 6.3 decades
18. _?_ years = 6.3 centuries
19. _?_ years = 1.2 decades
20. _?_ years = .73 century

Set 9 (after page 41)

Number	Round to nearest tenth.	Round to nearest one.	Round to nearest thousand.
1. 6734.89	?	?	?
2. 24,356.48	?	?	?
3. 5926.75	?	?	?
4. 3885.45	?	?	?
5. 68,339.849	?	?	?
6. 39,999.977	?	?	?
7. 9834.499	?	?	?
8. 44,444.49	?	?	?
9. 968.501	?	?	?
10. 426.452	?	?	?

Set 10 (after page 43)

1. $8.54 + 3.79$
2. $18.9 + 6.7$
3. $7.65 + 3.82$
4. $.374 + .296$
5. $5.08 + 0.39$
6. $2.93 + 4.67$
7. $9.67 - 1.07$
8. $.462 - .399$
9. $72.1 - 50.9$
10. $.516 - .384$
11. $8.26 - 4.19$
12. $95.6 - 83.1$
13. $82.0 + 27.9$
14. $58.4 + 6.9$
15. $4.63 + 3.29$
16. $39.8 + 27.5$
17. $7.09 + 5.65$
18. $3.62 + 5.83$
19. $89.0 - 42.8$
20. $9.28 - 3.56$
21. $80.2 - 9.3$
22. $.629 - .384$
23. $5.38 - 4.19$
24. $46.6 - 7.4$

Set 11 (after page 53) **Solve. Write flow charts first.**

1. Jody bought a skirt for $17.95 and a blouse for $6.95. There was $1.25 in sales tax. How much did she pay in all?
2. Jody (exercise 1) gave the clerk two $20 bills and 15¢ in coins. How much change did she get?
3. 527 girls
   468 boys
   How many children?
4. 527 girls
   468 boys
   How many more girls?

5. Mr. Hart bought 2 cans of soup at a price of 2 for 49¢ and 2 cans of fruit juice at a price of 49¢ each. How much did he spend?

6. Mr. Hart (exercise 5) gave the clerk a $5 bill and got $3.63 in change. Did he get the correct change?

Set 12 (after page 69)

1. .47 ×5	2. .38 ×6	3. 9.5 ×9	4. 7.8 ×2	5. 2.6 ×6	6. 5.3 ×3
7. .736 ×2	8. 5.94 ×3	9. 36.7 ×4	10. .206 ×4	11. 28.4 ×3	12. 1.35 ×5
13. 89.7 ×7	14. .699 ×4	15. 4.93 ×8	16. 35.4 ×4	17. .936 ×8	18. 48.2 ×5
19. .842 ×9	20. 7.51 ×7	21. 49.6 ×8	22. .369 ×8	23. 8.25 ×7	24. .704 ×9

Set 13 (after page 73)

1. 426 ×50	2. 482 ×60	3. 591 ×80	4. 538 ×30	5. 103 ×40	6. 235 ×20
7. 812 ×300	8. 653 ×800	9. 294 ×500	10. 205 ×900	11. 245 ×700	12. 929 ×300
13. 3.74 ×50	14. 48.2 ×70	15. 3.91 ×90	16. .688 ×30	17. 64.3 ×60	18. 4.40 ×80
19. 9.28 ×700	20. .773 ×800	21. 7.15 ×400	22. 34.6 ×900	23. 9.65 ×600	24. .868 ×500

Set 14 (after page 75)

1. 32 ×82	2. 82 ×32	3. 94 ×29	4. 59 ×63	5. 26 ×68	6. 38 ×21
7. 8.12 ×32	8. 67.4 ×28	9. 9.31 ×17	10. .482 ×53	11. 39.5 ×33	12. 2.78 ×42
13. 42.6 ×65	14. .538 ×44	15. 8.04 ×82	16. 9.27 ×53	17. .682 ×64	18. 73.5 ×56
19. 2.90 ×837	20. .666 ×500	21. 7.42 ×160	22. 35.3 ×250	23. .462 ×342	24. 3.91 ×128

Set 15 (after page 79)

1. $45 \times .6$
2. $45 \times .06$
3. $4.5 \times .6$
4. $4.5 \times .06$
5. $.45 \times .6$
6. $.45 \times .06$
7. $.52 \times 18$
8. 9.3×6.4
9. $7.4 \times .35$
10. $.26 \times 1.4$
11. 5.8×2.9
12. 45×2.5
13. 3.84×1.9
14. 56.5×5.3
15. $81.3 \times .27$
16. 7.02×5.8
17. 51.8×6.4
18. 6.24×90
19. 5.36×40.2
20. 38.5×5.63
21. 4.93×2.81
22. 6.35×34.6
23. 71.5×11.5
24. 9.38×1.21

Set 16 (after page 83)

1. 6)594
2. 9)171
3. 5)385
4. 4)628
5. 3)126
6. 4)1.56
7. 9).36
8. 5)6.85
9. 4)4.32
10. 2)6.34
11. 8)73.4
12. 3)429
13. 5)834
14. 3)5.43
15. 5).296
16. 9).387
17. 7)2.66
18. 8)752
19. 9)828
20. 8)7.2

Set 17 (after page 87) **Round quotients to the nearest hundredth.**

1. 38)7.53
2. 49).891
3. 90)3.64
4. 14)7.34
5. 25)56.92
6. 57).548
7. 68)4.82
8. 26)2.96
9. 53).834
10. 69).78
11. 71)32.6
12. 66).326
13. 32)7.31
14. 48)6.05
15. 57)3.52
16. 85)53.4
17. 94)89.1
18. 83).729
19. 79).92
20. 42)3.11

Set 18 (after page 91) **Round quotients to the nearest tenth.**

1. .9)7.96
2. .04).245
3. .8).643
4. .03).928
5. .2).368
6. .7).2341
7. .09)3.826
8. .004).8543
9. .002)2.963
10. .05)4.321
11. .32)43.52
12. 5.6)2.007
13. .64)741.8
14. 2.8).4352
15. 1.3)3.896
16. 6.14)281.03
17. 7.38)5.961
18. 92.4)43.75
19. 3.86)517.4
20. 1.24)29.63

Set 19 (after page 99) **Give 3 equivalent fractions.**

1. $\frac{1}{2}$ 2. $\frac{1}{3}$ 3. $\frac{2}{3}$ 4. $\frac{3}{2}$ 5. $\frac{3}{4}$ 6. $\frac{5}{4}$ 7. $\frac{3}{7}$

8. $\frac{5}{8}$ 9. $\frac{1}{5}$ 10. $\frac{9}{5}$ 11. $\frac{10}{12}$ 12. $\frac{8}{12}$ 13. $\frac{2}{9}$ 14. $\frac{7}{9}$

15. $\frac{8}{13}$ 16. $\frac{9}{7}$ 17. $\frac{15}{14}$ 18. $\frac{7}{11}$ 19. $\frac{15}{12}$ 20. $\frac{20}{30}$ 21. $\frac{35}{40}$

Set 20 (after page 103) **Change to decimals.**

1. $\frac{1}{5}$ 2. $\frac{2}{5}$ 3. $\frac{3}{5}$ 4. $\frac{4}{5}$ 5. $\frac{5}{5}$ 6. $\frac{1}{3}$ 7. $\frac{2}{3}$

8. $\frac{1}{6}$ 9. $\frac{2}{6}$ 10. $\frac{3}{6}$ 11. $\frac{4}{6}$ 12. $\frac{5}{6}$ 13. $\frac{6}{6}$ 14. $\frac{1}{7}$

15. $\frac{2}{7}$ 16. $\frac{3}{7}$ 17. $\frac{4}{7}$ 18. $\frac{5}{7}$ 19. $\frac{6}{7}$ 20. $\frac{1}{9}$ 21. $\frac{2}{9}$

Set 21 (after page 109)

1. $\frac{3}{8}+\frac{4}{8}$ 2. $\frac{4}{7}+\frac{2}{7}$ 3. $\frac{5}{6}+\frac{1}{2}$ 4. $\frac{2}{3}+\frac{1}{6}$ 5. $\frac{3}{5}+\frac{1}{10}$

6. $\frac{1}{4}+\frac{1}{2}$ 7. $\frac{3}{4}+\frac{1}{2}$ 8. $\frac{3}{2}+\frac{1}{6}$ 9. $\frac{1}{6}+\frac{1}{2}$ 10. $\frac{2}{5}+\frac{1}{15}$

11. $\frac{1}{3}+\frac{1}{4}$ 12. $\frac{2}{3}+\frac{1}{2}$ 13. $\frac{3}{5}+\frac{1}{4}$ 14. $\frac{1}{5}+\frac{1}{6}$ 15. $\frac{1}{8}+\frac{5}{6}$

16. $\frac{2}{3}+\frac{1}{9}$ 17. $\frac{2}{3}+\frac{1}{10}$ 18. $\frac{3}{4}+\frac{3}{10}$ 19. $\frac{3}{4}+\frac{1}{6}$ 20. $\frac{2}{5}+\frac{3}{8}$

Set 22 (after page 111)

1. $\frac{3}{4}-\frac{1}{4}$ 2. $\frac{1}{2}-\frac{1}{4}$ 3. $\frac{5}{9}-\frac{1}{3}$ 4. $1-\frac{2}{3}$ 5. $2-\frac{1}{3}$

6. $\frac{7}{8}-\frac{3}{4}$ 7. $\frac{1}{2}-\frac{3}{8}$ 8. $\frac{3}{10}-\frac{1}{5}$ 9. $\frac{5}{6}-\frac{2}{3}$ 10. $\frac{2}{3}-\frac{1}{4}$

11. $\frac{7}{4}-1$ 12. $\frac{3}{4}-\frac{3}{8}$ 13. $\frac{5}{4}-\frac{5}{8}$ 14. $\frac{3}{4}-\frac{2}{3}$ 15. $\frac{5}{9}-\frac{1}{2}$

16. $\frac{8}{9}-\frac{3}{4}$ 17. $\frac{3}{4}-\frac{5}{8}$ 18. $\frac{3}{4}-\frac{3}{10}$ 19. $\frac{3}{4}-\frac{1}{6}$ 20. $\frac{2}{5}-\frac{3}{8}$

Set 23 (after page 115) **Add or subtract. Give fractional parts in lowest terms.**

1. $8\frac{2}{5} + 3\frac{3}{4}$
2. $9\frac{1}{6} + 8\frac{1}{3}$
3. $14\frac{5}{9} + 6\frac{2}{3}$
4. $6\frac{7}{8} + 9\frac{3}{8}$
5. $3\frac{2}{5} + 6\frac{1}{2}$
6. $31\frac{1}{3} + 24\frac{2}{9}$
7. $25\frac{1}{2} + 38\frac{3}{4}$
8. $6\frac{3}{4} + 6\frac{3}{2}$
9. $5\frac{1}{4} + 3\frac{1}{8}$
10. $5\frac{3}{4} + 9\frac{5}{8}$
11. $9\frac{1}{2} - 4\frac{3}{4}$
12. $12 - 9\frac{3}{5}$
13. $8\frac{1}{4} - 6\frac{3}{5}$
14. $4\frac{5}{9} - 2\frac{2}{3}$
15. $15 - 12\frac{5}{8}$
16. $15\frac{1}{6} - 8\frac{1}{8}$
17. $6\frac{5}{7} - 3$
18. $3\frac{1}{3} - 2\frac{1}{2}$
19. $7\frac{3}{4} - 4\frac{5}{8}$
20. $6\frac{2}{3} - 3\frac{1}{6}$

Set 24 (after page 119) **Reduce answers to lowest terms.**

1. $\frac{1}{2} \times \frac{1}{4}$
2. $\frac{4}{7} \times \frac{2}{5}$
3. $\frac{2}{3} \times \frac{4}{4}$
4. $\frac{5}{8} \times \frac{0}{6}$
5. $\frac{5}{9} \times \frac{3}{10}$
6. $\frac{1}{7} \times \frac{1}{8}$
7. $\frac{1}{2} \times \frac{3}{8}$
8. $\frac{1}{4} \times \frac{2}{2}$
9. $\frac{3}{4} \times \frac{3}{3}$
10. $\frac{3}{4} \times \frac{7}{7}$
11. $\frac{3}{4} \times \frac{13}{13}$
12. $\frac{3}{4} \times \frac{107}{107}$
13. $\frac{5}{8} \times \frac{7}{5}$
14. $\frac{1}{5} \times \frac{1}{4}$
15. $\frac{2}{5} \times \frac{3}{5}$
16. $\frac{3}{4} \times \frac{8}{7}$
17. $\frac{2}{3} \times \frac{3}{2}$
18. $\frac{3}{4} \times \frac{4}{3}$
19. $\frac{5}{8} \times \frac{8}{5}$
20. $\frac{3}{5} \times \frac{5}{3}$

Set 25 (after page 121) **Reduce answers to lowest terms.**

1. $\frac{1}{2} \div \frac{2}{3}$
2. $\frac{4}{9} \div \frac{1}{3}$
3. $\frac{3}{2} \div \frac{3}{4}$
4. $\frac{3}{4} \div \frac{1}{8}$
5. $\frac{9}{5} \div \frac{3}{8}$
6. $\frac{5}{6} \div \frac{1}{2}$
7. $\frac{1}{8} \div \frac{9}{5}$
8. $\frac{1}{5} \div \frac{5}{4}$
9. $\frac{3}{4} \div \frac{3}{4}$
10. $\frac{2}{3} \div \frac{2}{3}$
11. $\frac{3}{5} \div \frac{3}{5}$
12. $\frac{5}{6} \div \frac{5}{6}$
13. $\frac{3}{4} \div \frac{2}{2}$
14. $\frac{3}{4} \div \frac{7}{7}$
15. $\frac{3}{10} \div \frac{1}{10}$
16. $\frac{3}{10} \div \frac{1}{5}$
17. $\frac{1}{2} \div \frac{7}{2}$
18. $\frac{4}{5} \div 2$
19. $\frac{8}{7} \div 2$
20. $\frac{9}{5} \div 2$

Set 26 (after page 123) **Give fractional parts of answers in lowest terms.**

1. $4\frac{1}{2} \times 2$ 2. $2\frac{1}{3} \times 5$ 3. $6\frac{1}{4} \times 6$ 4. $2\frac{1}{3} \times 9$

5. $1\frac{1}{5} \times 2\frac{3}{8}$ 6. $3\frac{5}{6} \times 2\frac{5}{8}$ 7. $1\frac{3}{4} \times 4\frac{1}{6}$ 8. $2\frac{1}{9} \times 8\frac{3}{4}$

9. $3\frac{1}{4} \div 3\frac{1}{4}$ 10. $4\frac{1}{6} \div 4\frac{1}{6}$ 11. $7\frac{1}{3} \div 2\frac{1}{4}$ 12. $9\frac{1}{2} \div 3\frac{1}{2}$

13. $4\frac{5}{8} \div 6\frac{3}{4}$ 14. $6\frac{3}{4} \div 4\frac{5}{8}$ 15. $3 \div 6\frac{2}{3}$ 16. $4\frac{1}{2} \div 1\frac{1}{2}$

17. $6\frac{3}{5} \div 8\frac{2}{3}$ 18. $6\frac{1}{3} \div 7\frac{1}{5}$ 19. $5\frac{1}{4} \div 5\frac{5}{4}$ 20. $5\frac{2}{3} \div 9$

Set 27 (after page 131) **Solve.**

1. $2x = 7$ 2. $5x = 1$ 3. $3x = 5$ 4. $9x = 12$

5. $12x = 9$ 6. $\frac{1}{2}x = 4$ 7. $\frac{1}{3}x = 4$ 8. $\frac{1}{5}x = 4$

9. $\frac{2}{5}x = 4$ 10. $\frac{2}{3}x = 4$ 11. $\frac{3}{5}x = 6$ 12. $\frac{3}{5}x = 7$

13. $\frac{1}{2}x + \frac{1}{4} = 3\frac{1}{4}$ 14. $\frac{2}{3}x + \frac{2}{5} = 4\frac{2}{5}$ 15. $\frac{3}{4}x + \frac{1}{3} = \frac{9}{3}$ 16. $\frac{5}{6}x + \frac{1}{5} = \frac{3}{4}$

17. $\frac{1}{2}x - \frac{1}{4} = 2\frac{3}{4}$ 18. $\frac{3}{4}x - 2 = 8\frac{3}{8}$ 19. $\frac{5}{8}x - \frac{3}{4} = 2\frac{1}{5}$ 20. $\frac{2}{3}x - 2\frac{5}{6} = 4\frac{7}{8}$

Set 28 (after page 139) **The two figures are congruent. Complete the lists of corresponding parts.**

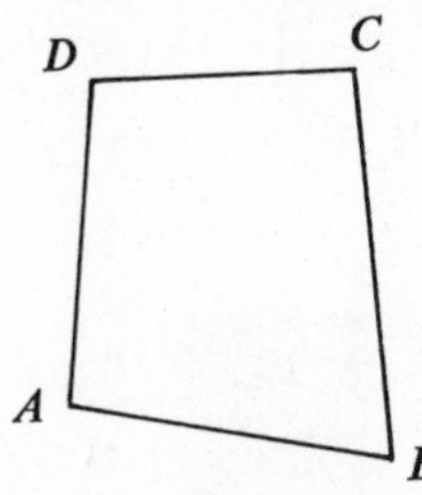

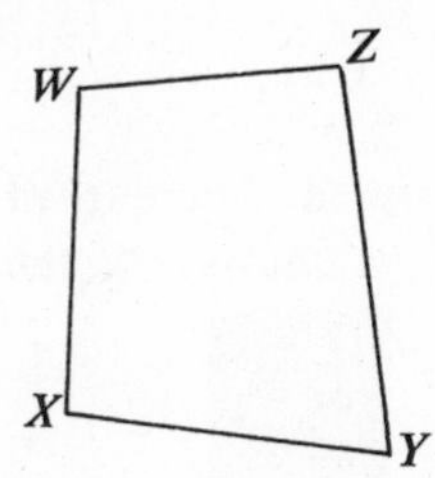

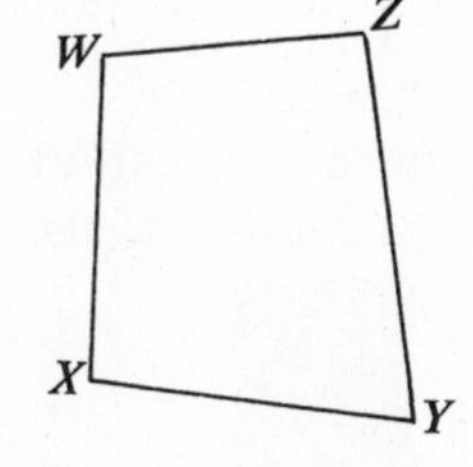

Corresponding parts

1. $\overline{AB}$ and ___?___ 2. $\overline{BC}$ and ___?___
3. $\overline{CD}$ and ___?___ 4. $\overline{DA}$ and ___?___
5. $\angle A$ and ___?___ 6. $\angle Y$ and ___?___
7. $\angle W$ and ___?___ 8. $\angle B$ and ___?___

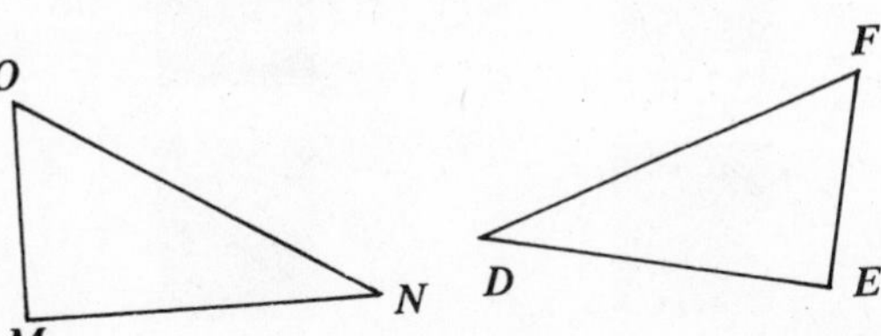

Corresponding parts

9. $\overline{MN}$ and ___?___ 10. $\overline{NO}$ and ___?___
11. $\overline{OM}$ and ___?___ 12. $\angle D$ and ___?___
13. $\angle E$ and ___?___ 14. $\angle F$ and ___?___

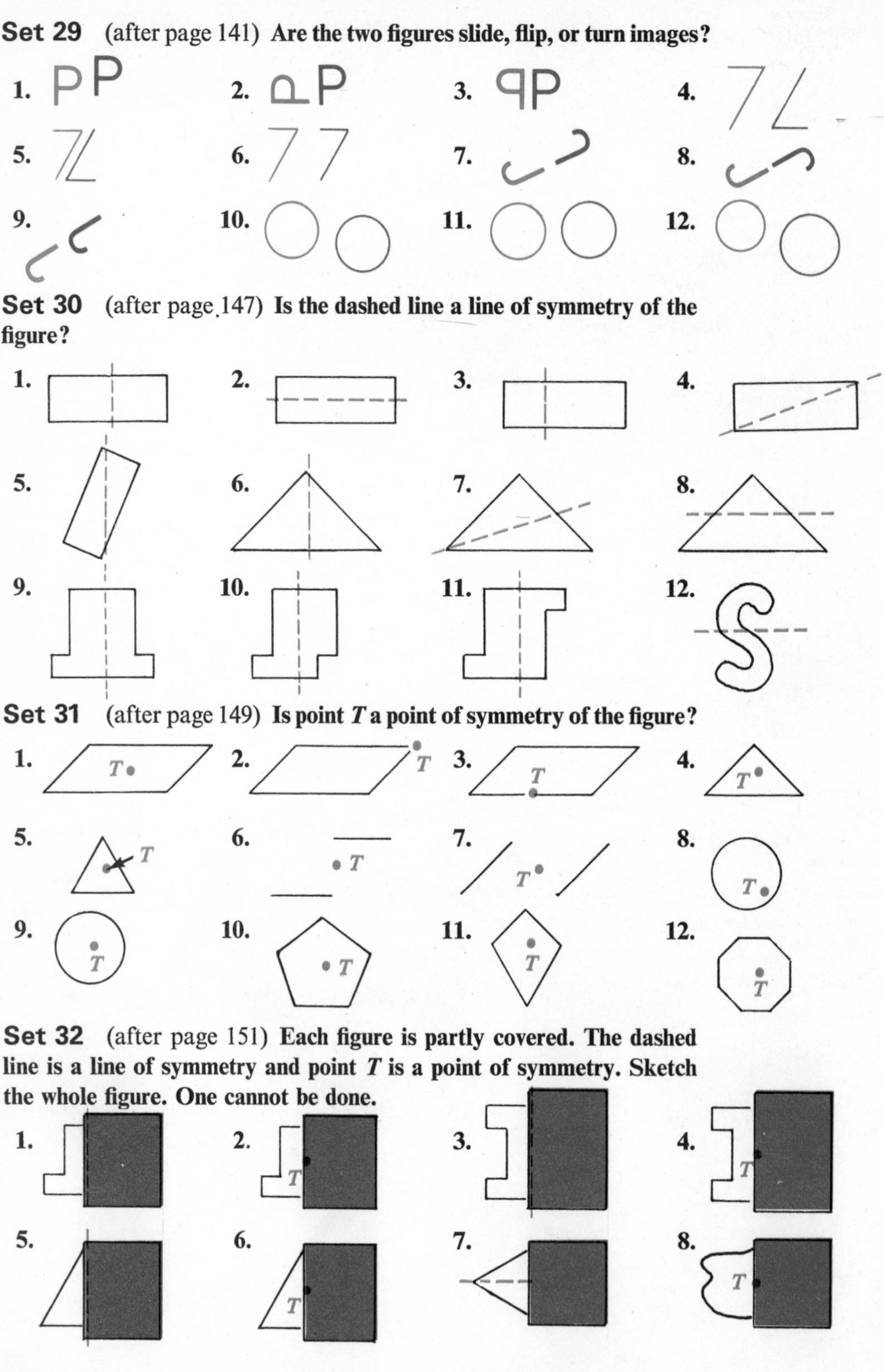

Set 29 (after page 141) **Are the two figures slide, flip, or turn images?**

Set 30 (after page 147) **Is the dashed line a line of symmetry of the figure?**

Set 31 (after page 149) **Is point *T* a point of symmetry of the figure?**

Set 32 (after page 151) **Each figure is partly covered. The dashed line is a line of symmetry and point *T* is a point of symmetry. Sketch the whole figure. One cannot be done.**

9. 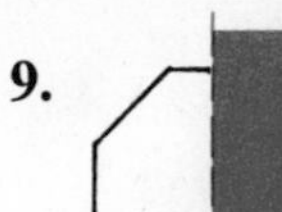

10. 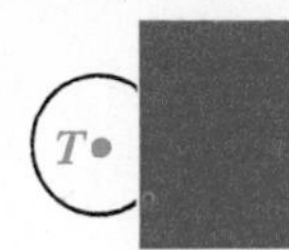

11. 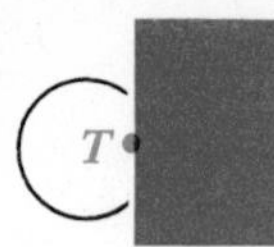

12. 

Set 33 (after page 165)

1. $\frac{2}{4} = \frac{x}{2}$
2. $\frac{5}{6} = \frac{a}{12}$
3. $\frac{f}{9} = \frac{4}{3}$
4. $\frac{5}{6} = \frac{11}{a}$
5. $\frac{8}{3} = \frac{13}{d}$
6. $\frac{3}{2} = \frac{5}{f}$
7. $\frac{g}{12} = \frac{1}{4}$
8. $\frac{h}{2} = \frac{9}{4}$
9. $\frac{c}{11} = \frac{3}{8}$
10. $\frac{7}{8} = \frac{w}{4}$
11. $\frac{z}{14} = \frac{7}{4}$
12. $\frac{20}{24} = \frac{k}{12}$
13. $\frac{6}{7} = \frac{9}{b}$
14. $\frac{a}{18} = \frac{5}{4}$
15. $\frac{3}{y} = 47$
16. $\frac{5}{9} = \frac{8}{g}$
17. $\frac{19}{j} = \frac{9}{5}$
18. $\frac{5}{9} = \frac{k}{5}$
19. $\frac{9}{4} = \frac{9}{w}$
20. $\frac{13}{x} = \frac{3}{5}$

Set 34 (after page 171) **Change to percents.**

1. $\frac{1}{4}$
2. $\frac{2}{4}$
3. $\frac{3}{4}$
4. $\frac{4}{4}$
5. $\frac{5}{4}$
6. $\frac{6}{4}$
7. $\frac{1}{3}$
8. $\frac{2}{3}$
9. $\frac{3}{3}$
10. $\frac{4}{3}$
11. $\frac{1}{8}$
12. $\frac{3}{8}$
13. $\frac{5}{8}$
14. $\frac{7}{8}$
15. $\frac{1}{6}$
16. $\frac{5}{6}$
17. $\frac{1}{5}$
18. $\frac{2}{5}$
19. $\frac{3}{5}$
20. $\frac{4}{5}$
21. $\frac{5}{5}$
22. $\frac{6}{5}$
23. $\frac{7}{5}$
24. $\frac{8}{5}$

Set 35 (after page 173) **Change to fractions in lowest terms.**

1. 10%
2. 20%
3. 30%
4. 40%
5. 50%
6. 60%
7. 70%
8. 80%
9. 85%
10. 90%
11. 250%
12. 175%
13. $66\frac{2}{3}\%$
14. $16\frac{2}{3}\%$
15. 1%
16. $\frac{1}{2}\%$
17. $\frac{1}{4}\%$
18. $87\frac{1}{2}\%$
19. $83\frac{1}{3}\%$
20. $12\frac{1}{2}\%$
21. $11\frac{1}{9}\%$

Set 36 (after page 175)

	1.	2.	3.	4.	5.	6.	7.	8.	9.	10.
Fraction	$\frac{3}{4}$	?	?	?	?	?	$\frac{3}{8}$	?	?	?
Decimal	?	.60	?	.08	?	1.5	?	.006	?	?
Percent	?	?	25%	?	140%	?	?	?	50%	$66\frac{2}{3}\%$

Set 37 (after page 179)

1. 75% of 164 = ___?___
2. 50% of 386 = ___?___
3. 35% of 146 = ___?___
4. $12\frac{1}{2}$% of 136 = ___?___
5. 100% of 48 = ___?___
6. 40% of 437 = ___?___
7. $33\frac{1}{3}$% of 132 = ___?___
8. 6% of 80 = ___?___
9. 150% of 27 = ___?___
10. 300% of 48 = ___?___
11. 40% of 380 = ___?___
12. 30% of 480 = ___?___
13. 8% of 500 = ___?___
14. 20% of 125 = ___?___
15. $83\frac{1}{3}$% of 42 = ___?___
16. 500% of 17 = ___?___
17. $62\frac{1}{2}$% of 264 = ___?___
18. 10% of 521 = ___?___
19. 50% of 12 = ___?___
20. 5% of 12 = ___?___
21. .5% of 12 = ___?___

Set 38 (after page 181)

1. 60% of 70 = ___?___
2. 6% of 70 = ___?___
3. .6% of 70 = ___?___
4. 50% of 30 = ___?___
5. 5% of 30 = ___?___
6. .5% of 30 = ___?___
7. 90% of 80 = ___?___
8. 9% of 80 = ___?___
9. .9% of 80 = ___?___
10. 25% of 40 = ___?___
11. 2.5% of 40 = ___?___
12. $\frac{1}{4}$% of 49 = ___?___
13. $66\frac{2}{3}$% of 75 = ___?___
14. $33\frac{1}{3}$% of 75 = ___?___
15. 100% of 80 = ___?___
16. 200% of 80 = ___?___
17. 300% of 80 = ___?___
18. 400% of 80 = ___?___
19. 100% of 2 = ___?___
20. 200% of 2 = ___?___
21. 150% of 2 = ___?___

Set 39 (after page 183)

1. 50% of ___?___ = 8
2. 50% of 8 = ___?___
3. 25% of ___?___ = 20
4. 25% of 20 = ___?___
5. 70% of ___?___ = 49
6. 70% of 49 = ___?___
7. 10% of ___?___ = 8
8. 200% of ___?___ = 36
9. 150% of ___?___ = 24
10. 1% of ___?___ = 12
11. 40% of ___?___ = 64
12. $33\frac{1}{3}$% of ___?___ = 15
13. $66\frac{2}{3}$% of ___?___ = 30
14. 250% of ___?___ = 50
15. 80% of ___?___ = 48
16. 90% of ___?___ = 54
17. 75% of ___?___ = 24
18. 75% of ___?___ = 12
19. 75% of ___?___ = 6
20. 10% of ___?___ = 6.7
21. 10% of ___?___ = .31

Set 40 (after page 185)

1. 10% of ___?___ = 6
2. 50% of ___?___ = 18
3. 200% of ___?___ = 38
4. 150% of ___?___ = 120
5. 5% of ___?___ = 8
6. 25% of ___?___ = 18
7. $37\frac{1}{2}\%$ of ___?___ = 27
8. 175% of ___?___ = 42
9. $33\frac{1}{3}\%$ of ___?___ = 30
10. 1% of ___?___ = 5
11. 20% of ___?___ = 6
12. 60% of ___?___ = 141
13. $12\frac{1}{2}\%$ of ___?___ = 42
14. $83\frac{1}{3}\%$ of ___?___ = 56
15. $16\frac{2}{3}\%$ of ___?___ = 27
16. $87\frac{1}{2}\%$ of ___?___ = 35
17. 40% of ___?___ = 48
18. $133\frac{1}{3}\%$ of ___?___ = 128
19. $62\frac{1}{2}\%$ of ___?___ = 135
20. 250% of ___?___ = 85
21. $66\frac{2}{3}\%$ of ___?___ = 108

Set 41 (after page 197)

1. 53 cm = ___?___ mm
2. 4 km = ___?___ m
3. 70 mm = ___?___ cm
4. 16 m = ___?___ dm
5. 43 mm = ___?___ cm
6. 7 km = ___?___ m
7. 3 m = ___?___ cm
8. 12 dm = ___?___ cm
9. 81 mm = ___?___ cm
10. 81 cm = ___?___ dm
11. 81 dm = ___?___ m
12. 81 m = ___?___ dm
13. 123 mm = ___?___ cm
14. 123 mm = ___?___ dm
15. 123 mm = ___?___ m
16. 123 cm = ___?___ dm
17. 6 m = ___?___ dm
18. 6 m = ___?___ cm
19. 6 m = ___?___ mm
20. 47 km = ___?___ m
21. 2.7 m = ___?___ cm
22. 2.7 m = ___?___ mm
23. 2.7 m = ___?___ km
24. 5.4 km = ___?___ m
25. 38.4 cm = ___?___ dm
26. 2 cm = ___?___ mm
27. 1628 m = ___?___ km
28. .385 m = ___?___ mm

Set 42 (after page 199)

1. 3 qt = ___?___ pt
2. 20 gal = ___?___ qt
3. 7 yd = ___?___ in.
4. 6 mi = ___?___ yd
5. 3 m = ___?___ cm
6. 20 m = ___?___ dm
7. 7 m = ___?___ mm
8. 6 km = ___?___ m
9. 15 lb = ___?___ oz
10. 35 tons = ___?___ lb
11. 5 c = ___?___ tbsp
12. 13 ft = ___?___ in
13. 15 m = ___?___ cm
14. 35 km = ___?___ m
15. 5 hm = ___?___ dm
16. 13 dm = ___?___ mm
17. 108 in. = ___?___ yd
18. 35 in. = ___?___ ft
19. 57 oz = ___?___ lb
20. 93 pt = ___?___ gal
21. 108 cm = ___?___ m
22. 35 mm = ___?___ dm
23. 57 cm = ___?___ m
24. 93 dm = ___?___ m

Set 43 (after page 203) **The last digit on the right shows the precision. For example: A measurement of 6.2*1* inches is correct to the nearest hundredth inch. A measurement of 27.*0* cm is correct to the nearest tenth cm. Give the percent of error.**

1. 1.2 cm	**2.** 31.2 mm	**3.** 51.2 cm	**4.** 1000.2 cm
5. 6 m	**6.** 6.1 m	**7.** 6.13 m	**8.** 7 km
9. 7.0 km	**10.** 7.00 km	**11.** 10 in.	**12.** 10.0 in.

Set 44 (after page 205)

1. $30° 15' 17'' + 21° 18' 24''$

2. $50° 27' 54'' + 32° 14' 18''$

3. $72° 52' 24'' + 18° 12' 10''$

4. $93° 47' 35'' + 17° 18' 40''$

5. $28° 36' 17'' + 51° 48' 29''$

6. $54° 42' 28'' + 37° 52' 44''$

7. $92° 53' 53'' + 22° 45' 45''$

8. $88° 55' 28'' + 16° 34' 34''$

9. $27° 35' 14'' - 14° 16' 10''$

10. $72° 48' 26'' - 12° 15' 30''$

11. $45° 37' 42'' - 17° 45' 10''$

12. $37° 25' 27'' - 14° 53' 45''$

13. $51° 38' 17'' - 42° 56' 29''$

14. $93° 17' 16'' - 92° 17' 17''$

15. $18° - 12° 52' 41''$

16. $75° - 74° 59' 59''$

Set 45 (after page 209) **Compute each area.**

1.
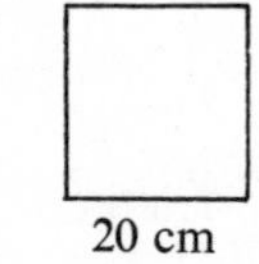

2.
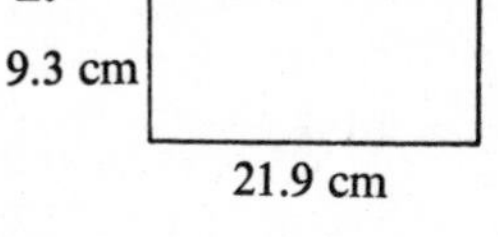

3.
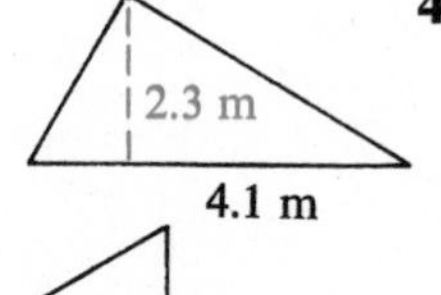

4.
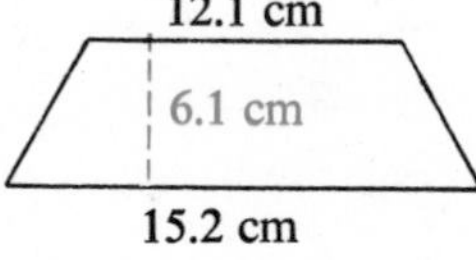

5.
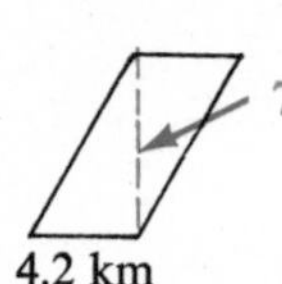

6.
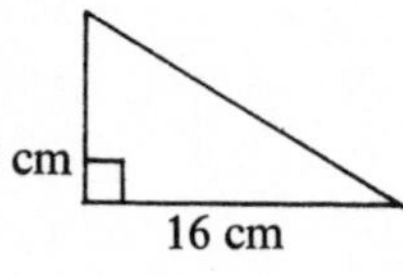

7.
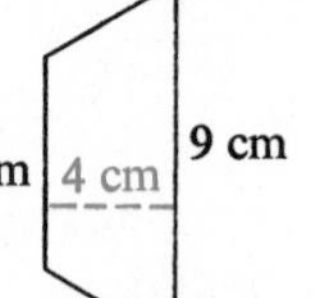

8.
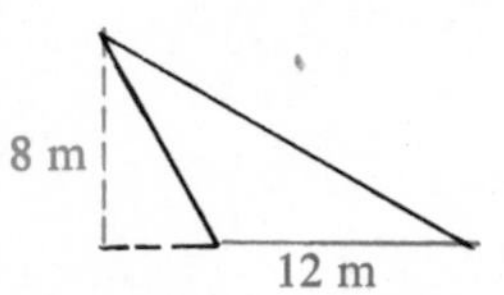

Set 46 (after page 221) **Give each volume and surface area. Use 3.14 as an approximation for π.**

1.
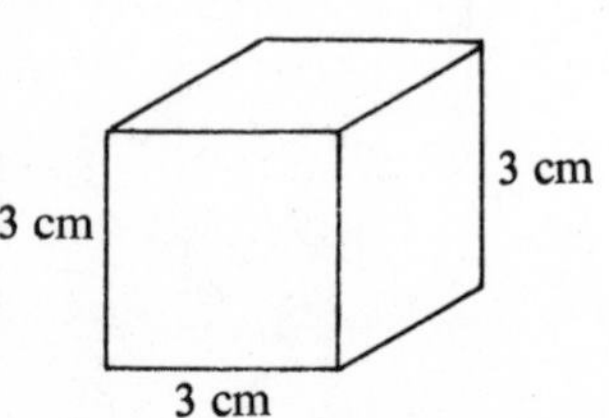

2.
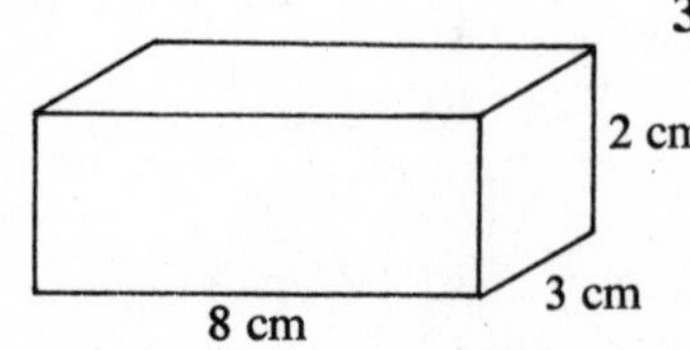

3.
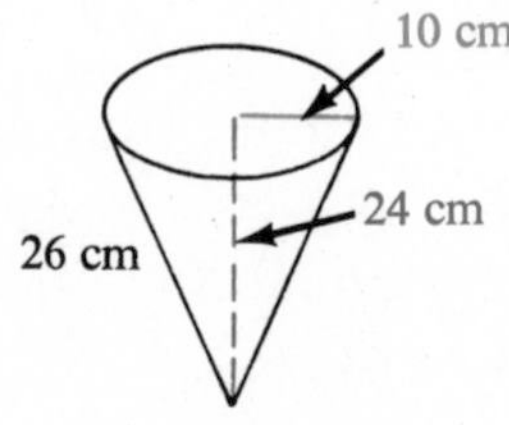

4.

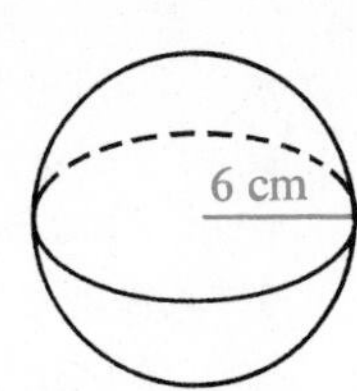

5.

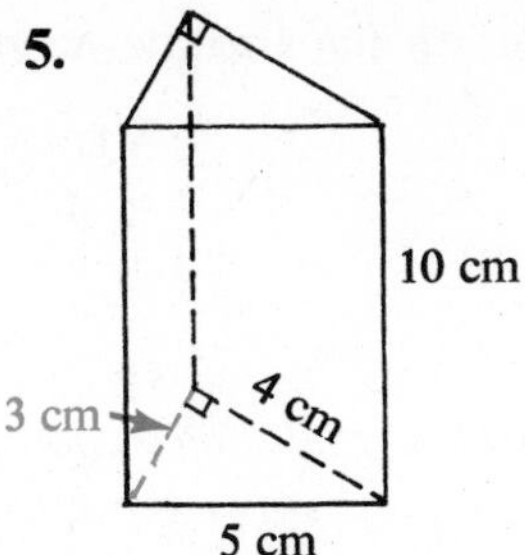

6.

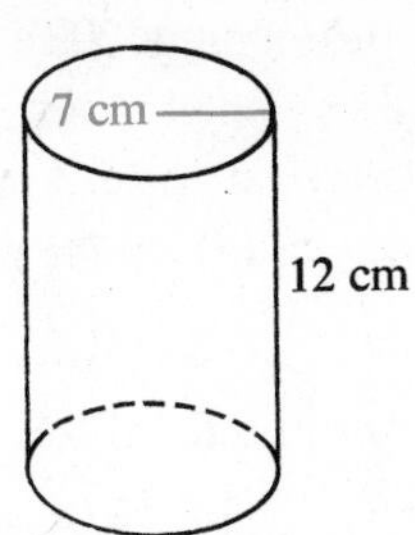

Set 47 (after page 223)

1. 2 *l* = ___?___ dl
2. 4 dl = ___?___ *l*
3. 24 *l* = ___?___ dal
4. 24 cl = ___?___ ml
5. 5.92 *l* = ___?___ cl
6. 3.9 kl = ___?___ hl
7. 53.7 ml = ___?___ cl
8. 56.2 hl = ___?___ kl
9. 34.5 cl = ___?___ ml
10. 3.5 cl = ___?___ ml
11. 7.48 kl = ___?___ dal
12. 3.92 hl = ___?___ *l*
13. 2.74 hl = ___?___ *l*
14. 4.3 dl = ___?___ cl
15. 8.6 dal = ___?___ dl
16. 7.9 dal = ___?___ *l*
17. .396 *l* = ___?___ dl
18. .396 *l* = ___?___ cl
19. .396 *l* = ___?___ ml
20. .396 *l* = ___?___ dal
21. 1.2 kl = ___?___ dal
22. 1.2 kl = ___?___ dl
23. 1.2 kl = ___?___ *l*
24. 1.2 kl = ___?___ hl

Set 48 (after page 227)

1. 7 g = ___?___ dg
2. 4 g = ___?___ dag
3. 4 g = ___?___ cg
4. 8 g = ___?___ mg
5. 41 g = ___?___ dg
6. 38 g = ___?___ cg
7. 72 g = ___?___ dag
8. 72 g = ___?___ hg
9. 2 kg = ___?___ hg
10. 2 kg = ___?___ dag
11. 2 kg = ___?___ g
12. 2 kg = ___?___ dg
13. 5.1 kg = ___?___ hg
14. 5.16 hg = ___?___ g
15. 6.41 g = ___?___ cg
16. 3.29 dg = ___?___ dag
17. 4.9 kg = ___?___ dag
18. 7.155 kg = ___?___ g
19. 3.75 dg = ___?___ mg
20. 63.8 hg = ___?___ g
21. 4673 mg = ___?___ cg
22. 4673 mg = ___?___ dg
23. 4673 mg = ___?___ g
24. 4673 mg = ___?___ dag

Set 49 (after page 229) **Convert from one unit to the other.**

1. 5 lb to kg
2. 5 kg to lb
3. 14 qt to *l*
4. 14 *l* to qt
5. 7 m to yd
6. 7 yd to m
7. 8 in. to cm
8. 8 cm to in.
9. 24 mi to km
10. 24 km to mi
11. 58 g to oz
12. 58 oz to g
13. 1 ton to kg
14. 1 gal to *l*
15. 1 pt to *l*
16. 20 oz to kg

Set 50 (after page 235) **Compute the earnings to the nearest cent.**

1. \$4.40 per hour
   40 hours
2. \$6.75 per hour
   37.5 hours
3. \$2.50 per hour
   $4\frac{1}{2}$ hours
4. \$6.34 per hour
   time and a half
   over 40 hours
   48.5 hours
5. 5% commission
   on sales of
   \$4,821
6. 9% commission
   on sales of
   \$56,320
7. \$824 per month
   12 months
8. \$925 per month
   7 months
9. \$600 plus 4%
   commission on
   sales of \$3,651
10. \$.032 per piece
    made; 1,535
    pieces made
11. \$3.25 per
    haircut;
    12 haircuts
12. \$5.25 per hour;
    $35\frac{1}{4}$ hours

Set 51 (after page 243) **Compute the tax to the nearest cent.**

1. 5% on \$48.20
2. $4\frac{1}{2}$% on \$12.14
3. 5% on \$17.95
4. $5\frac{1}{2}$% on \$83.75
5. $3\frac{1}{2}$% on \$123.60
6. 5% on \$.75
7. 5% on \$.12
8. $4\frac{1}{2}$% on \$.50
9. \$1.90 per \$100 val.;
   val.: \$732
10. \$2.30 per \$100 val.;
    val.: \$917.25
11. \$.027 per \$1 val.;
    val.: \$17.89
12. 11.5¢ per gal;
    18 gal

Set 52 (after page 249) **Compute the interest to the nearest cent.**

1. Principal: \$1,000
   Rate: 7% per year
   Time: 3 years
2. Principal: \$2,000
   Rate: $8\frac{1}{2}$% per year
   Time: 6 months
3. Principal: \$7,000
   Rate: 12% per year
   Time: 2 years
4. Principal: \$700
   Rate: 2% per month
   Time: 5 months
5. Principal: \$1,000
   Rate: 3% per month
   Time: 7 months
6. Principal: \$450
   Rate: 10% per year
   Time: 3 months
7. Principal: \$675
   Rate: 9% per year
   Time: 18 months
8. Principal: \$1,500
   Rate: $9\frac{1}{2}$% per year
   Time: 5 years
9. Principal: \$6,000
   Rate: $11\frac{3}{4}$% per year
   Time: 2 months
10. Principal: \$250
    Rate: $2\frac{1}{2}$% per month
    Time: 3 months
11. Principal: \$620
    Rate: $2\frac{1}{2}$% per month
    Time: 1 month
12. Principal: \$850
    Rate: $8\frac{1}{2}$% per year
    Time: 6 months

Set 53 (after page 271) **Give the end point of each trip.**

$^{-}7 \quad ^{-}6 \quad ^{-}5 \quad ^{-}4 \quad ^{-}3 \quad ^{-}2 \quad ^{-}1 \quad 0 \quad 1 \quad 2 \quad 3 \quad 4 \quad 5 \quad 6 \quad 7$

	1.	**2.**	**3.**	**4.**	**5.**	**6.**	**7.**	**8.**	**9.**	**10.**
Start at	0	0	5	5	3	3	6	7	3	4
Trip	6	$^{-}3$	$^{-}2$	$^{-}7$	8	$^{-}4$	12	7	$^{-}3$	$^{-}8$
End at	?	?	?	?	?	?	?	?	?	?

	11.	**12.**	**13.**	**14.**	**15.**	**16.**	**17.**	**18.**	**19.**	**20.**
Start at	12	12	$^{-}8$	$^{-}8$	$^{-}15$	23	31	$^{-}41$	$^{-}48$	$^{-}101$
Trip	$^{-}7$	13	$^{-}15$	16	$^{-}12$	$^{-}42$	$^{-}19$	17	53	101
End at	?	?	?	?	?	?	?	?	?	?

Set 54 (after page 273)

1. $^{-}5 + ^{-}6$ **2.** $^{-}8 + 0$ **3.** $^{-}5 + ^{+}9$ **4.** $^{+}9 + ^{+}5$ **5.** $0 + ^{+}9$

6. $^{-}6 + ^{-}6$ **7.** $^{-}5 + ^{-}9$ **8.** $^{+}3 + ^{+}9$ **9.** $^{-}9 + ^{+}13$ **10.** $^{+}8 + ^{-}9$

11. $^{-}3 + ^{-}11$ **12.** $^{+}11 + ^{-}15$ **13.** $^{+}14 + ^{-}14$ **14.** $^{+}9 + ^{+}7$ **15.** $^{-}10 + ^{-}1$

16. $^{-}11 + ^{+}11$ **17.** $^{-}20 + ^{+}13$ **18.** $^{+}13 + ^{-}13$ **19.** $0 + ^{-}19$ **20.** $^{+}5 + ^{+}13$

21. $^{+}9 + ^{+}11$ **22.** $^{-}5 + ^{+}12$ **23.** $0 + 0$ **24.** $^{+}16 + ^{-}16$ **25.** $^{-}8 + ^{+}15$

Set 55 (after page 275)

1. $^{+}7 - ^{-}5$ **2.** $^{+}7 - 0$ **3.** $^{+}6 - ^{-}4$ **4.** $^{+}4 - ^{+}6$ **5.** $^{+}12 - ^{+}5$

6. $^{-}3 - ^{+}9$ **7.** $^{-}5 - ^{-}3$ **8.** $0 - ^{+}6$ **9.** $^{-}8 - ^{-}2$ **10.** $^{+}8 - ^{+}3$

11. $^{-}2 - ^{-}6$ **12.** $^{-}2 - ^{-}9$ **13.** $^{+}12 - ^{-}3$ **14.** $0 - 0$ **15.** $^{+}3 - ^{-}9$

16. $^{+}4 - ^{-}6$ **17.** $^{-}9 - ^{-}4$ **18.** $^{-}4 - ^{+}11$ **19.** $^{+}3 - ^{+}8$ **20.** $^{-}1 - ^{-}5$

21. $^{+}6 - ^{+}14$ **22.** $^{+}13 - ^{-}6$ **23.** $^{-}4 - ^{+}6$ **24.** $^{-}8 - ^{-}7$ **25.** $^{+}7 - ^{-}15$

Set 56 (after page 277)

1. $^{-}6 \times ^{+}6$ **2.** $^{-}8 \times ^{-}8$ **3.** $^{+}7 \times ^{-}3$ **4.** $^{+}5 \times ^{+}5$ **5.** $^{-}4 \times ^{+}3$

6. $^{+}5 \times ^{+}7$ **7.** $0 \times ^{-}4$ **8.** $^{-}6 \times ^{+}7$ **9.** $^{-}9 \times ^{-}5$ **10.** $^{-}5 \times ^{-}8$

11. $^{-}9 \times ^{+}9$ **12.** $^{-}3 \times ^{-}9$ **13.** $^{-}9 \times ^{-}8$ **14.** $^{-}9 \times ^{+}5$ **15.** $^{+}4 \times ^{+}6$

16. $^{+}9 \times ^{-}7$ **17.** $^{+}8 \times ^{-}9$ **18.** $^{-}8 \times ^{-}4$ **19.** $^{-}7 \times ^{+}7$ **20.** $^{+}8 \times ^{+}9$

21. $^{+}9 \times ^{+}6$ **22.** $^{-}8 \times ^{+}6$ **23.** 0×0 **24.** $^{-}6 \times ^{-}9$ **25.** $^{-}8 \times ^{-}12$

Set 57 (after page 279)

1. $^-27 \div {}^-3$
2. $^-32 \div {}^+8$
3. $^+24 \div {}^-6$
4. $^+24 \div {}^+6$
5. $^+32 \div {}^+8$
6. $0 \div {}^-7$
7. $^-36 \div {}^-6$
8. $^-35 \div {}^+7$
9. $^-45 \div {}^-9$
10. $^+48 \div {}^-6$
11. $^-8 \div {}^-8$
12. $^+36 \div {}^+4$
13. $^-201 \div {}^-3$
14. $^+525 \div {}^-5$
15. $^-81 \div {}^+3$
16. $^+4.9 \div {}^-7$
17. $\frac{^+3}{4} \div \frac{^+1}{4}$
18. $\frac{^-3}{5} \div \frac{^+1}{5}$
19. $^-21 \div {}^+3$
20. $^+63 \div {}^-9$
21. $^+4.32 \div {}^-9$
22. $^-48 \div {}^-8$
23. $^-4.5 \div {}^-1.5$
24. $^+72 \div {}^-9$
25. $^+81 \div {}^+9$

Set 58 (after page 285)

1. $^+3x = {}^+27$
2. $^+4a = {}^+12$
3. $^-5g = {}^-45$
4. $^-6r = {}^+84$
5. $g + {}^-7 = {}^-3$
6. $h + {}^-7 = {}^+3$
7. $y + {}^-8 = {}^-16$
8. $a + {}^+7 = {}^-3$
9. $\frac{x}{^-4} = {}^-6$
10. $\frac{y}{^+3} = {}^-6$
11. $\frac{^-24}{g} = {}^-3$
12. $\frac{^-24}{y} = {}^+8$
13. $^-2a + {}^+3 = {}^-7$
14. $^+4h + {}^-6 = {}^-18$
15. $^+6r + {}^-12 = {}^+30$
16. $^-5c + {}^-3 = {}^-83$
17. $^+7g - {}^+3 = {}^+32$
18. $^+8x - {}^-4 = {}^+36$
19. $^+10m - {}^-6 = {}^-54$
20. $^-8g - {}^-5 = {}^+45$

Set 59 (after page 287)

1. $^+2a \geq {}^+6$
2. $^+3r \leq {}^+12$
3. $^-5g \geq {}^-30$
4. $^-3h \leq {}^-12$
5. $^-6x < {}^+54$
6. $^+7r > {}^-14$
7. $^-3a > {}^-21$
8. $^-4b \leq {}^-24$
9. $x + {}^+4 \neq {}^+7$
10. $g + {}^-7 \leq {}^+14$
11. $r + {}^-8 \geq {}^-3$
12. $m + {}^+9 > {}^+6$
13. $z - {}^-3 > {}^+4$
14. $r + {}^-8 \leq {}^+17$
15. $^+2a + {}^+4 > {}^+16$
16. $^+3r + {}^-8 \leq {}^+13$
17. $^-4x + {}^+3 \leq {}^-25$
18. $^-2r + {}^-6 \geq {}^+4$
19. $^+6y + {}^-3 \leq {}^+45$
20. $^-3a + {}^-7 \neq {}^-25$

Set 60 (after page 289) **Match.**

1. $x \leq {}^+3$ a.

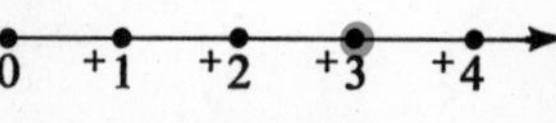

2. $x \geq {}^+3$ b. ⁻4 ⁻3 ⁻2 ⁻1 0 ⁺1 ⁺2 ⁺3 ⁺4

3. $x < {}^+3$ c. ⁻4 ⁻3 ⁻2 ⁻1 0 ⁺1 ⁺2 ⁺3 ⁺4

4. $x > {}^{+}3$ d. $^{-}4 \quad ^{-}3 \quad ^{-}2 \quad ^{-}1 \quad 0 \quad ^{+}1 \quad ^{+}2 \quad ^{+}3 \quad ^{+}4$

5. $x \leq {}^{-}3$ e. $^{-}4 \quad ^{-}3 \quad ^{-}2 \quad ^{-}1 \quad 0 \quad ^{+}1 \quad ^{+}2 \quad ^{+}3 \quad ^{+}4$

6. $x \geq {}^{-}3$ f. $^{-}4 \quad ^{-}3 \quad ^{-}2 \quad ^{-}1 \quad 0 \quad ^{+}1 \quad ^{+}2 \quad ^{+}3 \quad ^{+}4$

7. $x \neq {}^{-}3$ g. $^{-}4 \quad ^{-}3 \quad ^{-}2 \quad ^{-}1 \quad 0 \quad ^{+}1 \quad ^{+}2 \quad ^{+}3 \quad ^{+}4$

8. $x \neq {}^{+}3$ h. $^{-}4 \quad ^{-}3 \quad ^{-}2 \quad ^{-}1 \quad 0 \quad ^{+}1 \quad ^{+}2 \quad ^{+}3 \quad ^{+}4$

9. $x = {}^{-}3$ i. $^{-}4 \quad ^{-}3 \quad ^{-}2 \quad ^{-}1 \quad 0 \quad ^{+}1 \quad ^{+}2 \quad ^{+}3 \quad ^{+}4$

10. $x = {}^{+}3$ j. $^{-}4 \quad ^{-}3 \quad ^{-}2 \quad ^{-}1 \quad 0 \quad ^{+}1 \quad ^{+}2 \quad ^{+}3 \quad ^{+}4$

Set 61 (after page 295) **Tell how many events. Are they equally likely?**

1. Roll die with sides numbered 1, 2, 3, 4. Look at the bottom number.

2. Roll die with sides numbered 1–6. Look at top number.

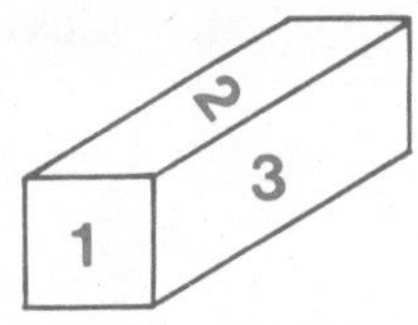

3. Spin this spinner. Look at the number the arrow points at.

4. Toss coin.
Roll die.

5. Toss coin.
Roll die.

6. Roll die.
Spin spinner.

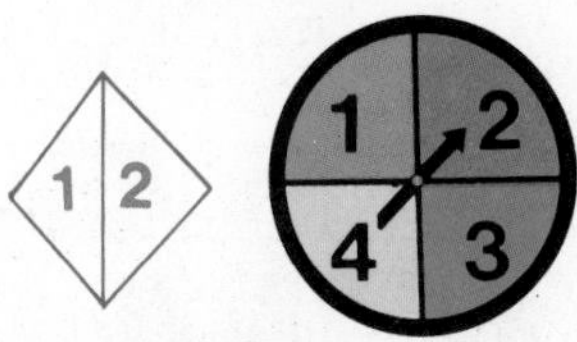

7. Toss dime.
Toss penny.

8. Toss coin.
Spin spinner.

9. Toss dime.
Toss penny.
Toss quarter.

Set 62 (after page 297)

Event: Toss this cube. The faces are numbered 1–6.

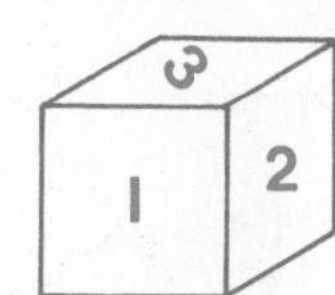

1. $P(1) =$ ___?___
2. $P(\text{even number}) =$ ___?___
3. $P(2) =$ ___?___
4. $P(\text{not } 2) =$ ___?___
5. $P(\text{odd number}) =$ ___?___
6. $P(\text{prime number}) =$ ___?___
7. $P(\text{less than } 2) =$ ___?___
8. $P(\text{greater than } 3) =$ ___?___
9. $P(1 \text{ or } 3) =$ ___?___
10. $P(1 \text{ and } 3) =$ ___?___

Set 63 (after page 299)

Event: Spin this spinner.

1. Odds in favor of 6 = ___?___
2. Odds in favor of 5 = ___?___
3. Odds against 6 = ___?___
4. Odds against 5 = ___?___
5. Odds in favor of even number = ___?___
6. Odds against even number = ___?___
7. Odds in favor of a number less than 2 = ___?___
8. Odds in favor of a prime number = ___?___

Set 64 (after page 301) **Give the sample space.**

1. Toss 4 coins.
2. Toss a coin; toss a die.
3. Toss a die; spin this spinner.

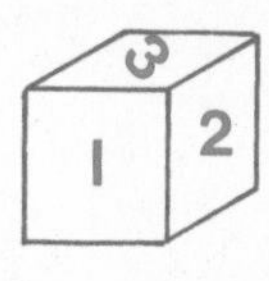

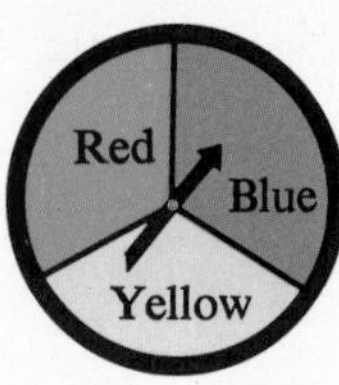

4. Pick 1 card. Replace, pick 1 card.

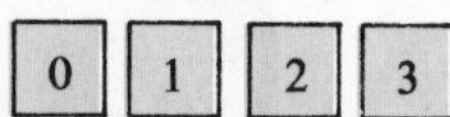

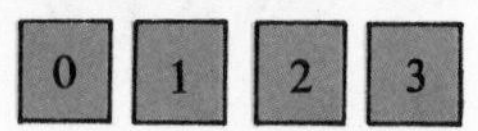

5. Pick 1 card, do not replace, pick 1 card.

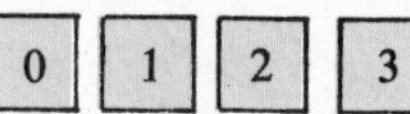

6. Pick 1 card, do not replace, pick 1 card.

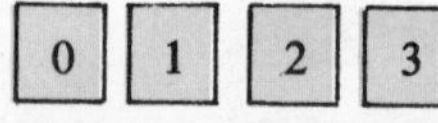

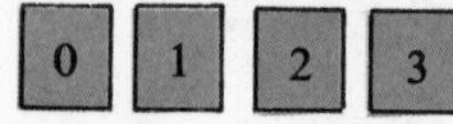

7. Pick 1 card, do not replace, pick 1 card.

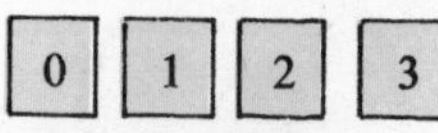

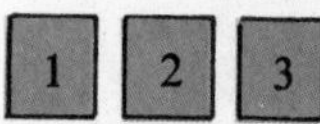

Set 65 (after page 303) **Give each probability.**

1. P(H, H, H, H) when 4 coins are tossed.
2. P(H, 6) when a coin and a die are tossed.
3. P(6, red) when a die is tossed and this spinner is spun.

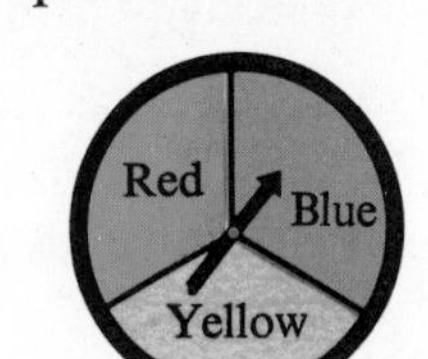

4. Pick 2 cards. Do not replace.
   a. $P(0, 0) =$ ___?___
   b. $P(1, 0) =$ ___?___
   c. $P(3, 1) =$ ___?___
   d. $P(0, 1) =$ ___?___

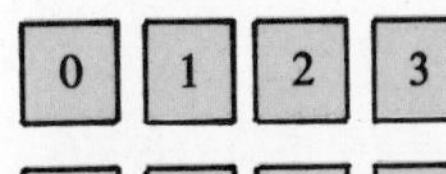

5. Pick 2 cards. Do not replace.
   a. $P(0, 0) =$ ___?___
   b. $P(1, 0) =$ ___?___
   c. $P(3, 1) =$ ___?___
   d. $P(0, 1) =$ ___?___

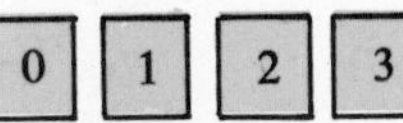

Set 66 (after page 313) **Give the range, mean, median, and mode.**

1. 3, 5, 8, 8, 10, 11, 14
2. 5, 6, 9, 9, 11, 12
3. 32, 38, 45, 49, 50
4. 26, 32, 34, 41, 42, 42, 46
5. 68, 69, 70, 71, 72
6. 39, 43, 56, 57, 65
7. 45, 45, 45, 45, 45, 45
8. 83, 86, 86, 89, 90, 91
9. 126, 124, 132, 128, 130
10. 153, 162, 147, 165, 147

Set 67 (after page 321) **Change to decimals.**

1. $\frac{1}{4}$ 2. $\frac{-2}{5}$ 3. $\frac{1}{6}$ 4. $\frac{-1}{5}$ 5. $\frac{-4}{3}$ 6. $\frac{3}{2}$ 7. $\frac{5}{6}$ 8. $\frac{-4}{5}$

9. $\frac{1}{3}$ 10. $\frac{-3}{4}$ 11. $\frac{-1}{2}$ 12. $\frac{1}{7}$ 13. $\frac{-2}{3}$ 14. $\frac{2}{9}$ 15. $\frac{5}{8}$ 16. $\frac{-7}{4}$

17. $\frac{-5}{4}$ 18. $\frac{-7}{2}$ 19. $\frac{-1}{9}$ 20. $\frac{3}{3}$ 21. $\frac{-3}{5}$ 22. $\frac{5}{2}$ 23. $\frac{3}{8}$ 24. $\frac{9}{2}$

Set 68 (after page 323) <, =, or >?

1. 7.21 ● 7.19
2. 3.48 ● 3.49
3. 7.45 ● 7.451
4. 2.81 ● 2.809
5. $\frac{1}{3}$ ● .3
6. $\frac{1}{3}$ ● .33
7. $\frac{1}{3}$ ● .333
8. $\frac{1}{3}$ ● .333333
9. $\frac{2}{3}$ ● .66
10. $\frac{2}{3}$ ● .666
11. $\frac{2}{3}$ ● .666666
12. $\frac{2}{3}$ ● .6
13. 1 ● .99
14. 1 ● .9999
15. 1 ● .99999
16. 1 ● .9
17. .265 ● .264999
18. 6.793 ● 6.79276
19. .003 ● .0029876

Set 69 (after page 325) **Match.**

1. Commutative property of addition
2. Commutative property of multiplication
3. Associative property of addition
4. Associative property of multiplication
5. Distributive property of multiplication over addition
6. Identity property of addition
7. Identity property of multiplication
8. Additive inverse property
9. Multiplicative inverse property

a. $7 \times (^-3 \times {}^-4) = (7 \times {}^-3) \times {}^-4$
b. $^+7 + 0 = {}^+7$
c. $8 + {}^-8 = 0$
d. $\frac{^-1}{4} \times \frac{1}{6} = \frac{1}{6} \times \frac{^-1}{4}$
e. $^-6 \times 1 = {}^-6$
f. $\frac{^-1}{4} \times {}^-4 = 1$
g. $7 + {}^-3 = {}^-3 + 7$
h. $4 + (3 + {}^-6) = (4 + 3) + {}^-6$
i. $6(^-1 + 1) = 6 \times {}^-1 + 6 \times 1$

Set 70 (after page 329)

1. $3a + {}^-7 = 20$
2. $3(c - 7) = 30$
3. $5x + 8 = {}^-17$
4. $2(a + 9) = 14$
5. $3(g - 4) = 78$
6. $4(x + {}^-4) = 32$
7. $4(x + {}^-4) = {}^-64$
8. $^-3(y + 3) = 21$
9. $^-10(r + 6) = 20$
10. $\frac{a + 5}{^-2} = {}^-2$
11. $\frac{b + {}^-3}{^-4} = 4$
12. $\frac{^-3c + {}^-4}{^-2} = {}^-10$

Set 71 (after page 331) **Write in decimal form correct to the nearest tenth.**

1. $\sqrt{81}$
2. $\sqrt{\frac{9}{4}}$
3. $\sqrt{64}$
4. $\sqrt{65}$
5. $\sqrt{66}$
6. $\sqrt{67}$
7. $\sqrt{68}$
8. $\sqrt{2025}$
9. $\sqrt{400}$
10. $\sqrt{1225}$
11. $\sqrt{751}$
12. $\sqrt{86.3}$
13. $\sqrt{574}$
14. $\sqrt{169}$

Set 72 (after page 333) **Give the coordinates.**

1. Point *A*
2. Point *B*
3. Point *C*
4. Point *D*
5. Point *E*
6. Point *F*
7. Point *G*
8. Point *H*
9. Point *I*
10. Point *J*
11. Point *K*
12. Point *L*

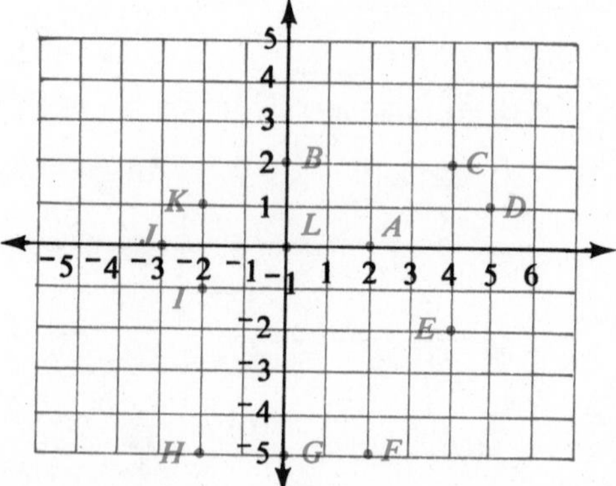

Set 73 (after page 335)

1. $x + y = 12$

	x	y
a.	1	?
b.	$^{-}3$	?
c.	5	?
d.	7	?
e.	18	?
f.	$^{-}9$	?

2. $5x + 2y = 10$

	x	y
a.	2	?
b.	0	?
c.	$^{-}2$	?
d.	$^{-}4$	?
e.	6	?
f.	3	?

3. $x + {}^{-}2y = {}^{-}8$

	x	y
a.	0	?
b.	$^{-}8$	?
c.	$^{-}4$	?
d.	4	?
e.	18	?
f.	$^{-}10$	?

4. $2x + {}^{-}2y = 0$

	x	y
a.	6	?
b.	1	?
c.	0	?
d.	$^{-}3$	?
e.	9	?
f.	$^{-}5$	?

Set 74 (after page 337) **Complete the table. Graph the solution set.**

1. $x - y = 0$

x	y
1	?
$^{-}4$	?
$^{-}6$	?
3	?

2. $x + y = 4$

x	y
3	?
$^{-}2$	?
0	?
$^{-}\frac{1}{2}$	?

3. $2x + y = 6$

x	y
3	?
0	?
2	?
$^{-}4$	?

4. $x + 2y = 6$

x	y
6	?
0	?
$^{-}2$	?
$^{-}4$	?

Set 75 (after page 345)

The two figures in each exercise are similar. Find the missing lengths.

1.

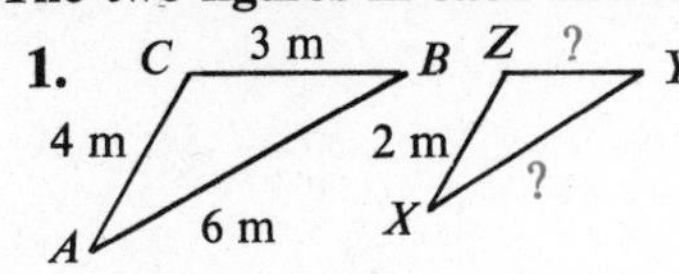

$m(\overline{XY}) =$ __?__

$m(\overline{YZ}) =$ __?__

2.

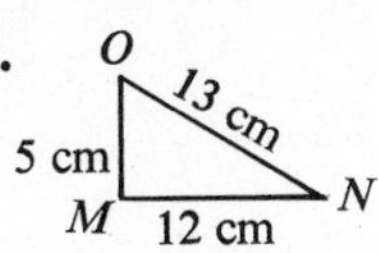

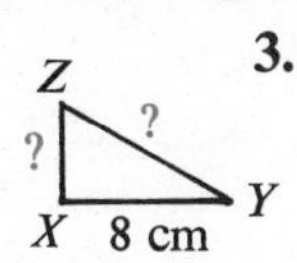

$m(\overline{XZ}) =$ __?__

$m(\overline{YZ}) =$ __?__

3.

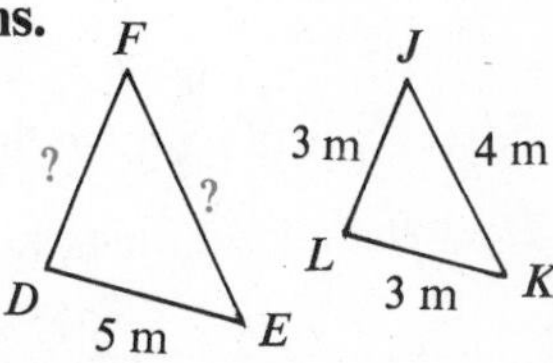

$m(\overline{DF}) =$ __?__

$m(\overline{EF}) =$ __?__

4.

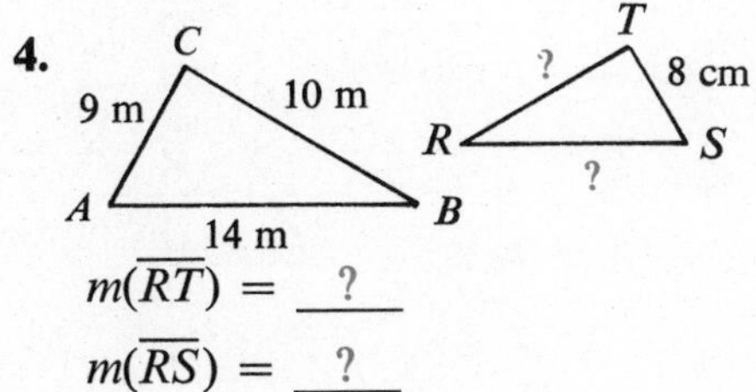

$m(\overline{RT}) =$ __?__

$m(\overline{RS}) =$ __?__

5.

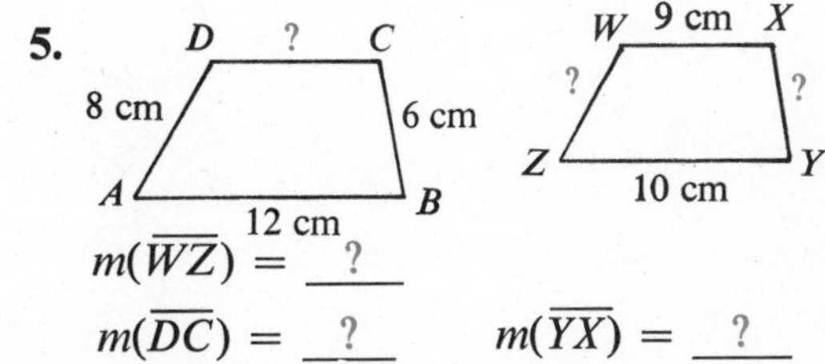

$m(\overline{WZ}) =$ __?__

$m(\overline{DC}) =$ __?__ $m(\overline{YX}) =$ __?__

Set 76 (after page 351)

Find the missing lengths to the nearest .1. Use the table of tangent values on page 351.

1. 40°, 70 m, ?

2. 60°, 90 cm, ?

3. ?, 100′, 70°

4. ?, 10°, 450 yd

5.

6.

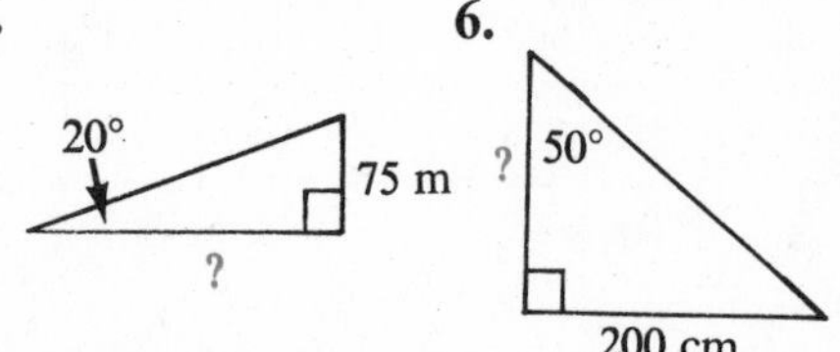

7.

8.

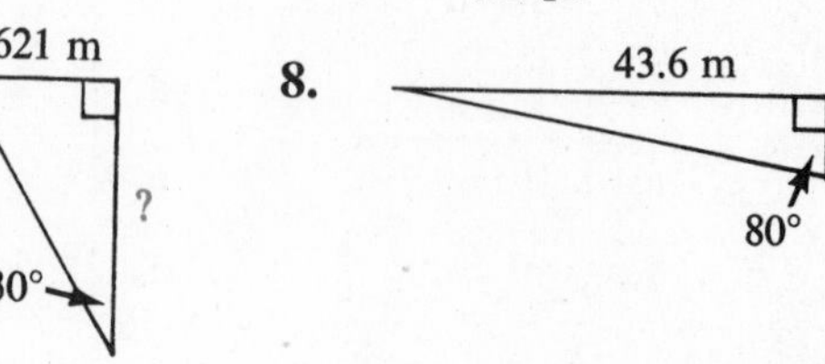

Set 77 (after page 359)

Find the missing lengths to the nearest .1.

1.

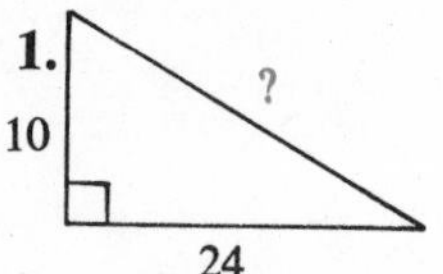

2.

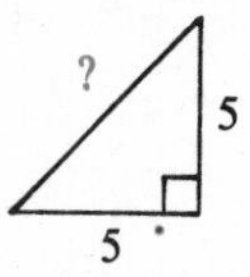

3. 3, 7, ?

4.

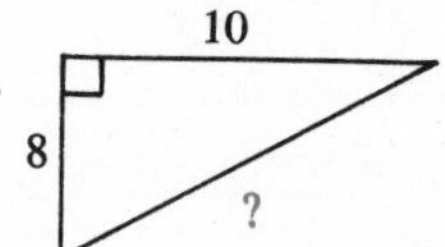

5.

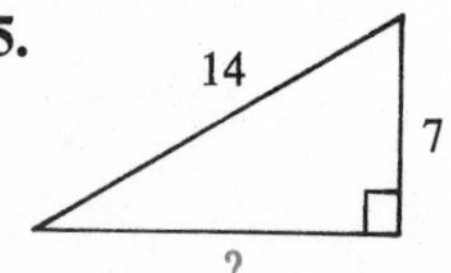

6.

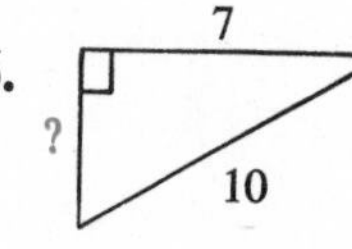

7.

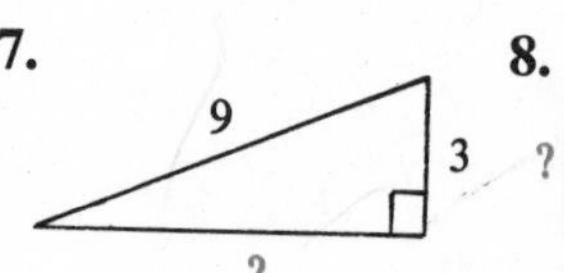

8.

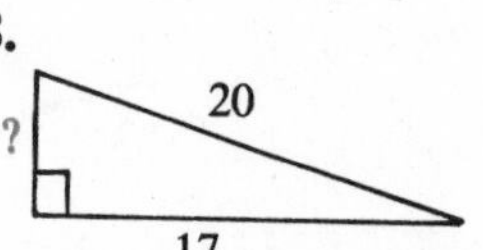

Set 78 (after page 361)

Find the missing lengths to the nearest .1.

1.

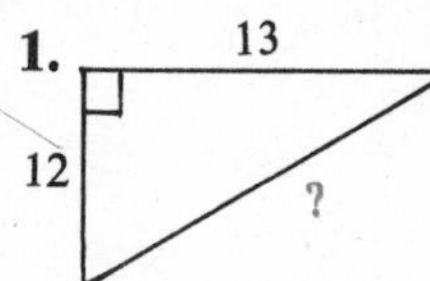

2. 17, 15, ?

3. ?, 8, 21

4.

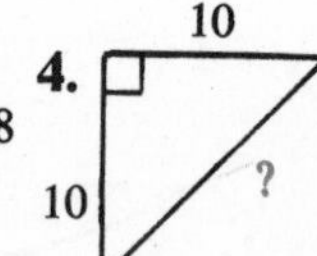

5.

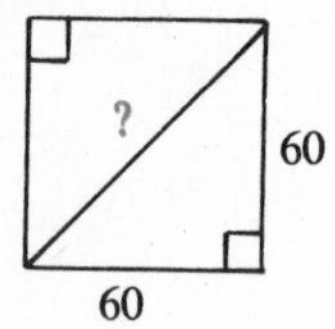

6.

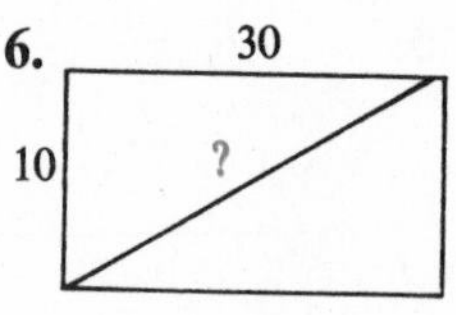

7.

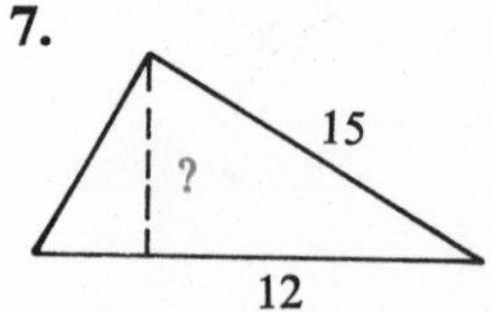

8.

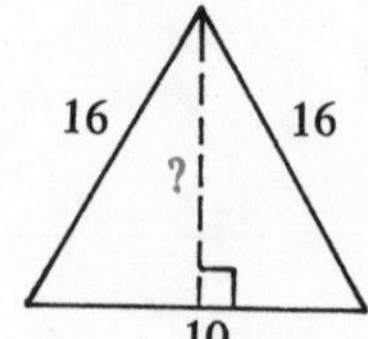

Skill maintenance

Set 1 (after page 5) **Simplify.**

1. $(9 + 3) \div 3$
2. $15 - 7 - 4$
3. $15 - (7 - 4)$
4. $20 \div 2 \div 2$
5. $5 \times 2 + 4 \times 3$
6. $6 + 2 \times 3 + 7$
7. $7 \times (4 + 2)$
8. $6 \times 7 + 3 \times 0$
9. $12 - 6 \times 2$
10. $18 \div (6 \div 3)$
11. $[8 + 2 - 6 + 3] \times 4$
12. $(20 \div 2 \times 2 + 1) \div 3$
13. $[(42 \div 6 + 1) \times 8 - 4] \div 6$

Set 2 (after page 9) **Substitute and simplify.**

a	b	A	c	d
3	6	2	0	5

1. $a \times b$
2. $a \times b - d$
3. $b \times (A - A)$
4. $A \times d - b$
5. $a + b$
6. $d \times (b - a)$
7. $a \times b \times c$
8. $c \times (b + A)$
9. $b \times A - d$
10. $a \times A \times d$
11. $d + c$
12. $b \times c \times d$
13. $a - a$
14. $a \times b \times c \times d$
15. $A \times b + a \times d$
16. $b \times d - A$
17. $b \times (d - A)$
18. $(b - b) \times d$
19. $A \times c$
20. $A \times (b - d)$

Set 3 (after page 11) **Match.**

1. Associative property of addition
2. Multiplying by 0 property
3. Multiplying by 1 property
4. Commutative property of addition
5. Distributive property
6. Associative property of multiplication
7. Commutative property of multiplication
8. Adding 0 property

a. $a + b = b + a$
b. $(ab)c = a(bc)$
c. $a \times 1 = a$
d. $a + 0 = a$
e. $(a + b) + c = a + (b + c)$
f. $ab = ba$
g. $a(b + c) = ab + ac$
h. $a0 = 0$

Set 4 (after page 13) **Simplify.**

1. 2^2
2. 3^1
3. 5^0
4. 2^3
5. 3^2
6. 4^1
7. 1^6
8. 4^3
9. 2^4
10. 5^2
11. 6^2
12. 2^5
13. 3^4
14. 4^2
15. 8^2
16. 5^3
17. 8^0
18. 7^3
19. 6^3
20. 12^0
21. 2^6
22. 7^2
23. 3^5
24. 9^3

Set 5 (after page 21) **True or false?**

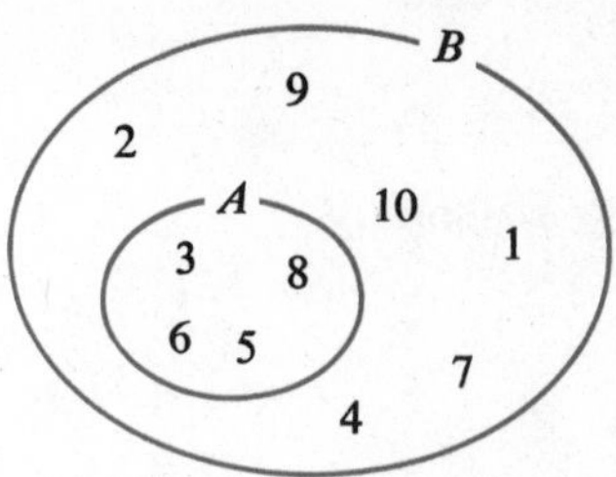

1. $A \subseteq B$
2. $A \cup B = \{1, 2, 4, 7, 9, 10\}$
3. $A \cap B = \{3, 5, 6, 8\}$
4. $\varnothing \subseteq B$
5. $\varnothing \subseteq A$

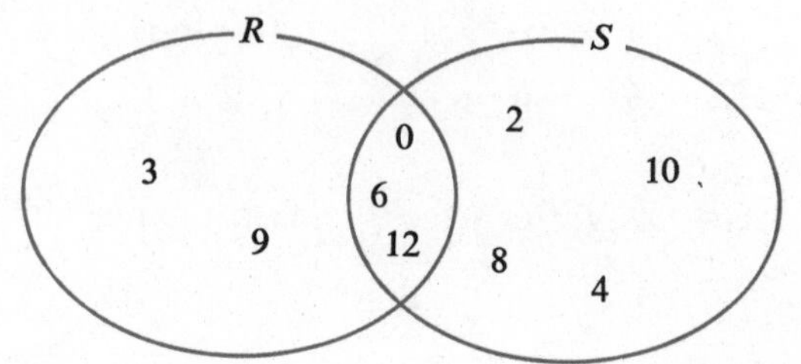

6. $R \cup S = \{0, 2, 3, 4, 6, 8, 9, 10, 12\}$
7. $R \cap S = \{0, 6, 12\}$
8. $R \subseteq S$
9. $S \subseteq R$
10. $R \cap S$ is the set of all common multiples of 2 and 3 that are less than 13.

Set 6 (after page 23) **Give the solution sets.**

1. $2x + 3 = 21$
2. $5(x + 3) = 40$
3. $\frac{7}{2}x = 14$
4. $6(x - 4) = 30$
5. $3x + 2 = 23$
6. $10x - 7 = 63$
7. $8(6 - x) = 16$
8. $3(2x - 4) = 18$
9. $2x > 8$
10. $2x \geq 8$
11. $x + 3 \neq 7$
12. $2x + 5 < 21$
13. $15 - 3x \leq 3$
14. $7x - 5 \neq 37$
15. $3(x + 4) < 27$
16. $3x + 4 \leq 28$

Set 7 (after page 29) **Solve.**

1. $3y + 7 = 28$
2. $7y = 0$
3. $18 - 8y = 2$
4. $\frac{2y}{4} = 4$
5. $16 - 4y = 0$
6. $\frac{36}{y} - 2 = 4$
7. $7(y - 3) = 35$
8. $6 + 5y = 51$
9. $3(2y + 1) = 21$
10. $\frac{3y + 1}{2} = 5$
11. $5(y + 4) = 40$
12. $6(y + 4) = 48$
13. $7y + 3 = 31$
14. $\frac{18 + 6y}{3} = 6$
15. $10(y - 6) = 0$
16. $9(y - 3) = 54$
17. $\frac{16 - y}{3} = 5$
18. $25 - 8y = 1$
19. $\frac{48}{8y + 8} = 6$
20. $3(y + 3) = 39$
21. $3y + 3 = 39$
22. $4(2y - 1) = 36$
23. $5(2y + 1) = 45$
24. $10y + 5 = 45$

Set 8 (after page 31) **Solve.**

1. $2x - 3 = 21$
2. $5x + 7 = 42$
3. $6(x + 1) = 54$
4. $7(12 - x) = 49$
5. $\frac{x + 9}{6} = 3$
6. $\frac{15 - x}{2} = 3$
7. $\frac{2}{4}x = 4$
8. $20 - 5x = 5$
9. $3(2x + 1) = 27$
10. $5(10 - 3x) = 20$
11. $7(20 - 2x) = 14$
12. $4(25 - 3x) = 16$
13. $\frac{2x + 3}{3} = 7$
14. $\frac{12 - 2x}{2} = 3$
15. $\frac{5x + 4}{2} = 22$
16. $\frac{7 + 3x}{5} = 5$

Set 9 (after page 33) **Substitute and simplify.**

a	A	n	x
2	3	5	6

1. x^2
2. $n + x$
3. $n(a - a)$
4. $(x - n)^2$
5. $(x + A)^n$
6. $an - n$
7. $a^a - (x - n)$
8. $3A + n$
9. $An + x$
10. $x(n - A)$
11. A^3
12. $a(n + x)$
13. $x(n - A)$
14. $Ax \div a$
15. n^2
16. anx
17. A^a
18. a^3
19. $An - x$
20. $x + 5a$

Set 10 (after page 37) **Complete.**

1. $f: a \rightarrow 3a - 1$
   a. (1, __?__)
   b. (3, __?__)
   c. (7, __?__)
   d. (__?__, 14)
   e. (__?__, 23)
   f. (__?__, 29)

2. $g: c \rightarrow c^2 - 1$
   a. (5 __?__)
   b. (9, __?__)
   c. (4, __?__)
   d. (__?__, 99)
   e. (__?__, 35)
   f. (__?__, 48)

3. $h: x \rightarrow 2(x + 1)$
   a. (5, __?__)
   b. (3, __?__)
   c. (8, __?__)
   d. (__?__, 20)
   e. (__?__, 16)
   f. (__?__, 10)

Set 11 (after page 45) **Complete.**

1. $f(x) = 5x$
   a. $f(1) =$ __?__
   b. $f(6) =$ __?__
   c. $f(7) =$ __?__
   d. $f($__?__$) = 45$
   e. $f($__?__$) = 50$
   f. $f($__?__$) = 10$

2. $g(x) = 7x - 3$
   a. $g(3) =$ __?__
   b. $g(6) =$ __?__
   c. $g(4) =$ __?__
   d. $g($__?__$) = 32$
   e. $g($__?__$) = 67$
   f. $g($__?__$) = 53$

3. $h(x) = 3x^2$
   a. $h(2) =$ __?__
   b. $h(5) =$ __?__
   c. $h(8) =$ __?__
   d. $h($__?__$) = 48$
   e. $h($__?__$) = 3$
   f. $(h$__?__$) = 0$

Set 12 (after page 47) **Substitute and simplify.**

d	m	N	n
5	3	2	4

1. dm
2. $\frac{d}{m}$
3. dN
4. d^n
5. $n - n$
6. d^m
7. $n - N$
8. $m(d + n)$
9. $\frac{mn}{N}$
10. $dN - m$
11. dn
12. $n(n + N)$
13. $nm - dN$
14. $(n - N)^m$
15. dmN
16. dNn
17. $\frac{(n - n)}{d}$
18. $(d - m)^n$
19. n^N
20. $\frac{N^d}{n}$
21. m^N
22. $dmNn$
23. $\frac{dmn}{N}$
24. dmn

Set 13 (after page 49) **True or false?**

1. $9 + 8 \leq 15$
2. $17 - 9 \neq 10$
3. $16 - 8 = 8$
4. $8 + 6 > 4 + 9$
5. $3 + 9 \geq 5 + 7$
6. $6 + 9 \leq 8 + 7$
7. $17 - 8 \geq 3 + 6$
8. $3 + 7 = 15 - 5$
9. $9 + 5 \neq 2 \times 7$
10. $8 + 8 \neq 2 \times 8$
11. $3 \times 6 > 9 + 8$
12. $4 + 9 < 5 \times 2$
13. $16 + 0 \neq 15$
14. $5 + 8 = 8 + 5$
15. $7 \times 2 = 2 \times 7$
16. $(4 + 3) + 5 = 4 + 1 \times 3 + 5$
17. $8 \times 7 = 9 \times 6$
18. $63 \div 9 > 1 + 4$
19. $18 \div 3 < 42 \div 7$
20. $45 \div 5 \leq 15 - 5$
21. $(2 \times 4) \times 3 = 2 \times (4 \times 3)$
22. $8 \times 8 > 8 \times 7$
23. $32 \times 0 = 32$
24. $5(3 + 2) = 5 \times 3 + 5 \times 2$

Set 14 (after page 51)

1. $g: x \rightarrow 2x + 9$
   - a. $g(0) = \underline{\ ?\ }$
   - b. $g(5) = \underline{\ ?\ }$
   - c. $g(7) = \underline{\ ?\ }$
   - d. $g(\underline{\ ?\ }) = 17$
   - e. $g(\underline{\ ?\ }) = 27$
   - f. $g(\underline{\ ?\ }) = 29$
2. $f: x \rightarrow 3x - 4$
   - a. $f(2) = \underline{\ ?\ }$
   - b. $f(10) = \underline{\ ?\ }$
   - c. $f(6) = \underline{\ ?\ }$
   - d. $f(\underline{\ ?\ }) = 17$
   - e. $f(\underline{\ ?\ }) = 5$
   - f. $f(\underline{\ ?\ }) = 20$
3. $h: x \rightarrow x^2 + 5$
   - a. $h(0) = \underline{\ ?\ }$
   - b. $h(4) = \underline{\ ?\ }$
   - c. $h(6) = \underline{\ ?\ }$
   - d. $h(\underline{\ ?\ }) = 6$
   - e. $h(\underline{\ ?\ }) = 105$
   - f. $h(\underline{\ ?\ }) = 86$

Set 15 (after page 55)

1. 63.4 +29.4	**2.** .938 +.261	**3.** .97 +6.74	**4.** 35.6 +9.3	**5.** 6.49 +3.85	**6.** .716 +.384
7. 47.8 +42.9	**8.** 42.9 +47.8	**9.** 9.99 +3.82	**10.** 4.69 +.83	**11.** .555 +.328	**12.** 26.8 +93.4
13. .826 −.817	**14.** 5.67 −2.78	**15.** 70.6 −29.3	**16.** .300 −.286	**17.** 40.6 −34.8	**18.** 7.30 −7.18
19. .894 −.267	**20.** 79.4 −18.9	**21.** 5.63 −3.65	**22.** 40.1 −29.7	**23.** 9.26 −3.58	**24.** 43.2 −16.9

Set 16 (after page 57)

1. 5.3 −1.92	**2.** .43 −.286	**3.** .29 −.163	**4.** .47 −.283	**5.** .28 −.164	**6.** 2.4 −1.87
7. 8.64 −3.79	**8.** 7.09 −.4	**9.** 2.01 −1.99	**10.** 29 −7.4	**11.** 6.62 −.8	**12.** 16 −8.4
13. 5.48 −2.99	**14.** .841 −.729	**15.** 59.3 −26.7	**16.** 70.2 −36.9	**17.** 5.03 −2.84	**18.** 3.81 −2.67
19. .35 −.187	**20.** .27 −.186	**21.** 8 −3.94	**22.** 6 −4.25	**23.** 7.2 −5.94	**24.** 4.6 −2.83

Set 17 (after page 59) **List the elements in sets 1–20.**

$A = \{0, 5, 10\}$ $B = \{0, 3, 6, 9\}$ $C = \{0, 1, 2, 3, 4, 5, 6, 7, 8, 9, 10\}$

$D = \{0, 2, 4, 6, 8, 10\}$ $E = \{0, 4, 8\}$ $F = \{\ \}$

1. $A \cap D$	**2.** $D \cup B$	**3.** $A \cup E$	**4.** $E \cap C$	**5.** $B \cup C$
6. $A \cap C$	**7.** $B \cap C$	**8.** $F \cap B$	**9.** $D \cap B$	**10.** $A \cup B$
11. $C \cup F$	**12.** $A \cap E$	**13.** $A \cup D$	**14.** $A \cap B$	**15.** $D \cap E$
16. $A \cup A$	**17.** $A \cap A$	**18.** $D \cup C$	**19.** $A \cup C$	**20.** $D \cap C$

Set 18 (after page 61)

1. $6.3 + 4.27$ **2.** $8.5 + 9$ **3.** $4.7 + .83$ **4.** $.81 + 8$
5. $.03 + 65$ **6.** $9.21 + 3.4$ **7.** $16.8 + 5.3$ **8.** $200 + .02$
9. $15.4 + 7.6$ **10.** $15.4 + .76$ **11.** $8.3 + 7.4 + 9.7$ **12.** $5.67 + 3.84 + 6.53$
13. $84.1 + 67.8 + 53.2$ **14.** $12.67 + 14.35 + 29.77$
15. $.435 + .773 + 6.889$ **16.** $4.6 + 12 + .77 + 35.092$

Set 19 (after page 63)

1. $12 - 6.7$ **2.** $6.5 - 3.29$ **3.** $5.8 - 4.77$ **4.** $.84 - .621$
5. $.39 - .245$ **6.** $15 - 1.2$ **7.** $18.3 - 4.11$ **8.** $26.5 - 23.49$
9. $1003.4 - 921.6$ **10.** $300.4 - 126.8$ **11.** $47.5 - 28.6$ **12.** $6.004 - 5.29$
13. $3.25 - 1.6$ **14.** $.554 - .29$ **15.** $8.002 - 1.34$ **16.** $3.002 - .877$
17. $.503 - .284$ **18.** $16.03 - 5.8$ **19.** $5.02 - 1.55$ **20.** $100.003 - 99.9$

Set 20 (after page 71) **Match.**

1. Commutative property of addition
2. Commutative property of multiplication
3. Associative property of addition
4. Associative property of multiplication
5. Distributive property
6. Identity property of addition
7. Identity property of multiplication

a. $7 \times 1 = 7$
b. $6(3 + 4) = 6 \times 3 + 6 \times 4$
c. $1 + 0 = 0 + 1$
d. $1 + 0 = 0$
e. $1 \times 0 = 0 \times 1$
f. $3 + (4 + 0) = (3 + 4) + 0$
g. $3 \times (4 \times 0) = (3 \times 4) \times 0$

Set 21 (after page 77) **True or false?**

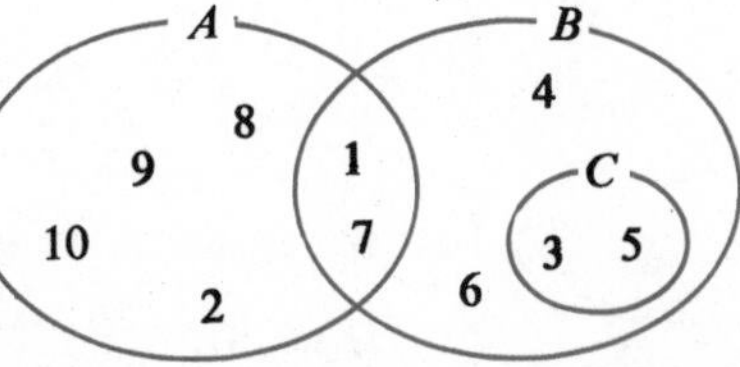

1. 7 is an element of A.
2. 7 is an element of B.
3. 7 is an element of $A \cap B$.
4. 7 is an element of $A \cup B$. **5.** 8 is an element of A. **6.** 8 is an element of B.
7. 8 is an element of $A \cap B$. **8.** 8 is an element of $A \cup B$. **9.** $A \subseteq B$
10. $B \subseteq A$ **11.** 3 is an element of C. **12.** 3 is an element of B.
13. 3 is an element of A. **14.** $C \subseteq B$ **15.** $B \subseteq C$
16. $C \subseteq A$ **17.** $A \subseteq C$ **18.** $\varnothing \subseteq B$

Set 22 (after page 81)

Number	Round to nearest hundredth.	Round to nearest tenth.	Round to nearest one.
1. 4.673	?	?	?
2. 2.485	?	?	?
3. 2.475	?	?	?
4. 3.500	?	?	?
5. 12.999	?	?	?
6. 8.67351	?	?	?
7. 298.436	?	?	?
8. 367.514	?	?	?
9. 44.449	?	?	?
10. 99.999	?	?	?

Set 23 (after page 85)

1. 52×10
2. 52×1000
3. 52×100
4. 326×10
5. 326×100
6. 326×1000
7. $.41 \times 10$
8. $.41 \times 100$
9. $.41 \times 1000$
10. 2.34×10
11. 2.34×100
12. 2.34×1000
13. 5.801×10
14. 5.801×100
15. 5.801×1000
16. 8.25×10
17. 8.25×100
18. 8.25×1000
19. 31.21×10
20. 31.21×100
21. 31.21×1000
22. 38.4×10
23. 38.4×100
24. 38.4×1000

Set 24 (after page 89)

1. $3a + 7 = 37$
2. $2(m + 6) = 16$
3. $28 = g^2 + 3$
4. $\frac{3x}{3} = 7$
5. $12n - 12 = 0$
6. $2k + 16 = 56$
7. $4(g - 4) = 8$
8. $5(10 - b) = 35$
9. $\frac{15}{3}y = 5$
10. $7(a + 6) = 63$
11. $6c + 5 = 59$
12. $6d = 0$
13. $\frac{a + 6}{3} = 4$
14. $12 + 9c = 12$
15. $3(b + 8) = 30$
16. $9y + 8 = 80$
17. $\frac{g - 6}{4} = 6$
18. $\frac{y + 9}{2} = 6$
19. $\frac{y - 8}{3} = 0$
20. $5(a + 9) = 60$
21. $6(n - 3) = 42$

Set 25 (after page 93) **Give the GCF and LCM of each pair of numbers.**

1. 9, 21	**2.** 25, 45	**3.** 8, 12	**4.** 35, 54
5. 14, 35	**6.** 42, 63	**7.** 40, 60	**8.** 15, 18
9. 36, 70	**10.** 48, 54	**11.** 18, 24	**12.** 5, 12
13. 33, 44	**14.** 21, 27	**15.** 35, 8	**16.** 20, 8

Set 26 (after page 101) **Give the union of each pair of sets.**

1. {a, b, c, d} {b, c, d, e}	**2.** {0, 3, 6, 9} {0, 6, 12}	**3.** {8, 7, 6, 5} {8, 9, 10, 11}	**4.** {0, 2, 4, 6} {1, 3, 5, 7}
5. {A, B, C, D} {A, B, C, D}	**6.** {2, 4, 6, 8} {2, 4, 6}	**7.** {2, 3, 5, 7} {4, 6, 8, 9}	**8.** {3, 5, 9, 12} {4, 8, 12, 16}
9. {x, r, s, b} {s, t, k, j, a}	**10.** {k, l, m, j} {0, 3, 9, 2}	**11.** { } {6, 4, 9}	**12.** { } { }

Set 27 (after page 105) **Round to the nearest .01.**

1. .3708	**2.** 9.166	**3.** .6585	**4.** 7.403	**5.** 3.892
6. .5745	**7.** 3.021	**8.** 3.174	**9.** .7956	**10.** .4263
11. 34.625	**12.** 7.3298	**13.** 593.853	**14.** 4.6102	**15.** .86052
16. 27.995	**17.** 3.6951	**18.** .29638	**19.** 56.194	**20.** 97.823

Set 28 (after page 107) **Round quotients to the nearest hundredth.**

1. $59\overline{)2.974}$	**2.** $84\overline{)3.678}$	**3.** $64\overline{)38.45}$	**4.** $18\overline{)42.16}$	**5.** $13\overline{)4.786}$
6. $27\overline{)3.675}$	**7.** $92\overline{)4.829}$	**8.** $18\overline{)20.03}$	**9.** $62\overline{)74.02}$	**10.** $24\overline{)1.294}$
11. $65\overline{)3.91}$	**12.** $23\overline{)4.278}$	**13.** $39\overline{)391.6}$	**14.** $70\overline{)35.29}$	**15.** $89\overline{)23.94}$
16. $348\overline{)3.821}$	**17.** $453\overline{)438.7}$	**18.** $276\overline{)9.295}$	**19.** $195\overline{)8.355}$	**20.** $141\overline{)8.648}$
21. $.08\overline{).432}$	**22.** $.4\overline{)76.4}$	**23.** $.07\overline{)3.99}$	**24.** $.6\overline{).042}$	**25.** $.9\overline{)3.78}$

Set 29 (after page 113)

1. $\begin{array}{r} 79 \\ -64.8 \\ \hline \end{array}$	**2.** $\begin{array}{r} 84.5 \\ -39.9 \\ \hline \end{array}$	**3.** $\begin{array}{r} 2.93 \\ -1.58 \\ \hline \end{array}$	**4.** $\begin{array}{r} .756 \\ -.259 \\ \hline \end{array}$	**5.** $\begin{array}{r} 6.39 \\ -2.67 \\ \hline \end{array}$	**6.** $\begin{array}{r} 58.2 \\ -13.8 \\ \hline \end{array}$

7. $\begin{array}{r} 5.04 \\ -3.68 \\ \hline \end{array}$ 8. $\begin{array}{r} .629 \\ -.469 \\ \hline \end{array}$ 9. $\begin{array}{r} 60.8 \\ -37.9 \\ \hline \end{array}$ 10. $\begin{array}{r} 6.35 \\ -2.96 \\ \hline \end{array}$ 11. $\begin{array}{r} 3.5 \\ -1.83 \\ \hline \end{array}$ 12. $\begin{array}{r} 2.78 \\ -.59 \\ \hline \end{array}$

13. $\begin{array}{r} .832 \\ -.369 \\ \hline \end{array}$ 14. $\begin{array}{r} 8.00 \\ -3.82 \\ \hline \end{array}$ 15. $\begin{array}{r} 38.6 \\ -27.9 \\ \hline \end{array}$ 16. $\begin{array}{r} 3.8 \\ -1.98 \\ \hline \end{array}$ 17. $\begin{array}{r} 7.39 \\ -2.91 \\ \hline \end{array}$ 18. $\begin{array}{r} 67.5 \\ -35.8 \\ \hline \end{array}$

19. $\begin{array}{r} 4.01 \\ -3.78 \\ \hline \end{array}$ 20. $\begin{array}{r} 32.7 \\ -19.9 \\ \hline \end{array}$ 21. $\begin{array}{r} 600.3 \\ -429.7 \\ \hline \end{array}$ 22. $\begin{array}{r} 8.001 \\ -1.395 \\ \hline \end{array}$ 23. $\begin{array}{r} 4.26 \\ -1.74 \\ \hline \end{array}$ 24. $\begin{array}{r} 52.3 \\ -35.9 \\ \hline \end{array}$

Set 30 (after page 117) **Round quotients to the nearest tenth.**

1. $.4\overline{)936}$ 2. $.9\overline{)6.75}$ 3. $.8\overline{)43.2}$ 4. $7\overline{)25.9}$ 5. $3\overline{)348}$

6. $.07\overline{)84.7}$ 7. $.03\overline{)6.24}$ 8. $.05\overline{)385}$ 9. $.6\overline{)5.22}$ 10. $.02\overline{).938}$

11. $4.7\overline{).2491}$ 12. $.36\overline{)10.08}$ 13. $.11\overline{).198}$ 14. $2.3\overline{)71.3}$ 15. $1.2\overline{)1.44}$

16. $8\overline{)184.68}$ 17. $.082\overline{)46.494}$ 18. $.65\overline{)35.295}$ 19. $4.2\overline{)162.12}$ 20. $.13\overline{).3328}$

Set 31 (after page 125)

1. $\begin{array}{r} .36 \\ \times 5 \\ \hline \end{array}$ 2. $\begin{array}{r} .77 \\ \times 3 \\ \hline \end{array}$ 3. $\begin{array}{r} 9.3 \\ \times 8 \\ \hline \end{array}$ 4. $\begin{array}{r} 8.0 \\ \times 6 \\ \hline \end{array}$ 5. $\begin{array}{r} 6.4 \\ \times 2 \\ \hline \end{array}$ 6. $\begin{array}{r} 3.8 \\ \times 2 \\ \hline \end{array}$

7. $\begin{array}{r} .29 \\ \times 7 \\ \hline \end{array}$ 8. $\begin{array}{r} 1.7 \\ \times 5 \\ \hline \end{array}$ 9. $\begin{array}{r} 5.4 \\ \times 8 \\ \hline \end{array}$ 10. $\begin{array}{r} .93 \\ \times 3 \\ \hline \end{array}$ 11. $\begin{array}{r} .062 \\ \times 7 \\ \hline \end{array}$ 12. $\begin{array}{r} .103 \\ \times 8 \\ \hline \end{array}$

13. $\begin{array}{r} 70.3 \\ \times 4 \\ \hline \end{array}$ 14. $\begin{array}{r} 7.03 \\ \times 4 \\ \hline \end{array}$ 15. $\begin{array}{r} .703 \\ \times 4 \\ \hline \end{array}$ 16. $\begin{array}{r} .533 \\ \times 7 \\ \hline \end{array}$ 17. $\begin{array}{r} .642 \\ \times 4 \\ \hline \end{array}$ 18. $\begin{array}{r} .03 \\ \times 8 \\ \hline \end{array}$

19. $\begin{array}{r} .742 \\ \times 9 \\ \hline \end{array}$ 20. $\begin{array}{r} 3.48 \\ \times 6 \\ \hline \end{array}$ 21. $\begin{array}{r} 90.5 \\ \times 3 \\ \hline \end{array}$ 22. $\begin{array}{r} 5.09 \\ \times 6 \\ \hline \end{array}$ 23. $\begin{array}{r} 7.56 \\ \times 5 \\ \hline \end{array}$ 24. $\begin{array}{r} .829 \\ \times 4 \\ \hline \end{array}$

Set 32 (after page 127)

1. $.4\overline{)31.6}$ 2. $.04\overline{)31.6}$ 3. $.3\overline{)25.2}$ 4. $.05\overline{).515}$ 5. $.4\overline{)38.4}$

6. $.2\overline{)29.4}$ 7. $.09\overline{).873}$ 8. $.08\overline{)36.2}$ 9. $.5\overline{)4.05}$ 10. $.8\overline{).648}$

11. $.09\overline{)9.18}$ 12. $.05\overline{)2.65}$ 13. $.3\overline{)25.2}$ 14. $.6\overline{)2.94}$ 15. $.7\overline{)3.85}$

16. $.02\overline{)90.6}$ 17. $.7\overline{)49.7}$ 18. $.02\overline{)6.38}$ 19. $.5\overline{).825}$ 20. $.06\overline{)42.6}$

Set 33 (after page 129)

1. 3.5×7	2. $.35 \times 7$	3. $.35 \times .7$	4. $.35 \times .07$	5. $3.5 \times .07$	6. $35 \times .07$
7. $.95 \times .8$	8. $6.9 \times .7$	9. $70 \times .9$	10. $5.3 \times .4$	11. $.18 \times .5$	12. $2.9 \times .2$
13. $3.06 \times .82$	14. 62.1×5.3	15. 4.98×4.5	16. 3.67×3.6	17. 23.8×2.5	18. $12.4 \times .12$
19. $.592 \times 65$	20. 784×5.5	21. $96.3 \times .73$	22. 8.17×90	23. 61.1×23.8	24. $.429 \times 16.1$

Set 34 (after page 133)

1. $f(t) = 3t$

a. $f(1) =$ ___?___
b. $f(2) =$ ___?___
c. $f(0) =$ ___?___
d. $f(3.4) =$ ___?___
e. $f\left(\frac{1}{3}\right) =$ ___?___
f. $f($___?___$) = 27$
g. $f($___?___$) = 102$
h. $f($___?___$) = 361$

2. $g(y) = 4y + 1$

a. $g(5) =$ ___?___
b. $g(0) =$ ___?___
c. $g(9) =$ ___?___
d. $g(5.6) =$ ___?___
e. $g\left(\frac{3}{4}\right) =$ ___?___
f. $g($___?___$) = 49$
g. $g($___?___$) = 401$
h. $g($___?___$) = 465$

3. $h(m) = m^2 - 1$

a. $h(1) =$ ___?___
b. $h(a) =$ ___?___
c. $h(10) =$ ___?___
d. $h(4.2) =$ ___?___
e. $h\left(\frac{5}{4}\right) =$ ___?___
f. $h($___?___$) = 24$
g. $h($___?___$) = 48$
h. $h($___?___$) = \frac{5}{4}$

Set 35 (after page 143) **Round quotients to the nearest tenth.**

1. $.07\overline{)6.28}$	2. $.02\overline{)3.51}$	3. $.6\overline{)2.97}$	4. $.5\overline{).348}$	5. $.3\overline{).386}$
6. $.9\overline{).629}$	7. $.04\overline{).511}$	8. $.05\overline{)2.97}$	9. $.003\overline{).038}$	10. $.08\overline{).347}$
11. $.83\overline{).1324}$	12. $.43\overline{).3916}$	13. $.31\overline{).9382}$	14. $2.4\overline{)1.356}$	15. $1.2\overline{)3.482}$
16. $.57\overline{)3.056}$	17. $6.4\overline{).2973}$	18. $3.9\overline{)4.901}$	19. $7.8\overline{)2.643}$	20. $4.2\overline{).3967}$

Set 36 (after page 145)

1. 23.51×10	2. 23.51×100	3. 23.51×1	4. $23.51 \times .01$
5. $68.2 \times .1$	6. 68.2×10	7. $68.2 \times .01$	8. 68.2×100

9. 4.51 × 100	**10.** 4.51 × .1	**11.** 4.51 × 10	**12.** 4.51 × .01
13. 6.03 × .01	**14.** 6.03 × 10	**15.** 6.03 × 100	**16.** 6.03 × .1
17. 526.3 × 100	**18.** 526.3 × 10	**19.** 506.3 × 1	**20.** 526.3 × .1
21. 54.54 × .1	**22.** 54.54 × .01	**23.** 54.54 × .001	**24.** 54.54 × .0001

Set 37 (after page 153) **Give the intersection of each pair of sets.**

1. {a, b, c, d} {a, b, c}	**2.** {0, 2, 4} {1, 3, 5}	**3.** {0, 2, 4, 6} {0, 2, 4}	**4.** {R, S, T} {R, S, T}
5. {16, 9, 14} {13, 11, 9}	**6.** {a, b, c} {1, 2, 3, 4}	**7.** {Bob, Sue} {Bob, Sarah}	**8.** {Bob, Rita} {Jim, Alice}
9. { } {1, 2, 3}	**10.** {1, 2, 3} {13, 2}	**11.** {2, 4, 6, 8, 10, 12} {3, 6, 9, 12, 15}	**12.** {1, 2, 3, 4, 6, 12} {1, 2, 3, 6, 9, 18}

Set 38 (after page 155)

1. $\begin{array}{r} 73 \\ 80 \\ +59 \\ \hline \end{array}$ **2.** $\begin{array}{r} 37 \\ 52 \\ +98 \\ \hline \end{array}$ **3.** $\begin{array}{r} 65 \\ 54 \\ +38 \\ \hline \end{array}$ **4.** $\begin{array}{r} 66 \\ 19 \\ +27 \\ \hline \end{array}$ **5.** $\begin{array}{r} 83 \\ 74 \\ +36 \\ \hline \end{array}$ **6.** $\begin{array}{r} 46 \\ 26 \\ +38 \\ \hline \end{array}$

7. $\begin{array}{r} 46 \\ 46 \\ +46 \\ \hline \end{array}$ **8.** $\begin{array}{r} 61 \\ 43 \\ +58 \\ \hline \end{array}$ **9.** $\begin{array}{r} 39 \\ 74 \\ +15 \\ \hline \end{array}$ **10.** $\begin{array}{r} 75 \\ 34 \\ +41 \\ \hline \end{array}$ **11.** $\begin{array}{r} 83 \\ 83 \\ +86 \\ \hline \end{array}$ **12.** $\begin{array}{r} 94 \\ 16 \\ +15 \\ \hline \end{array}$

13. $\begin{array}{r} 7.43 \\ .84 \\ +.42 \\ \hline \end{array}$ **14.** $\begin{array}{r} 6.80 \\ 5.00 \\ +2.43 \\ \hline \end{array}$ **15.** $\begin{array}{r} .714 \\ .026 \\ +.900 \\ \hline \end{array}$ **16.** $\begin{array}{r} 5.8 \\ 32.7 \\ +11.5 \\ \hline \end{array}$ **17.** $\begin{array}{r} .51 \\ 2.67 \\ +3.90 \\ \hline \end{array}$ **18.** $\begin{array}{r} 8.6 \\ 7.3 \\ +15.9 \\ \hline \end{array}$

19. $\begin{array}{r} 59.2 \\ 64.7 \\ +14.8 \\ \hline \end{array}$ **20.** $\begin{array}{r} .384 \\ .773 \\ +.091 \\ \hline \end{array}$ **21.** $\begin{array}{r} 2.63 \\ 5.71 \\ +4.77 \\ \hline \end{array}$ **22.** $\begin{array}{r} 29.4 \\ 14.6 \\ +93.8 \\ \hline \end{array}$ **23.** $\begin{array}{r} 2.61 \\ 4.75 \\ +9.77 \\ \hline \end{array}$ **24.** $\begin{array}{r} 18 \\ 6.34 \\ +.091 \\ \hline \end{array}$

Set 39 (after page 157) **Change to decimals.**

1. $\frac{1}{2}$ **2.** $\frac{1}{3}$ **3.** $\frac{1}{4}$ **4.** $\frac{1}{8}$ **5.** $\frac{1}{6}$ **6.** $\frac{1}{7}$ **7.** $\frac{1}{9}$ **8.** $\frac{5}{6}$

9. $\frac{5}{8}$ **10.** $\frac{5}{3}$ **11.** $\frac{3}{4}$ **12.** $\frac{3}{2}$ **13.** $\frac{3}{3}$ **14.** $\frac{2}{3}$ **15.** $\frac{4}{7}$ **16.** $\frac{11}{8}$

17. $\frac{7}{4}$ **18.** $\frac{7}{2}$ **19.** $\frac{7}{9}$ **20.** $\frac{9}{8}$ **21.** $\frac{5}{4}$ **22.** $\frac{5}{2}$ **23.** $\frac{4}{3}$ **24.** $\frac{2}{9}$

Set 40 (after page 163) **Round quotients to the nearest tenth.**

1. $3\overline{)1473}$	**2.** $8\overline{)4584}$	**3.** $9\overline{)5067}$	**4.** $6\overline{)2634}$	**5.** $7\overline{)3836}$
6. $6\overline{)350.4}$	**7.** $4\overline{).640}$	**8.** $3\overline{)9.630}$	**9.** $4\overline{)26.56}$	**10.** $5\overline{)36.05}$
11. $.008\overline{)6.680}$	**12.** $.06\overline{)37.62}$	**13.** $.05\overline{)2.870}$	**14.** $.08\overline{)18.72}$	**15.** $.9\overline{)6705}$
16. $.64\overline{).3104}$	**17.** $.31\overline{)2.139}$	**18.** $3.3\overline{)48.18}$	**19.** $.41\overline{)24.865}$	**20.** $2.4\overline{)31.68}$

Set 41 (after page 167)

1. 39×7.5	**2.** 7.5×6.8	**3.** $6.6 \times .53$	**4.** $.45 \times 2.7$	**5.** $3.6 \times .42$	**6.** 5.8×1.5
7. $6.3 \times .34$	**8.** $.34 \times 6.3$	**9.** $.58 \times 2.7$	**10.** 2.9×1.9	**11.** 9.3×2.3	**12.** 7.8×40
13. 3.86×7.3	**14.** 54.7×6.5	**15.** $34.2 \times .50$	**16.** 16.8×4.2	**17.** $2.95 \times .38$	**18.** 3.46×5.9
19. $.918 \times .267$	**20.** 2.57×1.59	**21.** 60.3×13.8	**22.** $58.4 \times .74$	**23.** $7.53 \times .90$	**24.** 2.91×5.6

Set 42 (after page 169)

1. $f: x \to 5x$

- **a.** $f(0) =$?
- **b.** $f(6) =$?
- **c.** $f(9) =$?
- **d.** $f(3.6) =$?
- **e.** $f\left(\frac{3}{4}\right) =$?
- **f.** $f($? $) = 6.5$
- **g.** $f($? $) = \frac{5}{6}$
- **h.** $f($? $) = 12$

2. $g: y \to 3y + 2$

- **a.** $g(0) =$?
- **b.** $g(6) =$?
- **c.** $g(10) =$?
- **d.** $g(6.7) =$?
- **e.** $g\left(\frac{3}{4}\right) =$?
- **f.** $g($? $) = 8$
- **g.** $g($? $) = 11.3$
- **h.** $g($? $) = 5\frac{3}{5}$

3. $h: y \to y^2 + 3$

- **a.** $h(0) =$?
- **b.** $h(5) =$?
- **c.** $h(10) =$?
- **d.** $h(4.7) =$?
- **e.** $h\left(\frac{3}{4}\right) =$?
- **f.** $h($? $) = 67$
- **g.** $h($? $) = 4.44$
- **h.** $h($? $) \doteq 3\frac{4}{9}$

Set 43 (after page 177)

1. $6.5 \times .02$	**2.** $6.5 \times .2$	**3.** $65 \times .2$	**4.** $65 \times .02$	**5.** $.65 \times .2$	**6.** $.65 \times .02$
7. $70 \times .6$	**8.** $.81 \times .03$	**9.** $7.4 \times .4$	**10.** $.39 \times 3$	**11.** 7.7×4.5	**12.** $.92 \times .60$

13. $4.1 \times .27$ **14.** $.39 \times .19$ **15.** $6.3 \times .40$ **16.** 8.8×3.5 **17.** 80.3×6.3 **18.** 9.17×50

19. 62.5×5.3 **20.** 8.03×4.9 **21.** 9.21×7.2 **22.** 78.4×4.3 **23.** 9.63×2.1 **24.** 3.56×1.1

Set 44 (after page 187) **Change to percents.**

1. $\frac{1}{2}$ **2.** $\frac{1}{3}$ **3.** $\frac{2}{3}$ **4.** $\frac{1}{4}$ **5.** $\frac{3}{4}$ **6.** $\frac{1}{5}$ **7.** $\frac{2}{5}$ **8.** $\frac{3}{5}$

9. .06 **10.** .08 **11.** .12 **12.** .35 **13.** .86 **14.** .91 **15.** 1.23 **16.** 2.34

17. .015 **18.** .136 **19.** .114 **20.** .236 **21.** $\frac{1}{8}$ **22.** $\frac{3}{8}$ **23.** $\frac{5}{6}$ **24.** $\frac{6}{5}$

Set 45 (after page 201)

1. $26 \times .7$ **2.** 4.7×5 **3.** 161×5 **4.** $9.2 \times .3$ **5.** $34 \times .9$ **6.** 7.8×3

7. $.53 \times 6$ **8.** $1.9 \times .6$ **9.** $.38 \times .4$ **10.** $7.0 \times .4$ **11.** $5.5 \times .8$ **12.** $.69 \times .2$

13. 3.33×6.5 **14.** 91.5×8.9 **15.** $30.6 \times .73$ **16.** 5.34×4.1 **17.** $72.8 \times .52$ **18.** 6.13×2.6

19. $.639 \times .438$ **20.** 5.22×22.6 **21.** $.183 \times 113$ **22.** $5.71 \times .64$ **23.** $96.2 \times .27$ **24.** 82.5×4.4

Set 46 (after page 207) **The two figures are congruent. Complete the list of corresponding parts.**

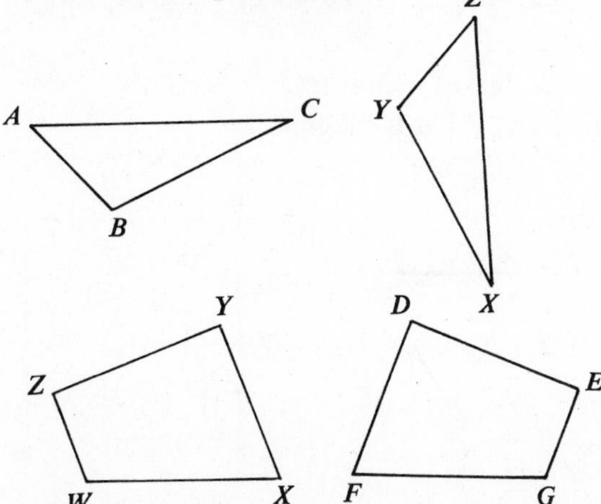

Corresponding parts

1. $\overline{AB}$ and ? **4.** $\angle Y$ and ?
2. $\overline{BC}$ and ? **5.** $\angle X$ and ?
3. $\overline{AC}$ and ? **6.** $\angle Z$ and ?

7. $\overline{GF}$ and ? **11.** $\angle W$ and ?
8. $\overline{GE}$ and ? **12.** $\angle X$ and ?
9. $\overline{DE}$ and ? **13.** $\angle Y$ and ?
10. $\overline{DF}$ and ? **14.** $\angle Z$ and ?

Set 47 (after page 211) **Round quotients to the nearest hundredth.**

1. $2\overline{)304}$ 2. $6\overline{)150}$ 3. $3\overline{)231}$ 4. $4\overline{)146}$ 5. $5\overline{)115}$
6. $.03\overline{)6.27}$ 7. $.07\overline{)4.97}$ 8. $.9\overline{)11.7}$ 9. $.8\overline{)7.28}$ 10. $.7\overline{)19.8}$
11. $.005\overline{)26.5}$ 12. $.04\overline{)292}$ 13. $.05\overline{)6.5}$ 14. $.08\overline{)11.2}$ 15. $.9\overline{)19.8}$
16. $3.4\overline{)2.397}$ 17. $5.7\overline{).3306}$ 18. $.93\overline{)2976}$ 19. $7.1\overline{)39.76}$ 20. $2.3\overline{)10.58}$

Set 48 (after page 213)

1. $\frac{1}{3}$ of 261 = ___?___ 2. $33\frac{1}{3}\%$ of 261 = ___?___ 3. $\frac{3}{4}$ of 60 = ___?___
4. 75% of 60 = ___?___ 5. 80% of 424 = ___?___ 6. $\frac{4}{5}$ of 424 = ___?___
7. $\frac{2}{3}$ of 60 = ___?___ 8. $66\frac{2}{3}\%$ of 60 = ___?___ 9. $\frac{1}{6}$ of 216 = ___?___
10. $16\frac{2}{3}\%$ of 216 = ___?___ 11. $\frac{3}{8}$ of 48 = ___?___ 12. $37\frac{1}{2}\%$ of 48 = ___?___
13. $\frac{5}{6}$ of 30 = ___?___ 14. $83\frac{1}{3}\%$ of 30 = ___?___ 15. $66\frac{2}{3}\%$ of 90 = ___?___
16. $12\frac{1}{2}\%$ of 80 = ___?___ 17. $16\frac{2}{3}\%$ of 120 = ___?___ 18. $83\frac{1}{3}\%$ of 240 = ___?___

Set 49 (after page 215) **Change to common fractions in lowest terms.**

1. 50% 2. 60% 3. 45% 4. 80% 5. 95% 6. 24%
7. 150% 8. 125% 9. $33\frac{1}{3}\%$ 10. $66\frac{2}{3}\%$ 11. $16\frac{2}{3}\%$ 12. $83\frac{1}{3}\%$
13. $12\frac{1}{2}\%$ 14. $37\frac{1}{2}\%$ 15. $62\frac{1}{2}\%$ 16. $87\frac{1}{2}\%$ 17. 250% 18. 25%
19. 2.5% 20. .25% 21. 300% 22. 30% 23. 3% 24. .3%

Set 50 (after page 217) **Each dashed line is a line of symmetry. Imagine flipping the figure about the line of symmetry. What is the flip image of each part?**

1. $\overline{AD}$ 2. $\overline{DC}$ 3. $\angle CDA$
4. $\overline{DB}$ 5. $\overline{DE}$ 6. $\overline{CA}$
7. $\overline{WX}$ 8. $\overline{XV}$ 9. $\overline{XU}$
10. $\overline{WZ}$ 11. $\overline{WU}$ 12. $\angle X$
13. $\angle W$

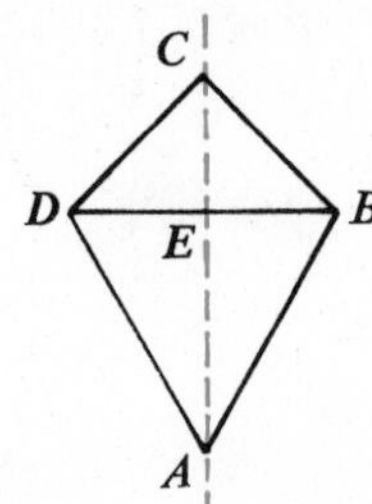

W U Z
X V Y

Set 51 (after page 219) **Round to the nearest hundredth.**

1. 6.683	**2.** .3964	**3.** 2.477	**4.** 7.815	**5.** .4369
6. 2.013	**7.** .0684	**8.** .9347	**9.** 6.830	**10.** 7.421
11. .0038	**12.** 2.964	**13.** 3.255	**14.** .7324	**15.** 2.795
16. .7413	**17.** 9.205	**18.** 0.035	**19.** .9834	**20.** 8.301
21. .0096	**22.** .0992	**23.** 23.995	**24.** 19.996	**25.** 99.998

Set 52 (after page 225) **Write as percents.**

1. .46	**2.** .27	**3.** .83	**4.** .06	**5.** .60	**6.** 1	**7.** 1.17
8. 1.34	**9.** .4	**10.** 1.7	**11.** 2.5	**12.** 1.67	**13.** .08	**14.** .8
15. 2.42	**16.** 3.71	**17.** $\frac{1}{2}$	**18.** $\frac{1}{5}$	**19.** $\frac{2}{2}$	**20.** $\frac{2}{10}$	**21.** $\frac{1}{4}$
22. $\frac{3}{10}$	**23.** $\frac{3}{2}$	**24.** $\frac{3}{5}$	**25.** $\frac{5}{10}$	**26.** $\frac{4}{4}$	**27.** $\frac{5}{4}$	**28.** $\frac{3}{4}$

Set 53 (after page 237)

1. $f(x) = 3(x + 4)$

- **a.** $f(9) =$ ___?___
- **b.** $f(15) =$ ___?___
- **c.** $f(3.4) =$ ___?___
- **d.** $f\left(\frac{1}{3}\right) =$ ___?___
- **e.** $f($___?___$) = 426$
- **f.** $f($___?___$) = 12\frac{1}{3}$
- **g.** $f($___?___$) = 15.24$

2. $g(x) = 3x + 4$

- **a.** $g(9) =$ ___?___
- **b.** $g(15) =$ ___?___
- **c.** $g(3.4) =$ ___?___
- **d.** $g\left(\frac{1}{3}\right) =$ ___?___
- **e.** $g($___?___$) = 426$
- **f.** $g($___?___$) = 12\frac{1}{3}$
- **g.** $g($___?___$) = 12.1$

3. $h(x) = \frac{x}{3} + 6$

- **a.** $h(0) =$ ___?___
- **b.** $h(9) =$ ___?___
- **c.** $h(624) =$ ___?___
- **d.** $h(16) =$ ___?___
- **e.** $h(3.24) =$ ___?___
- **f.** $h($___?___$) = 9$
- **g.** $h($___?___$) = 6\frac{1}{3}$

Set 54 (after page 239)

1. 7.2 cm = ___?___ mm	**2.** 8.4 m = ___?___ dm	**3.** 3 mm = ___?___ cm
4. 6.8 dm = ___?___ m	**5.** 3.8 dm = ___?___ m	**6.** 6 mm = ___?___ cm
7. 5 m = ___?___ dm	**8.** 12.8 cm = ___?___ mm	**9.** 19.8 cm = ___?___ dm
10. 3.8 m = ___?___ dm	**11.** 14.9 cm = ___?___ dm	**12.** 14.3 cm = ___?___ mm
13. 7.4 dm = ___?___ m	**14.** 15.9 cm = ___?___ dm	**15.** 9.5 cm = ___?___ mm
16. 9 dm = ___?___ m	**17.** 9.25 dm = ___?___ cm	**18.** 5.3 m = ___?___ dm
19. 2.9 dm = ___?___ m	**20.** 19.8 dm = ___?___ cm	**21.** 6 m = ___?___ dm
22. 8.2 mm = ___?___ cm	**23.** 4.38 dm = ___?___ cm	**24.** 2.9 m = ___?___ dm

Set 55 (after page 241)

1. $\begin{array}{r} 41 \\ 37 \\ +29 \\ \hline \end{array}$ **2.** $\begin{array}{r} 37 \\ 41 \\ +29 \\ \hline \end{array}$ **3.** $\begin{array}{r} 29 \\ 37 \\ +41 \\ \hline \end{array}$ **4.** $\begin{array}{r} 29 \\ 41 \\ +37 \\ \hline \end{array}$ **5.** $\begin{array}{r} 41 \\ 29 \\ +37 \\ \hline \end{array}$ **6.** $\begin{array}{r} 37 \\ 29 \\ +41 \\ \hline \end{array}$

7. $\begin{array}{r} 74 \\ 98 \\ +41 \\ \hline \end{array}$ **8.** $\begin{array}{r} 63 \\ 59 \\ +26 \\ \hline \end{array}$ **9.** $\begin{array}{r} 47 \\ 47 \\ +47 \\ \hline \end{array}$ **10.** $\begin{array}{r} 74 \\ 26 \\ +37 \\ \hline \end{array}$ **11.** $\begin{array}{r} 53 \\ 62 \\ +91 \\ \hline \end{array}$ **12.** $\begin{array}{r} 19 \\ 27 \\ +42 \\ \hline \end{array}$

13. $\begin{array}{r} .503 \\ .625 \\ +.439 \\ \hline \end{array}$ **14.** $\begin{array}{r} .356 \\ .291 \\ +.282 \\ \hline \end{array}$ **15.** $\begin{array}{r} .045 \\ .162 \\ +.158 \\ \hline \end{array}$ **16.** $\begin{array}{r} .43 \\ 6.89 \\ +.35 \\ \hline \end{array}$ **17.** $\begin{array}{r} .6 \\ 2.8 \\ +59.4 \\ \hline \end{array}$ **18.** $\begin{array}{r} .63 \\ 1.82 \\ +.95 \\ \hline \end{array}$

19. $\begin{array}{r} 92.8 \\ 13.5 \\ +36.4 \\ \hline \end{array}$ **20.** $\begin{array}{r} 92.8 \\ 36.4 \\ +13.5 \\ \hline \end{array}$ **21.** $\begin{array}{r} 13.5 \\ 36.4 \\ +92.8 \\ \hline \end{array}$ **22.** $\begin{array}{r} 14.6 \\ 17.3 \\ +18.9 \\ \hline \end{array}$ **23.** $\begin{array}{r} 56.9 \\ 47.8 \\ +66.4 \\ \hline \end{array}$ **24.** $\begin{array}{r} 83.6 \\ 83.6 \\ +83.6 \\ \hline \end{array}$

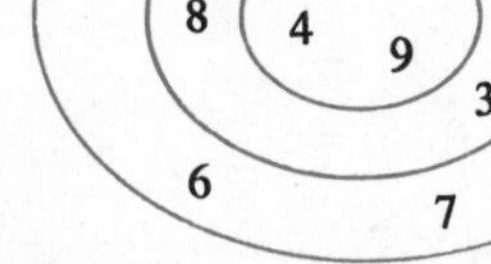

Set 56 (after page 245) **True or false?**

1. 1 is in A **2.** 1 is in B

3. 1 is in C **4.** $A \subseteq B$

5. $A \subseteq C$ **6.** 8 is in A

7. 8 is in B **8.** 8 is in C **9.** 4 is in A **10.** 4 is in B

11. 4 is in C **12.** $B \subseteq A$ **13.** $C \subseteq B$ **14.** $C \subseteq A$

Set 57 (after page 247)

1. $\begin{array}{r} 29 \\ \times 4 \\ \hline \end{array}$ **2.** $\begin{array}{r} 63 \\ \times 8 \\ \hline \end{array}$ **3.** $\begin{array}{r} 49 \\ \times 3 \\ \hline \end{array}$ **4.** $\begin{array}{r} 74 \\ \times 5 \\ \hline \end{array}$ **5.** $\begin{array}{r} 81 \\ \times 7 \\ \hline \end{array}$ **6.** $\begin{array}{r} 93 \\ \times 3 \\ \hline \end{array}$

7. $\begin{array}{r} .85 \\ \times .9 \\ \hline \end{array}$ **8.** $\begin{array}{r} 7.6 \\ \times .2 \\ \hline \end{array}$ **9.** $\begin{array}{r} 80 \\ \times .6 \\ \hline \end{array}$ **10.** $\begin{array}{r} 5.5 \\ \times .7 \\ \hline \end{array}$ **11.** $\begin{array}{r} 3.6 \\ \times 4 \\ \hline \end{array}$ **12.** $\begin{array}{r} 5.8 \\ \times 5 \\ \hline \end{array}$

13. $\begin{array}{r} 9.96 \\ \times .007 \\ \hline \end{array}$ **14.** $\begin{array}{r} 70.3 \\ \times .004 \\ \hline \end{array}$ **15.** $\begin{array}{r} .548 \\ \times .005 \\ \hline \end{array}$ **16.** $\begin{array}{r} 63.9 \\ \times .09 \\ \hline \end{array}$ **17.** $\begin{array}{r} 42.1 \\ \times .06 \\ \hline \end{array}$ **18.** $\begin{array}{r} 9.13 \\ \times .04 \\ \hline \end{array}$

19. $\begin{array}{r} 59.6 \\ \times 60.8 \\ \hline \end{array}$ **20.** $\begin{array}{r} 914 \\ \times 1.58 \\ \hline \end{array}$ **21.** $\begin{array}{r} 78.3 \\ \times .38 \\ \hline \end{array}$ **22.** $\begin{array}{r} 6.74 \\ \times 4.7 \\ \hline \end{array}$ **23.** $\begin{array}{r} 5.08 \\ \times 3.5 \\ \hline \end{array}$ **24.** $\begin{array}{r} 36.2 \\ \times .12 \\ \hline \end{array}$

Set 58 (after page 251) **Reduce to lowest terms.**

1. $\frac{9}{6}$ **2.** $\frac{8}{8}$ **3.** $\frac{2}{8}$ **4.** $\frac{4}{6}$ **5.** $\frac{2}{6}$ **6.** $\frac{3}{6}$ **7.** $\frac{24}{20}$ **8.** $\frac{20}{28}$

9. $\frac{2}{10}$ **10.** $\frac{4}{20}$ **11.** $\frac{4}{12}$ **12.** $\frac{12}{9}$ **13.** $\frac{16}{14}$ **14.** $\frac{10}{16}$ **15.** $\frac{6}{9}$ **16.** $\frac{4}{8}$

17. $\frac{3}{9}$ **18.** $\frac{6}{16}$ **19.** $\frac{5}{10}$ **20.** $\frac{10}{15}$ **21.** $\frac{5}{20}$ **22.** $\frac{16}{12}$ **23.** $\frac{12}{8}$ **24.** $\frac{5}{15}$

Set 59 (after page 253) **Change to mixed numerals.**

1. $\frac{10}{3}$ **2.** $\frac{17}{10}$ **3.** $\frac{16}{9}$ **4.** $\frac{11}{6}$ **5.** $\frac{6}{5}$ **6.** $\frac{4}{3}$ **7.** $\frac{5}{4}$ **8.** $\frac{3}{2}$

9. $\frac{13}{8}$ **10.** $\frac{7}{5}$ **11.** $\frac{21}{8}$ **12.** $\frac{7}{6}$ **13.** $\frac{5}{2}$ **14.** $\frac{5}{3}$ **15.** $\frac{7}{4}$ **16.** $\frac{8}{5}$

17. $\frac{11}{4}$ **18.** $\frac{7}{2}$ **19.** $\frac{8}{3}$ **20.** $\frac{9}{5}$ **21.** $\frac{9}{2}$ **22.** $\frac{9}{4}$ **23.** $\frac{7}{3}$ **24.** $\frac{13}{6}$

Set 60 (after page 255) **Substitute and simplify.**

j	r	s	t	x
1	2	5	0	3

1. $s - x$ **2.** $r^t + 5$ **3.** $s(r + x)$ **4.** $rs - sr$ **5.** $rs - t$

6. r^x **7.** $x(rs - j)$ **8.** stx **9.** 5^x **10.** $s^r - 9$

11. $s - r^r$ **12.** $t(r + x)$ **13.** $x^r - r^x$ **14.** $sx - r$ **15.** $r(x + j)$

16. $jrts$ **17.** $\frac{j + s}{x}$ **18.** $rx + s^r$ **19.** $\frac{rx - s}{j}$ **20.** $\frac{s + x}{j}$

Set 61 (after page 257)

1. $7\overline{)329}$ **2.** $9\overline{)288}$ **3.** $3\overline{)438}$ **4.** $2\overline{)586}$ **5.** $3\overline{)567}$

6. $.04\overline{)5.12}$ **7.** $.7\overline{)11.2}$ **8.** $.06\overline{)4.08}$ **9.** $5\overline{)3.90}$ **10.** $8\overline{)8.56}$

11. $.35\overline{)94.5}$ **12.** $2.6\overline{)28.6}$ **13.** $.11\overline{)3.85}$ **14.** $1.5\overline{)9.45}$ **15.** $1.2\overline{)28.8}$

16. $.78\overline{)397.8}$ **17.** $.49\overline{)2.793}$ **18.** $3.6\overline{)26.28}$ **19.** $.55\overline{)4950}$ **20.** $7.3\overline{).1314}$

Set 62 (after page 259)

1. $y\%$ of 6 = 18
2. $y\%$ of 18 = 6
3. $y\%$ of 9 = 12
4. $y\%$ of 12 = 9
5. $y\%$ of 8 = 4
6. $y\%$ of 4 = 8
7. $y\%$ of 5 = 2.5
8. $y\%$ of 36 = 12
9. $y\%$ of 32 = 16
10. $y\%$ of 16 = 12
11. $y\%$ of 20 = 15
12. $y\%$ of 18 = 12
13. $y\%$ of 24 = 36
14. $y\%$ of 11 = 22
15. $y\%$ of 100 = 20
16. $y\%$ of 100 = 2
17. $y\%$ of 100 = .2
18. $y\%$ of 50 = 30
19. $y\%$ of 50 = 8
20. $y\%$ of 50 = .8

Set 63 (after page 261)

1. 7.9 dm = __?__ m
2. 13.5 cg = __?__ mg
3. 8 l = __?__ dl
4. 5.8 cg = __?__ mg
5. 14.8 cm = __?__ dm
6. 6.4 mm = __?__ cm
7. 9 ml = __?__ cl
8. 4.6 dm = __?__ m
9. 2.6 m = __?__ dm
10. 14.5 cm = __?__ dm
11. 7.3 l = __?__ dl
12. 12.8 kg = __?__ g
13. 519 m = __?__ km
14. 15.3 cl = __?__ dl
15. 6.3 dl = __?__ l
16. 16.8 cg = __?__ dg
17. 8.4 cl = __?__ ml
18. 3.16 hg = __?__ g
19. 5.28 dag = __?__ g
20. 2.61 l = __?__ dl

Set 64 (after page 263) **Solve.**

1. $\frac{3}{8} = \frac{x}{9}$
2. $\frac{5}{2} = \frac{8}{x}$
3. $\frac{1}{5} = \frac{x}{7}$
4. $\frac{3}{x} = \frac{4}{9}$
5. $\frac{x}{15} = \frac{6}{15}$
6. $\frac{x}{16} = \frac{7}{8}$
7. $\frac{x}{19} = \frac{9}{5}$
8. $\frac{3}{5} = \frac{x}{7}$
9. $\frac{2}{9} = \frac{12}{x}$
10. $\frac{1}{6} = \frac{11}{x}$
11. $\frac{7}{x} = \frac{9}{4}$
12. $\frac{11}{x} = \frac{8}{3}$
13. $\frac{5}{9} = \frac{x}{27}$
14. $\frac{7}{3} = \frac{8}{x}$
15. $\frac{3}{2} = \frac{13}{x}$
16. $\frac{4}{8} = \frac{x}{6}$
17. $\frac{12}{13} = \frac{4}{x}$
18. $\frac{x}{9} = \frac{11}{8}$
19. $\frac{15}{x} = \frac{3}{8}$
20. $\frac{5}{x} = \frac{7}{4}$

Set 65 (after page 265) **Round to the nearest hundredth.**

1. 2.916
2. 3.743
3. 4.285
4. 5.783
5. 3.286
6. 7.358
7. 9.748
8. 0.069
9. 7.593
10. 8.296
11. 1.005
12. 5.002
13. 7.343
14. 4.951
15. 5.483
16. 6.999
17. 3.096
18. 2.895
19. 9.374
20. 6.008

Set 66 (after page 281) **Find each surface area and volume. Use 3.14 as an approximation for π.**

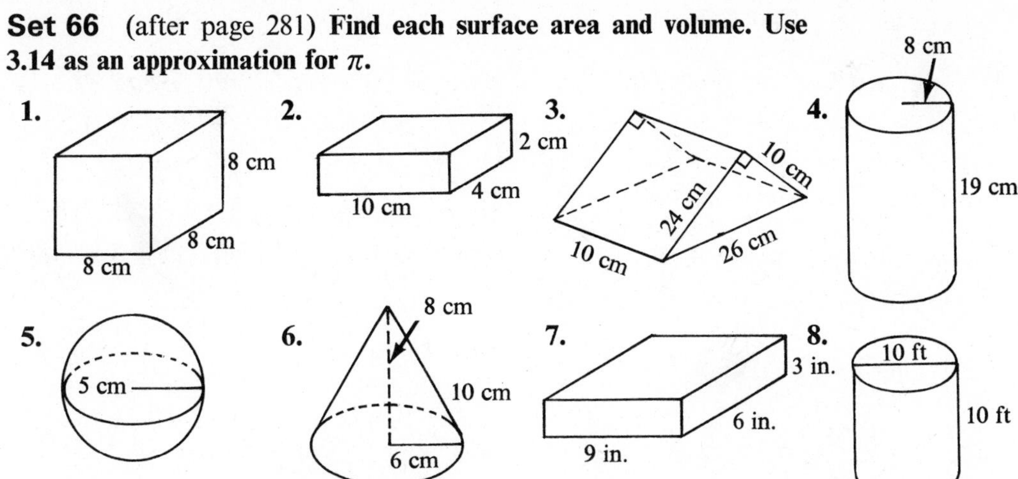

Set 67 (after page 283)

	Principal	Yearly rate	Time	Interest
1.	\$1000	$8\frac{1}{2}\%$	3 months	?
2.	\$450	10%	8 months	?
3.	\$100	6%	1 year	?
4.	\$300	9%	2 years	?
5.	\$3600	$9\frac{1}{2}\%$	18 months	?
6.	\$8000	$9\frac{3}{4}\%$	$1\frac{3}{4}$ years	?
7.	\$150	8%	$1\frac{1}{2}$ years	?
8.	\$600	9%	9 months	?
9.	\$2106	$8\frac{1}{4}\%$	$2\frac{1}{2}$ years	?
10.	\$1125	10%	4 months	?
11.	\$850	10%	2 months	?
12.	\$275	8%	6 months	?

Set 68 (after page 305) Solve.

1. $2x = {}^-8$
2. $3a = 21$
3. ${}^-2r = {}^-12$
4. ${}^-5a = 35$
5. $a - 9 = 1$
6. $a - 9 = 0$
7. $a - 9 = {}^-1$
8. $a - 9 = {}^-10$
9. $a - 2 = 6$
10. $a - 1 = 6$
11. $a - 0 = 6$
12. $a - {}^-1 = 6$
13. $2m + 3 = 11$
14. $2m + 3 = {}^-11$
15. $3x + 5 = {}^-7$
16. ${}^-3x + 5 = {}^-7$
17. $\frac{x}{3} = 6$
18. $\frac{x}{3} = {}^-6$
19. $\frac{12}{x} = 3$
20. $\frac{12}{x} = {}^-4$

Set 69 (after page 307)

1. 66×2
2. 47×5
3. 75×4
4. 86×7
5. 87×6
6. 93×3
7. $.29 \times .4$
8. $.37 \times .04$
9. $5.5 \times .03$
10. $7.3 \times .5$
11. $80 \times .9$
12. 9.2×6
13. 9.1×21
14. 9.1×2.1
15. $7.5 \times .26$
16. 4.6×30
17. 5.2×1.2
18. $.28 \times .18$
19. $62.4 \times .23$
20. 2.11×4.4
21. 5.26×35
22. 43.8×6.8
23. 7.42×10.2
24. 86.3×25.3

Set 70 (after page 309)

1. 4)748
2. 8)1608
3. 9)2007
4. 6)8592
5. 5)2465
6. 7)42.35
7. 3)2.982
8. 2)45.38
9. 8)64.40
10. 6).3960
11. 5.4)6242.4
12. 6.3)1.134
13. .31)93
14. 2.2)16.72
15. .15).1275
16. 2.5)59.75
17. .39)3.939
18. 1.26)34.02
19. 53.4)19.224
20. .812).38976

Set 71 (after page 311)

1. $\frac{2}{3} = \frac{x}{9}$
2. $\frac{5}{9} = \frac{20}{x}$
3. $\frac{5}{8} = \frac{x}{96}$
4. $\frac{24}{x} = \frac{3}{5}$
5. $\frac{3}{8} = \frac{5}{x}$
6. $\frac{7}{6} = \frac{8}{x}$
7. $\frac{8}{x} = \frac{5}{6}$
8. $\frac{9}{x} = \frac{3}{7}$
9. $\frac{6}{1} = \frac{8}{x}$
10. $\frac{3}{4} = \frac{x}{5}$
11. $\frac{8}{5} = \frac{7}{x}$
12. $\frac{x}{11} = \frac{7}{8}$
13. $\frac{12}{x} = \frac{4}{3}$
14. $\frac{x}{14} = \frac{11}{2}$
15. $\frac{15}{x} = \frac{3}{2}$
16. $\frac{17}{x} = \frac{5}{7}$
17. $\frac{9}{8} = \frac{x}{6}$
18. $\frac{8}{3} = \frac{x}{9}$
19. $\frac{13}{x} = \frac{4}{5}$
20. $\frac{16}{x} = \frac{9}{5}$

Set 72 (after page 315) **Round to the nearest tenth.**

1. .3279	**2.** 92.06	**3.** .2506	**4.** 7.137	**5.** 39.61
6. .6410	**7.** 8.671	**8.** 2.251	**9.** .7483	**10.** 4.463
11. 53.62	**12.** .2654	**13.** 1.937	**14.** 63.84	**15.** 20.05
16. 3.998	**17.** 3.756	**18.** 18.29	**19.** .5463	**20.** 19.73

Set 73 (after page 327)

1. $\frac{1}{5}$ of ___?___ = 6	**2.** $\frac{3}{8}$ of ___?___ = 9	**3.** $\frac{1}{3}$ of ___?___ = 15	**4.** $\frac{1}{2}$ of ___?___ = 7
5. $\frac{5}{3}$ of ___?___ = 45	**6.** $\frac{6}{5}$ of ___?___ = 36	**7.** $\frac{1}{4}$ of ___?___ = 10	**8.** $\frac{3}{3}$ of ___?___ = 18
9. $\frac{1}{8}$ of ___?___ = 12	**10.** $\frac{3}{4}$ of ___?___ = 24	**11.** $\frac{3}{2}$ of ___?___ = 9	**12.** $\frac{5}{8}$ of ___?___ = 40
13. $\frac{5}{2}$ of ___?___ = 10	**14.** $\frac{4}{3}$ of ___?___ = 24	**15.** $\frac{4}{5}$ of ___?___ = 40	**16.** $\frac{4}{4}$ of ___?___ = 32
17. $\frac{5}{8}$ of ___?___ = 35	**18.** $\frac{3}{8}$ of ___?___ = 24	**19.** $\frac{2}{3}$ of ___?___ = 102	**20.** $\frac{7}{2}$ of ___?___ = 7

Set 74 (after page 343) **Give the mean, median, and mode.**

1. 6, 6, 7, 7, 7, 8, 9, 10

2. 12, 15, 17, 18, 18, 19, 20, 28

3. 35, 36, 37, 38, 39, 40, 40, 40

4. 75, 79, 83, 83, 83, 88, 90, 97

5. 64, 64, 67, 93, 97, 106, 108

6. 38, 40, 47, 48, 48, 56, 75, 90

7. 12,000, 15,000, 18,000, 18,000, 25,000, 1,000,000

Set 75 (after page 347)

1. 9.5×3	**2.** 3.7×6	**3.** 8.5×4	**4.** $.75 \times 9$	**5.** 5.9×7	**6.** $.67 \times 2$
7. $5.03 \times .7$	**8.** $.304 \times .6$	**9.** 31.6×9	**10.** $4.33 \times .04$	**11.** $87.4 \times .09$	**12.** $6.03 \times .06$
13. 42.6×70	**14.** 6.12×40	**15.** 831×50	**16.** 72.8×30	**17.** 9.13×72	**18.** 80.6×16
19. 46.3×3.8	**20.** 9.71×4.1	**21.** $.634 \times .83$	**22.** 49.7×2.8	**23.** 6.05×17.3	**24.** 49.5×38.7

Set 76 (after page 349)

Give a decimal approximation correct to the nearest tenth.

1. $\sqrt{17}$ **2.** $\sqrt{15}$ **3.** $\sqrt{84}$ **4.** $\sqrt{59}$ **5.** $\sqrt{89}$ **6.** $\sqrt{3}$

7. $\sqrt{96}$ **8.** $\sqrt{50}$ **9.** $\sqrt{347}$ **10.** $\sqrt{586}$ **11.** $\sqrt{931}$ **12.** $\sqrt{1473}$

Set 77 (after page 353) **Round to the nearest .1.**

1. 243.16 **2.** 67.816 **3.** 4.3824 **4.** .53913 **5.** .054916

6. 28.917 **7.** 3.8381 **8.** 826.45 **9.** 37.348 **10.** 4.8326

11. .06811 **12.** 38.138 **13.** 62.555 **14.** 51.626 **15.** 6.3681

16. .96151 **17.** 43.672 **18.** 270.49 **19.** .09715 **20.** 59.997

Set 78 (after page 355) **Find the missing lengths. Use the table of tangent values on page 351.**

1.

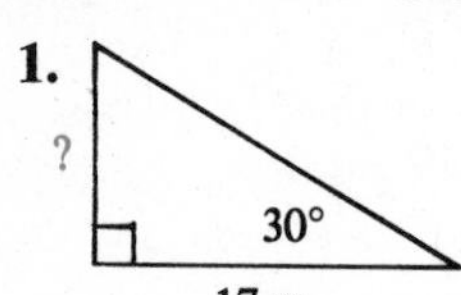

2. **3.**

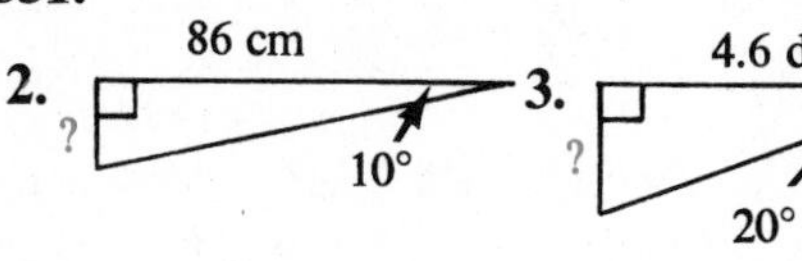

4.

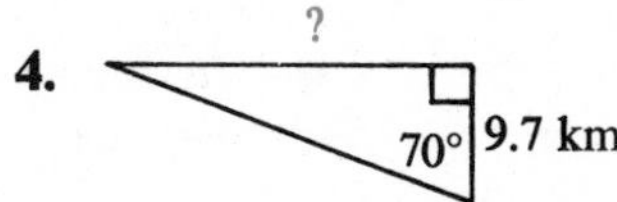

5.

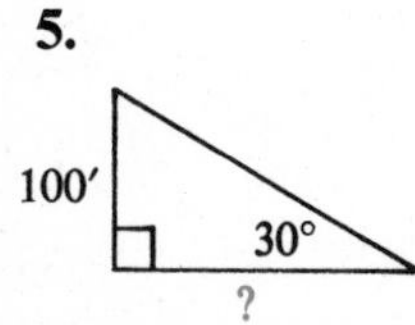

6.

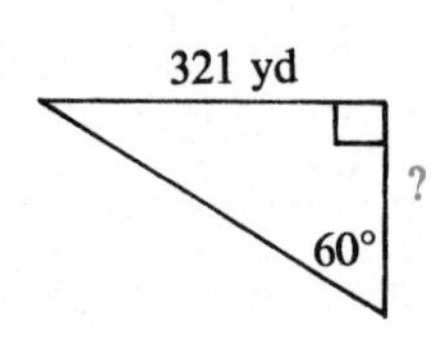

7.

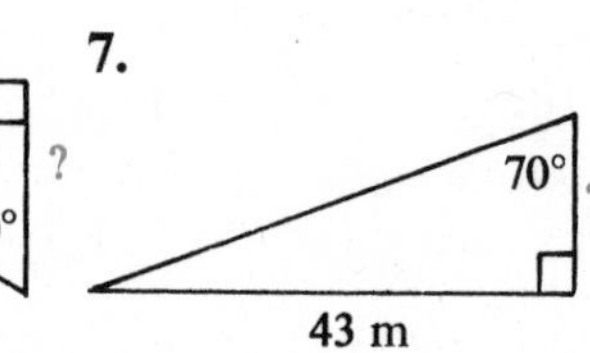

8.

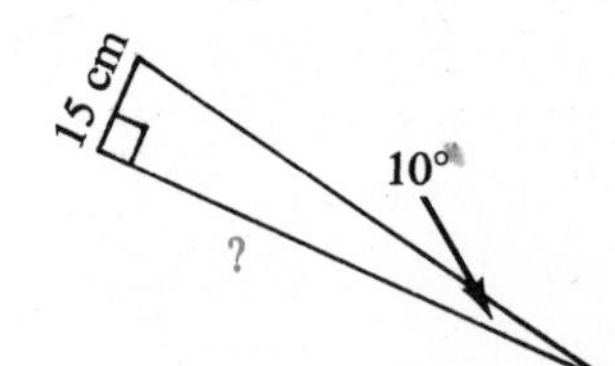

Set 79 (after page 357) **Are the two figures similar?**

1.

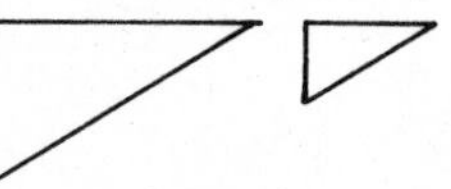

2.

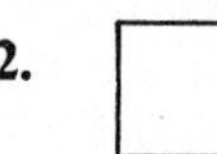

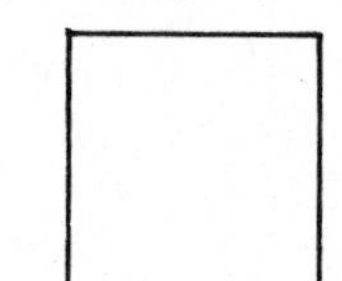

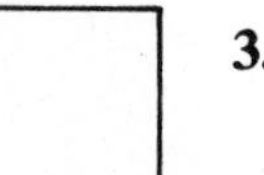

3.

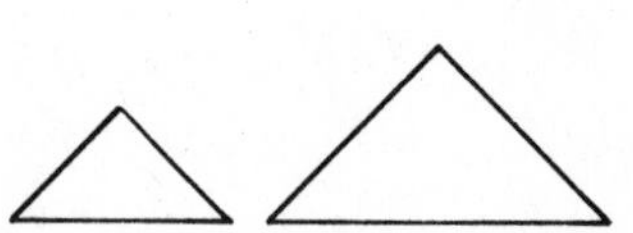

4.

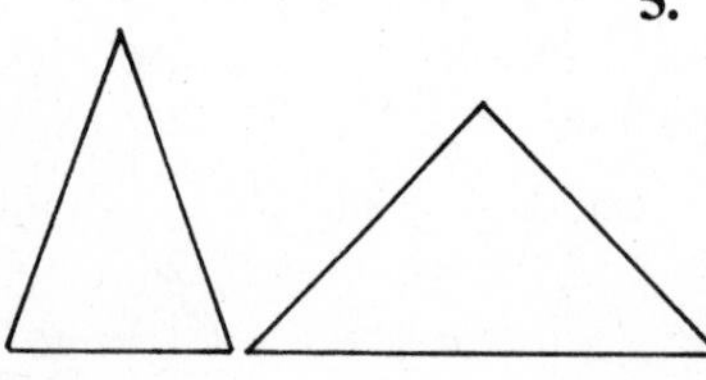

5.

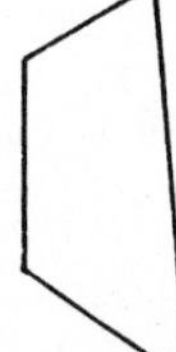

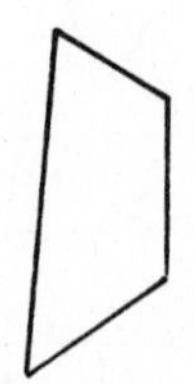

6.

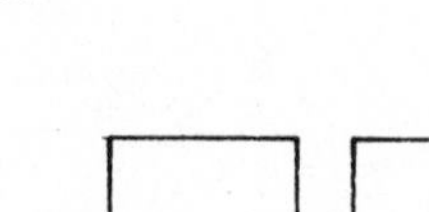

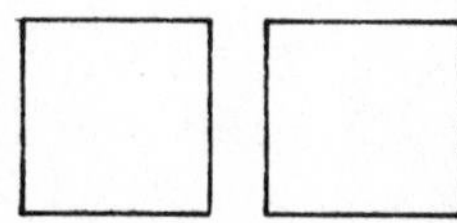

Skill Test

Whole numbers

	skill objective	test items			
1	Add any two numbers [*page 42*]	325 +412	296 +482	648 +229	5846 +8978
2	Subtract any two numbers [*page 42*]	473 −241	562 −149	821 −257	8000 −3841
3	Multiply by a 1-digit number [*page 68*]	132 ×2	19 ×3	526 ×7	4328 ×9
4	Multiply by 10 or 100 [*page 70*]	75 ×10	84 ×100	389 ×10	5762 ×100
5	Multiply by multiples of 10 and 100 [*page 72*]	48 ×20	572 ×40	321 ×600	4832 ×700
6	Multiply by a 2-digit number [*page 74*]	53 ×25	468 ×38	621 ×51	7033 ×94
7	Multiply by a 3-digit number [*page 74*]	483 ×114	872 ×205	608 ×217	4163 ×835
8	Divide by a 1-digit number [*page 82*]	4)628	3)281	8)526	7)8314
9	Divide by a 2-digit number [*page 86*]	20)831	43)2083	94)6821	42)8667

	skill objective	test items			
10	Divide by a 3-digit number [*page 86*]	$400\overline{)2974}$		$120\overline{)840}$	
		$421\overline{)16412}$		$832\overline{)4652}$	
11	Add with regrouping [*page 42*]	4.21 +3.17	5.81 +2.97	89.4 +9.8	4.238 +.876
12	Subtract with regrouping [*page 42*]	.821 −.118	2.63 −1.85	40.3 −28.7	17.6 −9.85
13	Multiply by a 1-digit whole number [*page 68*]	32.6 ×8	4.83 ×5	8.17 ×6	9.503 ×8
14	Multiply by 10 or 100 [*page 70*]	42.6 ×10	42.6 ×100	6.732 ×10	6.732 ×100
15	Multiply by multiples of 10 or 100 [*page 72*]	2.74 ×30	8.17 ×60	4.83 ×300	86.211 ×700
16	Multiply by a 2-digit whole number [*page 74*]	4.73 ×28	2.63 ×81	27.3 ×14	.817 ×46
17	Divide by a 1-digit whole number [*page 82*]	$2\overline{)91.8}$		$5\overline{)8.25}$	
		$8\overline{).416}$		$9\overline{)21.33}$	
18	Divide by a 2-digit whole number [*page 86*]	$30\overline{)5.7}$		$25\overline{)7.25}$	
		$57\overline{)121.41}$		$34\overline{)28.39}$	

Decimal numbers

	skill objective	test items			
Decimal numbers **19**	Divide by a 3-digit whole number [*page 86*]	$300\overline{)5.7}$		$250\overline{)7.25}$	
		$462\overline{)970.2}$		$513\overline{)1097.82}$	
20	Multiply [*page 78*]	$\begin{array}{r}.4\\ \times .3\\ \hline\end{array}$	$\begin{array}{r}2.7\\ \times .08\\ \hline\end{array}$	$\begin{array}{r}5.6\\ \times 3.9\\ \hline\end{array}$	$\begin{array}{r}4.21\\ \times 6.51\\ \hline\end{array}$
21	Divide [*page 90*]	$.8\overline{)1.64}$		$.05\overline{)3.1}$	
		$4.1\overline{)15.17}$		$.83\overline{)3.4943}$	
22	Divide and round to the nearest tenth [*page 90*]	$.6\overline{)43.1}$		$.8\overline{)2.67}$	
		$.43\overline{).87}$		$1.23\overline{)81.67}$	
23	Change fractions to decimals or repeating decimals [*page 102*]	$\frac{3}{4}$	$\frac{5}{8}$	$\frac{5}{6}$	$\frac{2}{11}$
Fractional numbers **24**	Find an equivalent fraction [*page 98*]	$\frac{3}{4} = \frac{x}{12}$		$\frac{5}{7} = \frac{z}{35}$	
		$\frac{8}{5} = \frac{m}{40}$		$\frac{5}{8} = \frac{g}{40}$	
25	Reduce a fraction to lowest terms [*page 100*]	$\frac{12}{18}$	$\frac{15}{25}$	$\frac{45}{81}$	$\frac{54}{72}$
26	Compare fractional numbers [*page 106*]	$<$ or $>$?			
		$\frac{3}{8} \bullet \frac{5}{8}$		$\frac{5}{7} \bullet \frac{5}{9}$	
		$\frac{2}{3} \bullet \frac{3}{5}$		$\frac{4}{9} \bullet \frac{3}{7}$	
27	Add fractional numbers [*page 108*]	$\frac{1}{4} + \frac{3}{8}$		$\frac{1}{6} + \frac{2}{3}$	
		$\frac{3}{4} + \frac{2}{3}$		$\frac{5}{7} + \frac{3}{8}$	

Fractional numbers

	skill objective	test items			
28	Subtract fractional numbers [*page 110*]	$\frac{3}{8} - \frac{1}{4}$	$\frac{2}{3} - \frac{1}{6}$		
		$\frac{3}{4} - \frac{2}{3}$	$\frac{5}{7} - \frac{3}{8}$		
29	Change mixed numerals to fractions [*page 112*]	$3\frac{1}{2}$	$2\frac{2}{3}$	$4\frac{3}{4}$	$5\frac{7}{8}$
30	Change fractions to mixed numerals [*page 112*]	$\frac{5}{2}$	$\frac{10}{3}$	$\frac{15}{4}$	$\frac{35}{8}$
31	Add, mixed numerals without regrouping [*page 114*]	$3\frac{1}{3} + 4\frac{1}{3}$	$7\frac{2}{3} + 5\frac{1}{4}$		
		$13\frac{1}{4} + 7\frac{1}{6}$	$10\frac{2}{3} + 3\frac{1}{4}$		
32	Add, mixed numerals with regrouping [*page 114*]	$4\frac{5}{7} + 3\frac{3}{7}$	$5\frac{2}{3} + 2\frac{1}{3}$	$6\frac{5}{6} + 3\frac{7}{8}$	$6\frac{2}{3} + 7\frac{3}{4}$
33	Subtract, mixed numerals without regrouping [*page 114*]	$4\frac{1}{3} - 3\frac{1}{3}$	$7\frac{2}{3} - 5\frac{1}{4}$		
		$13\frac{1}{4} - 7\frac{1}{6}$	$10\frac{2}{3} - 3\frac{1}{5}$		
34	Subtract, mixed numerals with regrouping [*page 114*]	$4\frac{2}{7} - 1\frac{4}{7}$	$5\frac{1}{2} - 3\frac{3}{4}$	$6\frac{5}{6} - 3\frac{7}{8}$	$10\frac{2}{3} - 7\frac{3}{4}$
35	Multiply fractional numbers [*page 118*]	$\frac{2}{3} \times \frac{4}{7}$	$\frac{3}{5} \times \frac{5}{8}$		
		$\frac{6}{7} \times \frac{5}{3}$	$\frac{12}{16} \times \frac{4}{3}$		
36	Multiply, mixed numeral by whole number [*page 122*]	$3\frac{2}{3} \times 3$	$4\frac{1}{5} \times 7$		
		$4\frac{3}{4} \times 5$	$7\frac{2}{3} \times 12$		

	skill objective	test items			
Fractional numbers					
37	Multiply, mixed numerals [*page 122*]	$2\frac{1}{2} \times 3\frac{1}{4}$	$2\frac{4}{5} \times 3\frac{1}{8}$		
		$5\frac{2}{3} \times 2\frac{3}{4}$	$6\frac{5}{7} \times 2\frac{4}{5}$		
38	Divide fractional numbers [*page 120*]	$\frac{3}{2} \div \frac{5}{4}$	$\frac{3}{4} \div \frac{3}{8}$		
		$\frac{2}{3} \div \frac{4}{5}$	$\frac{2}{5} \div \frac{3}{7}$		
39	Divide fractional and whole numbers [*page 120*]	$\frac{3}{5} \div 3$	$7 \div \frac{1}{2}$		
		$4 \div \frac{3}{4}$	$\frac{5}{8} \div 2$		
40	Divide mixed numerals [*page 122*]	$5\frac{3}{4} \div 1\frac{1}{4}$	$7\frac{4}{5} \div 2\frac{1}{4}$		
		$4\frac{1}{2} \div 1\frac{1}{2}$	$3\frac{2}{3} \div 2\frac{3}{5}$		
41	Find a fractional part of a quantity [*page 178*]	$\frac{1}{4}$ of \$24 = \$__?__	$\frac{3}{5}$ of 15¢ = __?__¢		
		$\frac{5}{4}$ of \$80 = \$__?__	$\frac{4}{7}$ of 56¢ = __?__¢		
42	Find a quantity given a fractional part of it [*page 182*]	$\frac{1}{3}$ of \$__?__ = \$8	$\frac{5}{6}$ of __?__¢ = 20¢		
		$\frac{4}{5}$ of \$__?__ = \$20	$\frac{7}{5}$ of __?__¢ = 35¢		
43	Change a fraction to a percent [*page 170*]	$\frac{1}{2}$	$\frac{4}{5}$	$\frac{5}{4}$	$\frac{2}{3}$
Percents					
44	Change a percent to a fraction [*page 172*]	10%	25%	$33\frac{1}{3}$%	160%
45	Change a percent to a decimal [*page 174*]	27%	30%	150%	1.3%

	skill objective	test items			
Percents					
46	Change a decimal to a percent *[page 174]*	.3	.03	.85	3.21
47	Find a percent of a number *[page 178]*	25% of 80 = ___?___ $33\frac{1}{3}$% of 93 = ___?___		142% of 81 = ___?___ 1.2% of 16 = ___?___	
48	Find a quantity given a percent of it *[page 182]*	40% of ___?___ = 16 8% of ___?___ = 16		75% of ___?___ = 18 150% of ___?___ = 60	
49	Find what percent one number is of another *[page 186]*	12 = ___?___ % of 24 18 = ___?___ % of 12		12 = ___?___ % of 18 2 = ___?___ % of 24	
Integers					
50	Add integers *[page 272]*	$^{+}7 + {}^{+}4$ $^{-}8 + {}^{+}3$		$^{+}9 + {}^{-}4$ $^{-}8 + {}^{-}7$	
51	Subtract integers *[page 274]*	$^{+}8 - {}^{+}12$ $^{-}8 - {}^{+}4$		$^{+}7 - {}^{-}3$ $^{-}8 - {}^{-}5$	
52	Multiply integers *[page 276]*	$^{+}2 \times {}^{+}7$ $^{-}8 \times {}^{+}6$		$^{+}5 \times {}^{-}3$ $^{-}8 \times {}^{-}5$	
53	Divide integers *[page 278]*	$^{+}18 \div {}^{+}3$ $^{-}27 \div {}^{+}9$		$^{+}24 \div {}^{-}3$ $^{-}36 \div {}^{-}4$	

Answers for Checkups

page 9 **1.** 17 **2.** 20 **3.** 6 **4.** 1 **5.** 10 **6.** 66
7. 6 **8.** 9 **9.** 8 **10.** 35 **11.** 7 **12.** 6

page 11 **1.** 5 **2.** 7 **3.** 9 **4.** 3 **5.** 10 **6.** 3 **7.** 7 **8.** 4

page 13 **1.** T **2.** F **3.** T **4.** T **5.** F **6.** T

page 17 **1.** $4a$ **2.** 6×7 **3.** ab **4.** $2(3 + 7)$ **5.** $2(3a)$
6. abc **7.** 8 **8.** 9 **9.** 1,000,000 **10.** 81
11. Commutative property of addition
12. Associative property of multiplication
13. Multiplying by 1 property **14.** Distributive property

page 25 **1.** 5 **2.** 7 **3.** 9 **4.** 3 **5.** 10 **6.** 3 **7.** 7 **8.** 4

page 27 **1.** {a, b, c, d, e, f, g} **2.** {c, g} **3.** {a, b, c, d, e, f} **4.** {c, d}
5. ∅ **6.** {c, d, h, m} **7.** T **8.** F **9.** T **10.** T

page 41 **1.** 6 **2.** 16 **3.** 6.2 **4.** 6.23 **5.** 36.23 **6.** 26.541 **7.** 8
8. 28 **9.** 8.6 **10.** 38.2 **11.** 5.342 **12.** 5.3426 **13.** 6,200,000
14. 5,770,000 000

page 47 **1.** 8.6 **2.** .8 **3.** .33 **4.** 1.257 **5.** 1.58 **6.** 8.16
7.—9. Answers will vary.

page 57 **1.** C = 7.2 **2.** 6, 12, 18, 24, 30, 36, 42, 48, 54

page 77 **1.** 9.6 **2.** 34.2 **3.** 3.36 **4.** 487.8
5. 195.3 **6.** 27.52 **7.** 3.525 **8.** 17506.3

page 83 **1.** .64 **2.** 3.36 **3.** .208 **4.** .335
5. 9.88 **6.** .2378 **7.** 5.852 **8.** 156.006

page 93 **1.** 2.6 **2.** .071 **3.** 2.5 **4.** .64 **5.** .13 **6.** .17 **7.** 38
8. .87 **9.** .64 **10.** 2.4 **11.** 5.9 **12.** 1520 **13.** 65.07

page 107 1. 1.5 2. .75 3. $.\overline{6}$ 4. .625 5. $.1\overline{6}$ 6. 4.5
7. $1.\overline{6}$ 8. .0625 9. .375 10. $\frac{3}{10}$ 11. $\frac{3}{100}$ 12. $\frac{3}{1000}$
13. $\frac{5}{4}$ 14. $\frac{3}{4}$ 15. $\frac{8}{100}$, or $\frac{2}{25}$ 16. $\frac{11}{8}$ 17. $\frac{15}{8}$ 18. $\frac{205}{100}$, or $\frac{41}{25}$

page 109 1. $\frac{1}{2}$ 2. 2 3. $\frac{1}{4}$ 4. 0 5. $\frac{1}{3}$ 6. 3
7. $\frac{1}{5}$ 8. $\frac{3}{2}$ 9. $\frac{1}{5}$ 10. $\frac{1}{3}$ 11. $\frac{1}{2}$ 12. $\frac{7}{2}$
13. $\frac{3}{2}$ 14. $\frac{1}{4}$ 15. 4 16. $\frac{1}{2}$ 17. $\frac{1}{5}$ 18. $\frac{1}{3}$

page 113 1. $\frac{1}{2}$ 2. $\frac{4}{9}$ 3. $\frac{7}{8}$ 4. $\frac{9}{4}$ 5. $\frac{3}{2}$ 6. $\frac{41}{24}$
7. $\frac{1}{2}$ 8. $\frac{2}{9}$ 9. $\frac{1}{6}$ 10. $\frac{1}{8}$ 11. $\frac{13}{24}$ 12. $\frac{11}{30}$

page 119 1. $\frac{7}{8}$ 2. $\frac{29}{12}$ 3. $\frac{3}{2}$ 4. $\frac{3}{4}$ 5. $3\frac{5}{6}$ 6. $\frac{11}{16}$
7. $\frac{1}{8}$ 8. $\frac{1}{12}$ 9. $\frac{4}{7}$ 10. $\frac{5}{8}$ 11. $\frac{1}{6}$ 12. $\frac{5}{24}$

page 123 1. 1 2. $\frac{12}{7}$ 3. $\frac{20}{9}$ 4. 1 5. $\frac{5}{9}$ 6. $\frac{2}{3}$
7. 24 8. $\frac{1}{3}$ 9. $\frac{5}{6}$ 10. $\frac{9}{4}$ 11. 0 12. $\frac{9}{4}$

page 127 1. $3\frac{3}{8}$ 2. $48\frac{5}{9}$ 3. $23\frac{3}{4}$ 4. $19\frac{7}{32}$ 5. $24\frac{3}{4}$ 6. $66\frac{1}{2}$
7. $2\frac{2}{33}$ 8. $1\frac{4}{17}$ 9. $5\frac{8}{9}$ 10. $5\frac{13}{28}$ 11. $3\frac{1}{26}$ 12. $3\frac{32}{33}$

page 133 1. $\frac{7}{48}$ 2. $\frac{35}{36}$ 3. $\frac{35}{24}$ 4. $\frac{19}{12}$ 5. $\frac{11}{20}$ 6. $\frac{49}{27}$

page 149 1. $\triangle NMO$ 2. $\overline{NM}$ 3. $\angle N$ 4. red one 5. a 6. m

page 153 1. 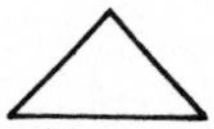 2. 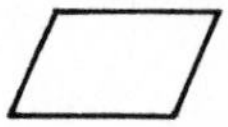 3. 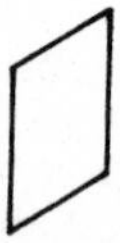 4. 4 cm 5. 5 cm 6. 14 cm
7. 8 cm

page 169 1. $\frac{1}{2}$ 2. $\frac{1}{4}$ 3. $\frac{1}{2}$ 4. $\frac{8}{5}$ 5. $\frac{1}{3}$ 6. $\frac{4}{3}$
7. $\frac{7}{10}$ 8. $\frac{5}{3}$ 9. $\frac{3}{5}$ 10. $\frac{3}{2}$ 11. $\frac{1}{2}$ 12. $\frac{1}{3}$
13. $\frac{1}{3}$ 14. $\frac{1}{4}$ 15. $\frac{2}{7}$ 16. $\frac{5}{3}$ 17. $\frac{8}{3}$ 18. $\frac{1}{2}$

page 173	1. $1\frac{7}{8}$	2. $15\frac{3}{4}$	3. $7\frac{1}{2}$	4. $16\frac{1}{2}$	5. $3\frac{1}{2}$	6. 18
	7. $2\frac{1}{2}$	8. $2\frac{5}{8}$	9. $6\frac{2}{3}$	10. $67\frac{1}{2}$	11. $10\frac{1}{9}$	12. $7\frac{17}{18}$
page 179	1. $\frac{1}{2}$	2. $\frac{1}{3}$	3. $\frac{3}{4}$	4. $\frac{4}{5}$	5. $\frac{5}{1}$	6. $\frac{3}{2}$
	7. $\frac{4}{3}$	8. $\frac{3}{2}$	9. $\frac{3}{4}$	10. $\frac{7}{6}$	11. $\frac{1}{2}$	12. $\frac{7}{5}$
	13. $\frac{3}{4}$	14. $\frac{6}{1}$	15. $\frac{4}{3}$	16. $\frac{6}{1}$	17. $\frac{1}{3}$	18. $\frac{1}{2}$
page 187	1. 34	2. 45.9	3. 153.6	4. 78	5. 208	6. 26.52
	7. 67.5	8. 81	9. .98	10. 2000	11. 48.24	12. 236.8
page 201	1. 130	2. 56.8	3. 3.2	4. 1500	5. 6000	6. 2.5
	7. 4.6	8. 820	9. 3.54	10. 2300	11. 180	12. 1300
page 209	1. .5%	2. .8%	3. 1.4%	4. 1.2%	5. .3%	6. .6%

page 225	1. 30	2. 400	3. 1.9	4. 3.4	5. 25.3
	6. 5.84	7. 26	8. .038	9. 2340	10. 6380

page 241 — 1. \$297 — 2. \$219.46 — 3. \$675

page 245 — 1. \$1722.75 — 2. \$205 — 3. \$3

page 251 — 1. \$45 — 2. \$17.33 — 3. \$480 — 4. \$98

page 253 — 1. \$1500 — 2. \$33.40

page 257 — \$141.30

page 263 — 1. \$80; $8\frac{1}{3}\%$ — 2. \$250; \$282.04

page 265 — 1. \$2443.75 — 2. \$2936.25 — 3. \$16406.25 — 4. \$150 — 5. \$975

page 275	1. $^{-}4$	2. $^{+}.9$	3. $^{-}1$	4. $\frac{^{+}1}{2}$	5. 0	6. $^{-}8$
	7. $\frac{^{+}3}{8}$	8. $\frac{^{-}3}{8}$	9. 0	10. $\frac{^{+}2}{9}$	11. $\frac{^{-}3}{8}$	12. $\frac{^{-}1}{2}$

page 277 **1.** $^-7$ **2.** $^+7$ **3.** $^+14$ **4.** $^-14$ **5.** $^-3$ **6.** $^-6$

7. $^+15$ **8.** $^+5.7$ **8.** $\frac{^-7}{8}$ **10.** $^+1\frac{1}{2}$ **11.** $\frac{^-2}{45}$ **12.** $^-5\frac{3}{4}$

page 283 **1.** $^-24$ **2.** $\frac{^+1}{6}$ **3.** $^+1$ **4.** $\frac{^-7}{10}$ **5.** $^+1$ **6.** $\frac{^-25}{24}$

7. $^+3$ **8.** $^-2$ **9.** $\frac{^+18}{5}$ **10.** $^-.9$ **11.** $\frac{^-15}{2}$ **12.** $^+40$

page 301 **1.** True **2.** True

page 309 **1.** $\frac{1}{4}$ **2.** $\frac{1}{8}$ **3.** $\frac{1}{4}$ **4.** 0 **5.** $\frac{3}{4}$ **6.** $\frac{3}{8}$

page 315

	Range	Mean	Median	Mode
1.	1—5	3	3	none
2.	2—8	4.6	4	4
3.	3—22	10.7	8.5	none
4.	12—12	12	12	12

	Range	Mean	Median	Mode
5.	3—8	5.6	5	5
6.	3—14	8.7	9	none
7.	16—20	18	18	none
8.	16—58	34	31	none

page 323 **1.** $^-.8$ **2.** $^-.75$ **3.** $1.\overline{3}$ **4.** $^-2.5$ **5.** 1.75

6. $^-.\overline{714285}$ **7.** $1.\overline{6}$ **8.** 5.8 **9.** 1.625 **10.** $^-.\overline{18}$

page 333 **1.** 6.1 **2.** 7.3 **3.** 8.3 **4.** 4.7

5. 6.6 **6.** 9.4 **7.** 7.8 **8.** 10.4

page 337 **1.** 4.4 **2.** 5.3 **3.** 6.2 **4.** 7.1 **5.** 7.7

6. 8.1 **7.** 8.5 **8.** 10.4 **9.** 14.1 **10.** 17.3

page 349 **1.** yes **2.** no **3.** $\overline{XY}$ **4.** $\angle B$ **5.** 6.75″

page 357 **1.** 15.7 m **2.** 27.8 m **3.** 55 cm

page 361 **1.** $\overline{AC}$, $\overline{CB}$ **2.** 10′ **3.** 13.4 m

acute angle An angle of less than 90 degrees.

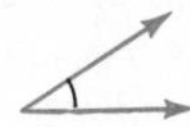

addend A number to be added.

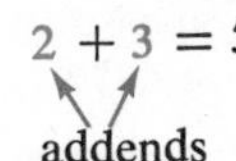

adding 0 property The sum of any number and zero is that number.

$29 + 0 = 29$

additive inverse property Two numbers whose sum is 0 are additive inverses of each other.

$^{-}8 + {}^{+}8 = 0$

additive inverses

angle Union of two rays.

angle of a polygon An angle formed by two adjacent sides of a polygon.

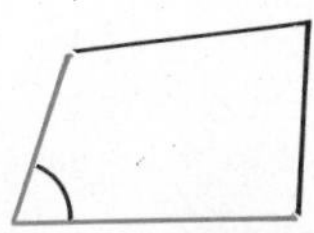

are A unit of area in the metric system. 1 are = 100 square meters.

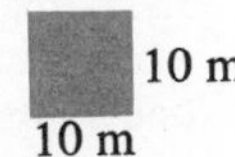

area The measure of a region or surface. A square is used as a unit.

associative property of addition The way in which the addends are grouped does not affect the sum.

$$(5 + 8) + 9 = 5 + (8 + 9)$$

associative property of multiplication The way in which the factors are grouped does not affect the product.

$$(3 \times 2) \times 5 = 3 \times (2 \times 5)$$

average See *mean.*

bar graph A graph made up of rectangular bars to show some information.

base (of a three-dimensional figure) Study the examples.

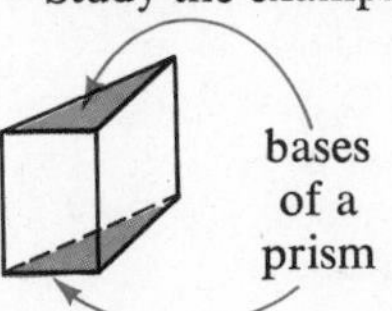

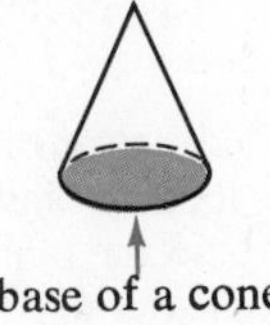

basic counting principle If a first event has ***m*** outcomes and if, after the first event, a second event has ***n*** outcomes, then the first event followed by the second event has $m \times n$ outcomes.

bisect a segment To divide a segment into two congruent parts.

A ———— B

bisects $\overline{AB}$

cancel Divide both numerator and denominator numbers by the same number, usually before multiplying.

$$\frac{5}{\cancel{8}_4} \times \frac{\cancel{2}^1}{7}$$

center of circle The point from which all points on the circle are the same distance.

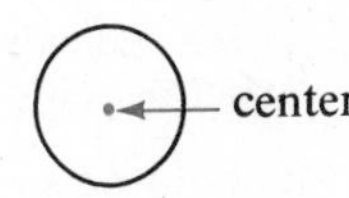

centigram A unit of weight in the metric system. A hundredth of a gram.

1 cg = .01 g

centiliter A unit of capacity in the metric system. A hundredth of a liter.

1 cl = .01 *l*

centimeter A unit of length in the metric system. A hundredth of a meter.

1 cm = .01 m

circle The set of all points in a plane that are the same distance from a given point.

circle graph A pictorial representation of numerical facts, where each fact is represented by a "slice" of a circular region. The whole region represents the total quantity.

circumference The distance around a circle.

$C = \pi d$

closure property of addition A set of numbers is closed under addition if the sum of any two numbers in the set is a number in the set.

closure property of multiplication A set of numbers is closed under multiplication if the product of any two numbers in the set is a number in the set.

common factor A number that is a factor of two or more numbers.

1 and 3 are common factors.

common multiple A number that is a multiple of two or more numbers.

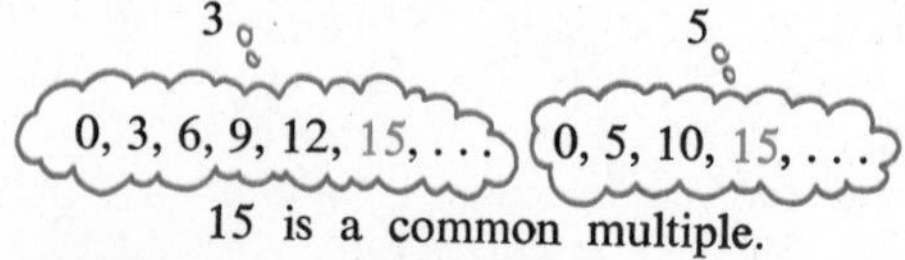

15 is a common multiple.

commutative property of addition The order of the addends does not affect the sum. $3 + 5 = 5 + 3$

commutative property of multiplication The order of the factors does not affect the product. $6 \times 7 = 7 \times 6$

complex fraction A fraction in which either the numerator or the denominator or both are fractions. $\frac{\frac{6}{7}}{\frac{2}{3}}$ $\frac{8}{\frac{3}{4}}$ $\frac{\frac{5}{2}}{6}$

composite number A whole number other than 0 having more than two factors.

compound interest Interest that is added to the principal at regular intervals. This makes the principal grow and earn more and more interest.

computer program The detailed instructions that tell a computer exactly what to do.

cone (right circular) A solid figure with one circular base and one curved lateral face.

congruent figures Figures that have the same size and shape. Two figures are congruent if a tracing of one fits the other.

conversion fraction A fraction whose two terms are different names for the same quantity. It is used to convert from one measurement unit to another.

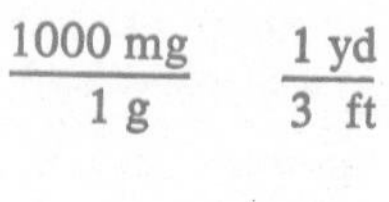

coordinate axes Two perpendicular lines used as a reference for graphing number pairs (ordered pairs). The horizontal line is the first component axis, and the vertical line is the second component axis.

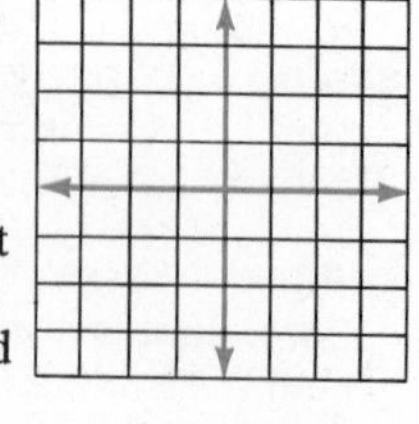

coordinates A number pair (ordered pair) matched with a point of the coordinate plane.

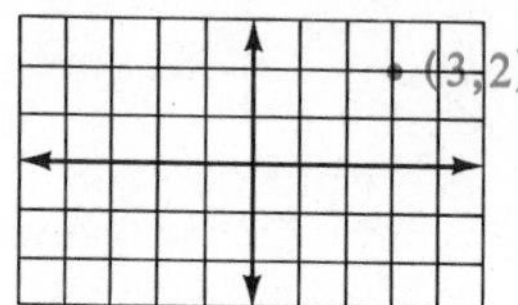

corresponding parts Parts that match when a tracing of one figure is placed on a congruent figure.

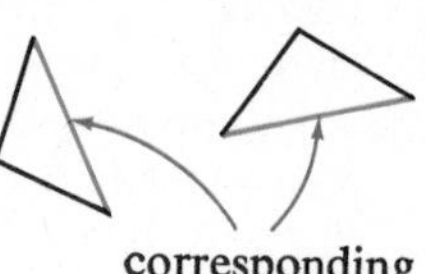

corresponding parts

cylinder (right circular) A three-dimensional figure formed by two congruent circular regions in parallel planes and a "curved" rectangular region.

decigram A unit of weight in the metric system. A tenth of a gram. 1 dg = .1 g

deciliter A unit of capacity in the metric system. A tenth of a liter. 1 dl = .1 *l*

decimal (or decimal fraction) A base ten numeral that uses place value and a decimal point. 5.6, .08, 953.4

decimal point The dot that is located between the ones place and the tenths place in a decimal numeral. 67 83

decimeter A unit of length in the metric system. A tenth of a meter. 1 dm = .1 m

degree The basic unit used for measuring angles. It is $\frac{1}{360}$ of a full turn.

dekagram A unit of weight in the metric system. Ten grams. 1 dag = 10 g

dekaliter A unit of capacity in the metric system. Ten liters. 1 dal = 10 *l*

dekameter A unit of length in the metric system. Ten meters. 1 dam = 10 m

denominator The numeral below the fraction bar. $\frac{3}{8}$ ← denominator

dependent events Events such that the outcome of the first affects the outcome of the second. Draw a first and a second card without replacement.

difference The number that is the result of subtracting one number from another.

difference ↓ $8 - 2 = 6$

digits The basic symbols used to write numerals in a place-value system. In our base ten system the digits are 0, 1, 2, 3, 4, 5, 6, 7, 8, and 9.

distributive property The property that connects multiplication and addition. For all numbers a, b, and c, $a \times (b + c) = a \times b + a \times c$.

$$2 \times (3 + 4) = 2 \times 3 + 2 \times 4$$

dividend The number that is divided.

$3\overline{)18}$ with quotient 6; $18 \div 3 = 6$ — dividend (18)

divisor The number that one divides by.

$4\overline{)36}$ with quotient 9; $36 \div 4 = 9$ — divisor (4)

down payment The partial payment that is made at the time of purchase when buying on the installment plan.

edge (of a three-dimensional figure) A segment that is the side of a face.

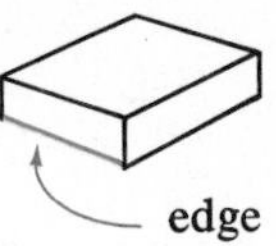

element A member of a set.

empty set The set having no elements. Represented by { } or O.

end point A point at the end of a segment or ray.

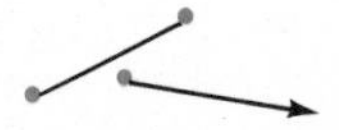

equally likely outcomes Outcomes such that each has the same chance of occurring.

equation A mathematical sentence containing an equal sign (=). $5x + 7 = 18$ $3 + 9 = 12$

equilateral triangle A triangle having three congruent sides.

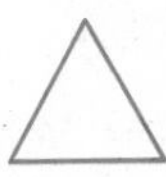

equivalent fractions Fractions that name the same fractional number. $\frac{1}{2}, \frac{2}{4}, \frac{3}{6}, \frac{4}{8}, \frac{5}{10}, \ldots$

error of measurement The difference between the measurement of a quantity and the quantity itself.

even number A whole number that has two as a factor. 0, 2, 4, 6, 8, 10, . . .

expanded form A number written so that the place value of a digit is represented by a power of ten instead of by its position in the numeral.

$$248 = 2 \times 10^2 + 4 \times 10^1 + 8 \times 10^0$$

exponent A numeral that tells the number of times that a number is used as a factor. $5^3 = 5 \times 5 \times 5$

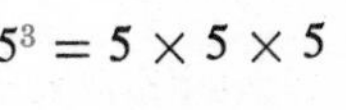

face (of a three-dimensional figure) A polygonal region of a three-dimensional figure.

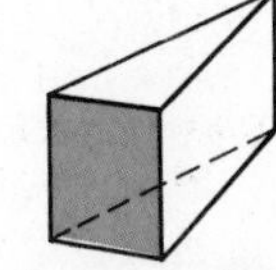

factor A number to be multiplied. $5 \times 8 = 40$

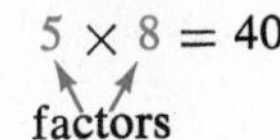

flip image The image obtained by tracing a figure and then flipping the tracing about a line.

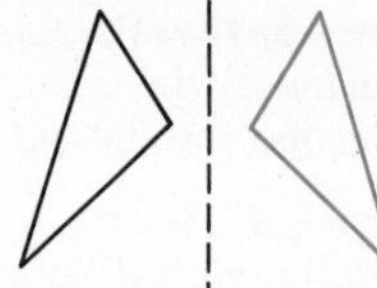

flip line The line about which a tracing of a figure is flipped.

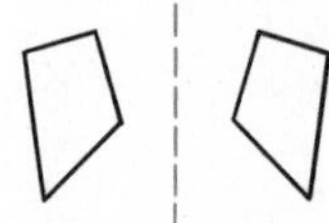

flow chart A diagram that gives step-by-step directions.

formula A general rule expressed by using symbols.

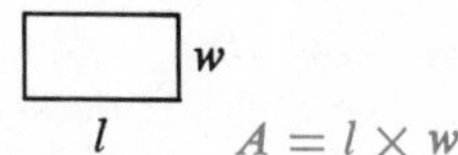

$A = l \times w$

fraction A numeral for a fractional number. Has the form of a/b where a and b are whole numbers and b is not 0.

$\frac{6}{5}$ $\frac{3}{8}$

fractional number A number that is a quotient of two whole numbers.

function A set of number pairs of which no two first numbers are the same.

Function rule
$n \rightarrow n + 3$
(0, 3)
(1, 4)
(2, 5)
.
.
.

gram A unit of weight in the metric system.

greatest common factor (GCF) The greatest number that is a factor of each of two or more numbers.

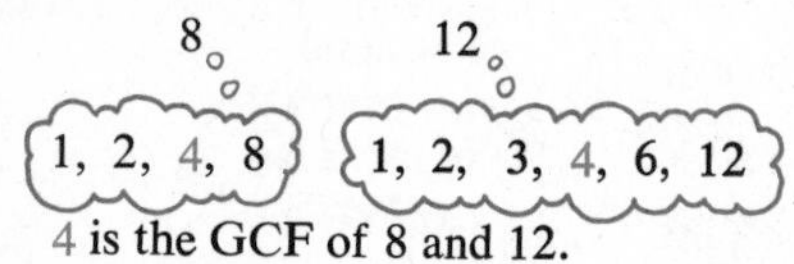

4 is the GCF of 8 and 12.

greatest possible error Half of the unit used in making the measurement.

hectare A unit of area in the metric system. One hundred ares.

1 hectare = 100 ares

hectogram A unit of weight in the metric system. One hundred grams.

1 hg = 100 g

hectoliter A unit of capacity in the metric system. One hundred liters.

1 hl = 100 *l*

hectometer A unit of length in the metric system. One hundred meters.

1 hm = 100 m

hypotenuse The side of a right triangle that is opposite the right angle. It is the longest side of a right triangle.

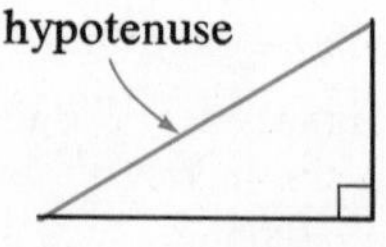

independent events Events such that the outcome of the first does not affect the outcome of the second.

Toss a coin. Roll a die.

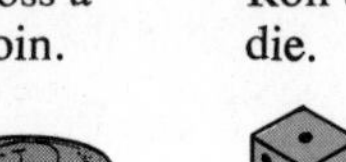

indirect measurement A measurement that is computed from other measurements rather than measured directly.

inequality A mathematical sentence containing an inequality sign, such as $<$, $>$, $\neq$, $\leqslant$, etc.

$3 + 6 < 11$

$2r + 5 \geqslant 6$

installment plan A plan for buying items by paying part of the total price at the time of purchase and the rest in regular payments (installments) over a period of time.

integer Any number in the set $\{\ldots, ^-3, ^-2, ^-1, 0, ^+1, ^+2, ^+3, \ldots\}$.

interest The amount of money that is charged for a loan.

intersection (of sets) The intersection of set A and set B, $A \cap B$, is the set of all elements that belong to both A and B.

$A = \{0, 1, 2, 3\}$
$B = \{2, 3, 4, 5\}$
$A \cap B = \{2, 3\}$

irrational number A number that is not rational; that is, a number that is not the quotient of two integers.

π, $\sqrt{2}$, .1010010001...

isosceles trapezoid A trapezoid with nonparallel sides congruent.

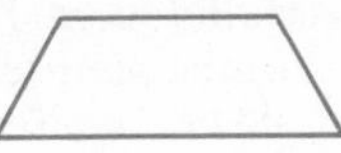

isosceles triangle A triangle having two congruent sides.

kilogram A unit of weight in the metric system. One thousand grams. 1 kg = 1000 g

kiloliter A unit of capacity in the metric system. One thousand liters. 1 kl = 1000 *l*

kilometer A unit of length in the metric system. One thousand meters. 1 km = 1000 m

kite A quadrilateral having two pairs of adjacent congruent sides.

lateral face In a prism, a face which is not a base.

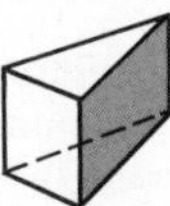

least common denominator The least common denominator of two fractions is the least common multiple of their denominator numbers.

The least common denominator of $\frac{3}{4}$ and $\frac{2}{6}$ is 12.

least common multiple (LCM) The smallest nonzero number that is a multiple of each of two or more numbers.

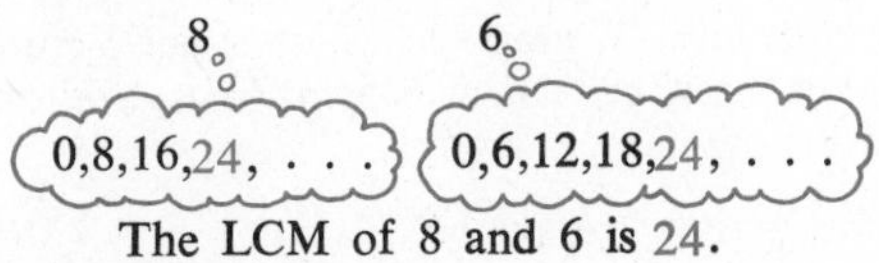

The LCM of 8 and 6 is 24.

leg of a right triangle Either of the two shortest sides of a right triangle.

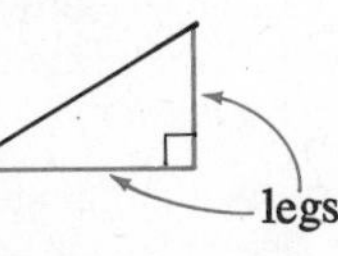

like fractions Fractions having the same denominator. $\frac{3}{8}, \frac{7}{8}$

line of symmetry A line that divides a figure into two congruent parts so that one part is a flip image of the other.

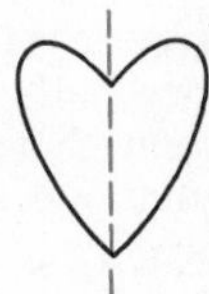

liter A unit of capacity in the metric system. A liter is 1000 cubic centimeters.

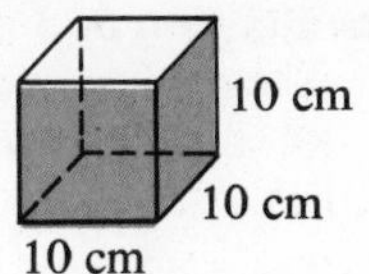

mean The arithmetic average. The sum of the numbers in a set divided by the number of numbers in the set.

{0, 8, 5, 7}

$$\frac{0 + 8 + 5 + 7}{4} = 5$$

The mean is 5.

median The median of a set of numbers is a number such that half of the numbers in the set are less and half are greater.

{63, 68, 74, 81, 86}

The median is 74.

meter A unit of length in the metric system. (A meter is a little longer than a yard.)

midpoint The point that bisects a segment.

milligram A unit of weight in the metric system. One thousandth of a gram. 1 mg = .001 g

milliliter A unit of capacity in the metric system. One thousandth of a liter. 1 ml = .001 *l*

millimeter A unit of length in the metric system. One thousandth of a meter. 1 mm = .001 m

mixed numeral A numeral consisting of a whole-number part and a fraction part. The fraction names a number that is less than 1. $3\frac{1}{4}$, $6\frac{7}{8}$

mode The number that occurs the greatest number of times in a set of data.

3, 6, 8, 9, 9, 11, 13

The mode is 9.

multiple of a number Any product of that number and a whole number.

Multiples of 3:

0, 3, 6, 9, 12, . . .

multiplying by 1 property The product of any number and 1 is that number. $8 \times 1 = 8$

multiplying by 0 property The product of any number and 0 is 0. $24 \times 0 = 0$

negative integer An integer that is less than 0.

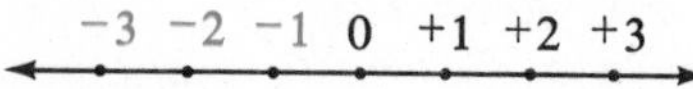

number line A line with its points labeled with numbers. $0 \quad \frac{1}{3} \quad \frac{2}{3} \quad 1 \quad \frac{4}{3} \quad \frac{5}{3}$

number pair An ordered pair of numbers. (5, 6), (8, 2)

numeral A name or symbol for a number. Numerals for ten: $10, 2 \times 5, 12 - 2$

numeration system A system for writing numerals for numbers.

numerator (of a fraction) The numeral above the fraction bar of a fraction. $\frac{9}{4}$ ← numerator

numerical expression A numeral. $6(7 + 3)$, 15, 7/3

obtuse angle An angle that is greater than 90 degrees and less than 180 degrees.

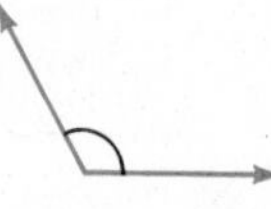

odd number A whole number that does not have 2 as a factor. 1, 3, 5, 7, . . .

odds The ratio of the number of successful outcomes to the number of unsuccessful outcomes.

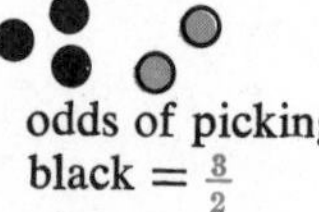

odds of picking black = $\frac{3}{2}$

open equation An equation with a placeholder in it. $5a + 7 = 47$

opposite faces Two faces of a three-dimensional figure that are in parallel planes.

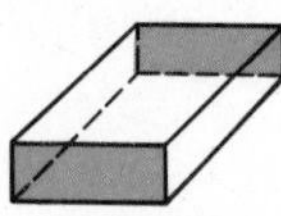

opposites Two numbers are opposites if their sum is 0. $^-3 + ^+3 = 0$

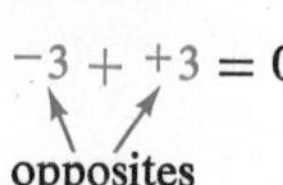

opposites

outcome A possible result.

parallel lines Two lines in the same plane that do not intersect.

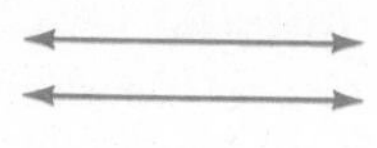

parallel segments Two segments that are contained in two parallel lines.

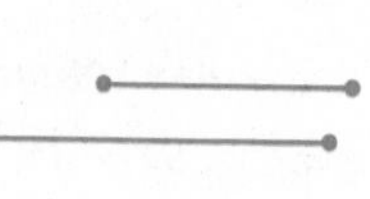

parallelogram A quadrilateral having opposite sides parallel.

percent A fractional number expressed as a fraction having a denominator of 100. The percent sign (%) is used for the unit fraction $\frac{1}{100}$.

percent of error The relative error stated as a percent.

perimeter The distance around a plane figure.

perpendicular bisector A line that bisects and is perpendicular to a segment.

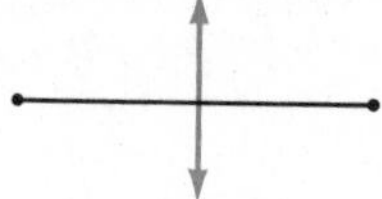

perpendicular lines Two lines that intersect at right angles.

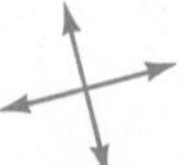

pi The number that is the ratio of the circumference of a circle to its diameter. It is represented by the Greek letter π and is approximately equal to $\frac{22}{7}$ or 3.14.

pictograph A graph in which small pictures or figures, instead of bars or lines, are used to show data.

placeholder A symbol, usually a letter, that holds a place for a numeral. $8x + 19 = 23$

plane A flat surface that extends endlessly in all directions.

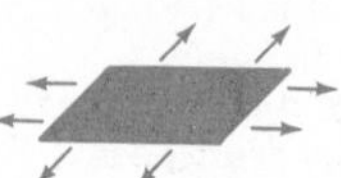

point of symmetry When a figure is its own image for a half-turn about a point, that point is a point of symmetry of the figure.

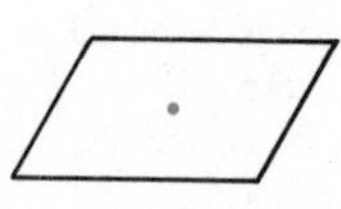

polygon A simple closed curve consisting of three or more segments, each pair of adjacent segments having a common end point.

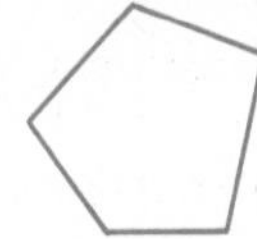

population A large group of people, objects, or events about which we wish to discover some characteristics.

positive integer An integer that is greater than 0.

$^+1, ^+2, ^+3, ^+4, ^+5, \ldots$

prime number A whole number having exactly two factors.

2, 3, 5, 7, 11, 13, . . .

principal The amount of money that is borrowed.

prism A three-dimensional figure with two congruent parallel faces that are polygons and with the remaining faces parallelograms.

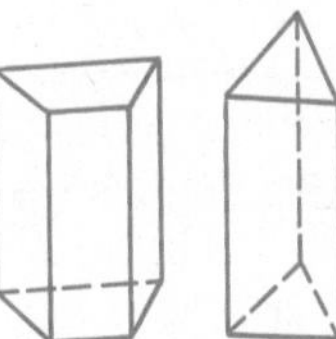

probability (of an outcome) The ratio of the number of ways that an equally likely outcome can occur to the total number of ways that all the equally likely outcomes can occur.

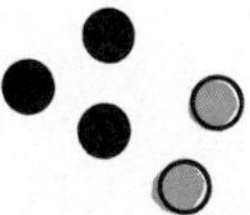

probability of picking black = $\frac{3}{5}$

product The number that is the result of multiplying two or more numbers.

$8 \times 9 = 72 \leftarrow$ product

proportion An equation stating that two ratios are equal. $\frac{5}{8} = \frac{30}{48}$

protractor An instrument used for measuring angles.

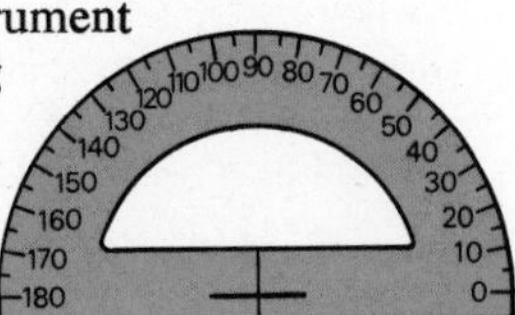

pyramid A solid figure with a base that is a polygon and with lateral faces that are triangles sharing a common vertex.

Pythagorean theorem The square of the hypotenuse of a right triangle is equal to the sum of the squares of the legs.

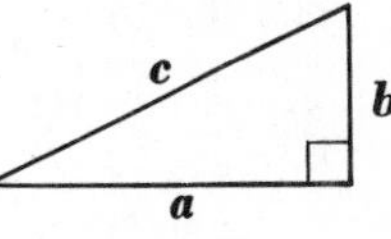

$a^2 + b^2 = c^2$

quadrilateral A polygon having four sides.

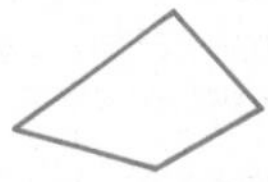

quotient The number that is the result of dividing one number by another.

$5\overline{)65}$ with quotient 13; $48 \div 6 = 8$ (quotient)

range The highest and lowest numbers in a set of numbers. Can also be thought of as the difference of the highest and lowest numbers.

{8, 13, 23, 27, 42, 51, 55}

The range is from 8 to 55.

rate A comparison by division of two quantities. $\frac{87 \text{ miles}}{2 \text{ hours}}$

rate of interest The percent of the principal that is charged as interest on a loan.

ratio A fractional number. It is used to compare two numbers. $\frac{5}{8}$, 8 cm:3 cm

rational number A number that is the quotient of two integers.

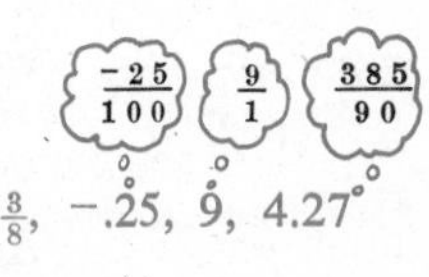

ray A part of a line that has one end point and continues endlessly in one direction.

real number A number that is either rational or irrational.

reciprocal Two numbers are reciprocals of each other if their product is 1.

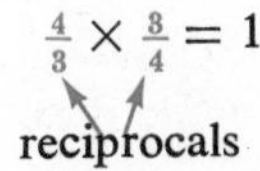

rectangle A quadrilateral with four congruent angles.

rectangular prism A prism whose faces are rectangles.

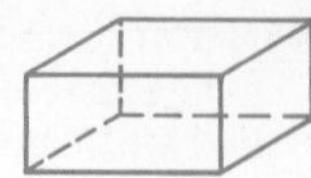

reduced to lowest terms A fraction such that the greatest common factor of its numerator and denominator numbers is 1.

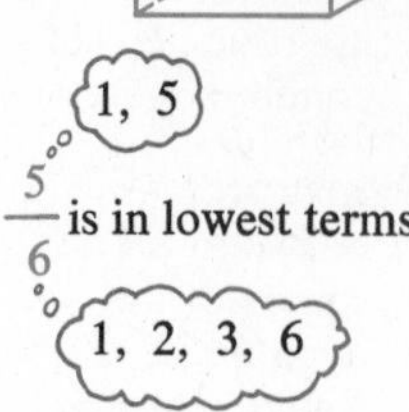

region The points of a plane that are bounded by a simple closed curve.

relative error The ratio of the greatest possible error of measurement to the actual measurement.

remainder In a division problem the number that is "left over." When it is added to the product of the divisor and quotient, the sum is the dividend.

$$\begin{array}{r} 3 \\ 8\overline{)29} \\ -24 \\ \hline 5 \end{array} \leftarrow \text{remainder}$$

repeating decimal A decimal fraction in which a digit or a group of digits repeats forever.

$.3333\ldots$

$1.\overline{47}$

replacement set The set of numbers that may be substituted for a placeholder.

rhombus A quadrilateral having four congruent sides.

right angle An angle of 90 degrees.

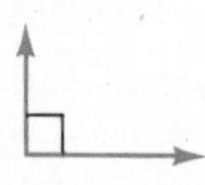

rounding (a number) Changing a number to an approximate number.

sample A group selected from a bigger population. The sample is examined carefully in order to make predictions about the population.

sample space The set of all possible outcomes of an event.

scale drawing A drawing of an object such that the ratio of a unit of length on the drawing to a unit of length on the object is fixed.

scalene triangle A triangle having no congruent sides.

scientific notation A notation for writing a number as the product of a number between 1 and 10 and a power of ten.

$186.3 = 1.863 \times 10^2$

segment A part of a line having two end points.

set A collection of things.

side (of an angle) One of the rays that make up the angle.

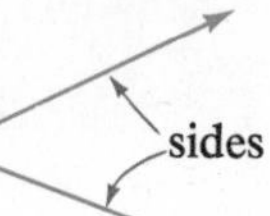

similar figures Two figures that have the same shape.

simple closed curve A curve that can be traced by beginning at any point and ending at the same point and that does not intersect itself.

simple interest Interest that is computed by using the formula $i = prt$, where p is principal, r is rate, and t is time.

simplify Change a numerical expression to the simplest numeral for the same number.

$5(3 + 4) \rightarrow 35$

slide image The image obtained by tracing a figure and then sliding the tracing in a "straight line."

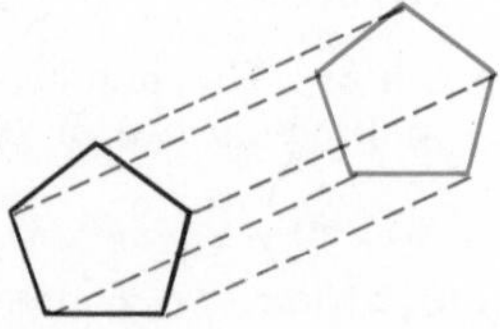

solution A number that makes an equation or inequality true.

solution set The set of all solutions of an equation or inequality.

solve Find the solution set of an equation or inequality.

sphere The set of all points in space that are the same distance from a given point.

square A quadrilateral with four congruent sides and four congruent angles.

square root The number that can be squared to get a given number. $\sqrt{49} = 7$

standard form A number written in its simplest place-value form. 586

statistics A branch of mathematics that studies numerical facts as a basis for drawing general conclusions and making predictions.

subset Set A is a subset of set B, $A \subseteq B$, if all the members of A are also members of B.

$A = \{0, 2, 4\}$
$B = \{0, 1, 2, 3, 4, 5\}$
$A \subseteq B$

substitute Replace a placeholder with a numeral.

$7a + 3$
↓
$7 \cdot 6 + 3$

sum The number that is the result of adding two or more numbers. $17 + 19 = 36$ ← sum

surface area The total area of the surface of a three-dimensional figure.

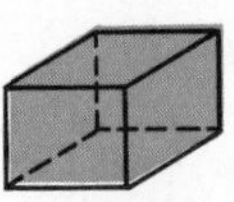

tangent ratio The ratio of the leg of a right triangle that is opposite a given angle to the leg adjacent to the given angle.

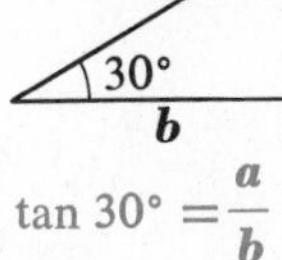

$\tan 30° = \frac{a}{b}$

terminating decimal A decimal fraction, such as .5 or 1.47, which is not a repeating decimal.

terms (of a fraction) The numerator and denominator numbers of a fraction. $\frac{3}{4}$ ← terms

time of a loan The length of time that the principal is borrowed.

trapezoid A quadrilateral having two parallel sides.

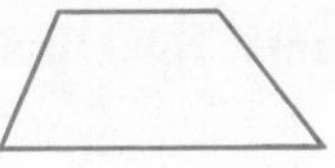

triangular prism A prism having two triangular faces in parallel planes.

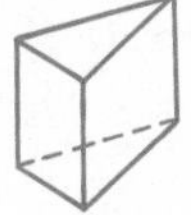

turn center The point about which a tracing of a figure is turned.

turn image The image obtained by tracing a figure and then turning the tracing about a point.

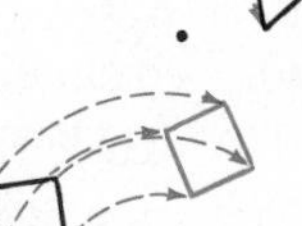

union (of sets) The union of set A and set B, $A \cup B$, is the set of all elements in either A or B.

$A = \{3, 5, 7\}$
$B = \{1, 2, 3\}$
$A \cup B = \{1, 2, 3, 5, 7\}$

unit A fixed quantity used as a standard for measuring length, area, volume, weight, etc.

unit fraction A fraction having a numerator of 1. $\frac{1}{8}, \frac{1}{32}$

vertex (of an angle) The common end point of the two rays.

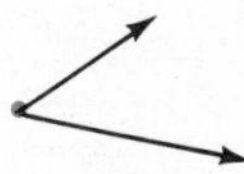

vertex (of a polygon) A point where two sides of a polygon intersect.

vertex (of a three-dimensional figure) A point where three or more edges intersect.

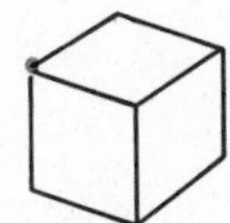

volume The measure of the space inside a three-dimensional figure. A cube is used as a unit.

whole number Any number in this set: $\{0, 1, 2, 3, \ldots\}$

word form (of a number) A number written in words. twenty-five

Symbols

$\{\ \}$	set	$\perp$	is perpendicular to
$\varnothing$	the empty set	$\boldsymbol{a}:\boldsymbol{b}$	the ratio of ***a*** to ***b***
$\subseteq$	is a subset of	$\%$	percent
$\neq$	is not equal to	$\approx$	is approximately equal to
$\leq$	is less than or equal to	π	pi
$\geq$	is greater than or equal to	$^\circ$	degree
$\cup$	union	$'$	foot
$\cap$	intersection	$''$	inch
$f(x)$	function notation	$'$	minute
(a, b)	ordered pair	$''$	second
$.\overline{37}$	.37373737. . .	$^{+}5$	positive 5
$\cong$	is congruent to	$^{-}5$	negative 5
$\angle$	angle	$P(2)$	the probability of the outcome 2
$\overline{AB}$	segment AB	$\sqrt{\ }$	square root
$\triangle$	triangle	$\sim$	is similar to
$\parallel$	is parallel to	tan 30°	tangent of 30°

Formulas

$P = a + b + c$	Perimeter of a triangle	$V = lwh$	Volume of a rectangular prism
$P = 4s$	Perimeter of a square	$V = Bh$	Volume of a prism
$P = 2(l + w)$	Perimeter of a rectangle	$V = \frac{1}{3}Bh$	Volume of a pyramid
$C = \pi d$	Circumference of a circle	$V = \frac{1}{3}\pi r^2 h$	Volume of a cone
$A = lw$	Area of a rectangle	$V = \frac{4}{3}\pi r^3$	Volume of a sphere
$A = s^2$	Area of a square	$i = prt$	Interest
$A = bh$	Area of a parallelogram	$F = \frac{9}{5}C + 32$	Temperature conversion to Fahrenheit
$A = \frac{1}{2}bh$	Area of a triangle	$C = \frac{5}{9}(F - 32)$	Temperature conversion to Celsius
$A = \frac{1}{2}(b_1 + b_2)h$	Area of a trapezoid	$a^2 + b^2 = c^2$	Pythagorean theorem
$A = \pi r^2$	Area of a circle	$V = \pi r^2 h$	Volume of a cylinder
$A = 4\pi r^2$	Area of a sphere		
$A = \pi rs$	Area of slant surface of a cone		

Index

PHOTOGRAPHS

Stephen V. Potter, Stock, Boston, page 39
Daniel S. Brody, Stock, Boston, page 39
Editorial Photocolor Archives, page 64
Courtesy of NASA, page 71
Wide World Photos, E.P.A., page 94
Pictorial Parade, E.P.A., page 117
Dan O'Neill, E.P.A., page 134
Dan O'Neill, E.P.A., page 188
Wide World Photos, page 188
Courtesy of American Stock Exchange, page 262
Pictorial Parade, E.P.A., page 316
Wide World Photos, E.P.A., page 316
Maps: Bonnie Pauley

2 3 4 5 6 7 8 9